GUIDE TO
GOLF
COURSES
IN
BRITAIN
&
IRELAND

Produced by AA Publishing
Atlas and town plans prepared by the AA's Cartographic
Department
Maps © The Automobile Association 1993

Directory generated by the AA Establishment Database, Information
Research and Control, Hotel and Touring Services

Cover design: The Paul Hampson Partnership

Editorial Contributor: John Ingham
Championship Courses Illustrations: Alan Roe

Head of Advertisement Sales
Christopher Heard, Tel 0256 20123 (ext 21544)
Advertisement Production
Karen Weeks, Tel 0256 20123 (ext 21545)

Typeset by Avonset, Midsomer Norton, nr Bath.
Printed and bound in Great Britain by William Clowes Limited,
Beccles and London

The contents of this book are believed correct at the time of going to press. Nevertheless, the Publishers cannot be held responsible for any errors or omissions or for changes in the details given in this guide or for the consequences of any reliance on the information provided in the same. Although every effort has been made to ensure accuracy we always welcome any information from readers to assist in such efforts and to keep the book up to date.

A CIP catalogue record for this book is available from the British Library

Published by AA Publishing, which is a trading name of Automobile Association Developments Limited whose registered office is Fanum House, Basingstoke, Hampshire RG21 2EA, Registered number 1878835.

ISBN 0 7495 0546X

CONTENTS

BRITAIN'S BEST PUBS

We have visited pubs up and down the country in search of the traditional, much loved 'local' with its friendly atmosphere and draught beers, but we have also looked for pubs that offer something exceptional such as adventurous food, facilities for children or reasonably priced accommodation.

Whatever your particular fancy, the hundreds of selected pubs in **BRITAIN'S BEST PUBS** will provide some exciting discoveries.

 Produced in association with Appletise plc

John Ingham,
golf journalist
and regular
contributor to
Golf Monthly,
looks at what is
happening to
the game of golf
and what these
changes are
doing to our
environment.

Do those Golden Fairways always harvest MEGABUCK$?

Golf has always been a fabulous game. You can play it from an early age until the end of time. But in the last few years, commercialism has taken a grip and one or two would-be participants, not short of a bob or two, seem to be making alarming changes.

The market is ripe for plunder. Your average overweight weekend player, fashionably dressed in cashmere, actually hates to practise and seldom admits that swinging a club in a proper arc calls for instruction, co-ordination, timing and hard work. Average players tell you that the teaching professionals keep something back, and that there is a secret to booming 300-yard tee shots. And the ordinary punter is right. The secret is flexibility and muscle achieved through unending practice - plus a sharp eye free of too much alcohol! The hapless teacher, expected to work a miracle, is on a hiding to nothing.

A tee too far!

Few unpaid players can hit the ball like the professionals who achieve success by belting out 1000 shots a day, every day, often until their hands literally split. And when the happy weekenders watch the top stars at courses like Royal St George's, they are expecting scores in the low 60s - forgetting that the experts are playing a specially toughened test where the rough has been allowed to grow into the fairway, and that the big boys are playing a links from the back tees measuring 6903 yards, with one fairway at the 4th almost unreachable over a mountain of sandhills. Unreachable, that is, for the play-for-fun brigade.

Do those Golden Fairways always harvest Megabucks?

It's an old yarn, but true. Joe Cook, a fairly well-known American comedian years ago, knew exactly what golfers were striving for when, in his palatial back garden, he built a single green, steeply bowl-shaped like a wine glass. Simply pitch from the verandah on to the prepared surface and the ball automatically whirlpooled round, into the base of the green - and into the hole! Joe was, without doubt, the most sympathetic golf course architect. But money spoiled his fun. He quickly discovered he could win a fistful of dollars from tipsy guests who would snatch his generous odds of 100-1 against a hole-in-one. The only problem for Joe, as he got older, was how to ensure he could reach the green. So the search for a magic 7-iron went on all his life.

Nothing much changes. Today, as athletic professionals spend a fortune on a diversion created so that people could enjoy themselves, our worldwide game has become an industry.

Big business comes to golf

Mr Golf Public is almost dying to part with his money, in spite of the recession, The slick businessman, observing that the game is suddenly populated with well-heeled folk aspiring to instant success and even greater heights on the social ladder, has stepped in. Building golf courses has become big business. The businessmen persuade overseas corporations to invest upwards of £2 million on what they describe as a championship course. In addition, these new fairways could be lined by what the brochure describes as 'tasteful' dwellings and they say it makes good sense to buy into what paid experts claim will surely hit the jackpot - in years to come!

With the right publicity, some 800 innocents will almost instantly fork out thousands of pounds to become what are called Founder Members.

Champion designers

Simply pitch from the verandah on to the prepared surface and the ball automatically whirlpooled round, into the base of the green - and into the hole!

Although champion Nick Faldo, undoubtedly England's best-ever player, seems interested in creating golf academies for youngsters, it is possible he could also become a famous golf course designer. Superstar Nick could be as good, if not better, than Spain's Seve Ballesteros, who has already proved his creative skills by shaping a course in Provence, France. Both realise that once they cease to win, they will quickly be forgotten by followers who often believe a new star of today is superior to the older men of yesterday.

Since champions have a dread of being called yesterday's men, they strive to create an influence that might last for ever, rather like an author penning something in concrete. In politics, you've cracked it if they name a street after you, or even a town. So now the famous golfer attempts to write his name in history by building a golf course that will endure as a monument! Jack Nicklaus has done this, so has Arnold Palmer - and in places as far-flung as the People's Republic of China where his course is called Arnold Palmer's Chung Shan course.

Unhappily for future weekenders these famous players build 7000-yard monsters, having convinced financial backers that instant championship tests attract admiration and publicity. It isn't always so.

Bigger is not always better

> "So many balls are lost in our lakes" says David, "that snorkel teams now have to bid for ball fishing rights. Believe me, the whole thing is a great source of revenue."

In the distant past, before mechanical earth-movers with wheels as large as those on an Airbus, Mother Nature, assisted by local greenfingers, created the great courses. Most of them look natural and from a distance you might not realise they were, in fact, golf courses at all. There was none of that dazzling white sand for bunkers, and the players were tested by whin bushes, heather and bracken. In fact Royal Ashdown Forest has no bunkers at all! These classic tests are the envy of the sporting world.

But today, despite examples well worth copying, international architects, aided by computer technology and public relations experts, persuade big business to literally throw money into the ground in an unnecessary revamping of whole tracts of landscape. The expense of it all often leads to receivership and a little-used sporting complex that is not only an environmental disaster, but one that priced itself out of a marketplace hit by recession.

Some of the high cost 'wonders' are staggering. In Taiwan, they removed the top of a mountain, while in Morocco they actually diverted a river to gain the most fertile land. In Wisconsin, USA there is a course that boasts 300,000 geraniums and marigolds as well as a series of lakes which look pretty if you fish, but to any golfer with arthritis are a nightmare as expensive balls sink without trace!

What price water?

In Florida, the director of golf at Turnberry Isle is David Podolan. He tells me the second-hand 'lake ball' business has become colossal, with hundreds of re-cycled balls exported to Britain - where they are advertised in magazines such as *Golf Monthly*. "So many balls are lost in our lakes" says David, "that snorkel teams now have to bid for ball fishing rights. Believe me, the whole thing is a great source of revenue."

However, five-times British Open champion Peter Thomson is hostile to what he calls gratuitous water on a golf course and launched a campaign some years ago. At his Rusacks Hotel at St Andrews, this intelligent senior citizen once put his views very clearly to me - after I'd said I had heard some wag suggesting the 18th green on the Old Course would look jollier if they turned the famous Valley of Sin into a grotto! Un-British? Don't dismiss it; they already have a grotto beside the 10th green at The Belfry, venue of the Ryder Cup!

In hot-climate countries, lakes are essential to assist in keeping sunburnt grass green. But they need not, according to former English champion Neil Coles, be in the line of fire. "Water storage lakes can be created just wide of the fairways," he says, pointing out that elderly players do not like to be confronted by a carry over water of more than 150 yards. In Britain, at present, artificial lakes are not essential for water storage purposes. However, it is now being pointed out that millions of gallons a year are taken out of the system to nourish overfed British fairways and greens during the drought of summer. If, in years to come, water is metered and sold by the gallon, many a golf course will be compelled to conserve rainwater and this must be a good thing.

A technicolour dream ....

"The red lights are flashing for those megabuck ventures and not just because the absurdly high costs are putting backers into receivership."

All this upheaval has changed the nature of the environment and today the Green Brigade are out in force, claiming that when farmers switch from cattle or corn, and sell out to the golf developers, serious problems arise for wildlife, and for the countryside itself.

"Golf has to be very careful," warns Bryan Griffith, a senior course designer who learned the craft with the late Commander John D Harris. "The red lights are flashing for those megabuck ventures and not just because the absurdly high costs are putting backers into receivership. Environmental opposition has stopped them, and quite right too!"

What do conservationists complain about? It seems they feel uneasy at the way Britain is copying the lush American courses seen on TV. What most viewers don't appreciate is that grassless patches in the United States are actually dyed green, while certain American 'lakes' are dyed blue, because it looks better on television!

This dye approach was actually used in England, at The Belfry for a televised Ryder Cup match where the dreaded water looked incredibly blue.

Problems at the grass roots! ....

The artificial army literally got to work in Britain at grass roots level. They talked the new wave of course builders into abandoning traditional turf, even though for years it had produced fine courses. While your old English grass used to be fed only on rainwater, the argument went that, with the greater traffic on modern courses, modern British links should buy grass called Bermuda, rye and bent. This new strain of seed, treated with costly fertiliser and further encouraged by a deluge of tap water that gushed from pop-up sprinklers, installed at a fortune, produced blobs of a type of hideous green never before seen in the United Kingdom. Not long before he died, Roger Wethered, past captain of the Royal and Ancient, told me modern greenkeeping methods from America had "ruined" the Old Course at St Andrews. He recalled that it used to be fast-running and slightly brown in the summer. It was a monument to the game, more than 500 years old - and should not have been dug up to fit underwater automatic watering which keeps it green, but weed-threatened, all year.

Mr Wethered's theory was that club golfers rather enjoy the changing seasons and the variable pace of their own course. He much objected to chemicals poured into the grass and said it encouraged wormcasts and bushy weeds never before seen at St Andrews. Suddenly the famous links tended to flood, and the cry went up that old greens should be dug up because the watering had compacted and killed them.

The solution to the problem: put down clinker beneath the putting surface, and re-sow. The greenkeeping traders made a killing.

Professionals admire consistent surfaces and uniform playing conditions. Weekenders rather enjoy a sporty course where luck plays a part on bone-hard approaches. And they don't like having to pay for expensive chemicals.

Says Malcolm Campbell, also an R & A member and something of an expert on golf course maintenance: "The major renovation work at Royal

Birkdale is a classic example of the effects of high phosphate build-up over the years, which resulted in the disappearance of traditional grasses."

Campbell claims imported grasses are susceptible to disease, such as that which caused the 1990 Open at Royal Birkdale so much adverse publicity. Competitors admitted they were shocked at the poor condition of certain greens. Later these were dug up and more traditional grasses planted.

The march of the Green Brigade

But the Green Brigade object to more that just foreign grass seed. They say the face of the English countryside is changed and that hedgerows are hacked down and trees inappropriate to the area are planted, together with the prolific flowering rhododendron bushes. Foxes, pheasants and a host of wild life has been disturbed while more than one group of badgers, supposedly protected, have been driven from their homes by persons unknown.

When the Surrey club of Wentworth built another course in what had been called the Big Wood, critics said dense scrub and decaying trees were cleared, leaving wild life no hiding place! In spite of protests, the course was officially opened on time by the Duke of Edinburgh and predicted demonstrations did not materialise.

At Wisley, a brand new course in Surrey, the construction experts couldn't win either way. New lakes were bulldozed in and certain locals claimed the water was poached from the River Wey, while others say it is tap water, millions of gallons of it, taken out of the system. Apparently tap water is lethal to some fish!

The National Rivers Authority, concerned about dwindling water supplies, went on record with the request that golf course owners dig reservoirs to conserve water. Clubs are currently exempt from hosepipe bans, but in an emergency this could change.

Less a golf club, more a leisure complex

And there are other critics of the way golf is going. While the 'planting' of artificial lakes is distasteful to some who object to what they describe as Marina Golf and Country Clubs, the real danger with these modern-looking courses - all of which have vast clubhouses that include sauna, swimming pool and squash courts - is the expense.

"the older golfers find they cannot pay the rocketing subscription from their pensions, and often they have to give up for financial reasons."

Donald McLeod, a senior Scotsman and founder member of the Golf Heritage of Great Britain, thinks the nouveau riche are bent on building bigger and better clubhouses, and fears the ordinary golfer will be priced out of the game by corporations who take over a club, and 'improve' everything - often turning the place into a gin palace.

"We created democratic golf in Britain and must resist to the death any take-over by business," he says, with emotion. "One of the saddest things" says this member at Richmond, Surrey, "is that the older golfers find they cannot pay the rocketing subscription from their pensions, and often they have to give up for financial reasons."

Obviously, the greater the cost of building, the more expensive will be the price of admission. It surprised few people that, to begin with, traffic

was slow at the most expensive 18-hole course ever built in Britain. More than £22 million was spent to create The Oxfordshire Golf Club just 38 miles from Heathrow. The owners tell me they don't ever expect to recoup the outlay, a record for any course in the United Kingdom.

Over coffee, Masaharu Tanaka and Shigeji Iida of the Nitto Kogyo Group of Japan told of the courses they own world-wide, including famed Turnberry in Scotland.

"Our object was to create the most significant course in England" said Mr Tanaka. We intend to foster cross-cultural understanding and to attract top people to the Oxfordshire." However, at a down-payment of £25,000 plus an annual subscription of £1000, I queried whether there had been a stampede to join from the local farmers.

The course, designed and built under the guidance of American millionaire Rees Jones, is backed by Edmund de Rothschild, former chairman of N M Rothschild and Sons, and is something of a Grand Design. Yes, it has lakes which will be stocked with fish and it also has the most sophisticated underground watering system, a marvel in design apparently. But there's more. There will be Japanese cultural evenings and flower arranging, plus tea ceremonies for members, and non-members who might like to join. Nothing has been spared.

Paying the price...........

John Ingham is a former golf correspondent of the London Evening Standard, *magazine editor and feature writer. He has extensive experience of golf, covering Open championships since the 1950s, reporting the triumphs of many champions. He has ghost written columns with Arnold Palmer, Jack Nicklaus and Peter Alliss, and travelled around the world on golfing assignments. A regular contributer to* Golf Monthly *for the last 17 years, he is also Press Officer for Alfred Dunhill golf competitions.*

However, several respected players feel that, for far too long, the British enjoyed cut-price golf without ever putting something back, either into the upkeep of the clubhouse itself or in the purchase of modern greenkeeping equipment. Peter Alliss, a former Ryder Cup player and winner of many professional tournaments in his day, came to see my local course one time and was greatly impressed, even though I had complained about the steep increase in subscription.

"When you consider you are within ten miles of the centre of London," he told me, "a course like this, of this stature, must be worth not less than £1000 a year."

And we both knew he was right. Anything similar in Japan or America might cost twenty times as much, and you'd be lucky to get in at all.

Yet I hark back to the days when Scotland and Ireland boasted the finest basic golf, with courses designed by God, a hut in which to change your shoes and enjoy a half pint when the game was over. The green fee at such a place, and I'm thinking of the old Ballybunion on the West Coast of Ireland, was the equal of a round of drinks, provided you included Matt Sullivan, who was always at the 19th hole with his grand stories.

But as Christy O'Connor Jnr said: "Times are changing. . ." He's wrong there. Times have changed! . . . But it's still the greatest sport under the sun.

HOW TO USE THIS BOOK

This guide contains over 2000 of those golf courses in Britain and Ireland that welcome visiting golfers. This includes some 200 newly-built courses. We have endeavoured to supply all the information you need to know before your visit by telling you what kind of course you can expect, what club facilities are available, including catering, accommodation, any leisure facilities and the green fees you can expect to pay.

Some courses want advance notice of any visit, and possibly a letter of introduction from your own club. They may also require a handicap certificate. If this is the case the directory will include this information. However, it is always a good idea to check with any course in advance as details in the directory can change, particularly green fees, during the currency of the guide.

Championship courses have been given special treatment with a full page entry, including a selection of places at which to eat as well as to stay. In addition, other courses that are considered to be of particular merit or interest have been placed within a shaded box and given a more detailed description. They may be very historic clubs or they may have been chosen because their courses are particularly testing or enjoyable to play. Some have been included because they are in holiday areas and have proved popular with visiting golfers. Such a selection cannot be either exhaustive or totally objective, and these courses do not represent any formal category on quality or other grounds.

THE DIRECTORY
The directory is arranged in country and county order. Each country is divided by county and within each county, the courses are in alphabetical order of the towns under which they are listed. If you are not sure where your chosen course may be, there is an alphabetical index of courses at the end of the directory.

MAP REFERENCES
Should you be travelling in an unfamiliar part of the country and want to know the choice of courses available to you, consult the atlas at the end of the book. In its directory entry, each course has a map number and Ordnance

Survey grid reference and there are directions to the course giving the nearest place located on the map.

CLUB NAME
NB Although we make every effort to obtain up to date information from golf clubs, in some cases we have been unable to verify details with the club's management. Where this is the case the course name is shown in bold italics and you would be strongly advised to check with the club in advance of your visit.

TELEPHONE CODES
The area codes shown against telephone numbers under Republic of Ireland courses are applicable within the Republic only. Similarly the area codes shown for entries in Great Britain and Northern Ireland cannot be used direct from the Republic. Check your telephone directory for details.

SYMBOLS AND ABBREVIATIONS
In order to maximise the space available, we have used certain symbols and abbreviations within the directory entries and these are explained in the panel below.

04 TO 21	atlas page and OS grid reference
☎	telephone number
IR£	Irish Punts (Republic only - the rates of exchange between Punts and pounds sterling are liable to fluctuate)
⊗	lunch
🍽	dinner
ⓑ	bar snacks
☕	tea/coffee
♀	bar open midday and evenings
🛏	accommodation at club
👔	changing rooms
🏬	well-stocked shop
🏌	clubs for hire
⌂	professional at club
★	hotel classification
✕	restaurant classification(applicable to championship course entry only)

ACCOMMODATION

For each course listed, we recommend the nearest AA-inspected hotel, giving its classification, full name and address, telephone number and total number of bedrooms, including the number with private bath or shower. In some cases the hotel will be with the grounds of the golf course itself. The hotels recommended in the Golf Guide are mostly in the ★★, ★★★, and ★★★★ star categories.

CLUB ACCOMMODATION

Some courses offer accommodation at their club. Where this facility exists, the 'bed' symbol (✍) will appear in the entry under club facilities. This has been listed as a further option for those who might wish to stay at the course. However, unless the club accommodation has an AA star-rating, the only accommodation appointed by the AA is the star-rated hotel that appears at the foot of each entry.

KEY TO HOTEL CLASSIFICATION

The AA system of star rating is the market leader in hotel classifications and has long been universally recognised as an accurate, objective indication of the facilities one can expect to find at any hotel in the AA scheme.

The AA recommended hotels are classified with one to five stars, as follows:

★ Hotels generally of a small scale with good but often simple furnishings, facilities and food. This category sometimes includes private hotels. Not all bedrooms have en-suite facilities. Often managed by the proprietor and with a personal atmosphere.

★★ Small to medium-sized hotels offering more facilities such as telephones and televisions in bedrooms. Can also include private hotels. At least half the bedrooms will have full en-suite facilities. Can be proprietor-managed or group-owned

★★★ Medium-sized hotels offering more spacious accommodation and a greater range of facilities and services. Generally included are full reception service as well as a formal restaurant and bar arrangements. You can expect all rooms to provide en-suite facilities, most of which will include a bath. Though often individually owned, this category encompasses a greater number of company owned properties.

★★★★ Generally large hotels with spacious accommodation including some private suites. Normally provides a full range of formal hotel services including room service and porterage and may well offer more than one dining operation. En-suite facilities in all rooms should include both bath and shower. High standards of comfort and food are expected at this level.

★★★★★ Large luxury hotels offering the highest international standards of accommodation, facilities, services and cuisine.

♨ This denotes an AA Country House hotel with a relaxed informal atmosphere and offering a personal welcome. Often secluded, they are not always rurally situated but are quiet.

PERCENTAGE RATINGS FOR QUALITY

AA hotels are also awarded percentages in addition to star ratings. These represent the difference in quality between hotels within a particular star rating. Hotels have been assessed for quality under a number of broad headings: hospitality, cleanliness, food, bedrooms, overall impression and the inspector's personal view.

50%-59% - a sound hotel meeting all the minimum standard for AA star rating and which overall provides modest but acceptable levels of accommodation, facilities and service.

60%-69% - a particularly sound hotel which exceeds the minimum requirements for its star rating by offering higher standards in certain areas

70%-85% - overall a very good hotel which can be strongly recommended for providing a high level of service, food and accommodation often with excellent standards in certain areas.

RED STARS

The AA recognises hotels that consistently provide outstanding levels of hospitality, service, food and comfort through its prestigious Red-star award scheme. These are given to a select group of hotels considered to be of the very best within their star rating. In such cases, a percentage score for quality is considered unnecessary. Red-star hotels in this guide are indicated by the word 'red' after the star classification.

ENGLAND

AVON

BACKWELL
Map 03 ST46

Tall Pines ☎ Lulsgate (0275) 472076
Parkland course with views over the Bristol Channel.
18 holes, 5800yds, Par 70, SSS 68.
Club membership 600.
Visitors must contact in advance.
Societies apply in writing.
Green Fees not confirmed.
Facilities ⊗ ⅢⅢ ⅃ ♥ ♀ ♨ 🖾 ⚑ ℓ Terry Murray.
Location Cooks Bridle Path, Downside
Hotel ★★★63% Walton Park Hotel, Wellington Ter, CLEVEDON ☎ (0275) 874253 38⇄ ♠

BATH
Map 03 ST76

Bath ☎ (0225) 463834
Considered to be one of the finest courses in the west, this is the site of Bath's oldest golf club. An interesting course situated on high ground overlooking the city and with splendid views over the surrounding countryside. The rocky ground supports good quality turf and there are many good holes. The 17th is a dog-leg right past, or over the corner of an out-of-bounds wall, and thence on to an undulating green.
18 holes, 6369yds, Par 71, SSS 70, Course record 65.
Club membership 825.
Visitors must contact in advance and have a handicap certificate.
Societies must apply in writing.
Green Fees not confirmed.
Facilities ⊗ ⅢⅢ by prior arrangement ⅃ ♥ ♀ ♨ 🖾 ⚑ ℓ Peter J Hancox.
Location Sham Castle, North Rd (1.5m SE city centre off A36)
Hotel ★★★64% Francis Hotel, Queen Square, BATH ☎ (0225) 424257 94 ⇄ ♠

Lansdown ☎ (0225) 422138
A flat parkland course in open situation.
18 holes, 6299yds, Par 71, SSS 70, Course record 65.
Club membership 790.
Visitors must contact in advance & have handicap certificate.
Societies must contact in advance.
Green Fees not confirmed.
Facilities ⊗ ⅢⅢ ⅃ ♥ ♀ ♨ 🖾 ⚑ ℓ Terry Mercer.
Leisure practice ground.
Location Lansdown (3m SW of exit 18 off M4)
Hotel ★★★64% Lansdown Grove Hotel, BATH ☎ (0225) 315891 45⇄ ♠

> A golf course name printed in ***bold italics***
> means we have been unable to verify
> information with the club's management for
> the current year

BRISTOL
Map 03 ST57

Bristol and Clifton ☎ (0275) 393474
A downland course with splendid turf and fine tree-lined fairways. The 222-yard (par 3) 13th with the green well below, and the par 4 16th, with its second shot across an old quarry, are outstanding. There are splendid views over the Bristol Channel towards Wales.
18 holes, 6270yds, Par 70, SSS 70.
Club membership 835.
Visitors must contact in advance & have a handicap certificate.
Societies must book in advance.
Green Fees £27 per weekday/round.
Facilities ⊗ ⅢⅢ by prior arrangement ⅃ ♥ ♀ ♨ 🖾 ⚑ ℓ Peter Mawson.
Leisure snooker.
Location Beggar Bush Ln, Failand (4m W on B3129 off A369)
Hotel ★★★68% Redwood Lodge Hotel & Country Club, Beggar Bush Ln, Failand, BRISTOL ☎ (0275) 393901 108⇄ ♠

Filton ☎ (0272) 694169
Parkland course with a par 4 testing hole 'dog-leg' 383 yds.
18 holes, 6042yds, Par 69, SSS 69.
Club membership 800.
Visitors must have handicap certificate but may not play at weekends.
Societies must contact in advance.
Green Fees £25 per day; £20 per round.
Facilities ⊗ ⅢⅢ by prior arrangement ⅃ ♥ ♀ ♨ 🖾 ⚑ ℓ
Location Golf Course Ln, Filton (5m NW off A38)
Hotel ★★★67% Forte Crest Hotel, Filton Rd, Hambrook, BRISTOL ☎ (0272) 564242 197⇄ ♠

Henbury ☎ (0272) 500044
A parkland course tree-lined and on two levels. The River Trym comes into play on the 7th drop-hole with its green set just over the stream. The last nine holes have the beautiful Blaise Castle woods for company.
18 holes, 6039yds, Par 70, SSS 70, Course record 62.
Club membership 800.
Visitors with member only weekends. Handicap certificate usually required.
Societies Tue & Fri only (minimum 20 players).
Green Fees £21 per round.
Facilities ⊗ ⅢⅢ by prior arrangement ⅃ ♥ ♀ ♨ 🖾 ℓ Nick Riley.
Location Henbury Hill, Westbury-on-Trym (3m NW of city centre on B4055 off A4018)
Hotel ★★★55% St Vincent Rocks Hotel, Sion Hill, Clifton, BRISTOL ☎ (0272) 739251 46⇄ ♠

Knowle ☎ (0272) 770660
A parkland course with nice turf but now somewhat naked after the loss of its fine elm trees. The first five holes climb up and down hill but the remainder are on a more even plane.
18 holes, 6016yds, Par 69, SSS 69.
Club membership 800. ▶

Visitors	must have handicap certificate. Must play with member at weekends. Must contact in advance and have an introduction from own club.
Societies	Thu only. Must contact in advance.
Green Fees	not confirmed.
Facilities	⊗ ⅏ by prior arrangement ⓑ ♨ ♀ ⚲ 🏠 ℓ Gordon Brand.
Location	Brislington (3m SE of city centre off A379)
Hotel	★★★(red)▲▲ Hunstrete House Hotel, CHELWOOD ☎ (0761) 490490 13⇔ 🐾 Annexe11 ⇔ 🐾

Mangotsfield ☎ (0272) 565501
An easy hilly parkland course. Caravan site.
18 holes, 5337yds, Par 68, SSS 66, Course record 65.
Club membership 500.

Visitors	may not play on competition days. Must contact in advance.
Societies	weekdays only, must contact 2 weeks in advance.
Green Fees	not confirmed.
Facilities	⊗ ⓑ ♨ ♀ ⚲ 🏠 ⅏ ℓ Craig Trewin.
Location	Carsons Rd, Mangotsfield (6m NE of city centre off B4465)
Hotel	★★★67% Forte Crest Hotel, Filton Rd, Hambrook, BRISTOL ☎ (0272) 564242 197⇔ 🐾

Shirehampton Park ☎ (0272) 822083
A lovely course in undulating parkland comprising two loops. There are views over the Portway beside the River Avon, where sliced balls at the opening hole are irretrievable.
18 holes, 5600yds, Par 67, SSS 68.
Club membership 600.

Visitors	with member only at weekends
Societies	Mon (if booked).
Green Fees	£18 per day (£25 weekends).
Facilities	⊗ ⓑ ♨ ♀ ⚲ 🏠 ℓ Brent Ellis.
Location	Park Hill, Shirehampton (4m W of city centre on A4)
Hotel	★★★68% Redwood Lodge Hotel & Country Club, Beggar Bush Ln, Failand, BRISTOL ☎ (0275) 393901 108⇔ 🐾

Woodlands ☎ Almondsbury (0454) 618121
Interesting parkland course, featuring five testing par 3's set around the course's six lakes.
18 holes, 5477yds, Par 69, SSS 67.
Club membership 70.

Visitors	no restrictions.
Societies	contact in advance.
Green Fees	£15 per round (£20 weekends).
Facilities	⊗ ⓑ ♨ ♀ ⚲ 🏠 ⅏ ℓ Tony Isaacs.
Leisure	fishing.
Location	Trench Ln, Almondsbury (N of Bristol off A38)
Hotel	★★★67% Forte Crest Hotel, Filton Rd, Hambrook, BRISTOL ☎ (0272) 564242 197⇔ 🐾

> Entries with a shaded background identify courses that are considered to be particularly interesting

CHIPPING SODBURY

Map 03 ST78

Chipping Sodbury ☎ (0454) 319042
Parkland courses of Championship proportions. The old course may be seen from the large opening tee by the clubhouse at the top of the hill. Two huge drainage dykes cut through the course and form a distinctive hazard on eleven holes.
New Course: 18 holes, 6912yds, Par 73, SSS 73.
Old Course: 9 holes, 6184yds, Par 70, SSS 69.
Club membership 770.

Visitors	must have a handicap certificate and may only play in the afternoons at weekends.
Societies	must contact in writing.
Green Fees	not confirmed.
Facilities	⊗ ⅏ by prior arrangement ⓑ ♨ ♀ ⚲ 🏠 ⅏ ℓ Mike Watts.
Location	0.5m N
Hotel	★★66% Cross Hands Hotel, OLD SODBURY ☎ (0454) 313000 24rm(3⇔17 🐾)

CLEVEDON

Map 03 ST47

Clevedon ☎ (0275) 874057
Situated on the cliff-top overlooking the Severn estuary and with distant views of the Welsh coast. Excellent parkland course in first-class condition overlooking the Severn estuary. Magnificent scenery and some tremendous 'drop' holes. Strong winds.
18 holes, 5889yds, Par 69, SSS 69.
Club membership 700.

Visitors	must contact in advance & have a handicap certificate. No play Wed morning.
Societies	Tue only.
Green Fees	£22 per day/round (£35 weekends & bank holidays).
Facilities	⊗ ⅏ ⓑ ♨ (Mon snacks only) ♀ ⚲ 🏠 ⅏ ℓ Martin Heggie.
Leisure	snooker.
Location	Castle Rd, Walton St Mary (1m NE of town centre)
Hotel	★★★64% Commodore Hotel, Beach Rd, Sand Bay, Kewstoke, WESTON-SUPER-MARE ☎ (0934) 415778 12⇔ 🐾 Annexe7rm(4 🐾)

CONGRESBURY

Map 03 ST46

Mendip Spring ☎ (0934) 852322
The 18-hole Brinsea course includes lakes and numerous water hazards covering some 12 acres of the course. The 12th is an island green surrounded by water and there are long drives on the 7th and 13th. The 9-hole Lakeside course is an easy walking course, mainly par 4. Floodlit driving range.
Brinsea: 18 holes, 6335yds, Par 71, SSS 70.
Lakeside: 9 holes, 2287yds, Par 68, SSS 65.
Club membership 500.

Visitors	must contact in advance.
Societies	apply in writing.
Green Fees	Brinsea £20 per day; Lakeside £10 per day.
Facilities	⊗ ⅏ ⅏ ⓑ ♨ ♀ ⚲ 🏠 ⅏ ℓ Christine Holt.
Leisure	heated indoor swimming pool, gymnasium, floodlit driving range.

Location	Honeyhall Ln (8m E of Weston-Super-Mare)
Hotel	★★★⚑69% Daneswood House Hotel, Cuck Hill, SHIPHAM ☎ (093484) 3145 & 3945 9⇥ ⋔ Annexe ⇥ ⋔

KEYNSHAM   Map 03 ST66

Stockwood Vale ☎ Bristol (0272) 866505
Undulating public course with interesting par 3s and good views.
9 holes, 4010yds, Par 64, SSS 61.
Club membership 150.

Visitors	no restrictions, but booking system is available.
Societies	must contact in advance.
Green Fees	£9 per 18 holes, £4.50 per 9 holes (£11/£5.50 weekends).
Facilities	⛾ ⚎ ⚏ David Holder.
Leisure	covered driving range.
Location	Stockwood Ln
Hotel	★★73% Chelwood House Hotel, CHELWOOD ☎ (0761) 490730 11⇥ ⋔

LONG ASHTON   Map 03 ST57

Long Ashton ☎ (0275) 392316
A high downland course with nice turf, some wooded areas and a spacious practice area. Good drainage ensures pleasant winter golf.
18 holes, 6077yds, Par 70, SSS 70, Course record 64.
Club membership 800.

Visitors	must contact in advance and have a handicap certificate.
Societies	must contact the secretary in advance.
Green Fees	£22 per round; £28 per 36 holes (weekend rates on application).
Facilities	⊗ ⫸ by prior arrangement ⚎ ⚏ Denis Scanlan.
Leisure	snooker.
Location	The Clubhouse (0.5m N on B3128)
Hotel	★★★68% Redwood Lodge Hotel & Country Club, Beggar Bush Ln, Failand, BRISTOL ☎ (0275) 393901 108⇥ ⋔

West Bristol ☎ Bristol (0275) 393707
A new course for 1993 designed by Peter Alliss and Clive Clark. In undulating hills south of Bristol, with lakes, pools and a rising landscape to give a challenging course.
18 holes, 6288yds, Par 72.
Club membership 780.

Visitors	must contact in advance and have handicap certificate, weekends may be limited.
Societies	must contact in advance.
Green Fees	£20 (£25 weekends & bank holidays).
Facilities	⊗ ⫸ ⛾ ⚎ ⚏ ⚏
Hotel	★★★68% Redwood Lodge Hotel & Country Club, Beggar Bush Ln, Failand, BRISTOL ☎ (0275) 393901 108⇥ ⋔

MIDSOMER NORTON   Map 03 ST65

Fosseway Country Club ☎ (0761) 412214
Very attractive parkland course, not demanding but with lovely views.
9 holes, 4278yds, Par 68, SSS 65, Course record 54.
Club membership 380.

Visitors	may not play on Wed evenings, Sat & Sun mornings & competitions days.
Societies	by arrangement.
Green Fees	£10 per day (£15 weekends & bank holidays).
Facilities	⊗ ⫸ ⚎ ⚏ (all day) ⚏ ⇔
Leisure	heated indoor swimming pool, squash, snooker, outdoor bowling green.
Location	Charlton Ln (SE of town centre off A367)
Hotel	★★★68% Centurion Hotel, Charlton Ln, MIDSOMER NORTON ☎ (0761) 417711 44⇥ ⋔

SALTFORD   Map 03 ST66

Saltford ☎ (0225) 873220 & 872043
Parkland course with easy walking and panoramic views over the Avon Valley. The par 4, 2nd and 13th are notable.
18 holes, 6081yds, Par 69, SSS 69.
Club membership 800.

Visitors	must contact in advance & have handicap certificate.
Societies	must telephone in advance.
Green Fees	£21 per round, £25 per two rounds weekdays.
Facilities	⊗ ⫸ ⛾ ⚎ ⚏ ⚏ ⛾ ⚎ ⚏ Dudley Millinstead.
Location	Golf Club Ln (S side of village)
Hotel	★★★(red)⚑ Hunstrete House Hotel, CHELWOOD ☎ (0761) 490490 13⇥ ⋔ Annexe11⇥ ⋔

WESTON-SUPER-MARE   Map 03 ST36

Puxton Park ☎ (0934) 876942
A Pay and Play course built on flat moorland dissected by a network of waterways.
18 holes, 6636yds, Par 72, SSS 71.
Club membership 250.

Visitors	must contact in advance.
Societies	apply in advance.
Green Fees	£8 per round (£10 weekends & bank holidays).
Facilities	⚎ (in summer) ⚎ ⚏ ⚏ ⛾ ⚎ ⚏ Colin Ancsell.
Location	Puxton Ln, Hewish (2m junc 21 of M5 on A370)
Hotel	★★★64% Commodore Hotel, Beach Rd, Sand Bay, Kewstoke, WESTON-SUPER-MARE ☎ (0934) 415778 12⇥ ⋔ Annexe7rm(4 ⋔)

Weston-Super-Mare ☎ (0934) 626968
A compact and interesting layout with the opening hole adjacent to the beach. The sandy, links-type course is slightly undulating and has beautifully maintained turf and greens. The 15th is a testing 455-yard, par 4.
18 holes, 6251yds, Par 70, SSS 70.
Club membership 900.

Visitors	may not play on competition days. Must contact in advance.
Societies	must contact in writing.
Green Fees	£20 per day (£28 weekends & bank holidays). ▶

Facilities	⊗ ⅢI by prior arrangement
	ⓑ ⬛ ♀ ⚲ 📠 ⚑ (
Leisure	snooker.
Location	Uphill Rd North (S side of town centre off A370)
Hotel	★★63% Beachlands Hotel, 17 Uphill Rd North, WESTON-SUPER-MARE
	☎ (0934) 621401 18⇄ ⮧

Worlebury ☎ (0934) 625789

Fairly easy walking and extensive views of the Severn estuary and Wales, on this seaside course situated on the ridge of Worlebury Hill.

18 holes, 5936yds, Par 70, SSS 69, Course record 65.

Club membership 600.

Visitors	must have handicap certificate, in possession of own clubs & trolley & dressed correctly.
Societies	must contact in writing.
Green Fees	£20 per day (£30 weekends & bank holidays).
Facilities	⊗ ⅢI by prior arrangement ⓑ ⬛ ♀ ⚲ 📠 ⚑ (Gary Marks.
Leisure	snooker.
Location	Monks Hill (5m NE off A370)
Hotel	★★★53% Royal Pier Hotel, Birnbeck Rd, WESTON-SUPER-MARE
	☎ (0934) 626644 40rm(38⇄ ⮧)
Additional hotel	★★★64% Commodore Hotel, Beach Rd, Sand Bay, Kewstoke, WESTON-SUPER-MARE
	☎ (0934) 415778 12⇄ ⮧ Annexe7rm(4 ⮧)

WICK Map 03 ST77

Tracy Park ☎ Bristol (0272) 372251

This course, situated on the south-western escarpment of the Cotswolds, is undulating with fine views. The clubhouse dates back to 1600 and is a building of great beauty and elegance, set in the 220 acre estate of this golf and country club. Natural water hazards affect a number of holes.

27 holes, 6850yds, Par 72, SSS 73.

Club membership 1000.

Visitors	must contact in advance.
Societies	must telephone in advance and confirm in writing.
Green Fees	not confirmed.
Facilities	⊗ ⅢI by prior arrangement
	ⓑ ⬛ ♀ ⚲ 📠 ⚑ (Grant Aitken.
Leisure	hard tennis courts, heated outdoor swimming pool, squash, snooker, croquet.
Location	Tracy Park, Bath Rd (S side of village off A420)
Hotel	★★★64% Lansdown Grove Hotel, BATH
	☎ (0225) 315891 45⇄ ⮧

BEDFORDSHIRE

ASPLEY GUISE Map 04 SP93

Aspley Guise & Woburn Sands

☎ Milton Keynes (0908) 583596

A fine undulating course in expansive heathland interspersed with many attractive clumps of gorse, broom and bracken. Some well-established silver birch are a feature. The 7th, 8th and 9th are really tough holes to complete the first half.

18 holes, 6135yds, Par 71, SSS 70.

Club membership 580.

Visitors	with member only at weekends. Must have a handicap certificate
Societies	normally booked 12 mths ahead.
Green Fees	£26 per day; £21 per round.
Facilities	⊗ & ⅢI by prior arrangement ⓑ & ⬛ ♀ (limited winter) ⚲ 📠 (Trevor Hill.
Location	West Hill (2m W of M1 junc 13)
Hotel	★★62% Swan Revived Hotel, High St, Newport Pagnell, MILTON KEYNES
	☎ (0908) 610565 42rm(40⇄ ⮧)

BEDFORD Map 04 TL04

Bedford & County ☎ (0234) 352617

Pleasant parkland course with views over Bedford and surrounding countryside. The 15th is a testing par 4.

18 holes, 6347yds, Par 70, SSS 70.

Club membership 600.

Visitors	handicap certificate required, weekends with member only.
Societies	welcome Mon,Tue,Thu & Fri, telephone in advance.
Green Fees	not confirmed.
Facilities	⊗ ⅢI ⓑ ⬛ ♀ ⚲ 📠 (E Bullock.

Location Green Ln, Clapham (2m N off A6)
Hotel ★★★74% Woodlands Manor Hotel, Green Ln, Clapham, BEDFORD
☎ (0234) 363281 22⇥ ▮ Annexe3 ⇥ ▮

Bedfordshire ☎ (0234) 261669
An easy walking, parkland course with tree hazards.
18 holes, 6196yds, Par 70, SSS 69.
Club membership 600.
Visitors may not play at weekends. Must contact in advance.
Societies must telephone in advance.
Green Fees not confirmed.
Facilities ⊗ ⊤ by prior arrangement ▮ ▮ ♀ ⅃ ➪ ▮ Gary Buckle.
Location Bromham Rd, Biddenham (1m W on A428)
Hotel ★★★74% Woodlands Manor Hotel, Green Ln, Clapham, BEDFORD
☎ (0234) 363281 22⇥ ▮ Annexe3 ⇥ ▮

Mowsbury ☎ (0234) 771041
Parkland municipal course in rural surroundings. Long and testing 14-bay driving range and squash facilities.
18 holes, 6514yds, Par 72, SSS 71.
Club membership 800.
Visitors no restrictions.
Societies apply in writing.
Green Fees not confirmed.
Facilities ⊗ & ⊤ by prior arrangement ▮ ▮ ♀ ⅃ ➪ ᛘ ▮ J MacFarlane.
Leisure squash.
Location Cleat Hill, Kimbolton Rd (2m N of town centre on B660)
Hotel ★★★74% Woodlands Manor Hotel, Green Ln, Clapham, BEDFORD ☎ (0234) 363281 22⇥ ▮ Annexe3⇥ ▮

COLMWORTH Map 04 TL15

Colmworth ☎ (0234) 378181
An easy walking course with well-bunkered greens, opened in 1991. The course is often windy and plays longer than the yardage suggests. Water comes into play on 3 holes.
18 holes, 6439yds, Par 71, SSS 71 or 9 holes, 750yds, Par 27.
Club membership 208.
Visitors advisable to contact in advance, tee reserved for members Sat & Sun until 10am & between 1-1.30pm.
Societies must contact in advance.
Green Fees £10 per 18 holes (£15 weekends).
Facilities ▮ ▮ ♀ ⅃ ➪ ᛘ ▮ Austin Curtis.
Location New Rd (5m W of Bedford, off B660)
Hotel ★★★67% The Barns Hotel, Cardington Rd, Fenlake, BEDFORD ☎ (0234) 270044 49⇥ ▮

DUNSTABLE Map 04 TL02

Dunstable Downs ☎ (0582) 604472
A fine downland course set on two levels with far-reaching views and frequent sightings of graceful gliders. The 9th hole is one of the best short holes in the country. There is a modernised clubhouse.
18 holes, 6184yds, Par 70, SSS 70.
Club membership 600.

Visitors weekends with member only.
Societies telephone in advance.
Green Fees not confirmed.
Facilities ⊗ ⊤ by prior arrangement ▮ ▮ ♀ ⅃ ➪ ▮ Michael Weldon.
Location Whipsnade Rd (2m S off B4541)
Hotel ★★★67% Old Palace Lodge Hotel, Church St, DUNSTABLE ☎ (0582) 662201 49⇥

LEIGHTON BUZZARD Map 04 SP92

Leighton Buzzard ☎ (0525) 373811
Parkland course with easy walking.
18 holes, 6101yds, Par 71, SSS 70.
Club membership 595.
Visitors may not play Tue pm. With member only weekends and bank holidays. Must contact in advance and have an introduction from own club.
Societies apply in writing.
Green Fees not confirmed.
Facilities ⊗ ⊤ ▮ ▮ ♀ ⅃ ➪ ▮
Location Plantation Rd (1.5 N of town centre off A418)
Hotel ★★★60% Swan Hotel, High St, LEIGHTON BUZZARD ☎ (0525) 372148 38⇥ ▮

LUTON Map 04 TL02

South Beds ☎ (0582) 591500
27-hole downland course, slightly undulating.
Galley Course: 18 holes, 6342yds, Par 71, SSS 71, Course record 66.
Warden Course: 9 holes, 2424yds, Par 32.
Club membership 960.
Visitors must contact in advance, restricted Tue.
Societies apply in writing.
Green Fees not confirmed.
Facilities ⊗ ⊤ ▮ ▮ ♀ ⅃ ➪ ▮ Eddie Cogle.
Leisure snooker.
Location Warden Hill (3m N off A6)
Hotel ★★★69% Strathmore Thistle Hotel, Arndale Centre, LUTON ☎ (0582) 34199 150⇥ ▮

Stockwood Park ☎ (0582) 413704
Municpal parkland course.
18 holes, 5973yds, Par 69, SSS 69.
Club membership 750.
Visitors no restrictions.
Societies Mon, Tue & Thu only.
Green Fees not confirmed.
Facilities ⊗ ▮ ▮ ♀ ⅃ ➪ ᛘ ▮ Glyn McCarthy.
Leisure pool tables.
Location London Rd (1m S on A6)
Hotel ★★★64% Forte Crest Hotel, Waller Av, Dunstable Rd, LUTON ☎ (0582) 575911 93⇥ ▮

> A golf course name printed in ***bold italics***
> means we have been unable to verify
> information with the club's management for
> the current year

MILLBROOK

Map 04 TL03

Millbrook ☎ Ampthill (0525) 840252
Long parkland course, on rolling countryside high above the
Bedfordshire plains, with several water hazards. Laid out on
well-drained sandy soil with many fairways lined with silver
birch, pine and larch.
18 holes, 6530yds, Par 74, SSS 71.
Club membership 550.
Visitors welcome weekdays & with member at
weekends.
Societies weekdays except Thu.
Green Fees not confirmed.
Facilities ⊗ ⽊ ⻐ ⬛ ♀ ⚲ ⚱ (T K Devine.
Location E side of village off A507
Hotel ★★★⬥72% Flitwick Manor Hotel, Church Rd,
FLITWICK ☎ (0525) 712242 15⇆ ⚑

SANDY

Map 04 TL14

John O'Gaunt ☎ Potton (0767) 260360
Two tree-lined parkland courses.
18 holes, 6214yds, Par 71, SSS 71.
Carthagena Course: 18 holes, 5590yds, Par 69, SSS 67.
Club membership 1300.
Visitors must contact in advance and have handicap
certificate at weekends.
Societies apply in writing.
Green Fees £35 per day/round (£50 weekends).
Facilities ⊗ ⽊ ⻐ ⬛ ♀ ⚲ ⚱ (Peter Round.
Location Sutton Park (3m NE of Biggleswade on B1040)
Hotel ★★64% Abbotsley Golf Hotel, Eynesbury
Hardwicke, ST NEOTS
☎ (0480) 474000 15⇆ ⚑

SHEFFORD

Map 04 TL13

Beadlow Manor Hotel & Golf & Country Club
☎ (0525) 860800
27 hole golf and leisure complex. Golf courses of undulating
nature with water hazards on numerous holes.
18 holes, 6231yds, Par 71, SSS 70.
Club membership 750.
Visitors must have an introduction from own club.
Green Fees not confirmed.
Facilities ♀ ⚲ ⚱ ⚒ (
Location 2m W on A507
Hotel ★★★⬥72% Flitwick Manor Hotel, Church Rd,
FLITWICK ☎ (0525) 712242 15⇆ ⚑

TILSWORTH

Map 04 SP92

Tilsworth ☎ Leighton Buzzard (0525) 210721
An undulating parkland course upgraded from 9 to 18 holes
in 1992. 30-bay floodlit driving range.
18 holes, 5443yds, Par 70, SSS 66, Course record 66.
Club membership 350.
Visitors must contact in advance but may not play Sun
mornings
Societies apply in writing.
Green Fees £5 per 9 holes (£6 weekends). £8 per 18 holes
(£10 weekends)..
Facilities ⊗ ⽊ ⻐ ⬛ (no catering Sun) ♀ ⚲ ⚱ ⚒ (
Nick Webb.

Location Dunstable Rd (.5m NE off A5)
Hotel ★★★67% Old Palace Lodge Hotel, Church St,
DUNSTABLE ☎ (0582) 662201 49 ⇆

WYBOSTON

Map 04 TL15

Wyboston Lakes ☎ Huntingdon (0480) 219200 & 212501
Parkland course, with narrow fairways, small greens, set
around four lakes and a river.
18 holes, 5721yds, Par 69, SSS 69.
Club membership 300.
Visitors must contact in advance at weekends.
Societies must telephone in advance.
Green Fees £10 per day/round (£14 weekends & bank
holidays).
Facilities ⊗ ⽊ ⻐ ⬛ ♀ ⚲ ⚱ ⚒ ⊠ (Paul Ashwell.
Leisure fishing.
Location NE side of village off A1
Hotel ★★★74% Woodlands Manor Hotel, Green Ln,
Clapham, BEDFORD
☎ (0234) 363281 22⇆ ⚑ Annexe3⇆ ⚑

● BERKSHIRE ●

ASCOT

Map 04 SU96

Berkshire ☎ (0344) 21496
Two heathland courses with splendid tree-lined fairways.
Red Course: 18 holes, 6369yds, Par 72, SSS 70.
Blue Course: 18 holes, 6260yds, Par 71, SSS 70.
Club membership 950.
Visitors only on application to secretary.
Societies must telephone in advance.
Green Fees £60 per day; £45 per round.
Facilities ⊗ ⻐ ⬛ ♀ ⚲ ⚱ ⚒ (
Location Swinley Rd (2.5m NW of M3 jct 3 on A332)
Hotel ★★★★59% The Berystede, Bagshot Rd,
Sunninghill, ASCOT
☎ (0344) 23311 91⇆ ⚑

Lavender Park ☎ (0344) 884074
Public parkland course. Driving range with 9-hole par 3
course, floodlit until 22.30 hrs.
9 holes, 1102yds, Par 28, SSS 29, Course record 20.
Club membership 50.
Visitors no restrictions.
Societies welcome.
Green Fees not confirmed.
Facilities ⊗ & ⬛ (Mon-Fri) ♀ ⚲ ⚒ (T Bowers.
Leisure snooker, golf driving range.
Location Swinley Rd (3.5m SW on A332)
Hotel ★★★★59% The Berystede, Bagshot Rd,
Sunninghill, ASCOT
☎ (0344) 23311 91⇆ ⚑

Mill Ride ☎ Winkfield Row (0344) 886777
Opened for play in 1991, this 18-hole course combines good
golfing country and attractive surroundings with a
challenging design. The holes require as much thinking as
playing.
18 holes, 6833yds, Par 72, SSS 72, Course record 68.

Visitors   must contact in advance.
Societies   apply in advance.
Green Fees   £40 per day; £30 per round (£40 weekends).
Facilities   ⊗ ⅶ ⅃ ☚ ♀ ⚘ 🏠 ⚐ 🏐 (Suzy Baggs.
Leisure   sauna, driving range & practice facilities.
Location   Mill Ride Estate, North Ascot (1.5m NW of
                 Ascot)
Hotel   ★★★★59% The Berystede, Bagshot Rd,
                 Sunninghill, ASCOT ☎ (0344) 23311 91⇄ ♠

Royal Ascot ☎ (0344) 25175
Heathland course exposed to weather.
18 holes, 5709yds, Par 68, SSS 68, Course record 63.
Club membership 600.
Visitors   must be guest of member.
Societies   Wed & Thu only, must contact in advance.
Green Fees   not confirmed.
Facilities   ⊗ ⅃ ☚ ♀ ⚘ 🏠 (Garry Malia.
Location   Winkfield Rd (0.5m N on A330)
Hotel   ★★★★59% The Berystede, Bagshot Rd,
                 Sunninghill, ASCOT ☎ (0344) 23311 91⇄ ♠

Swinley Forest ☎ (0344) 20197
An attractive and immaculate course of heather and pine
situated in the heart of Swinley Forest. The 17th is as
good a short hole as will be found, with a bunkered
plateau green. Course record holder is P. Alliss.
18 holes, 6001yds, Par 68, SSS 69, Course record 64.
Club membership 350.
Visitors   by invitation only.
Societies   must contact in writing.
Green Fees   £50 per day (£60 weekends).
Facilities   ⊗ ⅃ ☚ ♀ ⚘ 🏠 ⚐ (R C Parker.
Location   1.5m S, off A330
Hotel   ★★★★59% The Berystede, Bagshot Rd,
                 Sunninghill, ASCOT
                 ☎ (0344) 23311 91⇄ ♠

BINFIELD   Map 04 SU87

Blue Mountain Golf Centre ☎ (0344) 300200
An 18-hole Pay and Play course.
18 holes, 6097yds, Par 70, SSS 70.
Club membership 950.
Visitors   no restrictions.
Societies   must contact in advance.
Green Fees   £14 (£18 weekends).
Facilities   ⊗ ⅶ ⅃ ☚ ♀ ⚘ 🏠 ⚐ (Neil Dainton.
Location   Wood Ln (5m SW of Reading, on B3048)
Hotel   ★★★66% Reading Moat House, Mill Ln,
                 Sindlesham, WOKINGHAM
                 ☎ (0734) 351035 96⇄

CHADDLEWORTH   Map 04 SU47

West Berkshire ☎ (04882) 574
Challenging and interesting downland course with testing 635
yds (par 5) 5th hole.
18 holes, 7069yds, Par 73, SSS 74.
Club membership 800.
Visitors   must contact in advance but are restricted
                 weekends.
Societies   by arrangement.
Green Fees   not confirmed.

Facilities   ⊗ ⅃ ☚ ♀ ⚘ 🏠 (
Location   1m S of village off A338
Hotel   ★★★60% The Chequers, Oxford St, NEWBURY
                 ☎ (0635) 38000 45⇄ Annexe11⇄

COOKHAM   Map 04 SU88

Winter Hill ☎ Bourne End (0628) 527613
Parkland course set in a curve of the Thames with wonderful
views across the Thames to Cliveden.
18 holes, 6408yds, Par 72, SSS 71, Course record 69.
Club membership 800.
Visitors   not permitted weekends. Must contact in
                 advance.
Societies   must apply in writing.
Green Fees   £23 per day (Mon-Fri).
Facilities   ⊗ ⅶ by prior arrangement ⅃ ☚ ♀ ⚘ 🏠 (
Location   Grange Ln (1m NW off B4447)
Hotel   ★★★★70% Compleat Angler Hotel, Marlow
                 Bridge, MARLOW ☎ (0628) 484444 64⇄ ♠

CROWTHORNE   Map 04 SU86

East Berkshire ☎ (0344) 772041
An attractive heathland course with an abundance of
heather and pine trees. Walking is easy and the greens are
exceptionally good. Some fairways become tight where
the heather encroaches on the line of play. The course is
testing and demands great accuracy.
18 holes, 6345yds, Par 69, SSS 70, Course record 65.
Club membership 500.
Visitors   must have a handicap certificate; must play
                 with member at weekends & bank holidays.
                 Must contact in advance and have an
                 introduction from own club.
Societies   Thu & Fri only; must contact in advance.
Green Fees   not confirmed.
Facilities   ⊗ ⅃ ☚ (11am-4pm) ♀ ⚘ 🏠 (Arthur Roe
Location   Ravenswood Ave (W side of town centre off
                 B3348)
Hotel   ★★★★♨80% Pennyhill Park Hotel,
                 London Rd, BAGSHOT
                 ☎ (0276) 71774 22⇄ ♠ Annexe54 ⇄ ♠

DATCHET   Map 04 SU97

Datchet ☎ (0753) 543887 & 541872
Meadowland course, easy walking.
9 holes, 5978yds, Par 70, SSS 69, Course record 63.
Club membership 405.
Visitors   may play weekdays before 3pm.
Societies   Tue only.
Green Fees   £24 per day; £16 per round.
Facilities   ⊗ ⅃ ☚ ♀ ⚘ 🏠 (Bill Mainwaring.
Location   Buccleuch Rd (NW side of Datchet off B470)
Hotel   ★★58% The Manor Hotel, The Village Green,
                 DATCHET ☎ (0753) 543442 30⇄ ♠

If you know of a golf course that welcomes
visitors and is not already in this guide, we
should be grateful for information

HURLEY

Map 04 SU88

Temple ☎ Maidenhead (0628) 824248
An open parkland course with many excellent, fast
greens relying on natural slopes rather than heavy
bunkering. On one 'blind' punchbowl hole there is
actually a bunker on the green. Good drainage assures
play when many other courses are closed.
18 holes, 6206yds, Par 70, SSS 70, Course record 63.
Club membership 650.

Visitors	may not play before 9.15am or 2.15pm Mon-Wed & Fri or before 11.15am weekends & must contact in advance.
Societies	must book one year in advance.
Green Fees	£40 per day (£50 weekends).
Facilities	⊗ ⅏ 🏌 ♥ ♀ ⚒ 📷 ↑ ℓ Alan Dobbins.
Leisure	squash, putting green & practice ground.
Location	Henley Rd (1m SE on A432)
Hotel	★★★★70% Compleat Angler Hotel, Marlow Bridge, MARLOW ☎ (0628) 484444 64⇆ℝ

MAIDENHEAD

Map 04 SU88

Maidenhead ☎ (0628) 24693
A pleasant parkland course on level ground with easy
walking to good greens. Perhaps a little short but there
are many natural features and some first-rate short holes.
18 holes, 6364yds, Par 70, SSS 70, Course record 65.
Club membership 650.

Visitors	may not play after noon on Fri or at weekends. Must contact in advance and have a handicap certificate.
Societies	must contact in writing.
Green Fees	£27 per day.
Facilities	⊗ ⅏ by prior arrangement 🏌 ♥ ♀ ⚒ 📷 ↑ ℓ Clive Dell.
Location	Shoppenhangers Rd (S side of town centre off A308)
Hotel	★★★★73% Fredrick's Hotel, Shoppenhangers Rd, MAIDENHEAD ☎ (0628) 35934 37⇆ℝ

NEWBURY

Map 04 SU46

Donnington Valley ☎ (0635) 551199
Undulating, short, but testing course with mature trees and
elevated greens, some protected by water.
18 holes, 4002yds, Par 61, SSS 60.
Club membership 520.

Visitors	must contact in advance.
Societies	booking required in advance .
Green Fees	not confirmed.
Facilities	⊗ ⅏ 🏌 ♥ ♀ 📷 ↑ ⊨ ℓ Nick Mitchell.
Leisure	snooker, clay pigeon shooting.
Location	Old Oxford Rd, Donnington (2m N of Newbury)
Hotel	★★★65% Millwaters, London Rd, NEWBURY ☎ (0635) 528838 32⇆ℝ

Newbury & Crookham ☎ (0635) 40035
A well-laid out, attractive course running mostly through woodland, and giving more of a challenge than its length suggests.
18 holes, 5880yds, Par 68, SSS 68, Course record 61.
Club membership 800.

Visitors	must play with member on weekends & bank holidays. Handicap certificate required.
Societies	must contact in advance.
Green Fees	£27.50 per day/round.
Facilities	⊗ ⅏ 🏌 ♥ ♀ ⚒ 📷 ℓ David Harris.
Location	Bury's Bank Rd, Greenham (2m SE off A34)
Hotel	★★★60% The Chequers, Oxford St, NEWBURY ☎ (0635) 38000 45⇆Annexe11⇆

READING

Map 04 SU77

Calcot Park ☎ (0734) 427124
A delightfully sporting parkland course just outside the
town. Hazards include a lake and many trees. The 6th is
the longest, 497 yard par 5, with the tee-shot hit downhill
over cross-bunkers to a well-guarded green. The 13th (188
yards) requires a big carry over a gully to a plateau green.
18 holes, 6283yds, Par 70, SSS 70, Course record 66.
Club membership 735.

Visitors	must have handicap certificate, but may not play weekends & bank holidays.
Societies	must apply in writing.
Green Fees	not confirmed.
Facilities	⊗ ⅏ 🏌 ♥ ♀ ⚒ 📷 ↑ ℓ
Location	Bath Rd, Calcot (2.5m W on A4)
Hotel	★★★61% The Copper Inn, Church Rd, PANGBOURNE ☎ (0734) 842244 22⇆ℝ

Mapledurham ☎ (0734) 463353
18-hole course designed by Bob Sandow. Flanked by hedgerows and mature woods, it is testing for players of all levels.
18 holes, 5621yds, Par 69, SSS 67.
Club membership 600.

Visitors	no restrictions.
Societies	must contact in advance.
Green Fees	£13 per 18 holes; £6.50 per 9 holes (£16/£8 weekends).
Facilities	⊗ ⅏ 🏌 ♥ ♀ ⚒ 📷 ↑ ℓ Douglas Burton.
Location	Chazey Heath, Mapledurham (on A4074 to Oxford)
Hotel	★★★★61% Caversham Hotel, Caversham Bridge, Richfield Av, READING ☎ (0734) 391818 112⇆ℝ

Reading ☎ (0734) 472909
Tree-lined Parkland course, part hilly and part flat.
18 holes, 6212yds, Par 70, SSS 70, Course record 67.
Club membership 700.

Visitors	must have handicap certificate. With member only Fri & weekends.
Societies	advisable to book one year in advance.
Green Fees	£27 per weekday.
Facilities	⊗ ⅏ 🏌 (ex Mon) ♥ ♀ ⚒ 📷 ℓ Tim Morrison.
Location	17 Kidmore End Rd, Emmer Green (2m N off B481)
Hotel	★★★★60% Ramada Hotel, Oxford Rd, READING ☎ (0734) 586222 196⇆ℝ

SINDLESHAM

Map 04 SU76

Bearwood ☎ Arborfield Cross (0734) 760060
Flat parkland course with one water hazard - over part of a
lake. Also 9-hole pitch and putt.
9 holes, 2802yds, Par 35.
Club membership 570.

Visitors   must have handicap certificate. With member only on weekends & bank holidays. Must have an introduction from own club.
Green Fees not confirmed.
Facilities   ⊗ (ex Mon) 🏌 ⚑ ♀ ♨ 🏠 ⚲ A Hanson.
Leisure   riding, 9 hole pitch & putt course.
Location   Mole Rd (1m SW on B3030)
Hotel   ★★★66% Reading Moat House, Mill Ln, Sindlesham, WOKINGHAM
     ☎ (0734) 351035 96⇄

SONNING   Map 04 SU77

Sonning ☎ (0734) 693332
A quality parkland course and the scene of many county championships. Wide fairways, not overbunkered, and very good greens. Holes of changing character through wooded belts.
18 holes, 6366yds, Par 70, SSS 70, Course record 65.
Visitors   weekdays only. Handicap certificate required.
Societies   must apply in writing.
Green Fees £30 per day/round.
Facilities   ⊗ & ⽊ by prior arrangement 🏌 ⚑ ♀ ♨ 🏠 ⚲ R McDougall.
Location   Duffield Rd (1m S off A4)
Hotel   ★★★★60% Ramada Hotel, Oxford Rd, READING ☎ (0734) 586222 196⇄ ☞

STREATLEY   Map 04 SU58

Goring & Streatley ☎ Goring (0491) 873229
A parkland/moorland course that requires 'negotiating'. Four well-known first holes lead up to the heights of the 5th tee, to which there is a 300ft climb. Wide fairways, not overbunkered, with nice rewards on the way home down the last few holes.
18 holes, 6275yds, Par 71, SSS 70.
Club membership 750.
Visitors   with member only at weekends.
Societies   must telephone in advance.
Green Fees £28 per day;£19 after 4pm (weekends and bank holidays with member only).
Facilities   ⊗ ⽊ 🏌 ⚑ ♀ ♨ 🏠 ⚲ Roy Mason.
Location   N of village off A417
Hotel   ★★★★68% Swan Diplomat Hotel, High St, STREATLEY ☎ (0491) 873737 46⇄ ☞

SUNNINGDALE   Map 04 SU96

SUNNINGDALE See page 23

Sunningdale Ladies ☎ Ascot (0344) 20507
A short 18-hole heathland course designed for ladies golf.
18 holes, 3616yds, Par 60, SSS 60.
Club membership 350.
Visitors   telephone in advance.
Societies   Ladies societies only.
Green fees £22-£27 per round.
Facilities   ⊗ 🏌 (ex Sun) ⚑ ♀ ♨
Location   Cross Rd (1m S off A30)
Hotel   ★★★★59% The Berystede, Bagshot Rd, Sunninghill, ASCOT ☎ (0344) 23311 91⇄ ☞

WOKINGHAM   Map 04 SU86

Downshire ☎ Bracknell (0344) 422708 & 302030
Municipal parkland course with many water hazards, easy walking. Testing holes: 7th (par 4), 15th (par 4), 16th (par 3).
18 holes, 6382yds, Par 73, SSS 70.
Visitors   must contact in advance.
Societies   must apply in writing.
Green Fees £9/11 per round (£11/13 weekends).
Facilities   ⊗ ⽊ 🏌 ⚑ ♀ ♨ 🏠 ⚲ ⚲ Paul Watson.
Location   Easthampstead Park (3m SW of Bracknell)
Hotel   ★★★★59% The Berystede, Bagshot Rd, Sunninghill, ASCOT ☎ (0344) 23311 91 ⇄ ☞

Sand Martins ☎ (0734) 792711
Two different 9-hole loops:the front nine is mostly tree-lined with ponds and the back nine is similar to a links course.
18 holes, 6235yards, Par 70.
Club membership 850.
Visitors   no restrictions.
Societies   must apply in writing.
Green Fees £40 per 36 holes; £25 per 18 holes.
Facilities   ⊗ ⽊ 🏌 ⚑ ♀ ♨ 🏠 ⚲ Willie Milne.
Location   Finchampstead Rd
Hotel   ★★★66% Reading Moat House, Mill Ln, Sindlesham, WOKINGHAM
     ☎ (0734) 351035 96⇄

● BUCKINGHAMSHIRE ●

AYLESBURY   Map 04 SP81

Ellesborough ☎ Wendover (0296) 622114
Once part of the property of Chequers, and under the shadow of the famous monument at the Wendover end of the Chilterns. A downland course, it is rather hilly with most holes enhanced by far-ranging views over the Aylesbury countryside.
18 holes, 6276yds, Par 71, SSS 71, Course record 64.
Club membership 780.
Visitors   must have a handicap certificate, but may not play Tue mornings. With member only at weekends. Must contact in advance.
Societies   Wed & Thu only.
Green Fees £30 per day; £20 per round.
Facilities   ⊗ ⽊ 🏌 ⚑ ♀ ♨ 🏠 ⚲ Paul Warner.
Location   Butlers Cross (1m E of Ellesborough on B4010)
Hotel   ★★★(red) Bell Inn, ASTON CLINTON
     ☎ (0296) 630252 6⇄ ☞ Annexe15⇄ ☞

BEACONSFIELD   Map 04 SU99

Beaconsfield ☎ (0494) 676545
An interesting and, at times, testing tree-lined and parkland course which frequently plays longer than appears on the card! Each hole differs to a considerable degree and here lies the charm. Walking is easy, except perhaps to the 6th and 8th. Well bunkered.
18 holes, 6487yds, Par 72, SSS 71.
Club membership 862.   ▶

<table>
<tr><td>Visitors</td><td>must contact in advance and have a handicap certificate. Must play with member at weekends and bank holidays</td></tr>
<tr><td>Societies</td><td>must contact in writing</td></tr>
<tr><td>Green Fees</td><td>not confirmed.</td></tr>
<tr><td>Facilities</td><td>⊗ ⅏ by prior arrangement ⓑ ⓛ ♀ ♨ 🏨 ♈ ⓣ Michael Brothers.</td></tr>
<tr><td>Location</td><td>Seer Green (2m E,S of Seer Green)</td></tr>
<tr><td>Hotel</td><td>★★★67% Bellhouse Hotel, Oxford Rd, BEACONSFIELD ☎ (0753) 887211 136⇆</td></tr>
</table>

BLETCHLEY   Map 04 SP83

Windmill Hill ☎ Milton Keynes (0908) 378623
Long, open-parkland course designed by Henry Cotton and opened in 1972. Municipal.
18 holes, 6773yds, Par 73, SSS 72.
Club membership 430.

Visitors no restrictions.
Societies bookings for tee times: contact Sandie Hayward.
Green Fees £6 (£8.80 weekends).
Facilities ⊗ ⅏ ⓑ by prior arrangement ⓛ ♀ ♨ 🏨 ♈ ⓣ C Clingan.
Leisure floodlit driving range, pool table.
Location Tattenhoe Ln (W side of town centre on A421)
Hotel ★★★60% Swan Hotel, High St, LEIGHTON BUZZARD ☎ (0525) 372148 38⇆ ⓡ

BOW BRICKHILL   Map 04 SP93

WOBURN See page 25

BUCKINGHAM   Map 04 SP63

Buckingham ☎ (0280) 813282
Undulating parkland course cut by a stream.
18 holes, 5869yds, Par 70, SSS 69, Course record 67.
Club membership 680.

Visitors with member only at weekends. Must contact in advance.
Societies must contact by telephone.
Green Fees not confirmed.
Facilities ⊗ ⅏ ⓑ ⓛ ♀ ♨ 🏨 ⓣ Tom Gates.
Leisure snooker.
Location Tingewick Rd (1.5m W on A421)
Hotel ★★★66% Buckingham Lodge Hotel, Ring Rd South, BUCKINGHAM ☎ (0280) 822622 70⇆ ⓡ

BURNHAM   Map 04 SU98

Burnham Beeches ☎ (0628) 661448
In the centre of the lovely Burnham Beeches countryside. Wide fairways, carefully maintained greens, some hills, and some devious routes to a few holes. A good finish.
18 holes, 6449yds, Par 70, SSS 71.
Club membership 670.

Visitors must contact in advance. May play on weekdays only and must have a handicap certificate or introduction from own club.
Societies welcome
Green Fees £37.50 per day; £25 per round.
Facilities ♨ 🏨 ♈ ⓣ

<table>
<tr><td>Location</td><td>Green Ln (0.5m NE)</td></tr>
<tr><td>Hotel</td><td>★★★64% Burnham Beeches Moat House, Grove Rd, BURNHAM ☎ (0628) 603333 75⇆</td></tr>
</table>

Lambourne ☎ Maidenhead (0628) 662936 & 666755
A championship standard 18-hole course.
18 holes, 6746yds, Par 72, SSS 72.
Club membership 600.

Visitors must contact in advance, with introduction from own club. With member only at weekends.
Green Fees £30-£40.
Facilities ⊗ ⅏ ⓑ ⓛ ♀ ♨ 🏨
Leisure sauna, gymnasium.
Location Dropmore Rd
Hotel ★★★64% Burnham Beeches Moat House, Grove Rd, BURNHAM ☎ (0628) 603333 75⇆

CHALFONT ST GILES   Map 04 SU99

Harewood Downs ☎ Little Chalfont (0494) 762308 & 762184
A testing undulating parkland course with sloping greens and plenty of trees.
18 holes, 5958yds, Par 69, SSS 69, Course record 64.
Club membership 750.

Visitors must contact in advance & have handicap certificate.
Societies apply by phone then confirm in writing.
Green Fees £27 per day; £20 per round.
Facilities ⊗ ⅏ by prior arrangement ⓑ ⓛ ♀ ♨ 🏨 ⓣ G C Morris.
Location Cokes Ln (2m N off A413)
Hotel ★★★67% Bellhouse Hotel, Oxford Rd, BEACONSFIELD ☎ (0753) 887211 136 ⇆

CHARTRIDGE   Map 04 SP90

Chartridge Park ☎ High Wycombe (0494) 791772
Parkland course set in idyllic surroundings. Currently the UK's longest 9-hole course.
9 holes, 5836yds, Par 66, SSS 68, Course record 66.
Club membership 500.

Visitors may play mid-week only, must contact in advance.
Societies must telephone in advance.
Green Fees £13 per 18 holes.
Facilities ⊗ ⅏ ⓑ ⓛ ♀ ♨ 🏨 ♈ ⓣ Peter Gibbins.
Location 3m NW of Chesham
Hotel ★★★63% The Crown Hotel, High St, AMERSHAM ☎ (0494) 721541 23rm(13⇆1 ⓡ)

CHESHAM   Map 04 SP90

Chesham & Ley Hill ☎ (0494) 784541
Heathland course on hilltop with easy walking. Subject to wind.
9 holes, 5296yds, Par 67, SSS 66, Course record 64.
Club membership 430.

Visitors may play Mon & Thu, Wed after noon, Fri before 1.30pm.
Societies subject to approval, Thu only.
Green Fees not confirmed.

▶

Sunningdale

Sunningdale ☎ Ascot (0344) 21681   **Map 04 SU96**

*J*ohn Ingham writes: Many famous golfers maintain that Sunningdale, on the borders of Berkshire, is the most attractive inland course in Britain. The great Bobby Jones once played the 'perfect' round of 66 made up of threes and fours on the Old Course. Later, Norman von Nida of Australia shot a 63 while the then professional at the club, Arthur Lees, scored a 62 to win a huge wager.

To become a member of this club takes years of waiting. Maybe it is the quality of the courses, maybe the clubhouse atmosphere and perhaps the excellence of the professionals shop has something to do with it; but added up, it has to be the most desirable place to spend a day.

Founded just over ninety years ago, the Old Course was designed by Willie Park, while H.S. Colt created the New Course in 1923. Most golfers will agree that there isn't one indifferent hole on either course. While the Old Course, with silver birch, heather and perfect turf, is lovely to behold, the New Course alongside is considered by many to be its equal. But just as golfers want to play the Old Course at St Andrews, and miss the redesigned Jubilee, so visitors to Sunningdale opt for the Old, and fail to realise what they are overlooking by not playing the New.

The classic Old Course is not long, measuring just 6341 yards, and because the greens are normally in excellent condition, anyone with a 'hot' putter can have an exciting day, providing they keep teeshots on the fairway and don't stray into the gorse and the pine trees that lie in wait. On a sunny day, if you had to be anywhere in the world playing well, then we opt for the elevated 10th tee on the Old. What bliss!

Membership	850
Visitors	weekdays only. Must contact in advance, and have a letter of introduction from their own club and a handicap certificate
Societies	
Green fees	one year's notice required
Facilities	£80 per day
	⊗ ᒪ ☷ ♀ ⚒ 🏠 ᛚ (Keith Maxwell)
Location	Ridgemount Rd (1m S of Sunningdale, off A30)

36 holes. Old Course: 18 holes, 6586yds, Par 72, SSS 70, Course record 62 (Nick Faldo) New Course: 18 holes 6676yds, Par 70, SSS 72, Course record 64 (Gary Player)

WHERE TO STAY AND EAT NEARBY

HOTELS:

ASCOT

★★★★ 59% Berystede, Bagshot Rd, Sunninghill. ☎ (0344) 23311. 91 ⇄ 🐾 European cuisine

★★ 66% Highclere, 19 Kings Rd, Sunninghill. ☎ (0344) 25220. 12 ⇄ 🐾 European cuisine

BAGSHOT

★★★★❀❀ ♨ 80% Pennyhill Park, London Rd.
☎ (0276) 71774. 22 Annexe 54 ⇄ 🐾.
English & French cuisine

RESTAURANTS:

BRAY

✕✕✕✕❀❀❀❀ The Waterside, River Cottage, Ferry Road.
☎ Maidenhead (0628) 20691.
French cuisine

EGHAM

✕✕❀❀ La Bonne Franquette, 5 High St ☎ (0784) 439494. French cuisine

Facilities   ⊗ & ◼ by prior arrangement 🏌 🍺 ♀ ♨
Location   Ley Hill Common (2m E)
Hotel   ★★★63% The Crown Hotel, High St,
              AMERSHAM ☎ (0494) 721541
              23rm(13⇄1 ♠)

DAGNALL   Map 04 SP91

Whipsnade Park ☎ (044284) 2330
Parkland course situated on downs overlooking the Chilterns
adjoining Whipsnade Zoo. Easy walking, good views.
18 holes, 6800yds, Par 72, SSS 72, Course record 66.
Club membership 500.
Visitors   with member only at weekends. Must contact in
               advance.
Societies   must contact in advance.
Green Fees £31 per day; £21 per round.
Facilities ⊗ ◼ 🏌 🍺 ♀ ♨ 🏠 ⛳ 𝄡 Michael Lewendon.
Location   Studham Ln (1m E off B4506)
Hotel   ★★★67% Old Palace Lodge Hotel, Church St,
               DUNSTABLE ☎ (0582) 662201 49⇄

DENHAM   Map 04 TQ08

Buckinghamshire ☎ Uxbridge (0895) 835777
A John Jacobs designed championship-standard course.
Visitors only welcome as guests of members to this beautiful
course in 269 acres of lovely grounds including mature trees,
lakes and rivers.
18 holes, 6880yds, Par 72, SSS 73.
Club membership 324.
Visitors   with member only or introduced by member.
Societies   by invitation.
Green Fees £47 (£60 weekends).
Facilities ⊗ ◼ 🏌 🍺 ♀ ♨ 🏠 ⛳ 𝄡 John O'Leary.
Leisure   fishing.
Location   Denham Court
Hotel   ★★61% Ethorpe Hotel, Packhorse Rd,
               GERRARDS CROSS ☎ (0753) 882039 29⇄ ♠

Denham ☎ Uxbridge (0895) 832022
A beautifully maintained parkland/heathland course,
home of many county champions. Slightly hilly and
calling for good judgement of distance in the wooded
areas.
18 holes, 6440yds, Par 70, SSS 71, Course record 66.
Club membership 550.
Visitors   must contact in advance & have handicap
               certificate. Must play with member Fri-Sun.
Societies   must book one year in advance.
Green Fees Apr-Oct: £48 per day; £32 per round. Rest
               of year £25 per round.
Facilities ⊗ & 🏌 (ex Mon) 🍺 ♀ ♨ 🏠 ⛳ 𝄡
               John Sheridan.
Location   Tilehouse Ln (2m NW)
Hotel   ★★61% Ethorpe Hotel, Packhorse Rd,
               GERRARDS CROSS
               ☎ (0753) 882039 29⇄ ♠

For an explanation of symbols and
abbreviations, see page 11

FLACKWELL HEATH   Map 04 SU89

Flackwell Heath ☎ Bourne End (0628) 520027
Open heath and tree-lined course on hills overlooking
Loudwater and the M40. Quick drying.
18 holes, 6207yds, Par 71, SSS 70.
Club membership 800.
Visitors   with member only at weekends. A handicap
               certificate is usually required.
Societies   Wed & Thu only. Must contact in writing.
Green Fees £27 per day.
Facilities ⊗ ◼ by prior arrangement 🏌 🍺 ♀ ♨ 🏠 ⛳
               Stephen Bryan.
Location   Treadaway Rd, High Wycombe (NE side of
               town centre)
Hotel   ★★★67% Bellhouse Hotel, Oxford Rd,
               BEACONSFIELD ☎ (0753) 887211 136⇄

GERRARDS CROSS   Map 04 TQ08

Gerrards Cross ☎ (0753) 883263
A wooded parkland course which has been modernised in
recent years and is now a very pleasant circuit with
infinite variety. The best part lies on the plateau above
the clubhouse where there are some testing holes.
18 holes, 6295yds, Par 69, SSS 70.
Club membership 820.
Visitors   must contact in advance & have a letter of
               introduction from their club or a handicap
               certificate.
Societies   must book one year ahead.
Green Fees £35 per day; £28 per round.
Facilities ⊗ ◼ by prior arrangement 🏌 🍺 ♀ ♨ 🏠 ⛳
               Matthew Barr.
Location   Chalfont Park
               (NE side of town centre off A413)
Hotel   ★★★67% Bellhouse Hotel, Oxford Rd,
               BEACONSFIELD ☎ (0753) 887211 136⇄

HALTON   Map 04 SP81

Chiltern Forest ☎ Aylesbury (0296) 630899
Extended to 18 holes in 1992, this very hilly wooded
parkland course is on two levels. The surrounding woodland
makes the course very scenic.
18 holes, 5765yds, Par 70, SSS 70.
Club membership 670.
Visitors   must play with member at weekends.
Societies   must contact in advance.
Green Fees £24 per day.
Facilities ⊗ ◼ 🏌 🍺 ♀ ♨ 🏠 ⛳ C Skeet.
Location   Aston Hill (1m NE off A4011)
Hotel   ★★68% Rose & Crown Hotel, High St, TRING
               ☎ (044282) 4071 27⇄ ♠

HIGH WYCOMBE   Map 04 SU89

Hazelmere Golf & Country Club ☎ (0494) 714722
Undulating parkland. Two long Par 5s.
18 holes, 5873yds, Par 70, SSS 68, Course record 66.
Club membership 700.
Visitors   weekdays only.
Societies   apply in advance.
Green Fees £34 per day; £25 per round.   ▶

Woburn

Bow Brickhill ☎ **(0908) 370756**   **Map O4 SP93**

John Ingham writes: Come off the M1 motorway at Junction 13 and you are quickly at Woburn, with its magnificent stately home, wildlife safari park and surrounding echoes of Henry VIII and the Dukes of Bedford. Within the last 20 years two new attractions have been added - two golf courses designed by the famed Charles Lawrie of Cotton Pennink.

To create these beautiful courses, the bulldozers got among pine and chestnut and literally cut fairways through some of the most picturesque country in all England - but it had been country seen by very few. From the very back tees, both courses are somewhat long for the weekend amateur. The Duke's measures 6940 yards and makes for a stiff test for any class of golfer, while the 'easier' Duchess, measuring a very respectable 6616 yards, requires a high degree of skill on its fairways guarded by towering pines.

Today, under the direction of Alex Hay, a Scottish TV golf commentator, the two courses are best known as the home of the British Masters, a golf tournament sponsored by Rothmans, who also sponsor the club.

The town of Woburn and the Abbey are both within Bedfordshire, while the golf and country club actually lie over the border in Buckinghamshire. Although just 45 miles from London, you will feel very much in the wilds and the local pubs and people, plus some wonderful countryside, make this area an excellent place to stay for a few days.

And, if you can hit the ball straight, you might get near the course record of 64 achieved by professional Peter Mitchell and Andrew Murray!

Membership 900

Visitors   must play with a member at weekends. Must contact in advance and have an introduction from own club

Societies must telephone in advance

Green fees £67.50 per day - includes carvery lunch

Facilities ⊗ ▥ by prior arrangement (groups only) ▦ ♀⚲ 🏠 ໂ (Alex Hay)

Leisure   hard tennis courts

Location 0.5miles S E of Bow Brickhill

36 holes. Dukes Course: 18 holes, 6940 yds, Par 72 , SSS 74
Duchess Course: 18 holes, 6641yds, Par 72, SSS 72

WHERE TO STAY AND EAT NEARBY

HOTELS:

APSLEY GUISE
★★★69%Moore Place, The Square ☎ (0908) 282000, 39 ⇥ ▯ Annexe 15 ⇥ ໂ

Flitwick
★★★❀❀❀ ♣♣ 72% Flitwick Manor, Church Rd. ☎ (0525)712242,15 ⇥ ໂ

WOBURN
★★❀ 69% The Bell Inn, 34 Bedford St ☎ (0525)290280. 21 ⇥ ໂ Annexe 6 (4 ⇥ ໂ). English & French cuisine

RESTAURANTS:

MARSTON MORTAINE
✕✕✕❀❀ Moretayne Manor, Woburn Rd. ☎ (0234)767003. British, French & Italian cuisine

WOBURN
✕✕✕❀❀ Paris House, Woburn Park ☎ (0525) 290692. French cuisine

Facilities ⊗ 🅰 🅱 🍺 ♀ ⛄ 🏠 (Steve Morvell.
Leisure snooker.
Location Penn Rd, Hazelmere (2m NE, A404 towards Amersham)
Hotel ★★★63% The Crown Hotel, High St, AMERSHAM ☎ (0494) 721541 23rm(13⇄1 ⋒)

IVER   Map 04 TQ08

Iver ☎ (0753) 655615
Pay and play parkland course; fairly flat.
9 holes, 2994yds, Par 72, SSS 70.
Club membership 500.
Visitors no restrictions.
Societies must contact in advance.
Green Fees not confirmed.
Facilities ⊗ 🅱 🍺 ♀ ⛄ 🏠 🍴 (Gerry Isles.
Leisure practice range.
Location Hollow Hill Ln, Langley Park Rd (1.5m SW off B470)
Hotel ★★★★65% Heathrow/Slough Marriott, Ditton Road, Langley, SLOUGH ☎ (0753) 544244 350⇄ ⋒

IVINGHOE   Map 04 SP91

Ivinghoe ☎ Cheddington (0296) 668696
Testing parkland course with water on three holes. Easy walking on rolling countryside.
9 holes, 4508yds, Par 62, SSS 62, Course record 61.
Club membership 250.
Visitors may only play after 8am.
Societies must contact in advance.
Green Fees not confirmed.
Facilities ⊗ 🅰 🅱 🍺 ♀ ⛄ 🏠 🍴 (Bill Garrad.
Location Wellcroft (N side of village)
Hotel ★★★(red) Bell Inn, ASTON CLINTON ☎ (0296) 630252 6⇄ ⋒ Annexe15⇄ ⋒

LITTLE CHALFONT   Map 04 SU99

Little Chalfont ☎ (0494) 764877
Gently undulating flat course surrounded by woods.
9 holes, 5852yds, Par 68, SSS 68.
Club membership 300.
Visitors no restrictions.
Societies must contact in advance.
Green Fees not confirmed.
Facilities ⊗ 🅰 🅱 🍺 ♀ ⛄ 🏠 🍴 (Mr Williams.
Leisure practice area.
Location Lodge Ln (Between Little Chalfont & Chorleywood)
Hotel ★★★63% The Crown Hotel, High St, AMERSHAM ☎ (0494) 721541 23rm(13⇄1 ⋒)

LOUDWATER   Map 04 SU89

Wycombe Heights Golf Centre ☎ Penn (049481) 2862
Opened in 1991 and designed by the John Jacobs Partnership. The golf centre includes a 24-bay driving range.
18 holes, 6200yds, Par 70, SSS 72.
Club membership 1000.

Visitors no restrictions.
Societies apply in writing.
Green Fees £10 (£13 weekends).
Facilities ⊗ 🅰 🅱 🍺 ♀ ⛄ 🏠 🍴 (Wayne Owers.
Leisure driving range.
Location Rayners Ave
Hotel ★★★62% Forte Posthouse, Handy Cross, HIGH WYCOMBE ☎ (0494) 442100 106⇄ ⋒

MENTMORE   Map 04 SP91

Mentmore Golf & Country Club ☎ Aylesbury (0296) 662020
Two 18-hole courses in the wooded parkland of Mentmore House. Long Par 5 at the 9th on the Rosebery Course.
Rosebery: 18 holes, 6777yds, Par 72, SSS 72.
Rothschild: 18 holes, 6763yds, Par 72, SSS 72.
Club membership 650.
Visitors must have handicap certificate & contact in advance, weekends subject to competitions.
Societies by prior arrangement.
Green Fees £38 per day; £25 per round.
Facilities ⊗ 🅰 (Fri-Sat from 7pm) 🅱 🍺 ♀ ⛄ 🏠 🍴 (Pip Elson.
Leisure heated indoor swimming pool, sauna, steam room, jacuzzi.
Location 4m S of Leighton Buzzard
Hotel ★★★60% Swan Hotel, High St, LEIGHTON BUZZARD ☎ (0525) 372148 38⇄ ⋒

MILTON KEYNES   Map 04 SP83

Abbey Hill ☎ (0908) 563845
Undulating municipal course within the new city. Tight fairways and well-placed bunkers. Stream comes into play on five holes. Also Par 3 course.
18 holes, 6177yds, Par 68, SSS 69.
Club membership 600.
Visitors no restrictions
Societies must telephone (0908) 562408 in advance
Green Fees not confirmed.
Facilities ⊗ 🅰 🅱 🍺 ♀ ⛄ 🏠 🍴 (
Leisure pool table, darts.
Location Two Mile Ash (2m W of new town centre off A5)
Hotel ★★62% Swan Revived Hotel, High St, Newport Pagnell, MILTON KEYNES ☎ (0908) 610565 42rm(40⇄ ⋒)

PRINCES RISBOROUGH   Map 04 SP80

Whiteleaf ☎ (0844) 274058
Short, 9-hole parkland course requiring great accuracy, fine views.
9 holes, 5391yds, Par 66, SSS 66, Course record 64.
Club membership 350.
Visitors with member only at weekends. Must contact in advance.
Societies must contact the secretary in advance.
Green Fees not confirmed.
Facilities ⊗ 🅰 🅱 🍺 ♀ ⛄ 🏠 (K Ward.
Location Whiteleaf (1m NE off A4010)
Hotel ★★★(red) Bell Inn, ASTON CLINTON ☎ (0296) 630252 6⇄ ⋒ Annexe15⇄ ⋒

STOKE POGES

Map 04 SU98

Farnham Park ☎ (028814) 3332
Fine, public parkland course in pleasing setting.
18 holes, 6172yds, Par 71, SSS 69.
Club membership 900.
Visitors   no restrictions.
Societies   must contact in advance.
Green Fees   weekdays £7.70 (£10.25 weekends).
Facilities   ㋡ 🍴 ♀ ☂ 🏠 ⚑ ℓ Paul Harrison.
Leisure   pool table, darts.
Location   Park Rd (W side of village off B416)
Hotel   ★★★★65% Heathrow/Slough Marriott, Ditton
Road, Langley, SLOUGH
☎ (0753) 544244   350㋡ ⎙

> **Stoke Poges** ☎ Slough (0753) 26385
> Judgement of the distance from the tee is all important on
> this first-class parkland course. There are many
> outstanding par 4's around 440 yds, several calling for
> much thought. Fairways are wide and the challenge
> seemingly innocuous.
> *18 holes, 6654yds, Par 71, SSS 72.*
> *Club membership 720.*
> **Visitors**   may not play weekends, Tue mornings and
> Wednesdays. Must contact in advance and
> have a handicap certificate.
> **Societies**   must contact in advance.
> **Green Fees**   £45 per day; £30 per round.
> **Facilities**   ☂ 🏠 ⚑ ℓ
> **Leisure**   snooker, sauna.
> **Location**   Park Rd (1.5m W off B416)
> **Hotel**   ★★★★65% Heathrow/Slough Marriott,
> Ditton Road, Langley, SLOUGH
> ☎ (0753) 544244   350㋡ ⎙

WAVENDON

Map 04 SP93

Wavendon Golf Centre ☎ Milton Keynes (0908) 281811
Pleasant parkland course set in 96 acres of mature trees.
18 holes, 5479yds, Par 67, SSS 67.
Club membership 300.
Visitors   must book 3 days in advance. Casual smart dress
required.
Societies   must contact in advance by telephone.
Green Fees   £9 (£12 weekends & bank holidays).
Facilities   ㋡ (Sun only) ⫟ (Wed-Sun) 🍴 🍴 ♀ ☂ 🏠 ⚑ ℓ
P Sounders.
Leisure   9 hole Par 3 course.
Location   Lower End Rd (just off A421)
Hotel   ★★★69% Moore Place Hotel, The Square,
ASPLEY GUISE ☎ (0908) 282000
39㋡   Annexe15㋡

WESTON TURVILLE

Map 04 SP81

Weston Turville Golf & Squash Club ☎ Aylesbury (0296)
24084 & 25949
Parkland course, with views of the Chiltern Hills. Flat easy
walking with water hazards.
18 holes, 6002yds, Par 69, SSS 69.
Club membership 600.
Visitors   no restrictions.
Societies   must contact in advance.

Green Fees £15 (£20 weekends).
Facilities   ㋡ 🍴 🍴 ♀ ☂ 🏠 ⚑ ℓ Tom Jones.
Leisure   squash.
Location   New Rd (0.5m N off B4544)
Hotel   ★★★(red) Bell Inn, ASTON CLINTON
☎ (0296) 630252   6㋡ ⎙ Annexe15㋡ ⎙

WEXHAM STREET

Map 04 SU98

Wexham Park ☎ (0753) 663271
Gently undulating parkland course. Two courses.
*18 holes, 5836yds, Par 69, SSS 68 or 9 holes, 2283yds, Par
32, SSS 32.*
Club membership 500.
Visitors   no restrictions
Societies   may not play at weekends; must contact in
advance.
Green Fees   not confirmed.
Facilities   ㋡ ⫟ by prior arrangement 🍴 🍴 ♀ ☂ 🏠 ⚑ ℓ
Location   0.5m S
Hotel   ★★★★65% Heathrow/Slough Marriott, Ditton
Road, Langley, SLOUGH
☎ (0753) 544244   350㋡ ⎙

WING

Map 04 SP82

Aylesbury Vale ☎ Leighton Buzzard (0525) 240196
The course, which is gently undulating and played over
water, was opened in the autumn of 1991. There are five
ponds to add interest. In addition there is a 10-bay driving
range, a practice fairway and practice putting green as well as
an In-Golf Simulator.
18 holes, 6622yds, Par 72, SSS 72, Course record 70.
Club membership 550.
Visitors   must have handicap certificate & must contact in
advance.
Societies   telephone to book in advance.
Green Fees   £10 Mon-Thu; £12 Fri; £17.50 weekends.
Facilities   ㋡ ⫟ 🍴 🍴 ♀ ☂ 🏠 ⚑ ℓ Lee Scarbrow.
Leisure   golf simulator.
Location   Wing Rd (2m NW on unclassified Stewkley
road)
Hotel   ★★★60% Swan Hotel, High St, LEIGHTON
BUZZARD ☎ (0525) 372148   38㋡ ⎙

CAMBRIDGESHIRE

BRAMPTON

Map 04 TL27

Brampton Park ☎ Huntingdon (0480) 811772
Set in truly attractive countryside, bounded by the River
Great Ouse and bisected by the River Lane. Great variety
with mature trees, lakes and water hazards. One of the most
difficult holes is the 4th, a Par 3 island green, named
'Fowler's Folly'.
18 holes, 3245yds, Par 71, SSS 73.
Club membership 600.
Visitors   must be accompanied by member and contact in
advance.
Societies   must telephone in advance.
Green Fees   not confirmed.   ▶

Facilities ⊗ ⅷ by prior arrangement ⓑ ▦♀♨⌂ℓ
Michael Torrens.
Location Buckden Rd
Hotel ★★64% Grange Hotel, 115 High St,
BRAMPTON ☎ (0480) 459516 9rm(1⇌7 ↰)

CAMBRIDGE

Map 05 TL45

Cambridgeshire Moat House
☎ (0954) 780098 & 780555
Undulating parkland course with lake and water hazards,
easy walking. Many leisure facilities. Course record
holders, Paul Way and Peter Townsend.
18 holes, 6734yds, Par 72, SSS 72.
Club membership 500.
Visitors must book in advance.
Societies must telephone in advance.
Green Fees £19 per day (£25 weekends & bank holidays).
Facilities ⊗ ⅷ ⓑ ▦♀♨⌂↿⇆ℓ David Vernon.
Leisure hard tennis courts, heated indoor swimming
pool, squash, sauna, solarium, gymnasium.
Location Moat House Hotel, Bar Hill (5m NW on A604)
Hotel ★★★63% Cambridgeshire Moat House,
BAR HILL ☎ (0954) 780555 100⇌↰

Gog Magog ☎ (0223) 247626
Situated just outside the centre of the university town,
Gog Magog, established in 1901, is known as the nursery
of Cambridge under-graduate golf. The course is on high
ground, and it is said that if you stand on the highest
point and could see far enough to the east the next
highest ground would be the Ural Mountains! The
courses (there are two of them) are open but there are
enough trees and other hazards to provide plenty of
problems. Views from the high parts are superb. The
nature of the ground ensures good winter golf.
Old Course: 18 holes, 6354yds, Par 70, SSS 70.
New Course: 9 holes, 5833yds, Par 69, SSS 68.
Club membership 1100.
Visitors must contact in advance & have handicap
certificate. With member only at weekends.
Societies by reservation.
Green Fees £35 per day; £29 per round.
Facilities ⊗ ⅷ by prior arrangement ⓑ ▦♀♨⌂ℓ
Ian Bamborough.
Location Shelford Bottom (3m SE on A1307)
Hotel ★★★68% Gonville Hotel, Gonville Place,
CAMBRIDGE ☎ (0223) 66611 62⇌↰

ELY

Map 05 TL58

Ely City ☎ (0353) 662751
Parkland course slightly undulating with water hazards
formed by lakes and natural dykes. Magnificent views of
Cathedral. Lee Trevino is the professional record holder.
18 holes, 6602yds, Par 72, SSS 72, Course record 66.
Club membership 1000.
Visitors must have handicap certificate. It is advisable to
contact the club in advance.
Societies must contact club in advance.
Green Fees £22 per day (£30 weekends & bank holidays).
Facilities ⊗ ⅷ ⓑ ▦♀♨⌂↿ℓ Fred Rowden.
Location Cambridge Rd (SW side of city centre on A10)
Hotel ★★★61% Fenlands Lodge Hotel, Soham Rd,
Stuntney, ELY ☎ (0353) 667047 9⇌↰

GIRTON

Map 05 TL46

Girton ☎ Cambridge (0223) 276169
Flat, open parkland course with easy walking.
18 holes, 6088yds, Par 69, SSS 69.
Club membership 750.
Visitors with member only at weekends. Must
contact in advance.
Societies by arrangement.
Green Fees £25 per weekday (£19 with handicap
certificate).
Facilities ⊗ ⅷ ⓑ ▦♀♨⌂↿ℓ Scott Thomson.
Location Dodford Ln (NW side of village)
Hotel ★★★65% Forte Posthouse, Lakeview,
Bridge Rd, Impington, CAMBRIDGE
☎ (0223) 237000 118⇌↰

MARCH

Map 05 TL49

March ☎ (0354) 52364
Nine-hole parkland course.
9 holes, 6210yds, Par 70, SSS 70, Course record 65.
Club membership 400.
Visitors with member only at weekends.
Societies apply in writing.
Green Fees £15 per 18 holes.
Facilities ⓑ ▦ (Fri-Sun only) ♀♨⌂ℓ Richard Keys.
Location Frogs Abbey, Grange Rd (14m W of
Peterborough)
Hotel ★67% Olde Griffin Hotel, High St, MARCH
☎ (0354) 52517 20rm(16⇌3 ↰)

PETERBOROUGH

Map 04 TL19

Elton Furze ☎ (0832) 280189
A new course opened in 1993. Wooded parkland 18-hole
course in lovely surroundings.
18 holes, 6291yds, Par 70, SSS 70.
Club membership 400.
Visitors on Tue & Thu only, without member.
Societies apply in writing, Tue & Thu only.
Green Fees £30 per day; £20 per round (Tue & Thu only
unless with member).
Facilities ▦♀♨⌂ℓ Frank Kiddie.
Location Bullock Rd, Haddon (4m SW of Peterborough,
off A605)
Hotel ★★★★63% Swallow Hotel, Lynchwood,
ALWALTON ☎ (0733) 371111 163⇌

Orton Meadows ☎ (0733) 237478
Municipal, parkland course on either side of the Nene Valley
Railway, with lakes and water hazards. Also 12-hole pitch
and putt course.
18 holes, 5800yds, Par 68, SSS 68, Course record 67.
Club membership 850.
Visitors no restrictions.
Societies must telephone in advance.
Green Fees £7.50 per round (£10 weekends & bank
holidays).
Facilities ♨⌂↿ℓ Neil Grant.
Leisure 12 hole pitch & putt.
Location Ham Ln, Oundle Rd (3m W of town on A605)
Hotel ★★★66% The Haycock Hotel, WANSFORD
☎ (0780) 782223 51⇌↰

Peterborough Milton ☎ (0733) 380489
Well-bunkered parkland course set in the grounds of the Earl
Fitzwilliam's estate. Easy walking.
18 holes, 6221yds, Par 71, SSS 70.
Club membership 800.
Visitors   handicap certificate required.
Societies   Tue-Thu only, must contact in advance.
Green Fees £30 per day; £20 per round (£25 weekends).
Facilities   ⊗ ⅷ ⅃ ▆ ♀ ♨ 🏠 ⚑ Michael Gallagher.
Location   Milton Ferry (2m W on A47)
Hotel   ★★★66% The Haycock Hotel, WANSFORD
            ☎ (0780) 782223 51⇄ ⌂

Thorpe Wood ☎ (0733) 267701
Gently undulating, municipal parkland course designed by
Peter Alliss and Dave Thomas.
18 holes, 7086yds, Par 71, SSS 74.
Club membership 850.
Visitors   phone for reservations.
Societies   must telephone in advance.
Green Fees £7.50 per round (£10 weekends & bank
            holidays).
Facilities   ♨ 🏠 ⚑ Dennis & Roger Fitton.
Location   Thorpe Wood (3m W of city centre on A47)
Hotel   ★★★60% Bull Hotel, Westgate,
            PETERBOROUGH ☎ (0733) 61364 103⇄

PIDLEY   Map 04 TL37

Lakeside Lodge ☎ Ramsey (0487) 740540
A well designed, spacious course incorporating eight lakes
and a modern clubhouse. Also 9-hole Par 3 and 25-bay
driving range.
18 holes, 6600yds, Par 72, SSS 73.
Par 3: 9 holes, 820yds, Par 27.
Club membership 500.
Visitors   no restrictions.
Societies   must telephone in advance.
Green Fees £4 for 9 holes, £7 per 18 holes; (£7/£14
            weekends).
Facilities   ⊗ ⅷ ⅃ ▆ ♀ ♨ 🏠 ⚑ Alistair Headley.
Leisure   fishing, driving range.
Location   Fen Rd
Hotel   ★★★65% Slepe Hall Hotel, Ramsey Rd,
            ST IVES ☎ (0480) 63122 16rm(15⇄ ⌂)

RAMSEY   Map 04 TL28

Ramsey ☎ (0487) 812600
Flat, parkland course with water hazards.
18 holes, 6133yds, Par 71, SSS 70, Course record 66.
Club membership 750.
Visitors   must have a handicap certificate; must play with
            member at weekends & bank holidays.
Societies   must contact secretary in advance.
Green Fees £20 per day/round.
Facilities   ⊗ ⅷ by prior arrangement ⅃ ▆ ♀ ♨ 🏠 ⚑
            Stuart Scott.
Leisure   bowling green.
Location   4 Abbey Ter (S side of town)
Hotel   ★★★72% The Old Bridge Hotel,
            HUNTINGDON ☎ (0480) 52681 26⇄ ⌂

ST IVES   Map 04 TL37

St Ives (Hunts) ☎ (0480) 468392
Picturesque parkland course.
9 holes, 3302yds, Par 68, SSS 69.
Club membership 305.
Visitors   telephone for details.
Green Fees not confirmed.
Facilities   ♀ ♨ 🏠
Location   Westwood Rd (W side of town centre off
            A1123)
Hotel   ★★★65% Slepe Hall Hotel, Ramsey Rd,
            ST IVES ☎ (0480) 63122 16rm(15⇄ ⌂)

ST NEOTS   Map 04 TL16

Abbotsley Golf & Squash Club ☎ Huntingdon (0480)
215153 & 474000
Two courses - main Abbotsley course (parkland with tree-
lined fairways) hosts County Championship. Cromwell
course, opened in 1991, is maturing well. Courses surround
moated country house and hotel. Residential golf schools 30
weeks of the year plus floodlit, covered driving range.
Abbotsley: 18 holes, 5829yds, Par 70, SSS 72.
Cromwell: 18 holes, 6311yds, Par 73.
Club membership 650.
Visitors   may not play before 10am at weekends.
Societies   must contact by telephone.
Green Fees Abbotsley: £18 per day (£22 weekends);
            Cromwell: £10 per day (£12 weekends).
Facilities   ⊗ ⅷ ⅃ ▆ ♀ ♨ 🏠 ⚑ 🏳 ⚑ Vivien Saunders.
Leisure   squash, snooker, sauna, solarium, floodlit
            covered driving range.
Location   2m SE off B1046
Hotel   ★★64% Abbotsley Golf Hotel, Eynesbury
            Hardwicke, ST NEOTS
            ☎ (0480) 474000 15⇄ ⌂

St Neots ☎ Huntingdon (0480) 472363
Undulating parkland course with lake and water hazards,
close to the Kym and Great Ouse rivers. Easy, level walking.
18 holes, 6027yds, Par 69, SSS 69.
Club membership 600.
Visitors   must have handicap certificate. With member
            only at weekends.
Societies   must contact in advance.
Green Fees £30 per day; £20 per round.
Facilities   ⊗ ⅷ ⅃ ▆ ♀ ♨ 🏠 ⚑ 🏳 Graham Bithrey.
Leisure   snooker.
Location   Crosshall Rd (W side of town centre on A45)
Hotel   ★★64% Grange Hotel, 115 High St,
            BRAMPTON ☎ (0480) 459516 9rm(1⇄7 ⌂)

TOFT   Map 05 TL35

Comberton ☎ Cambridge (0223) 264700
A new course for 1993. Set in 207 acres to a Peter Allis/Clive
Clark design with sweeping fairways, lakes and well-guarded
greens.
18 holes, 6687yds, Par 73.
Club membership 750.
Visitors   must contact in advance, must have handicap
            card, weekends are limited.
Societies   contact in advance.   ▶

Green Fees £20 (£25 weekends & bank holidays).
Facilities ⊗ ⅲ ㄸ ♥ ♀ 冬 ⋒ ⛳ ℂ
Location Comberton Rd (3m W of Cambridge, on B1046)
Hotel ★★★62% Royal Cambridge Hotel,
Trumpington St, CAMBRIDGE
☎ (0223) 351631 46⇆ ⋒

CHESHIRE

ALDERLEY EDGE

Map 07 SJ87

Alderley Edge ☎ (0625) 585583
Well-wooded, undulating pastureland course. A stream
crosses 7 of the 9 holes.
9 holes, 5828yds, Par 68, SSS 68.
Club membership 400.
Visitors may not play Tue and Sat.
Societies Thu only.
Green Fees £18 per day; (£22 weekends).
Facilities ⊗ ⅲ ㄸ ♥ ♀ 冬 ⋒ ℂ A Sproston.
Leisure snooker.
Location Brook Ln (1m NW on B5085)
Hotel ★★★73% Alderley Edge Hotel, Macclesfield
Rd, ALDERLEY EDGE
☎ (0625) 583033 32⇆ ⋒

ALSAGER

Map 07 SJ75

Alsager Golf & Country Club ☎ (0270) 875700
An 18-hole parkland course situated in rolling Cheshire
countryside. Clubhouse is well appointed with good facilities
and a friendly atmosphere.
18 holes, 6206yds, Par 70, SSS 70, Course record 69.
Club membership 600.
Visitors must play with member at weekends. Must
contact in advance.
Societies Mon, Wed & Thu only; must contact in writing.
Green Fees not confirmed.
Facilities ⊗ ⅲ ㄸ ♥ ♀ 冬 ⋒ ⛳ ℂ Nick Rothe.
Leisure snooker.
Location Audley Rd (2m NE M6 junct 10)
Hotel ★★★66% Manor House Hotel, Audley Rd,
ALSAGER ☎ (0270) 884000 57⇆ ⋒

CHESTER

Map 07 SJ46

Chester ☎ (0244) 677760
Meadowland course on two levels contained within a loop of
the River Dee. The car park overlooks the racecourse across
the river.
18 holes, 6500yds, Par 72, SSS 71.
Club membership 700.
Visitors must contact in advance.
Societies must telephone in advance.
Green Fees £21 per day (£26 weekends).
Facilities ⊗ ⅲ by prior arrangement ㄸ ♥ ♀ 冬 ⋒ ⛳ ℂ
Georg Parton.
Leisure snooker.
Location Curzon Park (1m SW of city centre)
Hotel ★★★★71% Moat House International, Trinity
St, CHESTER ☎ (0244) 322330 150⇆

Upton-by-Chester ☎ (0244) 381183
Pleasant, tree-lined, parkland course. Not easy for low-
handicap players to score well. Testing holes are 2nd (par 4),
14th (par 4) and 15th (par 3).
18 holes, 5808yds, Par 69, SSS 68, Course record 62.
Club membership 700.
Visitors restricted competition days Sat & Sun. Must
contact in advance.
Societies apply in writing.
Green Fees not confirmed.
Facilities ⊗ ⅲ ㄸ ♥ ♀ 冬 ⋒ ℂ P A Gardner.
Leisure snooker.
Location Upton Ln, Upton-by-Chester (N side off A5116)
Hotel ★★★★62% Mollington Banastre Hotel,
Parkgate Rd, CHESTER
☎ (0244) 851471 64⇆

Vicars Cross ☎ (0244) 335174
Tree-lined parkland course, with undulating terrain.
18 holes, 6243yds, Par 72, SSS 70.
Club membership 660.
Visitors Mon-Thu day ticket only. Advisable to contact
in advance.
Societies Apr-Oct, Tue & Thu only.
Green Fees £20 per day/round, £14 after 4pm.
Facilities ⊗ ⅲ ㄸ ♥ (no catering Monday) ♀ 冬 ⋒ ℂ
J A Forsythe.
Leisure snooker.
Location Tarvin Rd, Great Barrow (4m E on A51)
Hotel ★★★66% Rowton Hall Hotel, Whitchurch
Road,Rowton, CHESTER
☎ (0244) 335262 42⇆ ⋒

CONGLETON

Map 07 SJ86

Astbury ☎ (0260) 272772
Parkland course in open countryside, bisected by a canal.
Large practice area.
18 holes, 6269yds, Par 71, SSS 70.
Club membership 700.
Visitors with member only at weekends. Must have a
handicap certificate. Must have an introduction
from own club.
Societies Thu by written request.
Green Fees £25 per day.
Facilities ⊗ ⅲ by prior arrangement ㄸ ♥ ♀ 冬 ⋒ ℂ
Nigel Griffith.
Leisure snooker.
Location Peel Ln, Astbury (1.5m S between A34 and
A527)
Hotel ★★★63% Saxon Cross Hotel, Holmes Chapel
Rd, SANDBACH ☎ (0270) 763281 52⇆ ⋒

Congleton ☎ (0260) 273540
Superbly-manicured parkland course with views over three
counties from the balcony of the clubhouse.
9 holes, 5103yds, Par 68, SSS 65.
Club membership 400.
Visitors may not play during competitions.
Societies must apply in writing to Secretary.
Green Fees £14 per day (£20 weekends & bank holidays).
Facilities ⊗ ⅲ & ㄸ by prior arrangement ♥ (Normally
no catering Mon) ♀ 冬 ⋒ ℂ John Colclough.
Leisure snooker.

Location	Biddulph Rd (1.5m SE on A527)
Hotel	★★★65% Chimney House Hotel, Congleton Rd, SANDBACH ☎ (0270) 764141 48⇥ ⋔

CREWE   Map 07 SJ75

Crewe ☎ (0270) 584099
Undulating parkland course.
18 holes, 6229yds, Par 70, SSS 70, Course record 66.
Club membership 600.

Visitors	with member only weekends and bank holidays.
Societies	Tue only, telephone to arrange.
Green Fees	£25 per day; £20 after 1pm.
Facilities	⊗ ⊞ by prior arrangement ⅙ ♥ ♀ ⚐ ⌂ ⌁
Leisure	snooker.
Location	Fields Rd, Haslington (2.25m NE off A534)
Hotel	★★★62% Hunters Lodge Hotel, Sydney Rd, Sydney, CREWE ☎ (0270) 583440 & 588216 42⇥ ⋔

DELAMERE   Map 07 SJ56

Delamere Forest ☎ Sandiway (0606) 882807
Played mostly on open heath there is great charm in the way this course drops down into the occasional pine sheltered valley.
18 holes, 6305yds, Par 72, SSS 70, Course record 63.
Club membership 600.

Visitors	restricted weekends and bank holidays. Must contact in advance.
Societies	telephone to arrange.
Green Fees	£35 per day; £25 per round (£30 per round weekends and bank holidays).
Facilities	⊗ & ⊞ by prior arrangement(ex Fri) ⅙ ♥ ♀ ⚐ ⌂ ⌁ Ellis B Jones.
Location	Station Rd (1.5m NE, off B5152)
Hotel	★★★64% Hartford Hall Hotel, School Ln, Hartford, NORTHWICH ☎ (0606) 75711 20⇥

DISLEY   Map 07 SJ98

Disley ☎ (0663) 62071
Parkland/moorland course with trees. Often breezy. Good views. Testing hole: 5th (par 5).
18 holes, 6015yds, Par 70, SSS 69.
Club membership 400.

Visitors	restricted Thu, Fri, weekends & bank holidays.
Societies	must contact in advance.
Green Fees	not confirmed.
Facilities	⊗ ⊞ ⅙ ♥ (no catering Mon) ♀ ⚐ ⌂ ⌁ Andrew Esplin.
Leisure	snooker.
Location	Stanley Hall Ln, Jacksons Edge (NW side of village off A6)
Hotel	★★70% Red Lion Inn, 112 Buxton Rd, High Ln, STOCKPORT ☎ (0663) 765227 6⇥ ⋔

ECCLESTON   Map 07 SJ46

Eaton ☎ (0244) 680474
A very testing well-wooded parkland course.
18 holes, 6446yds, Par 72, SSS 71.
Club membership 530.

Visitors	must contact in advance & have handicap certificate.
Societies	must contact in advance.
Green Fees	not confirmed.
Facilities	⅙ ♥ ♀ ⚐ ⌂ ⌁ A Mitchell.
Location	Eaton Park (1m S)
Hotel	★★★★(red) The Chester Grosvenor Hotel, Eastgate St, CHESTER ☎ (0244) 324024 86⇥ ⋔

ELLESMERE PORT   Map 07 SJ47

Ellesmere Port ☎ 051-339 7689
Municipal parkland course with natural hazards of woods, brook and ponds.
18 holes, 6384yds, Par 70, SSS 72, Course record 66.
Club membership 300.

Visitors	must contact in advance.
Societies	by arrangement with professional.
Green Fees	not confirmed.
Facilities	♀ ⚐ ⌂ ⌁ ⌁ David John Yates.
Leisure	squash.
Location	Chester Rd, Hooton (NW side of town centre on A41)
Hotel	★★63% Berni Royal, Childer Thornton, ELLESMERE PORT ☎ 051-339 8101 47⇥ ⋔

FRODSHAM   Map 07 SJ57

Frodsham ☎ (0928) 32159 due to change to 732159
Undulating inland course with pleasant views from all parts. Crossed by two footpaths so extreme care needed.
18 holes, 6289yds, Par 70, SSS 70, Course record 71.
Club membership 600.

Visitors	must contact in advance.
Societies	telephone for bookings.
Green Fees	£18 per day; £16 per round (£25/£20 weekends).
Facilities	⊗ ⊞ ⅙ ♥ ♀ ⚐ ⌂ ⌁ ⌂ ⌁ Graham Tonge.
Location	Simons Ln (3m NE of Helsby)
Hotel	★★★64% Forest Hill Hotel & Leisure Complex, Overton Hill, FRODSHAM ☎ (0928) 35255 58⇥ ⋔

HELSBY   Map 07 SJ47

Helsby ☎ (0928) 722021
Quiet parkland course with natural hazards.
18 holes, 6049yds, Par 70, SSS 69.
Club membership 600.

Visitors	weekends and bank holidays with member only. Must contact in advance.
Societies	Tue & Thu.
Green Fees	£27.50 per day; £20 per round.
Facilities	⊗ & ⊞ (ex Mon) ⅙ ♥ ♀ ⚐ ⌂ ⌁ Ian Wright.
Leisure	snooker.
Location	Towers Ln (1m S off A56)
Hotel	★★★★(red) The Chester Grosvenor Hotel, Eastgate St, CHESTER ☎ (0244) 324024 86⇥ ⋔

For an explanation of symbols and abbreviations, see page 11

KNUTSFORD   Map 07 SJ77

Heyrose ☎ Pickmere (0565) 733664 & 733623
An 18-hole course in wooded and gently undulating terrain.
Both the course and the comfortable clubhouse have
attractive views.
18 holes, 6449yds, Par 73, SSS 71.
Club membership 700.
Visitors   by arrangement with secretary, handicap
              certificate may be required, advisable to contact
              in advance.
Societies   apply in writing.
Green Fees £16 (£21 weekends & bank holidays).
Facilities   ⊗ � by prior arrangement ▙ ☕ ♀ △ 🏠 ℓ
              Martin Redrup.
Leisure   snooker.
Location   Budworth Rd, Tabley
              (1.5m from junc 19 on M6)
Hotel   ★★62% Wincham Hall, Hall Ln, Wincham,
              NORTHWICH ☎ (0606) 43453 10rm(9⇄ ☏)

Knutsford ☎ (0565) 633355
Parkland course set in a beautiful old deer park. It demands
some precise iron play.
9 holes, 6288yds, Par 70, SSS 70.
Club membership 230.
Visitors   are not permitted weekends and restricted Wed.
              Must contact in advance.
Green Fees £15 for 18 holes (£20 weekends and bank
              holidays).
Facilities   ⊗ & ☕ by prior arrangement ♀ △
Location   Mereheath Ln (N side of town centre off A50)
Hotel   ★★★61% The Swan Hotel, BUCKLOW HILL
              ☎ (0565) 830295 70⇄ ☏

> **Mere Golf & Country Club**
>   ☎ Bucklow Hill (0565) 830155
> A gracious parkland championship course designed by
> James Braid in the Cheshire sand belt, with several holes
> close to a lake. The round has a tight finish with four
> testing holes.
> *18 holes, 6817yds, Par 71, SSS 73, Course record 64.*
> *Club membership 540.*
> **Visitors**   must contact in advance.
> **Societies** Mon,Tue & Thu only by prior arrangement.
> **Green Fees** £45 per day (midweek).
> **Facilities** ⊗ � ▙ ☕ ♀ △ 🏠 ℓ Peter Eyre.
> **Leisure**   hard tennis courts, heated indoor swimming
>   pool, squash, fishing, snooker, sauna,
>   solarium, gymnasium.
> **Location** Chester Rd, Mere (1m E of junc 19 of M6)
> **Hotel**   ★★★61% The Swan Hotel, BUCKLOW
>   HILL ☎ (0565) 830295 70⇄ ☏

LYMM   Map 07 SJ68

Lymm ☎ (092575) 5020
First ten holes are gently undulating with the Manchester
Ship Canal running alongside the 9th hole. The remaining
holes are comparatively flat.
18 holes, 6304yds, Par 71, SSS 70, Course record 68.
Club membership 620.

Visitors   must have a handicap certificate, may not play
              on Thu mornings, weekends or bank holidays
              unless guest of member. Must contact in
              advance.
Societies   Wed only, must contact in writing.
Green Fees not confirmed.
Facilities   ⊗ � ▙ ☕ ♀ △ 🏠 ⟑ ℓ Steve McCarthy.
Leisure   snooker.
Location   Whitbarrow Rd (.5m N off A6144)
Hotel   ★★★59% Lymm Hotel, Whitbarrow Rd,
              LYMM ☎ (092575) 2233
              22⇄ ☏ Annexe47⇄ ☏

MACCLESFIELD   Map 07 SJ97

Macclesfield ☎ (0625) 23227
Very hilly heathland course recently extended to 18-holes.
Situated on the edge of the Pennines with excellent views.
18 holes, 5625yds, Par 70, SSS 69, Course record 63.
Club membership 600.
Visitors   must have a handicap certificate.
Societies   by arrangement.
Green Fees £17 per day (£20 weekends & bank holidays).
Facilities   ⊗ � by prior arrangement ▙ ☕ ♀ △ 🏠 ℓ
              Tony Taylor.
Leisure   snooker.
Location   The Hollins (SE side of town centre off A523)
Hotel   ★★65% Crofton Hotel, 22 Crompton Rd,
              MACCLESFIELD ☎ (0625) 434113 8⇄ ☏

> **Tytherington** ☎ (0625) 434562
> Modern championship course in beautiful, mature
> parkland setting. Headquarters of the Women's European
> Tour and venue of the WPGET English Open and County
> matches. Country club facilities.
> *18 holes, 6737yds, Par 72, SSS 72, Course record 68.*
> *Club membership 2000.*
> **Visitors**   must contact in advance & have handicap
>   certificate.
> **Societies** weekdays only, apply in writing up to one
>   year in advance.
> **Green Fees** £25 per 18 hole weekdays (£30 weekends).
> **Facilities** ⊗ � ▙ ☕ ♀ △ 🏠 ⟑ ℓ Sandy Wilson.
> **Leisure**   hard tennis courts, heated indoor swimming
>   pool, squash, snooker, sauna, solarium,
>   gymnasium, bowls, clay shot, creche.
> **Location** 1m N of Macclesfield on A523
> **Hotel**   ★★★★61% Shrigley Hall Golf & Country
>   Club, Shrigley Park, POTT SHRIGLEY
>   ☎ (0625) 575757 156⇄

MOTTRAM ST ANDREWS   Map 07 SJ87

Mottram Hall ☎ Macclesfield (0625) 80064 & 828135
Championship standard course with flat parkland on the front
nine and undulating woodland on the back. The hotel offers
many leisure facilities.
18 holes, 6905yds, Par 72, SSS 72, Course record 66.
Club membership 450.
Visitors   must have current handicap certificate or letter
              of introduction from own club. Must contact in
              advance.
Societies   must contact in advance.
Green Fees not confirmed.
Facilities   ▙ ☕ ♀ △ 🏠 ⟑ 🛏 ℓ Tim Rastall.

Leisure	hard tennis courts, heated indoor swimming pool, squash, fishing, snooker, sauna, solarium, gymnasium, jacuzzi.
Location	Wilmslow Rd
Hotel	★★★★63% Mottram Hall Hotel, Wilmslow Rd, Prestbury, WILMSLOW ☎ (0625) 828135 133⇆ ☏

POTT SHRIGLEY   Map 07 SJ97

Shrigley Hall Hotel ☎ Bollington (0625) 575755 & 575757
Parkland course set in 262-acre estate with breathtaking views over the Peak District and Cheshire Plain. Designed by Donald Steel, this championship standard course provides a real sporting challenge while the magnificent hotel provides a wealth of sporting facilities as well as accommodation and food.
18 holes, 6305yds, Par 71, SSS 71, Course record 68.

Visitors	must contact in advance by telephone.
Societies	contact in advance.
Green Fees	£30 per day; £22 per round (£28 weekends).
Facilities	⊗ ⅢⅢ ┗ ☕ ♀ ♨ 🏠 ⛳ ☏ Granville Ogden.
Leisure	hard tennis courts, heated indoor swimming pool, squash, fishing, snooker, sauna, solarium, gymnasium.
Location	Shrigley Park
Hotel	★★★★61% Shrigley Hall Golf & Country Club, Shrigley Park, POTT SHRIGLEY ☎ (0625) 575757 156⇆

POYNTON   Map 07 SJ98

Davenport ☎ (0625) 876951
Undulating parkland course. Extensive view over Cheshire Plain from elevated 5th tee. Testing 17th hole, par 4.
18 holes, 6006yds, Par 69, SSS 69.
Club membership 750.

Visitors	no restrictions.
Societies	must contact in writing.
Green Fees	£24 per day/round (£30 weekends).
Facilities	⊗ & ⅢⅢ by prior arrangement ┗ ☕ ♀ ♨ 🏠 ⛳ ☏ Wyn Harris.
Leisure	snooker.
Location	Worth Hall, Middlewood Rd (1m E off A523)
Hotel	★★★68% Bramhall Moat House, Bramhall Ln South, BRAMHALL ☎ 061-439 8116 65⇆ ☏

PRESTBURY   Map 07 SJ97

Prestbury ☎ (0625) 829388
Rather strenuous parkland course, undulating, with many plateau greens. Good views.
18 holes, 6143yds, Par 71, SSS 71, Course record 64.
Club membership 725.

Visitors	must contact in advance and play with member weekends.
Societies	Thu only, contact in advance.
Green Fees	£26 per day.
Facilities	⊗ ⅢⅢ ┗ ☕ ♀ ♨ 🏠 ⛳ ☏ Nick Summerfield.
Leisure	snooker.
Location	Macclesfield Rd (S side of village off A538)
Hotel	★★★★63% Mottram Hall Hotel, Wilmslow Rd, Prestbury, WILMSLOW ☎ (0625) 828135 133⇆ ☏

RUNCORN   Map 07 SJ58

Runcorn ☎ (0928) 572093
Parkland course with tree-lined fairways and easy walking. Fine views over Mersey and Weaver valleys. Testing holes: 7th par 5; 14th par 5; 17th par 4.
18 holes, 6035yds, Par 69, SSS 69.
Club membership 575.

Visitors	welcome except between 9-10am, noon-1.30pm and Tue afternoon.
Societies	apply in writing.
Green Fees	£16 per day (£20 weekends).
Facilities	⊗ & ⅢⅢ (ex Thu) ┗ ☕ ♀ ♨ 🏠 ☏ Steve Dooley.
Leisure	snooker.
Location	Clifton Rd (1.25m S of Runcorn Station)
Hotel	★★★66% Forte Posthouse, Wood Ln, Beechwood, RUNCORN ☎ (0928) 714000 134⇆ ☏

SANDBACH   Map 07 SJ76

Malkins Bank ☎ Crewe (0270) 765931
Parkland course. Tight 13th hole with stream running through.
18 holes, 6071yds, Par 70, SSS 69.
Club membership 500.

Visitors	no restrictions. Advisable to book in advance.
Societies	apply for booking form to course professional
Green Fees	£3.50 per round (£4.10 weekends and bank holidays) for 9 holes; £5 per round (£6 weekends and bank holidays) for 18 holes.
Facilities	⊗ ┗ ☕ ♀ ♨ 🏠 ⛳ ☏ David Wheeler.
Location	Betchton Rd, Malkins Bank (1.5m SE off A533)
Hotel	★★★63% Saxon Cross Hotel, Holmes Chapel Rd, SANDBACH ☎ (0270) 763281 52⇆ ☏

Sandbach ☎ Crewe (0270) 762117
Meadowland, undulating course with easy walking. Limited facilities.
9 holes, 5094yds, Par 68, SSS 67.
Club membership 570.

Visitors	weekdays except Tue, and with member only weekends & bank holidays. Must contact in advance.
Societies	apply by letter.
Green Fees	not confirmed.
Facilities	⊗ ⅢⅢ ┗ ☕ ♀ ♨
Location	Middlewich Rd (0.5m W on A533)
Hotel	★★★63% Saxon Cross Hotel, Holmes Chapel Rd, SANDBACH ☎ (0270) 763281 52⇆ ☏

SANDIWAY   Map 07 SJ67

Sandiway ☎ (0606) 883247
Delightful undulating woodland and heath golf with long hills up to the 8th, 16th and 17th holes. Many dog-legged and tree-lined holes give opportunities for the deliberate fade or draw.
18 holes, 6435yds, Par 70, SSS 72.
Club membership 750.

Visitors	must contact in advance and have a handicap certificate.
Societies	apply by letter.
Green Fees	not confirmed. ▶

Facilities ⊗ 𝕀 🖳 ■ ♀ ⚲ 🏠 ⅌ 𝄆 William Laird.
Location 1m E on A556
Hotel ★★★64% Hartford Hall Hotel, School Ln,
Hartford, NORTHWICH
☎ (0606) 75711 20➥

TARPORLEY   Map 07 SJ56

Oaklands Golf & Country Club ☎ (0829) 733884
Opened in Spring 1990, this pleasant course has lovely views
over the Cheshire Plain plus many leisure facilities.
18 holes, 6169yds, Par 71, SSS 69.
Club membership 550.
Visitors with member only at weekends.
Societies must contact in advance.
Green Fees not confirmed.
Facilities ⊗ 𝕀 🖳 ■ ♀ ⚲ 🏠 𝄆 B Rimner, J Statham,
P Murray.
Leisure heated indoor swimming pool, snooker, sauna,
gymnasium.
Location Forest Rd
Hotel ★★★64% Willington Hall Hotel, Willington,
TARPORLEY ☎ (0829) 52321 10➥ 🐾

Portal Golf & Country Club ☎ (0829) 733933
Although only opened in May 1991 this course is set in
mature, wooded parkland. There are fine views over the
Chesire Plain and numerous water hazards. The 13th is just a
short iron through trees, but its green is virtually an island
surrounded by water.
18 holes, 7145yds, Par 73, SSS 73.
Club membership 100.
Visitors must contact in advance.
Societies must contact at least 2 weeks in advance.
Green Fees £45 per day; £30 per round.
Facilities ⊗ 𝕀 🖳 ■ ♀ ⚲ 🏠 𝄆 David John Clare.
Leisure hard tennis courts, croquet & polo.
Location Cobbler's Cross Ln
Hotel ★★★69% The Wild Boar, Whitchurch Rd,
Beeston, TARPORLEY
☎ (0829) 260309 37➥ 🐾

WARRINGTON   Map 07 SJ68

Birchwood ☎ (0925) 818819
Very testing parkland course with natural water hazards. The
11th hole is particularly challenging.
18 holes, 6808yds, Par 71, SSS 73.
Club membership 1150.
Visitors welcome except Sun.
Societies Mon-Thu only.
Green Fees not confirmed.
Facilities ⊗ 𝕀 🖳 ■ ♀ ⚲ 🏠 ⅌ 𝄆 Derrick Cooper.
Leisure snooker, sauna.
Location Kelvin Close, Birchwood (4m NE on A574)
Hotel ★★★67% Forte Posthouse, Lodge Ln, Newton-
Le-Willows, HAYDOCK
☎ (0942) 717878 136➥

> If visiting a brand new course, be sure to
> telephone before your visit to confirm the
> course information is correct

Leigh ☎ Culcheth (0925) 762943
A pleasant, well-wooded parkland course. Any
discrepancy in length is compensated by the wide variety
of golf offered here. The course is well maintained and
there is a comfortable clubhouse.
18 holes, 5853yds, Par 69, SSS 68.
Club membership 750.
Visitors may not play during competitions and before
9.30am or 12-1.30pm. Must have a handicap
certificate. Must have an introduction from
own club.
Societies must contact in writing.
Green Fees £24 per day (£30 weekends & bank
holidays).
Facilities ⊗ 𝕀 🖳 ■ ♀ ⚲ 🏠 𝄆
Leisure snooker.
Location Kenyon Hall, Kenyon (5m NE off A579)
Hotel ★★★64% Fir Grove Hotel, Knutsford Old
Rd, WARRINGTON
☎ (0925) 267471 40➥ 🐾

Poulton Park ☎ Padgate (0925) 812034
Tight, flat parkland course with good greens and many trees.
9 holes, 5379yds, Par 68, SSS 66, Course record 66.
Club membership 350.
Visitors may not play between 5-6pm weekdays and
noon-1.30pm Sat.
Societies contact in writing.
Green Fees £16 per day (£18 weekends).
Facilities ⊗ 𝕀 🖳 ■ ♀ ⚲ 🏠 𝄆 Tony Cuppello.
Leisure practice nets & putting green.
Location Dig Ln, Cinnamon Brow, Padgate (3m from
Warrington on A574)
Hotel ★★★64% Fir Grove Hotel, Knutsford Old Rd,
WARRINGTON
☎ (0925) 267471 40➥ 🐾

Walton Hall ☎ (0925) 63061
Wooded, municipal parkland course on Walton Hall estate.
18 holes, 6843yds, Par 72, SSS 73, Course record 69.
Club membership 420.
Visitors no restrictions.
Societies must contact in writing.
Green Fees not confirmed.
Facilities 🖳 ■ ♀ ⚲ 🏠 ⅌
Location Warrington Rd, Higher Walton (2.5m S off A56)
Hotel ★★★64% Fir Grove Hotel, Knutsford Old Rd,
WARRINGTON
☎ (0925) 267471 40➥ 🐾

Warrington ☎ (0925) 261620
Meadowland, with varied terrain and natural hazards.
18 holes, 6305yds, Par 72, SSS 70.
Club membership 400.
Visitors no restrictions.
Societies apply in writing.
Green Fees not confirmed.
Facilities ♀ ⚲ 🏠 𝄆
Location The Hill Warren, London Rd, Appleton (2.5m S
on A49)
Hotel ★★70% Rockfield Hotel, Alexandra Rd,
Grappenhall, WARRINGTON
☎ (0925) 262898 6➥ 🐾Annexe7rm(5➥ 🐾)

WIDNES

Map 07 SJ58

St Michael Jubilee ☎ 051-424 6230
Municipal parkland course dominated by the 'Stewards Brook'. It is divided into two sections which are split by the main road and joined by an underpass.
18 holes, 2648yds, Par 69, SSS 68.

Visitors	must be accompanied by member, contact in advance and have an introduction from own club.
Societies	must contact in writing.
Green Fees	not confirmed.
Facilities	♀ ♿ 🏠 (
Leisure	snooker.
Location	Dunalk Rd (W side of town centre off A562)
Hotel	★56% Rockland Hotel, View Rd, RAINHILL ☎ 051-426 4603 10rm(9⇄)

Widnes ☎ 051-424 2440
Parkland course, easy walking.
18 holes, 5719yds, Par 69, SSS 68.

Visitors	may play after 9am & after 4pm on competition days. Must contact in advance.
Societies	must contact in writing.
Green Fees	not confirmed.
Facilities	⊗ ⯑ by prior arrangement ₺ 🍺 ♀ ♿ 🏠 (S Forster.
Leisure	snooker.
Location	Highfield Rd
Hotel	★56% Rockland Hotel, View Rd, RAINHILL ☎ 051-426 4603 10rm(9⇄)

WILMSLOW

Map 07 SJ88

Wilmslow ☎ Mobberley (0565) 872148
A fine parkland championship course, of middle length, fair to all classes of player and almost in perfect condition.
18 holes, 6607yds, Par 72, SSS 72, Course record 68.
Club membership 830.

Visitors	restricted Wed, weekends & bank holidays. Must contact in advance.
Societies	must contact in advance.
Green Fees	£37.50 per day (£50 weekends); £25 per round (£40 weekends).
Facilities	⊗ & ⯑ by prior arrangement ₺ 🍺 ♀ ♿ 🏠 (John Nowicki.
Location	Great Warford, Mobberley (2m SW off B5058)
Hotel	★★★★60% Belfry Hotel, Stanley Rd, HANDFORTH ☎ 061-437 0511 81⇄

WINSFORD

Map 07 SJ66

Knights Grange ☎ (0606) 552780
Municipal parkland course with water hazards.
9 holes, 2860yds, Par 35, SSS 68.

Visitors	no restrictions. Advisable to book day before.
Societies	must contact the Manager in advance.
Green Fees	£2.40 (£3.20 weekends) for 9 holes; £3.60 (£4.80 weekends) for 18 holes.
Facilities	🍺 ♿ 🏠 ⛏
Location	Grange Ln (N side of town off A54)
Hotel	★★★64% Hartford Hall Hotel, School Ln, Hartford, NORTHWICH ☎ (0606) 75711 20⇄

CLEVELAND

BILLINGHAM

Map 08 NZ42

Billingham ☎ Stockton (0642) 533816
Parkland course on edge of urban-rural district, with hard walking and water hazards; testing 15th hole.
18 holes, 6460yds, Par 73, SSS 71.
Club membership 1000.

Visitors	with member only at weekends & bank holidays. Must have a handicap certificate.
Societies	must contact in writing.
Green Fees	not confirmed.
Facilities	⊗ & ⯑ (ex Mon) ₺ 🍺 (ex Mon) ♀ ♿ 🏠 (P S Bradley.
Leisure	snooker.
Location	Sandy Ln (1m W of town centre E of A19)
Hotel	★★★57% Billingham Arms Hotel, The Causeway, Billingham, STOCKTON-ON-TEES ☎ (0642) 553661 & 360880 69⇄ 🐾

EAGLESCLIFFE

Map 08 NZ41

Eaglescliffe and District ☎ (0642) 780098
This hilly course offers both pleasant and interesting golf to all classes of player. It lies in a delightful setting on a rolling plateau, shelving to the River Tees. There are fine views to the Cleveland Hills.
18 holes, 6275yds, Par 72, SSS 70.
Club membership 550.

Visitors	restricted Tue, Thu, Fri & weekends.
Societies	must contact in advance.
Green Fees	£20 per day (£26 weekends & bank holidays).
Facilities	♿ 🏠 (Nic Gilks.
Leisure	snooker.
Location	Yarm Rd (E side of village off A135)
Hotel	★★★★58% Swallow Hotel, 10 John Walker Square, STOCKTON-ON-TEES ☎ (0642) 679721 124⇄ 🐾

HARTLEPOOL

Map 08 NZ53

Castle Eden & Peterlee ☎ Wellfield (0429) 836510
Beautiful parkland course alongside a nature reserve. Hard walking, trees provide wind shelter.
18 holes, 6107yds, Par 70, SSS 69.
Club membership 750.

Visitors	with member only during 12-1.30pm & 4-6.30pm. Must contact in advance.
Societies	must contact in advance on (0429) 836689.
Green Fees	£20 per day (£30 weekends & bank holidays).
Facilities	⊗ ⯑ ₺ 🍺 ♀ ♿ 🏠 ⛏ (Graham J Laidlaw.
Leisure	snooker.
Location	Castle Eden (2m S of Peterlee on B1281 off A19)
Hotel	★★★67% Hardwick Hall Hotel, SEDGEFIELD ☎ (0740) 20253 17⇄ 🐾

> This guide is up-dated annually – make sure you use the up-to-date edition

Hartlepool ☎ (0429) 274398
A seaside course, half links, overlooking the North Sea. A good test and equally enjoyable to all handicap players. The 10th, par 4, demands a precise second shot over a ridge and between sand dunes to a green down near the edge of the beach, alongside which several holes are played.
18 holes, 6255yds, Par 70, SSS 70.
Club membership 600.
Visitors with member only on Sun.
Societies must apply in writing.
Green Fees £17 per day (£24 weekends).
Facilities ⊗ & ☾ by prior arrangement ♨ ☕ ♀ ⛺ ☗ ⟨ Malcolm E Cole.
Leisure snooker.
Location Hart Warren (N side off King Oswy Drive)
Hotel ★★★67% Hardwick Hall Hotel, SEDGEFIELD ☎ (0740) 20253 17⇌ ⚑

MIDDLESBROUGH Map 08 NZ42

Middlesbrough ☎ (0642) 311515
Undulating parkland course, prevailing winds. Testing 9th, 16th and 17th holes.
18 holes, 6111yds, Par 70, SSS 69, Course record 66.
Club membership 900.
Visitors restricted Tue & Sat.
Societies Wed, Thu & Fri only. Must contact the club in advance.
Green Fees £25 per day (£30 weekends & bank holidays).
Facilities ⊗ ☾ by prior arrangement ♨ ☕ ♀ ⛺ ☗ ⟨ Don Jones.
Leisure snooker.
Location Brass Castle Ln, Marton (3m S off A172)
Hotel ★★★56% Marton Way Toby Hotel, Marton Rd, MIDDLESBROUGH ☎ (0642) 817651 53⇌

Middlesbrough Municipal ☎ (0642) 315533
Parkland course with good views. The front nine holes have wide fairways and large, often well-guarded greens while the back nine demand shots over tree-lined water hazards and narrow entrances to subtley contoured greens. Driving range.
18 holes, 6326yds, Par 71, SSS 70, Course record 68.
Club membership 575.
Visitors tees should be booked in advance.
Societies by arrangement.
Green Fees £7.50 per day/round (£9.50 weekends & bank holidays).
Facilities ♨ ☕ ♀ ⛺ ☗ ⚲ ⟨ Alan Hope & Dave Symington.
Leisure 20 bay floodlit driving range.
Location Ladgate Ln 2.5m S of town centre on B1380 off A172)
Hotel ★★★56% Marton Way Toby Hotel, Marton Rd, MIDDLESBROUGH ☎ (0642) 817651 53⇌

REDCAR Map 08 NZ62

Cleveland ☎ (0642) 471798
Links championship course.
18 holes, 6707yds, Par 71, SSS 70.
Club membership 890.
Visitors must contact in advance & have handicap certificate.
Societies must apply in writing.
Green Fees £16 per day/round.
Facilities ⊗ ☾ ♨ ☕ (no catering Mon) ♀ ⛺ ☗ ⟨ M Nutter.
Leisure snooker.
Location Queen St (8m E of Middlesborough on A19/A172)
Hotel ★★★67% Park Hotel, Granville Ter, REDCAR ☎ (0642) 490888 26⇌ ⚑

Wilton ☎ (0642) 465265
Parkland course with some fine views.
18 holes, 6104yds, Par 70, SSS 69.
Club membership 750.
Visitors restricted Sat.
Societies must telephone in advance.
Green Fees not confirmed.
Facilities ⊗ ☾ by prior arrangement ♨ ☕ ♀ ⛺ ☗ ⟨ R Smith.
Location Wilton Castle (3m W on A174)
Hotel ★★★67% Park Hotel, Granville Ter, REDCAR ☎ (0642) 490888 26⇌ ⚑

SALTBURN-BY-THE-SEA Map 08 NZ62

Saltburn by the Sea ☎ (0287) 622812
Undulating meadowland course surrounded by woodland. Particularly attractive in autumn. There are fine views of the Cleveland Hills and of Tees Bay.
18 holes, 5803yds, Par 70, SSS 68.
Club membership 850.
Visitors may not play Sat & occasional Sun.
Societies apply in writing.
Green Fees £19 per day/round (£22 Sun).
Facilities ⊗ ☾ by prior arrangement ♨ ☕ ♀ ⛺ ☗ ⚲ ⟨ David Forsythe.
Leisure snooker.
Location Hob Hill, Guisborough Rd (S side of town centre on B1268)
Hotel ★★★56% Marton Way Toby Hotel, Marton Rd, MIDDLESBROUGH ☎ (0642) 817651 53⇌

SEATON CAREW Map 08 NZ52

Seaton Carew ☎ Hartlepool (0429) 266249
A championship links course taking full advantage of its dunes, bents, whins and gorse. Renowed for its par 4 (17th); just enough fairway for an accurate drive followed by another precise shot to a pear-shaped, sloping green that is severly trapped.
The Old Course: 18 holes, 6604yds, Par 72.
Brabazon Course: 18 holes, 6849yds, Par 73.
Club membership 650.
Visitors restricted after 10am at weekends & bank holidays.
Societies must apply in writing.
Green Fees £22 per day (£30 weekends & bank holidays).
Facilities ⊗ & ☾ by prior arrangement ♨ ☕ ♀ ⛺ ☗ ⟨ W Hector.
Leisure snooker.
Location Tees Rd (SE side of village off A178)
Hotel ★★★57% Billingham Arms Hotel, The Causeway, Billingham, STOCKTON-ON-TEES ☎ (0642) 553661 & 360880 69⇌ ⚑

STOCKTON-ON-TEES   Map 08 NZ41

Norton ☎ Stockton (0642) 676385 & 674636
An interesting parkland course with long drives from the 7th
and 17th tees. Several water hazards.
18 holes, 5870yds, Par 71, SSS 71.
Visitors   no restrictions.
Societies   apply in advance.
Green Fees £8.50 per 18 holes.
Facilities   ⊗ ⅷ ⅼ ⅾ ♀ ⅿ ⅾ 𝔯 Ernest Scott.
Location   Norton (at Norton 2m N off A19)
Hotel   ★★★57% Billingham Arms Hotel, The
                   Causeway, Billingham, STOCKTON-ON-TEES
                   ☎ (0642) 553661 & 360880 69⇆ 𝔯

Teesside ☎ (0642) 676249
Flat parkland course, easy walking.
18 holes, 6472yds, Par 72, SSS 71.
Club membership 600.
Visitors   with member only weekdays after 4.30pm,
                   weekends after 11am.
Societies   must contact in writing.
Green Fees £18 per day (£24 weekends & bank holidays).
Facilities   ⊗ ⅷ ⅼ ⅾ ♀ ⅿ ⅾ 𝔯 Ken Hall.
Location   Acklam Rd, Thornaby (1.5m SE on A1130)
Hotel   ★★★61% Forte Posthouse Teesside, Low Ln,
                   Thornaby-on-Tees, STOCKTON-ON-TEES
                   ☎ (0642) 591213 135⇆ 𝔯

CORNWALL &
ISLES OF SCILLY

BODMIN   Map 02 SX06

Lanhydrock ☎ (0208) 73600
Championship standard parkland/moorland course.
Picturesque but not hilly.
18 holes, 6142yds, Par 71, SSS 71.
Visitors   no restrictions.
Societies   welcome.
Green Fees £22 per round.
Facilities   ⊗ & ⅷ by prior arrangement ⅼ ⅾ ♀ ⅿ ⅾ ⅿ
Location   Lostwithiel Rd, Lanhydrock (2m SE)
Hotel   ★★59% Westberry Hotel, Rhind St, BODMIN
                   ☎ (0208) 72772 15rm(5⇆4 𝔯)Annexe8⇆ 𝔯
Additional   ★★69% Port Gaverne Hotel, PORT GAVERNE
Hotel   ☎ (0208) 880244 16⇆ 𝔯Annexe3⇆ 𝔯

BUDE   Map 02 SS20

Bude & North Cornwall ☎ (0288) 352006
Seaside links course with natural sand bunkers, superb greens
and breathtaking views. Club established in 1891.
18 holes, 6222yds, Par 71, SSS 70.
Club membership 900.
Visitors   must contact in advance, restricted weekdays
                   9.30am-12.30pm, 2-5pm & from 6.30pm
                   onwards. Closed Sat & Sun mornings.
Societies   weekdays only by arrangement.
Green Fees not confirmed.
Facilities   ⊗ ⅷ ⅼ ⅾ ♀ ⅿ ⅾ 𝔯 John Yeo.   ▶

Leisure	snooker.
Location	Burn View (N side of town)
Hotel	★★65% Camelot Hotel, Downs View, BUDE ☎ (0288) 352361 21⇄ ⌕

BUDOCK VEAN   Map 02 SW73

Budock Vean Hotel ☎ Falmouth (0326) 250288
Undulating parkland course.
9 holes, 5007yds, Par 68, SSS 65.
Visitors	cannot play on bank holidays. Must contact in advance and have an introduction from own club.
Societies	welcome if resident in hotel.
Green Fees	not confirmed.
Facilities	⊗ 🍴 🛏 ♣ ♀ 👤 🏊 ⌕ David Short.
Leisure	hard tennis courts, heated indoor swimming pool, snooker.
Location	Mawnan Smith (1.5m SW)
Hotel	★★★72% Budock Vean Hotel, MAWNAN SMITH ☎ (0326) 250288 58⇄ ⌕

CAMBORNE   Map 02 SW64

Tehidy Park ☎ Portreath (0209) 842208
A well-maintained parkland course providing good holiday golf.
18 holes, 6241yds, Par 72, SSS 70, Course record 64.
Club membership 1000.
Visitors	must contact in advance and have a handicap certificate.

Societies	must apply in writing.
Green Fees	£32 per day; £26 per round.
Facilities	⊗ 🍴 🛏 ♣ ♀ 👤 🏊 ⌕
Leisure	snooker.
Location	2m NE off A30
Hotel	★★★62% Penventon Hotel, REDRUTH ☎ (0209) 214141 50⇄ ⌕

CARLYON BAY   Map 02 SX05

Carlyon Bay Hotel ☎ (0726) 814228
Championship-length, cliff-top course moving into parkland. Magnificent views surpassed only by the quality of the course. The 230-yard (par 3) 18th with railway and road out-of-bounds, holds the player's interest to the end.
18 holes, 6501yds, Par 72, SSS 71.
Club membership 550.
Visitors	no restrictions.
Societies	must contact in advance.
Green Fees	not confirmed.
Facilities	⊗ 🍴 🛏 ♣ ♀ 👤 🏊 🏌 ⌕ Nigel Sears.
Location	2.5m E of St Austell off A3082
Hotel	★★★61% Carlyon Bay Hotel, Sea Rd, Carlyon Bay, ST AUSTELL ☎ (072681) 2304 73⇄ ⌕

For an explanation of symbols and abbreviations, see page 11

CONSTANTINE BAY
Map 02 SW87

Trevose ☎ Padstow (0841) 520208
A pleasant holiday seaside course with early holes close
to the sea on excellent springy turf. It is a good and
enjoyable test. Self-catering accommodation is available
at the club.
18 holes, 6608yds, Par 71, SSS 71.
Short Course: 9 holes, 1360yds, Par 29, SSS 29.
Club membership 650.
Visitors	must contact in advance & have handicap certificate for main course.
Societies	must apply in writing.
Green Fees	Main course: £25-£30 per day.
Facilities	⊗ ⅢⅢ ⮜ ⚑ ♀ ⚘ 🏠 ⚐ 🍴 ⚑ Gary Alliss.
Leisure	hard tennis courts, heated outdoor swimming pool, snooker.
Location	N side of village off B3276
Hotel	★★★76% Treglos Hotel, CONSTANTINE BAY ☎ (0841) 520727 44⇄ ⇗

FALMOUTH
Map 02 SW83

Falmouth ☎ (0326) 311262
Seaside/parkland course with outstanding coastal views.
Sufficiently bunkered to punish any inaccurate shots. Five
acres of practice grounds.
18 holes, 5680yds, Par 70, SSS 68, Course record 64.
Club membership 600.
Visitors	may not play on competition days. Must contact in advance.
Societies	must contact in advance.
Green Fees	£25 per day; £20 per round.
Facilities	⊗ ⅢⅢ by prior arrangement ⮜ ⚑ ♀ ⚘ 🏠 ⚐ 🍴 David J Short.
Leisure	practice fields, putting green.
Location	Swanpool Rd (SW side of town centre)
Hotel	★★★⚑76% Penmere Manor Hotel, Mongleath Rd, FALMOUTH ☎ (0326) 211411 39⇄ ⇗

LAUNCESTON
Map 02 SX38

Launceston ☎ (0566) 773442
Undulating parkland course with views over Tamar Valley to
Dartmoor and Bodmin Moor. Dominated by the 'The Hill' up
which the 8th and 11th fairways rise, and on which the 8th,
9th, 11th and 12th greens sit.
18 holes, 6407yds, Par 70, SSS 71, Course record 64.
Club membership 800.
Visitors	with member only at weekends. Must contact in advance and have an introduction from own club.
Societies	must apply in writing.
Green Fees	not confirmed.
Facilities	⊗ ⮜ ⚑ ♀ ⚘ 🏠 ⚐ 🍴 J Tozer.
Location	St Stephens (NW side of town centre on B3254)
Hotel	★★★71% Arundell Arms, LIFTON ☎ (0566) 784666 24⇄ ⇗ Annexe5⇄ ⇗

Use the AA *Hotels* or *Bed and Breakfast*
Guides to extend your choice of
accommodation

LELANT
Map 02 SW53

West Cornwall ☎ Penzance (0736) 753401
A seaside links with sandhills and lovely turf adjacent to
the Hayle estuary and St Ives Bay. A real test of the
player's skill, especially 'Calamity Corner' starting at the
5th on the lower land by the River Hayle. A small (3
hole) course is available for practice.
18 holes, 5645yds, Par 69, SSS 68, Course record 64.
Club membership 900.
Visitors	must have handicap certificate.
Societies	must apply in writing.
Green Fees	£20 per day (£25 weekends).
Facilities	⊗ & ⅢⅢ by prior arrangement ⮜ ⚑ ♀ ⚘ 🏠 🍴 Paul Atherton.
Leisure	snooker.
Location	N side of village off A3074
Hotel	★★66% Boskerris Hotel, Boskerris Rd, Carbis Bay, ST IVES ☎ (0736) 795295 13rm(11⇄ ⇗) Annexe5⇄ ⇗

LOOE
Map 02 SX25

Looe ☎ Widegates (05034) 239
Exposed and somewhat windy course on high moorland;
designed by Harry Vardon in 1934. Easy walking. Fine views
over Looe coastline.
18 holes, 5940yds, Par 70, SSS 68.
Club membership 620.
Visitors	no restrictions.
Societies	apply one week in advance.
Green Fees	£17 per round.
Facilities	⊗ ⅢⅢ ⮜ ⚑ ♀ ⚘ 🏠 ⚐ 🍴 Alistair Macdonald.
Location	Widegates (3.5m NE off B3253)
Hotel	★★★58% Hannafore Point Hotel, Marine Dr, Hannafore, LOOE ☎ (05036) 3273 37 ⇄ ⇗

LOSTWITHIEL
Map 02 SX15

Lostwithiel Golf & Country Club ☎ Bodmin (0208)
873550
An undulating, parkland course with water hazards.
Overlooked by Restormel Castle and the Rover Fowey flows
alongside the course. Driving range.
18 holes, 6098yds, Par 72, SSS 70.
Club membership 650.
Visitors	must have handicap certificate. Must contact in advance.
Societies	contact in advance.
Green Fees	summer £15 (£19 weekend); winter £11 (£15 weekend).
Facilities	⊗ ⅢⅢ ⮜ ⚑ ♀ ⚘ 🏠 ⚐ 🍴 ⚑ Martin Hammond.
Leisure	hard tennis courts, heated indoor swimming pool, fishing, snooker, floodlit undercover driving range.
Location	Lower Polscoe (1m outside Lostwithiel off A390)
Hotel	★★★63% Restormel Lodge Hotel, Hillside Gardens, LOSTWITHIEL ☎ (0208) 872223 21⇄ ⇗ Annexe12⇄

MAWNAN SMITH
See **Budock Vean**

MULLION

Map 02 SW61

Mullion ☎ (0326) 240685
Cliff top and links course with panoramic views over
Mounts Bay. Well-known ravine hole (7th). Most
southerly course in the British Isles.
18 holes, 6022yds, Par 69, SSS 69.
Club membership 755.
Visitors must have handicap certificate.
Societies must contact in advance.
Green Fees £18 per day/round.
Facilities ⊗ ⦿ ⓘ ⬤ ♈ ♇ ⚑ ⚒ ♈ ℓ Robin Goodway.
Location Cury Cross Lanes (1.5m NW off A3083)
Hotel ★★★74% Polurrian Hotel, MULLION
☎ (0326) 240421 40rm(38⇄ ℝ)

NEWQUAY

Map 02 SW86

Newquay ☎ (0637) 874354
Seaside course close to the beach and open to wind.
18 holes, 6140yds, Par 69, SSS 69, Course record 63.
Club membership 500.
Visitors must have a handicap certificate.
Societies must contact in advance.
Green Fees not confirmed.
Facilities ⦿ ⓘ ⬤ ♇ ⚑ ⚒ ⓘ ℓ
Leisure hard tennis courts, snooker.
Location Tower Rd (W side of town)
Hotel ★★62% Philema Hotel, 1 Esplanade Rd,
Pentire, NEWQUAY
☎ (0637) 872571 37rm(32⇄ ℝ)

Additional Hotel ★★★57% Barrowfield Hotel, Hilgrove Rd,
NEWQUAY ☎ (0637) 878878 81⇄ ℝ
Additional Hotel ★★★60% Kilbirnie Hotel, Narrowcliff,
NEWQUAY ☎ (0637) 875155 74⇄

Treloy ☎ (0637) 878554
An Executive course constructed in 1991 to American
specifications with large contoured and mounded greens.
Offers an interesting round for all categories of player.
9 holes, 2143yds, Par 32, SSS 31.
Visitors must contact in advance. Restricted competitions
& matches.
Societies must contact in advance.
Green Fees 18 holes: £11.50. 9 holes: £7.50.
Facilities ⬤ ⚑ ⚒ ⓘ ♈ ℓ
Location On A3059 Newquay to St Columb Major Road
Hotel ★★70% Whipsiderry Hotel, Trevelgue Road,
Porth, NEWQUAY
☎ (0637) 874777 24rm(5⇄14 ℝ)

PADSTOW

See **Constantine Bay**

PERRANPORTH

Map 02 SW75

Perranporth ☎ Truro (0872) 572454
There are three testing par 5 holes on the links course (2nd,
5th, 11th) and a fine view over Perranporth Beach from all
holes.
18 holes, 6286yds, Par 72, SSS 70.
Club membership 600.

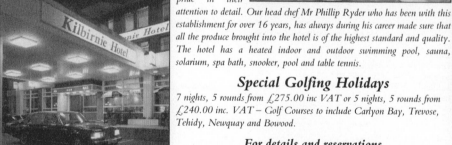

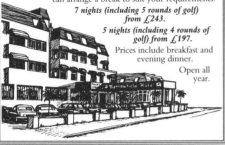

Barrowfield Hotel

AA
★★★

HILGROVE ROAD, NEWQUAY, CORNWALL
TEL: 0637 878878   FAX: 0637 879490

Fully inclusive golfing holidays at one of the south west's finest hotels.

Let us take the strain out of organising your golfing holiday. You choose from a choice of 10 courses and we'll do the rest.

Our choice of courses includes the superb St Mellion Nicklaus Course, the New Bowood Park Course and a good selection of Links, Parkland and Downland Courses.

We cater for individuals, group and non golfers.

Choose from our 7 nights and 5 night golf packages or we can arrange a break to suit your requirements.

7 nights (including 5 rounds of golf) from £243.

5 nights (including 4 rounds of golf) from £197.

Prices include breakfast and evening dinner.

Open all year.

Visitors   must contact in advance & have handicap certificate. Restricted Sun mornings & competition days.
Societies   must apply in writing.
Green Fees £20 per day (£25 weekends & bank holidays).
Facilities ⊗ ⅲ ⓑ 🍺 ♀ 🏋 🏠 ⊤� ℂ D Michell.
Leisure   snooker.
Location   Budnick Hill (0.75m NE on B3285)
Hotel   ★65% Beach Dunes Hotel, Ramoth Way, Reen Sands, PERRANPORTH
         ☎ (0872) 572263 7rm(3⇄ ℝ) Annexe3⇄ ℝ

PORTWRINKLE   Map 02 SX35

Whitsand Bay Hotel Golf & Country Club
☎ St Germans (0503) 30276
Seaside course laid-out on cliffs overlooking Whitsand Bay. Easy walking after 1st hole. The par 3 (3rd) hole is well-known.
18 holes, 5850yds, Par 68, SSS 69, Course record 63.
Club membership 450.
Visitors   must have handicap certificate.
Societies   must contact in advance.
Green Fees not confirmed.
Facilities ⊗ ⅲ ⓑ 🍺 ♀ 🏋 🏠 ⊤⟐ ℂ S Poole.
Leisure   heated indoor swimming pool, riding, sauna, solarium, games room, masseur, hairdresser.
Location   E side of village off B3247
Hotel   ★64% Whitsand Bay Hotel, Golf & Country Club, Portwrinkle, TORPOINT
         ☎ (0503) 30276 30rm(28⇄)

PRAA SANDS   Map 02 SW52

Praa Sands ☎ Penzance (0736) 763445
A beautiful parkland course with outstanding sea views from every tee and green.
9 holes, 4104yds, Par 62, SSS 60, Course record 59.
Club membership 300.
Visitors   restricted Fri afternoon & Sun morning (May-Sep).
Societies   must contact in advance.
Green Fees £12.50 per round.
Facilities ⊗ ⅲ ⓑ 🍺 ♀ 🏋 🏠 ⊤⟐ ℂ Mike Singleton.
Leisure   pool table & darts.
Location   Germoe Cross Roads (N side of village on A394)
Hotel   ★★♨71% Nansloe Manor Hotel, Meneage Rd, HELSTON ☎ (0326) 574691 7rm(6⇄ ℝ)

ROCK   Map 02 SW97

St Enodoc ☎ Trebetherick (020886) 3216
Seaside course with natural hazards.
Church Course: 18 holes, 6207yds, Par 69, SSS 70, Course record 65.
Holywell Course: 18 holes, 4142yds, Par 63, SSS 61.
Club membership 1200.
Visitors   may not play on bank holidays. Must have a handicap certificate of 24 or below for Church Course. Must contact in advance.
Societies   must contact in writing.
Facilities ⊗ ⅲ by prior arrangement ⓑ 🍺 ♀ 🏋 🏠 ⊤⟐ ℂ Nick Williams.
Leisure   practice ground, putting green.
Location   W side of village
Hotel   ★★67% St Enodoc Hotel, ROCK
         ☎ (020886) 3394 13⇄ ℝ

ST AUSTELL   Map 02 SX05

St Austell ☎ (0726) 72649
Very interesting inland parkland course designed by James Braid. Undulating, well-covered with tree plantations and well-bunkered. Notable holes are 8th (par 4) and 16th (par 3).
18 holes, 6007yds, Par 69, SSS 69.
Club membership 800.
Visitors   must have handicap certificate.
Societies   must apply in writing.
Green Fees not confirmed.
Facilities ⊗ ⅲ by prior arrangement ⓑ 🍺 ♀ 🏋 🏠 ℂ Mark Rowe.
Location   Tregongeeves Ln (1m SW off A390)
Hotel   ★★★63% Porth Avallen Hotel, Sea Rd, Carlyon Bay, ST AUSTELL
         ☎ (0726) 812802 & 812183 23rm(22⇄ ℝ)

ST JUST (NEAR LAND'S END)   Map 02 SW33

Cape Cornwall Golf & Country Club
☎ Penzance (0736) 788611
Coastal parkland, walled course. The walls are an integral part of its design. Country club facilities.
18 holes, 5650yds, Par 70, SSS 68.
Club membership 830.

▶

Visitors	may not play before 11.30am at weekends.
Societies	must contact in advance.
Green Fees	£14 per round (£20 weekends & bank holidays).
Facilities	⊗ ⅧⅢ Ⅼ ⬛ ⬤ ⅄ ⌂ ⌐ ⌐ (Bob Hamilton.
Leisure	heated indoor swimming pool, snooker, sauna, solarium, gymnasium.
Location	Cape Cornwall (1m W of St Just)
Hotel	★★★♨♨61% Higher Faugan Hotel, Newlyn, PENZANCE
	☎ (0736) 62076 11⇆ ⌐

St Mary's

Isle of Scilly ☎ (0720) 22692
Links course, glorious views.
9 holes, 6001yds, Par 73, SSS 69, Course record 69.
Club membership 300.

Visitors	only with member on Sun.
Societies	must apply in writing
Green Fees	£14 per day.
Facilities	⊗ ⅧⅢ Ⅼ ⬛ ⬤ ⅄ ⌂ ⌐
Location	1m N of Hugh Town
Hotel	★★69% Tregarthens Hotel, Hugh Town, ST MARY'S ☎ (0720) 22540
	28⇆ Annexe1⇆

St Mellion   Map 02 SX36

St Mellion International Golf & Country Club
☎ Liskeard (0579) 50101
St Mellion is a delightful family-run golfing complex put together by brothers Martin and Hermon Bond. They decided the Tamar Valley, made famous by Sherlock Holmes, deserved a championship golf course - so they chose to convert one of their farms. Their hearts were set on securing Jack Nicklaus as course architect. So they sent him a massive cheque, said to be £1 million, with a letter. It did the trick!
Today the rugged course, seen on TV for several professional events, certainly needs an expert touch if low scores are to be achieved. Without doubt a picturesque setting in Cornwall, some of the holes look inviting, but are dangerous. Maybe none more so than the short 11th, with the green nestling at the bottom of a valley guarded by sand bunkers and a stream! There are four holes in excess off 500 yards with the 16th, at 554 yards, being the longest. Not a course for the meek and mild.
Nicklaus Course: 18 holes, 6626yds, Par 72, SSS 72.
The Old Course: 18 holes, 5927yds, Par 70, SSS 68.
Club membership 4500.

Visitors	must contact in advance and have a handicap certificate.
Societies	must apply in writing.
Green Fees	Nicklaus Course: £42 per round; Old Course: £22.
Facilities	⊗ ⅧⅢ Ⅼ ⬛ ⬤ ⅄ ⌂ ⌐ ⇱ (Tony Moore.
Leisure	hard tennis courts, heated indoor swimming pool, squash, snooker, sauna, solarium, gymnasium, jacuzzi.
Location	.5m NW off A388
Hotel	★★★65% St Mellion Hotel, St Mellion Golf & County Club, ST MELLION ☎ (0579) 50101 Annexe24⇆ ⌐ (See advertisement on page 53)

Truro   Map 02 SW84

Killiow Park ☎ (0872) 70246
Picturesque parkland course with mature oaks and woodland and five holes played across or around water hazards. Floodlit, all-weather driving range.
18 holes, 3542yds, Par 60.
Club membership 450.

Visitors	may not play until after 10.30am at weekends. Must contact in advance.
Green Fees	not confirmed.
Facilities	⬛ ⅄ ⌂ ⌐
Location	Killiow, Kea (3m SW of Truro, off A39)
Hotel	★★★65% Brookdale Hotel, Tregolls Rd, TRURO ☎ (0872) 73513 & 79305 21⇆ ⌐

Truro ☎ (0872) 72640
Undulating parkland course.
18 holes, 5347yds, Par 66, SSS 66.
Club membership 1000.

Visitors	must contact in advance & have handicap certificate.
Societies	must apply in writing.
Green Fees	£18 per day (£22 weekends & bank holidays).
Facilities	⊗ ⅧⅢ Ⅼ ⬛ ⬤ ⅄ ⌂ ⌐ (Nigel Bicknell.
Leisure	snooker.
Location	Treliske (1.5m W on A390)
Hotel	★★★65% Brookdale Hotel, Tregolls Rd, TRURO ☎ (0872) 73513 & 79305 21⇆ ⌐

● CUMBRIA

Alston   Map 12 NY74

Alston Moor ☎ (0434) 381675
Parkland course with lush fairways and naturally interesting greens.
10 holes, 5780yds, Par 66, SSS 66, Course record 67.
Club membership 180.

Visitors	no restrictions.
Societies	must contact in advance.
Green Fees	£6 per day (£10 weekends).
Facilities	⊗ ⅧⅢ Ⅼ ⬛ (catering by arrangement) ⅄ ⌐
Location	The Hermitage (1.75m NE on B6277)
Hotel	★★68% Lowbyer Manor Country House Hotel, ALSTON ☎ (0434) 381230
	7⇆ ⌐ Annexe4⇆

Appleby-in-Westmorland   Map 12 NY62

Appleby ☎ (07683) 51432
This remotely situated heather and moorland course offers interesting golf with the rewarding bonus of several long par-4 holes that will be remembered. There are superb views.
18 holes, 5755yds, Par 68, SSS 68.
Club membership 830.

For an explanation of symbols and abbreviations, see page 11

Visitors	restricted weekends and bank holidays.
Societies	must contact in advance by letter.
Green Fees	£11 per day (£15 weekends & bank holidays).
Facilities	⊗ ℍ by prior arrangement 🄻 ⬤ ♀ ⛄ 🏠
Leisure	snooker.
Location	Brackenber Moor (1m E of Appleby .5m off A66)
Hotel	★★★🛦🛦70% Appleby Manor Country House Hotel, Roman Rd, APPLEBY-IN-WESTMORLAND ☎ (07683) 51571 23⇄ 🞀Annexe7⇄ 🞀

ASKAM-IN-FURNESS   Map 07 SD27

Dunnerholme ☎ Dalton-in-Furness (0229) 62675
Unique 10-hole (18 tee) links course with view of Lakeland hills, and a stream running through.
10 holes, 6181, Par 71, SSS 69.
Club membership 425.

Visitors	no restrictions.
Societies	must contact in advance.
Green Fees	not confirmed.
Facilities	🄻 ⬤ ♀ ⛄ 🏠
Location	Duddon Rd (1m N on A595)
Hotel	★★63% Eccle Riggs Hotel, Foxfield Rd, BROUGHTON IN FURNESS ☎ (0229) 716398 & 716780 12⇄ 🞀

BARROW-IN-FURNESS   Map 07 SD17

Barrow ☎ (0229) 825444
Pleasant course laid out on meadowland with extensive views of the nearby Lakeland fells.
18 holes, 6209yds, Par 71, SSS 70.
Club membership 850.

Visitors	must contact in advance & be members of a recognised golf club.
Societies	must contact in writing.
Green Fees	£15 per day/round (£25 weekends).
Facilities	⊗ ℍ 🄻 ⬤ ♀ ⛄ 🏠 🎯 ↧ Neale Hyde.
Location	Rakesmoor Ln, Hawcoat (2m N off A590)
Hotel	★★64% Lisdoonie Hotel, 307/309 Abbey Rd, BARROW-IN-FURNESS ☎ (0229) 827312 12⇄ 🞀

Furness ☎ (0229) 471232
Links golf with a fairly flat first half but a much sterner second nine played across subtle sloping ground. There are good views of the Lakes, North Wales and the Isle of Man.
18 holes, 6363mtrs, Par 71, SSS 71.
Club membership 1177.

Visitors	restricted, Ladies Day Wed, competition days and members only Fri from 2pm.
Societies	must contact in writing.
Green Fees	not confirmed.
Facilities	⊗ & ℍ by prior arrangement 🄻 ⬤ on request ♀ ⛄ 🏠
Leisure	snooker.
Location	Central Dr, Walney Island (1.75 E of town centre off A590)
Hotel	★★64% Lisdoonie Hotel, 307/309 Abbey Rd, BARROW-IN-FURNESS ☎ (0229) 827312 12⇄ 🞀

Birdie, Eagle, Albatross ...

... or even if you're looking for the elusive 'hole in one', Windermere is the place.

Situated only a mile from this 18 hole golf course, The Wild Boar Hotel with it's olde worlde charm offers you a friendly and welcome atmosphere.

Reflect, whilst sampling our excellent cuisine and extensive wine list, on the 67 par round.

All our rooms are ensuite and are equipped with every modern day facility to ensure your stay is an enjoyable one!

Discounted Green Fees for Residents
For your free colour brochure
telephone Windermere (05394) 45225

 Wild Boar Hotel   ★★★ 70%

Crook, Nr. Windermere, Cumbria LA23 3NF.

BOWNESS-ON-WINDERMERE   Map 07 SD49

Windermere ☎ Windermere (05394) 43123
Enjoyable holiday golf on a short, slightly hilly but sporting course in this delightful area of the Lake District National Park, with superb views of the mountains as the backcloth to the lake and the course.
18 holes, 5006yds, Par 67, SSS 65, Course record 58.
Club membership 943.

Visitors	must contact in advance & be member of recognised club with a handicap certificate.
Societies	must contact in writing.
Green Fees	£23 per day (£28 weekends & bank holidays).
Facilities	⊗ (ex Mon) ℍ 🄻 ⬤ ♀ ⛄ 🏠 🎯 ↧ W S M Rooke.
Leisure	fishing, snooker.
Location	Cleabarrow (1m E on B5284)
Hotel	★★★70% Wild Boar Hotel, Crook, WINDERMERE ☎ (05394) 45225 36⇄ 🞀

BRAMPTON   Map 12 NY56

Brampton ☎ (06977) 2255 & 2000
Challenging golf across glorious rolling fell country demanding solid driving and many long second shots. A number of particularly fine holes, the pick of which may arguably be, the 3rd and 11th. The course offers unrivalled panoramic views from its hilly position.
18 holes, 6420yds, Par 72, SSS 71, Course record 68.
Club membership 750. ▶

Visitors	some restrictions on Mon, Wed & Thu.
Societies	must contact in writing.
Green Fees	£16 per day (£20 weekends & bank holidays).
Facilities	⊗ ⅢⅢ by prior arrangement ⓑ ⬛ ♀ ⚘ 🏠 ⌕ (Stephen Harrisson.
Leisure	snooker.
Location	Talkin Tarn (1.5m SE of Brampton on B6413)
Hotel	★★★(red)⚤ Farlam Hall Hotel, Hallbankgate, BRAMPTON ☎ (06977) 46234 12↹ ✿Annexe1↹ ❀

CARLISLE   Map 11 NY35

Carlisle ☎ (0228) 513303
Majestic looking parkland course with great appeal. A complete but not too severe test of golf, with fine turf, natural hazards, a stream and many beautiful trees.
18 holes, 6080yds, Par 71, SSS 70.
Club membership 950.

Visitors	with member on Sat, restricted Tue afternoons and competition days. Must contact in advance and have a handicap certificate.
Societies	contact in advance for details
Green Fees	£25 per day; £18 round (Sun £30).
Facilities	⊗ ⅢⅢ ⓑ ⬛ ♀ ⚘ 🏠 ⌕ (John Smith More.
Leisure	snooker.
Location	Aglionby (On A69 1m E of M6 junc 43)
Hotel	★★★64% Cumbrian Hotel, Court Square, CARLISLE ☎ (0228) 31951 70↹ ❀

Stony Holme Municipal ☎ (0228) 34856
Municipal parkland course, bounded on three sides by the River Eden.
18 holes, 5783yds, Par 69, SSS 68, Course record 68.
Club membership 350.

Visitors	must contact in advance.
Societies	must telephone in advance.
Green Fees	not confirmed.
Facilities	⊗ ⅢⅢ ⓑ ⬛ ♀ ⚘ 🏠 ⌕ (S Ling.
Location	St Aidans Rd (3m E off A69)
Hotel	★★★58% Forte Posthouse, Parkhouse Rd, Kingstown, CARLISLE ☎ (0228) 31201 93↹ ❀

COCKERMOUTH   Map 11 NY13

Cockermouth ☎ Bassenthwaite Lake (07687) 76223
Fell-land course, fenced, with exceptional views and a hard climb on the 3rd and 11th holes. Testing holes: 10th and 16th (rearranged by James Braid).
18 holes, 5496yds, Par 69, SSS 67, Course record 65.
Club membership 586.

Visitors	restricted Wed, Sat & Sun.
Societies	must contact in advance.
Green Fees	not confirmed.
Facilities	ⓑ ⬛ (weekends only) ♀ ⚘
Leisure	snooker.
Location	Embleton (3m E off A66)
Hotel	★★★63% The Trout Hotel, Crown St, COCKERMOUTH ☎ (0900) 823591 23↹ ❀

CROSBY-ON-EDEN   Map 12 NY03

Eden ☎ Carlisle (0228) 23161
Open, championship-length course following the River Eden.
18 holes, 6973yds, Par 73, SSS 72, Course record 67.
Club membership 450.

Visitors	no restrictions.
Societies	must contact in advance.
Green Fees	£10 (£15 weekends & bank holidays).
Facilities	⊗ ⅢⅢ ⓑ ⬛ ♀ ⚘ 🏠 ⌕ (Philip Harrison.
Location	5m from M6 junc 44, on A689 towards Brampton
Hotel	★★★58% Newby Grange Hotel, CROSBY-ON-EDEN ☎ (0228) 573645 20↹ ❀

GRANGE-OVER-SANDS   Map 07 SD47

Grange Fell ☎ (05395) 32536
Hillside course with magnificent views over Morecambe Bay and the surrounding Lakeland mountains.
9 holes, 4826mtrs, Par 70, SSS 66, Course record 67.
Club membership 300.

Visitors	may normally play Mon-Sat.
Green Fees	£10 per day (£15 weekends & bank holidays).
Facilities	⬛ ♀ ⚘
Location	Fell Rd (1m W)
Hotel	★★70% Netherwood Hotel, Lindale Rd, GRANGE-OVER-SANDS ☎ (05395) 32552 32rm(29↹ ❀)

Grange-over-Sands ☎ (05395) 33180 or 33754
Parkland course with trees, ditches and easy walking.
18 holes, 5670yds, Par 70, SSS 69.
Club membership 600.

Visitors	may not play 8.30-9.30am & 11.45-1.15pm on Sat & Sun.
Societies	must contact in writing.
Green Fees	£15 per day; £10 per round (£20/£15 weekends & bank holidays).
Facilities	⊗ ⅢⅢ by prior arrangement ⓑ ⬛ ♀ ⚘ 🏠 ⌕ (Steve Sumner-Roberts.
Location	Meathop Rd (NW of town centre off B5277)
Hotel	★★★62% Grange Hotel, Station Square, GRANGE-OVER-SANDS ☎ (05395) 33666 41↹ ❀

KENDAL   Map 07 SD59

Kendal ☎ (0539) 724079 & 733708
Elevated moorland course affording breathtaking views of Lakeland fells and surrounding district.
18 holes, 5515yds, Par 66, SSS 67, Course record 57.
Club membership 700.

Visitors	must have a handicap certificate.
Societies	must contact in advance.
Green Fees	£16 per day (£20 weekends & bank holidays).
Facilities	⊗ ⅢⅢ & ⓑ (ex Mon) ⬛ ♀ ⚘ 🏠 ⌕ (D J Turner.
Leisure	pool table.
Location	The Heights (W side of town centre)
Hotel	★★★60% Woolpack Hotel, Stricklandgate, KENDAL ☎ (0539) 723852 54↹ ❀

KESWICK   Map 11 NY22

Keswick ☎ Threlkeld (07687) 79324
Varied fell and tree-lined course with commanding views of
Lakeland scenery.
18 holes, 6175yds, Par 71, SSS 72.
Club membership 879.
Visitors   must contact in advance, restricted on
          competition days.
Societies   must contact in advance.
Green Fees £15 per day (£20 weekends & bank holidays).
Facilities   ⊗ ⅊ ▙ ☂ ♀ ♨ ➡ ♈ 𝕴 Nigel Burkitt.
Leisure   fishing.
Location   Threlkeld Hall (4m E off A66)
Hotel   ★★★67% Borrowdale Hotel, BORROWDALE
          ☎ (07687) 77224   34➡ ♞

KIRKBY LONSDALE   Map 07 SD67

Kirkby Lonsdale ☎ Barbon (05242) 76366
Parkland course by the River Lune and Barbon Beck. The
beck is a water hazard.
18 holes, 6283yds, Par 70, SSS 70, Course record 71.
Club membership 600.
Visitors   may not play before 9.30am.
Societies   telephone in advance.
Green Fees £14 (£18 weekends & bank holidays).
Facilities   ⊗ ⅊ ▙ ♀ ♨ ➡ 𝕴 R Williams.
Location   Scaleber Ln, Barbon, Carnforth (6m S of
          Sedbergh)
Hotel   ★★69% Pheasant Inn, CASTERTON
          ☎ (05242) 71230   10➡ ♞

MARYPORT   Map 11 NY03

Maryport ☎ (0900) 812605
A tight seaside links course exposed to Solway breezes. Fine
views across Solway Firth.
18 holes, 6272yds, Par 71, SSS 71, Course record 70.
Club membership 380.
Visitors   no restrictions.
Societies   must apply in writing.
Green Fees not confirmed.
Facilities   ⊗ ⅊ ▙ & ♀ by prior arrangement ♀ ♨
Location   Bank End (1m N on B5300)
Hotel   ★★62% Ellenbank Hotel, Birkby, MARYPORT
          ☎ (0900) 815233   26➡ ♞

PENRITH   Map 12 NY53

Penrith ☎ (0768) 62217
A beautiful and well-balanced course, always changing
direction, and demanding good length from the tee. It is
set on rolling moorland with occasional pine trees and
some fine views.
18 holes, 6026yds, Par 69, SSS 69.
Club membership 870.
Visitors   restricted at weekends. Must contact in
          advance and have a handicap certificate.
Societies   restricted at weekends.
Green Fees £21 per day; £18 per round (£25 weekends
          & bank holidays).
Facilities   ⊗ ⅊ ▙ ☂ ♀ ♨ ➡ ♈ 𝕴 C B Thomson.

Leisure   snooker.
Location   Salkeld Rd (0.75m N off A6)
Hotel   ★★65% George Hotel, Devonshire St,
          PENRITH ☎ (0768) 62696   31➡ ♞

ST BEES   Map 11 NX91

St Bees ☎ (0946) 824300
Links course, down hill and dale, with sea views.
9 holes, 5082yds, Par 64, SSS 65.
Club membership 275.
Visitors   no restrictions.
Green Fees not confirmed.
Location   0.5m W of village off B5345
Hotel   ★★★56% Blackbeck Bridge Inn, EGREMONT
          ☎ (0946) 841661   22➡ ♞

SEASCALE   Map 06 NY00

Seascale ☎ (09467) 28202
A tough links requiring length and control. The natural
terrain is used to give a variety of holes and considerable
character. Undulating greens add to the challenge. Fine
views over the Western Fells, the Irish Sea and Isle of
Man.
18 holes, 6419yds, Par 71, SSS 71, Course record 65.
Club membership 750.
Visitors   must contact in advance and normally may
          not play before 9.30am.
Societies   must contact in advance.
Green Fees £18 per day (£22 weekends & bank
          holidays).
Facilities   ⊗ & ⅊ (ex Mon-Tue) ♀ ♨ ➡ ♈
Location   The Banks (NW side of village off B5344)
Hotel   ★★★56% Blackbeck Bridge Inn,
          EGREMONT ☎ (0946) 841661   22➡ ♞

SEDBERGH   Map 07 SD69

Sedbergh ☎ (05396) 20993
A grassland course with superb scenery.The permanent
greens were completed in May 1993.
9 holes, 5504yds, Par 70, SSS 68.
Club membership 300.
Visitors   must book to play on weekends & bank
          holidays.
Societies   must contact in advance.
Green Fees £18 per day; £12 per round (£21/£15 weekends).
Facilities   ⊗ ▙ ♀ ♨ ➡ ♈
Leisure   fishing.
Location   Catholes, Abbot Holme (1m S off A683)
Hotel   ★★70% Garden House Hotel, Fowl-ing Ln,
          KENDAL ☎ (0539) 731131   10➡ ♞

SILECROFT   Map 06 SD18

Silecroft ☎ Millom (0229) 774250
Seaside links course parallel to the coast of the Irish Sea.
Often windy. Easy walking. Spectacular views inland of
Lakeland hills.
9 holes, 5712yds, Par 68, SSS 68.
Club membership 365.   ▶

Visitors restricted weekends.
Societies must contact 14 days in advance.
Green Fees £10 per day/round.
Facilities ⚒
Location 1m SW
Hotel ★★63% Eccle Riggs Hotel, Foxfield Rd, BROUGHTON IN FURNESS
☎ (0229) 716398 & 716780 12⇄ ♠

SILLOTH   Map 11 NY15

Silloth on Solway ☎ (06973) 31304
Billowing dunes, narrow fairways, heather and gorse and the constant subtle problems of tactics and judgement make these superb links on the Solway an exhilarating and searching test. The 13th is a good long hole. Superb views.
18 holes, 6062yds, Par 72, SSS 71.
Club membership 600.
Visitors must contact in advance & have handicap certificate. Restricted Sat & Sun mornings.
Societies must contact in advance.
Green Fees £20 per day (£25 per round weekends & bank holidays).
Facilities ⊗ ⅂ ⅃ ♭ ☛ (no catering Mon) ♀ ⚒ ⌂ ⌐
Leisure snooker.
Location S side of village off B5300
Hotel ★★62% Golf Hotel, Criffel St, SILLOTH
☎ (06973) 31438 22⇄ ♠

ULVERSTON   Map 07 SD27

Ulverston ☎ (0229) 52824
Inland golf with many medium length holes on undulating parkland. The 17th is a testing par 4. Overlooking Morecambe Bay the course offers extensive views to the Lakeland Fells.
18 holes, 6142yds, Par 71, SSS 69, Course record 64.
Club membership 700.
Visitors must contact in advance and have a handicap certificate. May not play on competition days.
Societies must apply in writing.
Green Fees £14/£20 per day (£25 weekends & bank holidays).
Facilities ⊗ ⅂ & ♭ (ex Mon & Fri after 1.45pm) ☛ ♀ ⚒ ⌂ ⌐ M R Smith.
Location Bardsea Park (2m S off A5087)
Hotel ★★★69% Whitewater Hotel, The Lakeland Village, NEWBY BRIDGE
☎ (05395) 31133 35⇄ ♠

WINDERMERE   See **Bowness-on-Windermere**

WORKINGTON   Map 11 NX92

Workington ☎ (0900) 603460
Meadowland course, undulating, with natural hazards created by stream and trees. Good views of Solway Firth and Lakeland Hills.
18 holes, 6200yds, Par 72, Course record 65.
Club membership 900.
Visitors must have a handicap certificate.

Societies must contact in advance.
Green Fees £15 per round/day (£20 weekends & bank holidays).
Facilities ⊗ ⅂ & ♭ (ex Mon) ☛ ♀ ⚒ ⌂ ⌐ ⌐
A Drabble.
Leisure snooker.
Location Branthwaite Rd (1.75m off A596)
Hotel ★★★68% Washington Central Hotel, Washington St, WORKINGTON
☎ (0900) 65772 40 ⇄ ♠

• DERBYSHIRE •

ALFRETON   Map 08 SK45

Alfreton ☎ (O773) 832070
A small parkland course with tight fairways and many natural hazards.
9 holes, 5074yds, Par 66, SSS 65, Course record 62.
Club membership 340.
Visitors with member only Mon & weekends.
Societies apply in writing.
Green Fees £15 per day; £12 per round (18 holes).
Facilities ⊗ (ex Sun & Mon) ⅂ ♭ & ☛ (ex Mon)
♀ (ex Mon) ⚒ ⌂
Location Wingfield Rd, Oakerthorpe (1m W on A615)
Hotel ★★★★62% Swallow Hotel, Carter Ln East, SOUTH NORMANTON
☎ (0773) 812000 161⇄ ♠

ASHBOURNE   Map 07 SK14

Ashbourne ☎ (0335) 42078
Undulating parkland course.
9 holes, 5359yds, Par 66, SSS 66, Course record 61.
Club membership 350.
Visitors may not play on competition days. With member only at weekends.
Societies telephone in advance.
Green Fees £10 for 18 holes.
Facilities ⊗ ♭ ☛ ♀ ⚒
Leisure snooker.
Location Clifton (1.5m SW on A515)
Hotel ★★⚘75% Callow Hall, Mappleton Rd, ASHBOURNE
☎ (0335) 43403 & 42412 12⇄ ♠

BAKEWELL   Map 08 SK26

Bakewell ☎ (062981) 2307
Parkland course, hilly, with plenty of natural hazards to test the golfer. Magnificent views across the Wye Valley.
9 holes, 5240yds, Par 68, SSS 66, Course record 63.
Club membership 400.
Visitors no restrictions.
Societies must contact in advance.
Facilities ⊗ ⅂ ♭ ☛ (no catering Mon)
♀ (ex Mon) ⚒ ⌂
Location Station Rd (E side of town off A6)
Hotel ★★66% Milford House Hotel, Mill St, BAKEWELL ☎ (0629) 812130 12⇄ ♠

BAMFORD   Map 08 SK28

Sickleholme ☎ Hope Valley (0433) 651306
Downland type course in the lovely Peak District. Fine views.
18 holes, 6064yds, Par 69, SSS 69, Course record 63.
Club membership 700.
Visitors	'must contact in advance, restricted Wed mornings & weekends.
Societies	must contact in advance.
Green Fees	£22 per day (£30 weekends & bank holidays).
Facilities	⊗ ⅷ ㋩ 🍺 ♀ ⚏ 🏠 ⚑ P H Taylor.
Location	Saltergate Ln (0.75m S on A6013)
Hotel	★★★65% George Hotel, Main Rd, HATHERSAGE ☎ (0433) 50436 due to change to 650436 18⇥ 🐾

BUXTON   Map 07 SK07

Buxton & High Peak ☎ (0298) 23453
Bracing, well-drained meadowland course; the highest in
Derbyshire.
18 holes, 5980yds, Par 69, SSS 69, Course record 66.
Club membership 800.
Visitors	no restrictions.
Societies	apply in writing to Mrs S Arnfield.
Green Fees	£20 per day (£25 weekends & bank holidays).
Facilities	⊗ (ex Thu) ⅷ by prior arrangement ㋩ (ex Thu) 🍺 ♀ ⚏ 🏠 ⚑ Andrew Hoyles.
Leisure	snooker.
Location	Town End (1m NE off A6)
Hotel	★★★60% Palace Hotel, Palace Rd, BUXTON ☎ (0298) 22001 122⇥

Cavendish ☎ (0298) 23494
This parkland/moorland course with its comfortable
clubhouse nestles below the rising hills. Generally open
to the prevailing west wind, it is noted for its excellent
surfaced greens which contain many deceptive subtleties.
Designed by Dr Alastair McKenzie, good holes include
the 8th, 9th and 18th.
18 holes, 5833yds, Par 68, SSS 68, Course record 63.
Club membership 600.
Visitors	must contact in advance. Must play with member at weekends.
Societies	must contact in advance in writing.
Green Fees	£22 per day (£33 per round weekends & bank holidays).
Facilities	⊗ & ⅷ by prior arrangement ㋩ 🍺 ♀ ⚏ 🏠 ⚑ Paul Hunstone.
Leisure	snooker.
Location	Gadley Ln (0.75m W of town centre off A53)
Hotel	★★★68% Lee Wood Hotel, 13 Manchester Rd, BUXTON ☎ (0298) 23002 & 70421 36⇥ 🐾

CHAPEL-EN-LE-FRITH   Map 07 SK08

Chapel-en-le-Frith ☎ (0298) 812118
Scenic parkland course, with testing holes at the 15th (par 4)
and 17th (517 yds), par 5. Good views.
18 holes, 6119yds, Par 70, SSS 69.
Club membership 665.

Visitors	must contact in advance.
Societies	apply in writing.
Green Fees	£18 per day (£30 weekends & bank holidays).
Facilities	⊗ ⅷ ㋩ 🍺 (no catering Mon) ♀ ⚏ 🏠 ⚑
Location	The Cockyard, Manchester Rd (1m W on A6)
Hotel	★★★68% Lee Wood Hotel, 13 Manchester Rd, BUXTON ☎ (0298) 23002 & 70421 36⇥ 🐾

CHESTERFIELD   Map 08 SK37

Chesterfield ☎ (0246) 279256
A varied and interesting, undulating parkland course with
trees picturesquely adding to the holes and the outlook alike.
Stream hazard on back nine. Views over four counties.
18 holes, 6326yds, Par 71, SSS 70.
Club membership 500.
Visitors	must contact in advance and may not play at weekends. A handicap certificate is generally required.
Societies	apply in writing.
Green Fees	£25 per day; £20 per round.
Facilities	⊗ ⅷ ㋩ 🍺 ♀ ⚏ 🏠 ⚑ M McLean.
Location	Walton (2m SW off A632)
Hotel	★★★62% Chesterfield Hotel, Malkin St, CHESTERFIELD ☎ (0246) 271141 72⇥ 🐾

Grassmoor Golf Centre ☎ (0246) 856044
An 18-hole heathland course with interesting and challenging
water features. 26 bay floodlit driving range, practice bunkers
and putting area.
18 holes, 5800yds, Par 69, SSS 69.
Club membership 350.
Visitors	may book in advance.
Societies	telephone in advance.
Green Fees	£7.50 per 18 holes (£10 weekends).
Facilities	⊗ ⅷ ㋩ 🍺 ♀ ⚏ 🏠 ⚑ Darren Webster Clarke.
Leisure	driving range, practice bunkers.
Location	North Wingfield Rd, Grassmoor (between Chesterfield & Grassmoor, off B6038)
Hotel	★★★62% Chesterfield Hotel, Malkin St, CHESTERFIELD ☎ (0246) 271141 72⇥ 🐾

Stanedge ☎ (0246) 566156
Moorland course in hilly situation open to strong winds.
Some fairways are narrow. Accuracy is paramount.
9 holes, 4867yds, Par 64, SSS 64, Course record 64.
Club membership 300.
Visitors	with member only Sat & Sun, and may not play after 2pm weekdays.
Societies	apply in writing.
Green Fees	£15 per round (18 holes).
Facilities	🍺 ♀ ⚏
Leisure	pool table.
Location	Walton Hay Farm (5m SW off B5057)
Hotel	★★★62% Chesterfield Hotel, Malkin St, CHESTERFIELD ☎ (0246) 271141 72⇥ 🐾

Tapton Park ☎ (0246) 239500
Municipal parkland course with some fairly hard walking.
The 620 yd (par 5) 5th is a testing hole.
Tapton Main: 18 holes, 6013yds, Par 71, SSS 69.
Dobbin Clough: 9 holes, 2613yds, Par 34.
Club membership 750.

▶

Visitors   must contact in advance. No caddies allowed.
Societies   telephone in advance.
Green Fees not confirmed.
Facilities ⊗ ⊞ ⅃ ♥ ♀ ♨ 🕿 🏌 ⎰ Carl Weatherhead.
Location   Murray House, Tapton (0.5m E of Chesterfield
            Station)
Hotel   ★★★62% Chesterfield Hotel, Malkin St,
            CHESTERFIELD ☎ (0246) 271141 72⇆ ﹠

CODNOR   Map 08 SK44

Ormonde Fields ☎ Ripley (0773) 742987
Parkland course with undulating fairways and natural
hazards. The par 4 (4th) and the par 3 (11th) are notable.
There is a practice area.
18 holes, 6011yds, Par 69, SSS 69, Course record 70.
Club membership 500.
Visitors   restricted at weekends. Must contact in advance.
Societies   telephone in advance.
Green Fees not confirmed.
Facilities ⊗ ⊞ ⅃ ♥ ♀ ♨ 🕿 🏌
Location   Nottingham Rd (1m SE on A610)
Hotel   ★★★61% Forte Posthouse Nottingham/Derby,
            Bostocks Ln, SANDIACRE
            ☎ (0602) 397800 91⇆ ﹠

DERBY   Map 08 SK33

Allestree Park ☎ (0332) 550616
Municipal parkland course in rather hilly country.
18 holes, 5749yds, Par 68, SSS 68, Course record 66.
Club membership 275.
Visitors   restricted weekends & bank holidays.
Societies   restricted at weekends & bank holidays.
Green Fees not confirmed.
Facilities ⊗ & ⊞ by prior arrangement
            ⅃ ♥ ♀ ♨ 🕿 🏌 ⎰ Colin Henderson.
Leisure   fishing.
Location   Allestree Hall (3m N on A6)
Hotel   ★★69% Kedleston Country House Hotel,
            Kedleston Rd, DERBY
            ☎ (0332) 559202 & 556507 14⇆ ﹠

Derby ☎ (0332) 766323
Municipal parkland course. The front nine holes are rather
difficult.
18 holes, 5618yds, Par 70, SSS 69, Course record 64.
Club membership 450.
Visitors   starting time must be booked at weekends. Must
            contact in advance.
Societies   apply in writing in advance.
Green Fees not confirmed.
Facilities ⊗ ⊞ ⅃ ♥ ♀ ♨ 🕿 🏌 ⎰ C T C Henderson.
Location   Shakespeare St, Sinfin (3.5m S of city centre)
Hotel   ★★★62% International Hotel, Burton Rd
            (A5250), DERBY
            ☎ (0332) 369321 41⇆Annexe21⇆

Mickleover ☎ (0332) 518662
Undulating parkland course in pleasant setting.
18 holes, 5708yds, Par 68, SSS 68, Course record 63.
Club membership 650.
Visitors   no restrictions.
Societies   telephone in advance.
Green Fees £18 per day (£25 weekends & bank holidays).

Facilities ⊗ ⊞ ⅃ ♥ ♀ ♨ 🕿 🏌 ⎰ Paul Wilson.
Leisure   snooker.
Location   Uttoxeter Rd, Mickleover (3m W off
            A516/B5020)
Hotel   ★★★63% Forte Posthouse, Pasture Hill,
            Littleover, DERBY ☎ (0332) 514933 62⇆

DRONFIELD   Map 08 SK37

Hallowes ☎ (0246) 413734
Attractive moorland/meadowland course set in the
Derbyshire hills. Several testing Par 4's and splendid views.
18 holes, 6330yds, Par 71, SSS 70.
Club membership 600.
Visitors   may only play with member at weekends;
            restricted Wed. Must contact in advance and
            have a handicap certificate.
Societies   must contact in advance.
Green Fees £27 per day; £20 per round.
Facilities ⊗ ⊞ ⅃ ♥ ♀ ♨ 🕿 🏌 ⎰ Philip Dunn.
Leisure   snooker.
Location   Hallowes Ln (S side of town)
Hotel   ★★60% Chantry Hotel, Church St, DRONFIELD
            ☎ (0246) 413014 7⇆ ﹠

DUFFIELD   Map 08 SK34

Chevin ☎ (0332) 841864
A mixture of parkland and moorland, this course is rather
hilly which makes for some hard walking. The 8th calls for a
very hard drive, possibly the hardest in the area.
18 holes, 6057yds, Par 69, SSS 69, Course record 65.
Club membership 500.
Visitors   with member only weekends & bank holidays.
Societies   contact in advance.
Green Fees £25 per day.
Facilities ⊗ ⊞ ⅃ ♥ ♀ ♨ 🕿 🏌 ⎰ Willie Bird.
Leisure   snooker, practice ground.
Location   Golf Ln (N side of town off A6)
Hotel   ★★69% Kedleston Country House Hotel,
            Kedleston Rd, DERBY
            ☎ (0332) 559202 & 556507 14⇆ ﹠

GLOSSOP   Map 07 SK09

Glossop and District ☎ (0457) 865247
Moorland course in good position, excellent natural hazards.
11 holes, 5800yds, Par 68, SSS 68.
Club membership 250.
Visitors   may not play on bank holidays.
Societies   must apply in writing to professional.
Green Fees £15 per day (£20 weekends).
Facilities ⊗ ⊞ ⅃ ♥ (No catering Mon)
            ♀ (ex Mon) ♨ 🕿 ⎰ Gary S Brown.
Location   Hurst Ln, off Sheffield Rd (1m E off A57)
Hotel   ★★71% York House Hotel, York Place,
            Richmond St, ASHTON-UNDER-LYNE
            ☎ 061-330 5899 24⇆ ﹠Annexe10⇆

> If you know of a golf course that welcomes
> visitors and is not already in this guide, we
> should be grateful for information

HORSLEY
Map 08 SK34

Horsley Lodge ☎ Derby (0332) 780838
This course, opened in 1991 and set in 100 acres of
Derbyshire countryside, has some challenging holes. Also Par
3 course and floodlit driving range.
18 holes, 6434yds, Par 72, SSS 71, Course record 74.
Club membership 600.
Visitors   restricted during competitions.
Societies   must telephone in advance.
Green Fees   £15 per round.
Facilities   ⊗ ⅷ ᒪ ♥ ♀ ⚘ 🗑 ⚲ ⚑ ℓ Simon Berry.
Leisure   fishing, sauna, solarium.
Location   Smalley Mill Rd (off A608 Derby-Heanor Rd)
Hotel   ★★★71% Breadsall Priory Hotel, Golf &
                  Country Club, Moor Rd, MORLEY
                  ☎ (0332) 832235 14⇄ ꛱Annexe77⇄ ꛱

KEDLESTON
Map 08 SK34

Kedleston Park ☎ Derby (0332) 840035
The course is laid out in flat mature parkland with fine
trees and background views of historic Kedleston Hall
(National Trust). Many testing holes are included in each
nine and there is an excellent modern clubhouse.
18 holes, 6253yds, Par 70, SSS 70, Course record 64.
Club membership 978.
Visitors   welcome weekdays, must contact in advance
                  & have handicap certificate.
Societies   telephone in advance.
Green Fees   £35 per day; £25 per round.
Facilities   ⊗ ⅷ ᒪ ♥ ♀ ⚘ 🗑 ⚲ ℓ Jim Hetherington.
Leisure   snooker, sauna.
Location   Kedleston Quarndon (2m SE)
Hotel   ★★69% Kedleston Country House Hotel,
                  Kedleston Rd, DERBY
                  ☎ (0332) 559202 & 556507 14⇄ ꛱

MATLOCK
Map 08 SK36

Matlock ☎ (0629) 582191
Moorland course with fine views of the beautiful Peak
District.
18 holes, 5800yds, Par 70, SSS 68, Course record 65.
Club membership 650.
Visitors   with member only weekends & bank holidays.
Societies   telephone in advance.
Green Fees   £25 per day/round.
Facilities   ⊗ & ⅷ by prior arrangement ᒪ ♥ ♀ ⚘ 🗑 ℓ
                  Mike Deeley.
Leisure   snooker, crown green bowling.
Location   Chesterfield Rd (1m NE of Matlock on A632)
Hotel   ★★★69% New Bath Hotel, New Bath Rd,
                  MATLOCK ☎ (0629) 583275 55⇄

MICKLEOVER
Map 08 SK33

Pastures ☎ Derby (0332) 513921 (ext 348)
Small course laid-out on undulating meadowland in the
grounds of a psychiatric hospital, with good views across the
Trent valley. Fishing and snooker.
9 holes, 5005yds, Par 64, SSS 64, Course record 62.
Club membership 320.

Visitors   may not play on Sun. Must contact in advance.
Societies   must contact in advance.
Green Fees   £10 per day.
Facilities   (catering by arrangement)
                  ♀ (by arrangement) ⚘
Leisure   fishing, snooker, badminton, bowls, table tennis.
Location   Pastures Hospital (1m SW off A516)
Hotel   ★★★62% International Hotel, Burton Rd
                  (A5250), DERBY
                  ☎ (0332) 369321 41⇄Annexe21⇄

MORLEY
Map 08 SK34

Breadsall Priory ☎ Derby (0332) 834425
Set in 200 acres of mature parkland, the Old Course is built
on the site of a 13th-century priory. Full use had been made
of natural features and fine old trees. In contrast the Moorland
Course, opened in Spring 1992, designed by Donald Steel and
built by Brian Piersen, features Derbyshire stone walls and
open moors.
Priory Golf Course: 18 holes, 5871yds, Par 72, SSS 68.
Moorland Golf Course: 18 holes, 5820yds, Par 71, SSS 68.
Club membership 800.
Visitors   must contact in advance.
Societies   must contact in advance.
Green Fees   £31 per day; £22.50 per round (£26 per round
                  weekends).
Facilities   ⊗ ⅷ ᒪ ♥ ♀ ⚘ 🗑 ⚲ ℓ Andrew Smith.
Leisure   hard tennis courts, heated indoor swimming
                  pool, squash, snooker, sauna, solarium,
                  gymnasium, health & beauty salon.
Location   Moor Rd (0.75m W)
Hotel   ★★★71% Breadsall Priory Hotel, Golf &
                  Country Club, Moor Rd, MORLEY
                  ☎ (0332) 832235 14⇄ ꛱ Annexe77 ⇄ ꛱

NEW MILLS
Map 07 SK08

New Mills ☎ (0663) 743485
Moorland course with panoramic views and first-class greens.
9 holes, 5633yds, Par 68, SSS 67, Course record 67.
Club membership 350.
Visitors   must play with member at weekends & special
                  days. Must contact in advance.
Societies   must contact in advance.
Green Fees   not confirmed.
Facilities   ⊗ & ⅷ by prior arrangement
                  ᒪ ♥ ♀ ⚘ 🗑 ⚲ ℓ Andrew Hoyles.
Location   Shaw Marsh (0.5m N off B6101)
Hotel   ★★70% Red Lion Inn, 112 Buxton Rd, High
                  Ln, STOCKPORT ☎ (0663) 765227 6⇄ ꛱

RENISHAW
Map 08 SK47

Renishaw Park ☎ Eckington (0246) 432044
Part parkland and part meadowland with easy walking.
18 holes, 5949yds, Par 71, SSS 68.
Club membership 500.
Visitors   no restrictions.
Societies   apply in writing.
Green Fees   not confirmed.
Facilities   ⊗ ⅷ by prior arrangement ᒪ ♥ ♀ ⚘ 🗑 ⚲ ℓ
                  Simon Elliot.
Leisure   snooker.   ▶

Location	Golf House (0.5m NW on A616)
Hotel	★★★59% Sitwell Arms Toby Hotel, RENISHAW ☎ (0246) 435226 30⇥ ⋔

SHIRLAND

Map 08 SK35

Shirlands ☎ (0773) 834935
Rolling parkland and tree-lined course with extensive views of Derbyshire countryside.
18 holes, 6072yds, Par 71, SSS 69, Course record 71.
Club membership 700.

Visitors	must contact in advance.
Societies	contact Professional.
Green Fees	£25 per day; £15 per round (£20 per round weekends).
Facilities	⊗ ⋔ ⅊ ♨ ⚑ ⅋ ↑ ⎰ ℂ N B Hallam.
Leisure	bowling green.
Location	Lower Delves (S side of village off A61)
Hotel	★★★★62% Swallow Hotel, Carter Ln East, SOUTH NORMANTON ☎ (0773) 812000 161⇥ ⋔

STANTON-BY-DALE

Map 08 SK43

Erewash Valley ☎ Sandiacre (0602) 323258
Parkland/meadowland course overlooking valley and M1. Unique 4th and 5th in Victorian quarry bottom: 5th-testing par 3.
18 holes, 6487yds, Par 72, SSS 71, Course record 68.
Club membership 860.

Visitors	must contact in advance & have handicap certificate but may not play before noon weekends & bank holidays.
Societies	contact in advance.
Green Fees	£27 per day; £22 per round (£27 per round weekends).
Facilities	⊗ ⋔ by prior arrangement ⅊ ♨ ⚑ ⅋ ↑ ⎰ ℂ M J Ronan.
Leisure	snooker, bowling green.
Location	1m W
Hotel	★★★61% Forte Posthouse Nottingham/Derby, Bostocks Ln, SANDIACRE ☎ (0602) 397800 91⇥ ⋔

DEVON

AXMOUTH

Map 03 SY29

Axe Cliff ☎ Seaton (0297) 24371
Undulating links course with coastal views.
18 holes, 5057yds, Par 67, SSS 65.
Club membership 400.

Visitors	may only play after 11am on Wed & Sun.
Societies	must contact in advance.
Green Fees	not confirmed.
Facilities	⊗ (ex Tue) ⋔ by prior arrangement (summer only) ⅊ ♨ ⅊ ⚑
Location	0.75m S on B3172
Hotel	★★61% Anchor Inn, BEER ☎ (0297) 20386 9rm(2⇥2 ⋔)

BIGBURY-ON-SEA

Map 03 SX64

Bigbury ☎ (0548) 810557
Heathland course with easy walking. Exposed to winds, but with fine views over the sea and River Avon.
18 holes, 5902yds, Par 70, SSS 68, Course record 65.
Club membership 850.

Visitors	must have handicap certificate.
Societies	must apply in writing.
Green Fees	£20 per day (£24 weekends & bank holidays).
Facilities	⊗ ⋔ by prior arrangement ⅊ ♨ ⅊ ♨ ⚑ ↑ ℂ Simon Lloyd.
Location	Kingsbridge (1m S on B3392)
Hotel	★69% Henley Hotel, BIGBURY-ON-SEA ☎ (0548) 810240 8⇥ ⋔

BUDLEIGH SALTERTON

Map 03 SY08

East Devon ☎ (0395) 443370
An interesting course with downland turf, much heather and gorse, and superb views over the bay. The early holes climb to the cliff edge. The downhill 17th, has a heather section in the fairway leaving a good second to the green.
18 holes, 6239yds, Par 70, SSS 70.
Club membership 850.

Visitors	must contact in advance and have an introduction from own club.
Societies	must contact in advance.
Green Fees	not confirmed.
Facilities	⊗ ⅊ ♨ ⅊ ♨ ⚑ ↑ ℂ Trevor Underwood.
Location	North View Rd (W side of town centre off A376)
Hotel	★★★61% The Imperial, The Esplanade, EXMOUTH ☎ (0395) 274761 57⇥ ⋔

CHITTLEHAMHOLT

Map 02 SS62

Highbullen Hotel ☎ (0769) 540561
Mature parkland course with water hazards and outstanding scenic views to Exmoor and Dartmoor. Excellent facilities offered by the hotel.
9 holes, 2210yds, Par 31, SSS 29.
Club membership 100.

Visitors	no restrictions.
Green Fees	not confirmed.
Facilities	⅊ ♨ ⅊ ♨ ⚑ ↑ ⎰ ℂ Paul Weston.
Leisure	hard tennis courts, outdoor and indoor heated swimming pools, squash, snooker, sauna, solarium, gymnasium, indoor putting, steam room.
Location	0.5m SE of Village
Hotel	★★★♨70% Highbullen Hotel, CHITTLEHAMHOLT ☎ (0769) 540561 12⇥ Annexe25⇥ ⋔

CHULMLEIGH

Map 03 SS61

Chulmleigh ☎ (0769) 80519
Challenging par 3 courses on undulating meadowland.
18 holes, 1485yds, Par 54, SSS 54, Course record 52.
Club membership 150.

Visitors	may play without restriction but juniors should be accompanied by an adult.
Societies	must contact in advance.
Green Fees	£5 per round; £10 per day.
Facilities	ⓑ 🍺 ♀ 🏌 🏠 🦶 🍴
Location	Leigh Rd (SW side of village)
Hotel	★★73% Marsh Hall Hotel, SOUTH MOLTON ☎ (0769) 572666 7⇄ 🐾

CHURSTON FERRERS   Map 03 SX95

Churston ☎ Churston (0803) 842751
A cliff-top downland course with splendid views over Brixham harbour and Tor Bay. There is some gorse with a wooded area inland. A variety of shot is called for, with particularly testing holes at the 3rd, 9th and 15th, all par 4.
18 holes, 6219yds, Par 70, SSS 70, Course record 64.
Club membership 700.

Visitors	must be members of recognised golf club & have handicap certificate, play is restricted at times.
Societies	must contact in advance.
Green Fees	£22 per day (£27 weekends & bank holidays).
Facilities	⊗ ⁂ ⓑ 🍺 ♀ 🏌 🏠 🍴 R Penfold.
Location	NW side of village on A379
Hotel	★★62% Dainton Hotel, 95 Dartmouth Rd, Three Beaches, Goodrington, PAIGNTON ☎ (0803) 550067 & 525901 11⇄ 🐾

CREDITON   Map 03 SS80

Downes Crediton ☎ (0363) 773991 & 774464
Converted farmhouse course with lovely views. Parkland with hilly back nine.
18 holes, 5776yds, Par 70, SSS 68.
Club membership 700.

Visitors	must contact in advance, restricted at weekends.
Societies	must contact in advance.
Green Fees	£16 per day (£22 weekends).
Facilities	⊗ ⓑ 🍺 ♀ 🏌 🏠 🦶 🍴 H Finch.
Location	Hookway (1.5m SE off A377)
Hotel	★★★70% Barton Cross Hotel & Restaurant, Huxham, STOKE CANON ☎ (0392) 841245 & 841584 6⇄ 🐾

CULLOMPTON   Map 03 ST00

Padbrook Park ☎ (0884) 38286
A 9-hole, 18 tee parkland course with much mature woodland and two small lakes.
9 holes, 6108yds, Par 70, SSS 69.
Club membership 450.

Visitors	must contact in advance.
Societies	apply by telephone.
Green Fees	£8 per 18 holes; £5 per 9 holes (£14/£7 weekends).
Facilities	⊗ ⁂ ⓑ 🍺 ♀ 🏌 🏠 🍴 Stewart Adwick.
Leisure	fishing, riding, indoor bowling centre.
Location	13m NE of Exeter, 1m from junc 28 of M5
Hotel	★★70% Parkway House, SAMPFORD PEVERELL ☎ (0884) 820255 7⇄ 🐾

DAWLISH WARREN   Map 03 SX97

Warren ☎ (0626) 862255
Typical flat, genuine links course lying on spit between sea and Exe estuary. Picturesque scenery, a few trees but much gorse. Testing in windy conditions. The 7th hole provides the opportunity to go for the green across a bay on the estuary.
18 holes, 5973yds, Par 69, SSS 69.
Club membership 700.

Visitors	must contact in advance & have handicap certificate.
Societies	telephone in advance.
Green Fees	not confirmed.
Facilities	⊗ ⓑ 🍺 ♀ 🏌 🏠 🍴
Location	W side of village
Hotel	★★★60% Langstone Cliff Hotel, Dawlish Warren, DAWLISH ☎ (0626) 865155 64⇄ 🐾

EXETER   Map 03 SX99

Exeter ☎ Topsham (039287) 4139
A sheltered parkland course with some very old trees and known as the flattest course in Devon. 15th & 17th are testing par 4 holes.
18 holes, 6000yds, Par 69, SSS 69.
Club membership 850.

Visitors	must contact in advance and have a handicap certificate.
Societies	welcome Thu only, must telephone in advance.
Green Fees	£22 per day.
Facilities	⊗ ⁂ (Fri & Sat evenings only) ⓑ 🍺 ♀ 🏌 🏠 🍴
Leisure	hard tennis courts, outdoor and indoor heated swimming pools, squash, snooker, sauna, solarium, gymnasium, gym.
Location	Topsham Rd, Countess Wear (SE side of city centre off A379)
Hotel	★★★61% Countess Wear Lodge Hotel, Topsham Rd, Exeter Bypass, EXETER ☎ (0392) 875441 44⇄ 🐾

Woodbury Park ☎ Woodbury (0395) 33382
Two courses set in the lovely wooded parkland of Woodbury Castle. The 18-hole championship Oaks course is host to professional Championships and the 9-hole is a championship-standard training course.
Oaks: 18 holes, 6707yds, Par 72, SSS 72.
Acorn: 9 holes, 4582yds, Par 69, SSS 62.
Club membership 400.

Visitors	advisable to contact in advance.
Societies	contact in advance.
Green Fees	£20 per 18 holes; £8 per 9 holes (£25/£9 weekends).
Facilities	⊗ ⁂ by prior arrangement ⓑ 🍺 ♀ (Mon-Sat) 🏌 🏠 🦶
Leisure	fishing.
Location	Woodbury Castle, Woodbury
Hotel	★★70% Ebford House Hotel, Exmouth Rd, EBFORD ☎ (0392) 877658 18⇄ 🐾

> *Remember* – replace all divots, and repair ball-marks or damage by spikes on completion of the hole

HIGH BICKINGTON

Map 02 SS52

Libbaton ☎ (0769) 60269
Parkland course on undulating land with no steep slopes.
Floodlit driving range.
18 holes, 5812yds, Par 72, SSS 68.
Club membership 400.

Visitors may not play during competitions, advisable to phone in advance.
Societies must contact in advance.
Green Fees not confirmed.
Facilities ⊗ ⅏ ⓛ 🍺 ♀ ⚑ 🏠 ⚑ ℓ John Phillips.
Hotel ★★★♨70% Highbullen Hotel, CHITTLEHAMHOLT ☎ (0769) 540561 12⇌ Annexe25⇌ ↾

HOLSWORTHY

Map 02 SS30

Holsworthy ☎ (0409) 253177
Pleasant parkland course.
18 holes, 6012yds, Par 70, SSS 69, Course record 66.
Club membership 700.

Visitors may not play before 9.30am or 12-2.30pm Sat, before 2.30pm Sun or on competition days.
Societies must contact in writing.
Green Fees £15 per day (£20 weekends).
Facilities ⊗ ⅏ ⓛ 🍺 ♀ ⚑ 🏠 ℓ Tim McSherry.
Location Killatree (1.5m W on A3072)
Hotel ★★★♨70% Court Barn Country House Hotel, CLAWTON ☎ (040927) 219 8rm(4⇌3 ↾)

HONITON

Map 03 ST10

Honiton ☎ (0404) 44422
Level parkland course on a plateau 850ft above sea level.
Easy walking and good views. The 4th hole is a testing par 3.
The club was founded in 1896.
18 holes, 5940yds, Par 69, SSS 68, Course record 67.
Club membership 800.

Visitors must contact in advance & have handicap certificate.
Societies must contact in writing.
Green Fees £18 per day (£23 weekends).
Facilities ⊗ ⅏ ⓛ 🍺 (Mon-Sat during summer months only) ♀ ⚑ 🏠 ℓ Adrian Cave.
Location Middlehills (1.25m SE)
Hotel ★★66% Home Farm Hotel, Wilmington, HONITON ☎ (040483) 278 7rm(3⇌) Annexe6⇌ ↾

ILFRACOMBE

Map 02 SS54

Ilfracombe ☎ (0271) 862176
A sporting, clifftop, heathland course with views over the Bristol Channel and moors from every tee and green.
18 holes, 5893yds, Par 70, SSS 69, Course record 66.
Club membership 706.

Visitors must have handicap certificate, play is restricted at times.
Societies must contact in advance.
Green Fees £17 per day (£20 weekends & bank holidays).
Facilities ⊗ ⅏ ⓛ 🍺 ♀ ⚑ 🏠 ⚑ ℓ David Hoare.

Leisure pool & darts.
Location Hele Bay (1.5m E off A399)
Hotel ★★67% Elmfield Hotel, Torrs Park, ILFRACOMBE ☎ (0271) 863377 12rm(11 ↾) Annexe2⇌ ↾

IVYBRIDGE

Map 02 SX65

Dinnaton Sporting & Country Club
☎ Plymouth (0752) 892512
A 9-hole course, mainly Par 3 but with four recently added Par 4 holes. Floodlit driving range.
9 holes, 3850yds, Par 62, SSS 56.
Club membership 200.

Visitors a handicap certificate is appreciated.
Societies must telephone in advance.
Green Fees weekdays £10 (£12.50 weekends).
Facilities ⊗ ⅏ ⓛ 🍺 ♀ ⚑ 🏠 ⚑ 🏓 ℓ Paul Weston.
Leisure heated indoor swimming pool, squash, snooker, sauna, solarium, gymnasium, badminton courts, volleyball courts.
Location Blachford Rd
Hotel ★★♨74% Glazebrook House Hotel & Restaurant, SOUTH BRENT ☎ (0364) 73322 11⇌ ↾

MORETONHAMPSTEAD

Map 03 SX78

Manor House Hotel ☎ (0647) 40355
This enjoyable parkland course is a sporting circuit with just enough hazards (most of them natural) to make any golfer think. The Rivers Bowden and Bovey meander through the first eight holes. Driving range.
18 holes, 6016yds, Par 69, SSS 69, Course record 65.
Club membership 230.

Visitors must contact in advance and pre-arrange starting times.
Societies must contact in advance.
Facilities ⊗ & ⅏ by prior arrangement ⓛ ♀ ⚑ 🏠 ⚑ 🏓 ℓ Richard Lewis.
Leisure hard tennis courts, squash, fishing, snooker, 6 hole pitch & putt, driving range.
Location 3m W off B3212
Hotel ★★★♨77% The Bel Alp House, HAYTOR ☎ (0364) 661217 9⇌ ↾

MORTEHOE

Map 02 SS44

Easewell Farm Holiday Park ☎ Woolacombe (0271) 870225
Attached to a camping and caravan site, this 9-hole course has 2 par 3s and 7 par 4s. The gently sloping clifftop course has spectacular views across Morte Bay.
9 holes, 2426yds, Par 34, SSS 32, Course record 32.
Club membership 250.

Visitors no restrictions.
Societies must telephone in advance.
Green Fees £10 per 18 holes; £6 per 9 holes.
Facilities ⓛ 🍺 ♀ ⚑ 🏠 ⚑
Leisure heated indoor swimming pool, camping & caravan site.
Hotel ★★★73% Watersmeet Hotel, Mortehoe, WOOLACOMBE ☎ (0271) 870333 25rm(23⇌ ↾)

NEWTON ABBOT   Map 03 SX87

Newton Abbot (Stover) ☎ (0626) 52460
Wooded parkland course with a stream coming into play on eight holes. Fairly flat.
18 holes, 5886yds, Par 69, SSS 68, Course record 63.
Club membership 877.
Visitors   must have proof of membership of recognised club. Must contact in advance.
Societies by arrangement on Thu only.
Green Fees £22 per day.
Facilities ⊗ ⅏ by prior arrangement ⅃ ♥ ♀ ⚲ ⌂ ⱡ Malcolm Craig.
Location   Bovey Rd (3m N on A382)
Hotel   ★★59% Queens Hotel, Queen St, NEWTON ABBOT ☎ (0626) 63133 & 54106 24rm(20⇄ ⋔)

OKEHAMPTON   Map 02 SX59

Okehampton ☎ (0837) 52113
Interesting and beautiful moorland course with true Dartmoor turf.
18 holes, 5191yds, Par 68, SSS 67.
Club membership 550.
Visitors   must contact in advance & have handicap certificate.
Societies must contact in writing.
Green Fees £15 per day (£20 Sat, £17 Sun).
Facilities ⊗ ⅏ by prior arrangement ⅃ ♥ ♀ ⚲ ⌂ ⱡ ⱡ Phillip J Blundell.
Location   Tors Rd (1m S off A30)
Hotel   ★★62% Oxenham Arms, SOUTH ZEAL ☎ (0837) 840244 & 840577 8rm(7⇄ ⋔)

PLYMOUTH   Map 02 SX45

Elfordleigh ☎ (0752) 336428
Charming, saucer-shaped parkland course with alternate tees for 18 holes. Tree-lined fairways and three lakes. Fairly hard walking.
9 holes, 5664yds, Par 68, SSS 67.
Club membership 350.
Visitors   must contact in advance & have handicap certificate.
Societies by arrangement.
Green Fees not confirmed.
Facilities ⊗ ⅏ ⅃ ♥ ♀ ⚲ ⌂ ⱡ ⋈ ⱡ Andrew Rickard.
Leisure   hard tennis courts, outdoor and indoor heated swimming pools, squash, snooker, sauna, solarium, gymnasium, games room, jacuzzi, croquet.
Location   Plympton (8m NE off B3416)
Hotel   ★★★58% Novotel Plymouth, Marsh Mills Roundabout, 270 Plymouth Rd, PLYMOUTH ☎ (0752) 221422 100⇄ ⋔
Additional
Hotel   St Mellion (See advertisement)

Staddon Heights ☎ (0752) 402475
Seaside course that can be windy. Walking easy.
18 holes, 5874yds, Par 68, SSS 68.
Club membership 750.

Visitors   cannot play Sun.
Societies must apply to the secretary.
Green Fees £15 per day (£20 weekends).
Facilities ⊗ ⅏ ⅃ ♥ ♀ ⚲ ⌂ ⱡ John Cox.
Leisure   snooker.
Location   Plymstock (5m SW)
Hotel   ★★★65% Forte Posthouse, Cliff Rd, The Hoe, PLYMOUTH ☎ (0752) 662828 106⇄ ⋔
Additional
Hotel   St Mellion (See advertisement above)

SAUNTON   Map 02 SS43

Saunton ☎ Braunton (0271) 812436
Two traditional links courses (one championship). Windy, with natural hazards.
East Course: 18 holes, 6708yds, Par 71, SSS 73, Course record 66.
West Course: 18 holes, 6356yds, Par 71, SSS 71, Course record 68.
Club membership 1180.
Visitors   must have handicap certificate and be member of recognised golf club.
Societies must apply in writing.
Green Fees £28 (£33 weekends).
Facilities ⊗ ⅏ ⅃ ♥ ♀ ⚲ ⌂ ⱡ J McGhee.
Location   S side of village off B3231
Hotel   ★★★★59% Saunton Sands Hotel, SAUNTON ☎ (0271) 890212 92⇄ ⋔

SIDMOUTH

Map 03 SY18

Sidmouth ☎ (0395) 513451
Situated on the side of Peak Hill, offering beautiful coastal views. Club founded in 1889.
18 holes, 5100yds, Par 66, SSS 65.
Club membership 700.

Visitors	restricted on competition days. Must contact in advance.
Societies	must telephone in advance.
Green Fees	£18 per day.
Facilities	⊗ ⅢⅢ ⅃⃗ ♨ ♀ ⅄ 🛈 ⊓⃗ ⅃ Mervyn Kemp.
Location	Cotmaton Rd, Peak Hill (W side of town centre)
Hotel	★★★★65% Victoria Hotel, Esplanade, SIDMOUTH ☎ (0395) 512651 61⇌ 🛏

SOUTH BRENT

Map 03 SX66

Wrangaton (S Devon) ☎ (0364) 73229
Moorland/parkland course within Dartmoor National Park. Spectacular views towards sea and rugged terrain. Natural fairways and hazards include bracken, sheep and ponies.
18 holes, 6040yds, Par 69, SSS 69, Course record 68.
Club membership 600.

Visitors	must contact in advance & have handicap certificate, restricted on competition days.
Societies	must give one months notice in writing.
Green Fees	not confirmed.
Facilities	⊗ ⅢⅢ ⅃⃗ ♨ ♀ ⅄ 🛈 ⅃ John Cox.
Location	Golf Links Rd, Wrangaton (2.25 m SW off A38)
Hotel	★★♨♨74% Glazebrook House Hotel & Restaurant, SOUTH BRENT ☎ (0364) 73322 11⇌ 🛏

TAVISTOCK

Map 02 SX47

Hurdwick ☎ (0822) 612746
This Executive parkland course with many bunkers and fine views opened in 1990. The idea of Executive golf originated in America and the concept is that a round should take no longer than 3 hours whilst offering solid challenge, thus suiting the busy business person.
18 holes, 4553yds, Par 67, SSS 62, Course record 67.
Club membership 175.

Visitors	no restrictions.
Societies	must contact in advance.
Green Fees	£14 per day (£16 weekends & bank holidays).
Facilities	⅃⃗ ♨ ♀ ⅄ ⊓⃗
Location	Tavistock Hamlets (1m N)
Hotel	★★★62% Bedford Hotel, Plymouth Rd, TAVISTOCK ☎ (0822) 613221 31rm(30⇌ 🛏)

Tavistock ☎ (0822) 612344
Set on Whitchurch Down in south-west Dartmoor with easy walking and magnificent views over rolling countryside into Cornwall. Downland turf with some heather, and interesting holes on undulating ground.
18 holes, 6250yds, Par 70, SSS 70.
Club membership 700.

Visitors	may not play on competition days. Must contact in advance and have a handicap certificate.
Societies	must apply in writing.
Green Fees	weekdays £17; weekends £22.

Facilities	⊗ ⅢⅢ ⅃⃗ ♨ ♀ ⅄ 🛈 ⊓⃗ ⅃ Reg Cade.
Leisure	snooker.
Location	Down Rd (1m SE)
Hotel	★★★62% Bedford Hotel, Plymouth Rd, TAVISTOCK ☎ (0822) 613221 31rm(30⇌ 🛏)

TEDBURN ST MARY

Map 03 SX89

Fingle Glen ☎ (0647) 61817
9-hole course containing six par 4's and three par 3's set in 52 acres of rolling countryside. Testing 4th, 5th and 9th holes. 12-bay floodlit driving range.
9 holes, 2466yds, Par 33, SSS 31.
Club membership 450.

Visitors	no restrictions.
Societies	must telephone two weeks in advance.
Green Fees	not confirmed.
Facilities	⊗ ⅢⅢ ⅃⃗ ♨ ♀ ⅄ 🛈 ⊓⃗ ⊶ ⅃ Stephen Gould.
Leisure	driving range.
Location	5m from city centre on A30
Hotel	★★★61% Countess Wear Lodge Hotel, Topsham Rd, Exeter Bypass, EXETER ☎ (0392) 875441 44⇌ 🛏

TEIGNMOUTH

Map 03 SX97

Teignmouth ☎ (0626) 774194
This fairly flat heathland course is high up with a fine seascape from the clubhouse. Good springy turf with some heather and an interesting layout makes for very enjoyable holiday golf.
18 holes, 5880yds, Par 70, SSS 69.
Club membership 900.

Visitors	must contact in advance & have handicap certificate & must use yellow tees.
Societies	must contact Secretary for details.
Green Fees	£22 per day.
Facilities	⊗ ⅢⅢ ⅃⃗ ♨ ♀ ⅄ 🛈 ⊓⃗ ⅃ Peter Ward.
Location	Exeter Rd (2m NW off B3192)
Hotel	★★65% Ness House Hotel, Marine Dr, Shaldon, TEIGNMOUTH ☎ (0626) 873480 7⇌ 🛏 Annexe5rm

THURLESTONE

Map 03 SX64

Thurlestone ☎ Kingsbridge (0548) 560405
Situated on the edge of the cliffs with typical downland turf and good greens. The course, after an interesting opening hole, rises to higher land with fine seaviews, and finishes with an excellent 502-yard downhill hole to the clubhouse.
18 holes, 6303yds, Par 70, SSS 70, Course record 67.
Club membership 770.

Visitors	must contact in advance & have handicap certificate.
Green Fees	£25 per day.
Facilities	⊗ ⅢⅢ by prior arrangement ⅃⃗ ♨ ♀ ⅄ 🛈 ⊓⃗ ⅃ Neville Whitley.
Leisure	hard and grass tennis courts.
Location	S side of village
Hotel	★★★★65% Thurlestone Hotel, THURLESTONE ☎ (0548) 560382 68⇌ 🛏

TIVERTON
Map 03 SS91

Tiverton ☎ (0884) 252187
A parkland course where the many different species of tree are a feature and where the lush pastures ensure some of the finest fairways in the south-west. There are a number of interesting holes which visitors will find a real challenge.
18 holes, 6263yds, Par 71, SSS 71, Course record 65.
Club membership 930.

Visitors	must contact in advance & be member of a recognised golf club & have handicap certificate.
Societies	must contact in advance.
Green Fees	not confirmed.
Facilities	⊗ ⅢⅢ ⅃ ▬ ⅄ ⚲ ⚹ ℓ David Sheppard.
Location	Post Hill
Hotel	★★58% Hartnoll Hotel, Bolham, TIVERTON ☎ (0884) 252777 11⇆ Annexe5 ⚲

TORQUAY
Map 03 SX96

Torquay ☎ (0803) 314591
Unusual combination of cliff and parkland golf, with wonderful views over the sea and Dartmoor.
18 holes, 6198yds, Par 69, SSS 69, Course record 66.
Club membership 700.

Visitors	must contact in advance & have handicap certificate.
Societies	must apply in writing.
Green Fees	£20 per day/round (£25 weekends & bank holidays).
Facilities	⊗ ⅢⅢ ⅃ ▬ (no catering Mon) ⅄ ⚲ ⚹ ℓ M Ruth.
Location	30 Petitor Rd, St Marychurch (1.25m N)
Hotel	★★59% Norcliffe Hotel, 7 Babbacombe Downs Rd, Babbacombe, TORQUAY ☎ (0803) 328456 & 328023 28⇆ ⚲

TORRINGTON
Map 02 SS41

Torrington ☎ Great Torrington (0805) 22229
Hard walking on hilly commonland course. Small greens and outstanding views.
9 holes, 4373yds, Par 64, SSS 61, Course record 60.
Club membership 374.

Visitors	cannot play Sat & Sun mornings & bank holidays. Must contact in advance.
Societies	by arrangement.
Green Fees	£10 per day/round (£14 weekends & bank holidays).
Facilities	⊗ ⅃ ▬ ⅄ ⚲ ⚹
Location	Weare Trees, Great Torrington (1.25m NW)
Hotel	★★50% Beaconside Hotel, LANDCROSS ☎ (02372) 77205 9rm(4⇆2 ⚲)

Use the AA *Hotels* or *Bed and Breakfast* Guides to extend your choice of accommodation

UPOTTERY
Map 03 ST20

Otter Valley Golf Centre ☎ (0404) 86266 (5m NW of Honiton off A30, on Upottery Rd) This is a golf school set in beautiful Devon countryside. There are practice facilities with driving range, approach and chipping green areas. 3-day courses are designed for established golfers and offer playing opportunities at Woodbury Park Golf Club, 1992 venue of the Devon Professional Championship and Mizuro Assistants Championship. A 5-day course gives instruction to establish all aspects of your game and takes you through the basics of sound swing technique, giving you a written record and a video analysis. Beginners are prepared for the Tony Jacklin Club Certificate of Competence and taken through their first round on a golf course. Self-catering accommodation is available at the course.

WESTWARD HO!
Map 02 SS42

Royal North Devon ☎ Bideford (0237) 473817
Links course with sea views.
18 holes, 6644yds, Par 71, SSS 72, Course record 66.
Club membership 1089.

Visitors	must have handicap certificate or letter of introduction from club.
Societies	must apply in advance.
Green Fees	£25 per day; £21 per round.
Facilities	⊗ & ⅢⅢ by prior arrangement ⅃ ▬ ⅄ ⚲ ⚹ ℓ Graham Johnston.

▶

Location N side of village off B3236
Hotel ★★62% Culloden House Hotel, Fosketh Hill, WESTWARD HO! ☎ (0237) 479421 9rm(2⇌5 ⇌)

YELVERTON Map 02 SX56

Yelverton ☎ (0822) 852824
An excellent course on the moors with virtually no trees. It is exposed to high winds. The fairways are tight but there is plenty of room. The longest hole is the 8th, a 569-yard, par 5. Outstanding views.
18 holes, 6293yds, Par 70, SSS 70.
Club membership 800.

Visitors must be member of a club & have handicap certificate. Must contact in advance.
Societies by arrangement.
Green Fees not confirmed.
Facilities ⊗ Iain Parker.
Leisure snooker.
Location Golf Links Rd (1m S off A386)
Hotel ★★★69% Moorland Links Hotel, YELVERTON ☎ (0822) 852245 30⇌

DORSET

BELCHALWELL Map 03 ST70

Mid-Dorset ☎ Blandford (0258) 861386
Set in an area of outstanding natural beauty, rich in wildlife, which provides a picturesque backdrop to this stimulating, undulating course. Modern clubhouse with magnificent views.
18 holes, 5938mtrs, Par 70, SSS 71.
Club membership 350.

Visitors no restrictions.
Societies welcome by prior arrangement.
Green Fees not confirmed.
Facilities ⊗ Andrew Pakes.
Hotel ★★★66% Crown Hotel, 8 West St, BLANDFORD FORUM ☎ (0258) 456626 32⇌

BLANDFORD FORUM Map 03 ST80

Ashley Wood ☎ (0258) 452253
Undulating downland course with superb views and excellent drainage.
9 holes, 6630yds, Par 70, SSS 70, Course record 67.
Club membership 550.

Visitors ladies only Tues mornings. Must contact in advance and have a handicap certificate.
Societies contact in writing.
Green Fees £17 per day (weekend £24 per day).
Facilities ⊗ & by prior arrangement Spencer Taylor.
Leisure practise ground & putting green.
Location Wimborne Rd (2m E on B3082)
Hotel ★★★66% Crown Hotel, 8 West St, BLANDFORD FORUM ☎ (0258) 456626 32⇌

BOURNEMOUTH Map 04 SZ09

Knighton Heath ☎ (0202) 572633
Undulating heathland course on high ground inland from Bournemouth.
18 holes, 5987yds, Par 68, SSS 69.
Club membership 700.

Visitors with member only weekends & bank holidays. Must have handicap certificate.
Societies must book in advance.
Green Fees on application.
Facilities ⊗ by prior arrangement Jane Miles.
Location Francis Av, West Howe (N side of town centre off A348)
Hotel ★★★58% Bournemouth Heathlands Hotel, 12 Grove Rd, East Cliff, BOURNEMOUTH ☎ (0202) 553336 116⇌

Queen's Park ☎ (0202) 396198
Undulating parkland course of pine and heather, with narrow, tree-lined fairways. Public course played over by 'Boscombe Golf Club' and 'Bournemouth Artisans Golf Club'.
18 holes, 6505yds, Par 72, SSS 72.

Visitors must contact in advance.
Societies must contact in advance.
Green Fees not confirmed.
Facilities ⊗ Richard Hill.
Location Queens Park Dr West (2m NE of town centre off A338)
Hotel ★★64% Hotel Riviera, West Cliff Gardens, BOURNEMOUTH ☎ (0202) 552845 34⇌

For a Golfing Break in the New Forest
OUR OWN THREE, 18 HOLE COURSES
Come and stay at the 200 year old Bell Inn Hotel, ideally located 1½ miles off the M27 in a New Forest village, and play our three contrasting 18 hole courses.
The first tee is only a wedge away from the front door, with reserved tee times for all our guests.
For our full colour brochure please telephone: 0703 812214
AA ★★★
The Bell Inn
HOTEL AND GOLF CLUB
Brook, Lyndhurst, Hampshire SO43 7HE
Telephone: (0703) 812214 Fax: (0703) 813958

BRIDPORT
Map 03 SY49

Bridport & West Dorset ☎ (0308) 421095
Seaside links course on the top of the east cliff, with fine views over Lyme Bay and surrounding countryside. At the 13th hole (par 3), the green is 70 ft below the tee.
18 holes, 4930yds, Par 67, SSS 64, Course record 61.
Club membership 700.
Visitors may not play 8-9.30am & noon-2pm or on competition days.
Societies must contact in advance.
Green Fees £18 per day (after 2pm £12), (£22 weekends, after 2pm £18).
Facilities ⊗ ⅷ & ⓛ (Tue-Sat) ♥ ♀ ♨ ☎ ℓ John Parish.
Location East Cliff, West Bay (2m S)
Hotel ★★★61% Haddon House Hotel, West Bay, BRIDPORT
☎ (0308) 23626 & 25323 13⇄ ⚲

BROADSTONE
Map 04 SZ09

Broadstone (Dorset) ☎ (0202) 692595
Typical heathland course.
18 holes, 6183yds, Par 69, SSS 70, Course record 64.
Club membership 800.
Visitors may not play weekends & bank holidays. Must have handicap certificate. Must contact in advance.
Societies contact in advance.
Green Fees not confirmed.
Facilities ⊗ & ⅷ by prior arrangement
ⓛ ♥ ♀ ♨ ☎ ℯ ℓ Nigel Tokely.
Location Wentworth Dr (N side of village off B3074)
Hotel ★★★61% King's Head Hotel, The Square, WIMBORNE ☎ (0202) 880101 27⇄ ⚲

CHRISTCHURCH
Map 04 SZ19

Dudmoor Farm ☎ (0202) 483980
A non-membership golf course with tree-lined par 3 and 4 fairways.
9 holes, 1428mtrs, Par 31.
Visitors no restrictions
Societies advisable to contact.
Green Fees £4.50 per 18 holes.
Facilities ♥ ♨ ℯ ⚌
Leisure squash, fishing.
Location Fairmile Rd, Dudmoor Ln
Hotel ★★★74% Waterford Lodge Hotel, 87 Bure Ln, Friars Cliff, Mudeford, CHRISTCHURCH
☎ (0425) 272948 & 278801 20⇄

Iford Bridge ☎ (0202) 473817
Parkland course with the River Stour running through. Driving range.
9 holes, 2377yds, Par 34, SSS 32.
Club membership 350.
Visitors no restrictions.
Societies must contact in advance.
Green Fees not confirmed.
Facilities ♀ ☎ ℯ ℓ
Leisure hard and grass tennis courts, driving range, bowls.
Location Barrack Rd (W side of town centre on A5)

Hotel ★★★74% Waterford Lodge Hotel, 87 Bure Ln, Friars Cliff, Mudeford, CHRISTCHURCH
☎ (0425) 272948 & 278801 20⇄

DORCHESTER
Map 03 SY69

Came Down ☎ (0305) 813494
Scene of the West of England Championships on several occasions, this fine course lies on a high plateau commanding glorious views over Portland. Three par 5 holes add interest to a round. The turf is of the springy, downland type.
18 holes, 6244yds, Par 70, SSS 71, Course record 67.
Club membership 700.
Visitors must contact in advance & have handicap certificate. May play after 9am weekdays & after 11am Sun.
Societies by arrangement on Wed only.
Green Fees £20 per day (£25 per day weekends).
Facilities ⊗ ⅷ by prior arrangement ⓛ ♥ ♀ ♨ ☎ ℓ Robert Preston.
Location Came Down
Hotel ★★★67% King's Arms Hotel, DORCHESTER ☎ (0305) 265353 31⇄

FERNDOWN
Map 04 SU00

Ferndown ☎ (0202) 872022
Fairways are gently undulating amongst heather, gorse and pine trees giving the course a most attractive appearance. There are a number of dog-leg holes and, on a clear day, there are views across to the Isle of Wight.
Old Course: 18 holes, 6452yds, Par 71, SSS 71.
Presidents: 9 holes, 5604yds, Par 70, SSS 68.
Club membership 700.
Visitors must contact in advance & have handicap certificate but may not play before 9.30am at weekends.
Societies welcome Tue & Fri only, apply by letter.
Green Fees Old Course: £35 per day (£40 weekends). Presidents: £15 per day (£20 weekends).
Facilities ⊗ ⅷ by prior arrangement ⓛ ♥ ♨ ☎ ℯ ℓ Doug Sewell.
Location 119 Golf Links Rd (S side of town centre off A347)
Hotel ★★★★65% Dormy Hotel, New Rd, FERNDOWN ☎ (0202) 872121 130⇄ ⚲

HIGHCLIFFE
Map 04 SZ29

Highcliffe Castle ☎ (0425) 272210
Picturesque parkland course with easy walking.
18 holes, 4686yds, Par 64, SSS 63, Course record 58.
Club membership 500.
Visitors must have handicap certificate or be a member of recognised club.
Societies Tue only.
Green Fees £18 per day; (£27 weekends). Reduced after 4pm.
Facilities ⊗ ⅷ by prior arrangement ⓛ ♥ ♀ ♨ ☎ ℯ R E Crockford.
Location 107 Lymington Rd (SW side of town on A337)
Hotel ★★★74% Waterford Lodge Hotel, 87 Bure Ln, Friars Cliff, Mudeford, CHRISTCHURCH
☎ (0425) 272948 & 278801 20⇄

LYME REGIS
Map 03 NY39

Lyme Regis ☎ (0297) 442963
Undulating cliff-top course with magnificent views of Golden
Cap and Lyme Bay.
18 holes, 6220yds, Par 71, SSS 70, Course record 68.
Club membership 575.
Visitors   must contact in advance & have handicap
certificate or be a member of recognised golf
club. No play on Thu & Sun mornings.
Societies   Tue, Wed & Fri; must contact in writing.
Green Fees £24 per day (£20 after 2pm).
Facilities   ⊗ ⊞ (Tue-Sat) ⌾ ⬛ ♀ ⌾ ⌾ (Andrew Black.
Location   Timber Hill (1.5m N on A3052)
Hotel   ★★★70% Alexandra Hotel, Pound St, LYME
REGIS ☎ (0297) 442010 26rm(23⇄ ⋒)

LYTCHETT MATRAVERS
Map 03 SY99

Bulbury Woods ☎ Morden (092945) 574
Parkland course in 40 acres of woodland, with extensive
views over the Purbecks, Poole Bay and Wareham Forest.
Not too hilly.
18 holes, 6020yds, Par 70, SSS 69, Course record 63.
Club membership 650.
Visitors   are advised to contact in advance.
Societies   must contact in advance.
Green Fees £25 per day; £15 per round (£30/£18 weekends).
Facilities   ⊗ ⊞ by prior arrangement ⌾ ⬛ ♀ ⌾ ⌾ (
John Sharkey.
Location   Halls Rd (2m W of Lytchett Minster)
Hotel   ★★★(red) Priory Hotel, Church Green,
WAREHAM ☎ (0929) 552772 & 551666
15⇄ ⋒ Annexe4⇄ ⋒

POOLE
Map 04 SZ09

Parkstone ☎ Canford Cliffs (0202) 707138
Very scenic heathland course with views of Poole Bay.
Club founded in 1910.
18 holes, 6250yds, Par 72, SSS 70, Course record 64.
Club membership 800.
Visitors   must contact in advance and have handicap
certificate.
Societies   by prior arrangement.
Green Fees not confirmed.
Facilities   ⊗ ⊞ by prior arrangement
⌾ ⬛ ♀ ⌾ ⌾ ⹁ (Mark Thomas.
Location   Links Rd, Parkstone (E side of town centre
off A35)
Hotel   ★★★78% Salterns Hotel, 38 Salterns Way,
Lilliput, POOLE ☎ (0202) 707321 16⇄

SHERBORNE
Map 03 ST61

Sherborne ☎ (0935) 814431
A sporting course of first-class fairways with far-
reaching views over the lovely Blackmore Vale and the
Vale of Sparkford. Parkland in character, the course has
many well-placed bunkers. The dog-leg 2nd calls for an
accurately placed tee shot, and another testing hole is the
7th, a 194-yard, par 3. There is a practice area.
18 holes, 5949yds, Par 70, SSS 68.
Club membership 700.

Visitors   must contact in advance & have handicap
certificate.
Societies   must contact well in advance.
Green Fees £20 per day (£25 weekends).
Facilities   ⊗ ⊞ (ex Sun) ⌾ ⬛ ♀ ⌾ ⌾ (
Stewart Wright.
Location   Higher Clatcombe (2m N off B3145)
Hotel   ★★★61% Forte Posthouse, Horsecastles Ln,
SHERBORNE ☎ (0935) 813191 59⇄ ⋒

STURMINSTER MARSHALL
Map 03 ST90

Sturminster Marshall ☎ Blandford (0258) 858444
Opened in June 1992, this 9-hole is Pay-and-Play. A
membership scheme allows players to gain an official
handicap. Course was designed by John Sharkey.
9 holes, 4650yds, Par 68, SSS 63.
Club membership 350.
Visitors   no restrictions.
Societies   welcome.
Green Fees £8 per 18 holes; £5 per 9 holes.
Facilities   ⊗ ⌾ ⬛ ♀ ⌾ ⌾ ⹁ (John Sharkey.
Location   Moor Ln
Hotel   ★★★66% Crown Hotel, 8 West St,
BLANDFORD FORUM ☎ (0258) 456626 32⇄

SWANAGE
Map 04 SZ07

Isle of Purbeck ☎ Studland (092944) 361
A heathland course sited on the Purbeck Hills with grand
views across Swanage, the Channel and Poole Harbour.
Holes of note include the 5th, 8th, 14th, 15, and 16th
where trees, gorse and heather assert themselves. The
very attractive clubhouse is built of the local stone.
Purbeck: 18 holes, 6295yds, Par 70, SSS 71.
Dene: 9 holes, 4014yds, Par 60, SSS 63.
Club membership 600.
Visitors   handicap certificate required for Purbeck
course.
Societies   must contact in advance.
Green Fees Purbeck: £30 per day; £22.50 round
(£35/£27.50 weekends). Dene: £10 (£12
weekends).
Facilities   ⊗ ⊞ ⌾ ⬛ ♀ ⌾ ⌾ ⹁ (Kevin Spurgeon.
Location   2.5m N on B3351
Hotel   ★★★64% The Pines Hotel, Burlington Rd,
SWANAGE ☎ (0929) 425211
51rm(49⇄ ⋒)

VERWOOD
Map 04 SU00

Crane Valley ☎ (0202) 814088
Two secluded undulating parkland courses - a 9-hole Pay and
Play and an 18-hole Par 72 for golfers holding a handicap
certificate.
Valley: 18 holes, 6424yds, Par 72, SSS 71.
Woodland: 9 holes, 4120yds, Par 66, SSS 60.
Club membership 400.
Visitors   must have handicap certificate for Valley course.
Societies   contact in advance.
Green Fees Valley, £9.50 per round; Woodland £5 per
round.
Facilities   ⊗ ⊞ ⌾ ⬛ ♀ ⌾ ⌾ ⹁ ⋈ (Alan Egford.
Location   6m N of Ferndown

Hotel ★★72% Struan Hotel & Restaurant, Horton Rd,
Ashley Heath, RINGWOOD
☎ (0425) 473553 & 473029 10⇥ ▮

CO DURHAM

WAREHAM Map 03 SY98

East Dorset ☎ Bere Regis (0929) 472244
Long 18-hole parkland course with natural water
features. A second 9-hole, 18-tee course is set amongst
trees and rhododendrons. Floodlit 22-bay driving range,
club fitting centre, indoor putting area and extensive golf
shop.
*Lakeland: 18 holes, 6580yds, Par 72, SSS 73, Course
record 71.*
Woodland: 9 holes, 2440yards, Par 33.
Club membership 600.
Visitors must contact in advance and handicap
certificate required for Lakeland course.
Societies apply in writing.
Green Fees Lakeland, £35 per day; £25 per round.
Woodland, £26 per day; £20 per round.
Facilities ⊗ ▥ ⬤ ▮ ♀ △ 📷 ⛳ ⬤ (Kim Thomas.
Leisure floodlit driving range.
Location Hyde (5m NW on unclass Puddletown
Rd,off A352)
Hotel ★★67% Kemps Country House Hotel, East
Stoke, WAREHAM ☎ (0929) 462563
5rm(1⇥3 ▮) Annexe10⇥ ▮

Wareham ☎ (0929) 554147
Heathland/parkland course. The club was founded in 1926.
18 holes, 5603yds, Par 69, SSS 67.
Club membership 600.
Visitors must have a handicap certificate & should
contact the club in advance. Must be
accompanied by a member at weekends & bank
holidays.
Societies must contact in advance.
Green Fees £18 per day.
Facilities ⊗ ▥ by prior arrangement ⬤ ▮ ♀ △
Location Sandford Rd
Hotel ★★★71% Springfield Country Hotel, Grange
Road, Stoborough, WAREHAM
☎ (0929) 552177 32⇥ ▮

WEYMOUTH Map 03 SY67

Weymouth ☎ (0305) 773981
Seaside parkland course. The 5th is played off an elevated
green over copse.
18 holes, 6030yds, Par 70, SSS 69, Course record 63.
Club membership 730.
Visitors must contact in advance & have proof of
membership or handicap certificate.
Societies telephone in advance.
Green Fees £18 per day (£24 weekends).
Facilities ⊗ ▥ by prior arrangement ⬤ ▮ ♀ △ 📷 (
Des Lochrie.
Location Links Rd, Westham (N side of town centre off
B3157)
Hotel ★★63% Hotel Rex, 29 The Esplanade,
WEYMOUTH
☎ (0305) 781004 31⇥ ▮

BARNARD CASTLE Map 12 NZ01

Barnard Castle ☎ Teesdale (0833) 38355
Flat moorland course high above the River Tees and
presenting fine views. A small stream runs in front of, or
alongside, many of the holes adding challenge and
enjoyment to the game.
18 holes, 5838yds, Par 71, SSS 68.
Club membership 600.
Visitors must be member of recognised club.
Societies by arrangement.
Green Fees £18 per day; £15 per round (£24 weekends).
Facilities ⊗ ▥ ⬤ ▮ (limited catering Mon)
♀ △ 📷 ⛳ (J Harrison.
Leisure snooker.
Location Harmire Rd (0.75m N on B6278)
Hotel ★★71% Rose & Crown Hotel,
ROMALDKIRK ☎ (0833) 50213
8⇥ ▮ Annexe5⇥ ▮

BEAMISH Map 12 NZ25

Beamish Park ☎ 091-370 1382
Parkland course. Designed by Henry Cotton and W
Woodend.
18 holes, 6205yds, Par 71, SSS 70.
Club membership 520.
Visitors restricted except before 9am & 12.15-1.45pm.
Societies by arrangement.
Green Fees not confirmed.
Facilities ⊗ ▥ ⬤ ▮ ♀ △ 📷 (C Cole.
Leisure snooker.
Location 1m NW off A693
Hotel ★★★64% Beamish Park Hotel, Beamish Burn
Rd, MARLEY HILL
☎ (0207) 230666 47⇥ ▮

BISHOP AUCKLAND Map 08 NZ22

Bishop Auckland ☎ (0388) 602198 & 663648
A rather hilly parkland course with many well-
established trees offering a challenging round. A small
ravine adds interest to several holes including the short
7th, from a raised tee to a green surrounded by a stream,
gorse and bushes. Pleasant views down the Wear Valley.
18 holes, 6420yds, Par 72, SSS 71.
Club membership 820.
Visitors must contact in advance, may play on
weekdays only.
Societies weekdays only; must contact in advance.
Green Fees £22 per day; £18 per round.
Facilities ⊗ ▥ ▥ (no catering Mon) ▮ ♀ △ 📷 (
David Skiffington.
Leisure snooker, driving range & practice fairway.
Location Durham Rd (1m NE on A689)
Hotel ★★★63% Park Head Hotel, New Coundon,
BISHOP AUCKLAND
☎ (0388) 661727 8⇥ ▮ Annexe7⇥

BURNOPFIELD
Map 12 NZ15

Hobson Municipal ☎ (0207) 71605
Meadowland course opened in 1981.
18 holes, 6080yds, Par 71, SSS 69, Course record 68.
Club membership 600.
Visitors no restrictions.
Societies must contact in advance.
Green Fees not confirmed.
Facilities ⊗ �🏌 🖳 ⬛ ♀ ♨ 🏠 ⚑ 🏊 ⎝ Jack Ord.
Leisure practice area.
Location Hobson (0.75m S on A692)
Hotel ★★★66% Swallow Hotel-Gateshead, High West
St, GATESHEAD ☎ 091-477 1105 103⇌ ☞

CHESTER-LE-STREET
Map 12 NZ25

Chester-le-Street ☎ Durham (091) 3883218
Parkland course in castle grounds, good views, easy walking.
18 holes, 6054yds, Par 70, SSS 69, Course record 67.
Club membership 650.
Visitors restricted weekends & bank holidays. Must
contact in advance and have an introduction
from own club or handicap certificate.
Societies must apply in writing.
Green Fees £20 per day(£25 weekends & bank holidays).
Facilities ⊗ �🏌 by prior arrangement 🖳 ⬛ ♀ ♨ 🏠 ⚑ ⎝
A Hartley.
Leisure snooker, pool table.
Location Lumley Park (0.5m E off B1284)
Hotel ★★★70% Ramside Hall Hotel, Carrville,
DURHAM ☎ 091-386 5282 82⇌ ☞

CONSETT
Map 12 NZ15

Consett & District ☎ (0207) 502186
Undulating parkland/moorland course.
18 holes, 6011yds, Par 71, SSS 69, Course record 63.
Club membership 650.
Visitors advised to telephone for Wed and weekends.
Societies must contact in advance.
Green Fees £15 per day (£22 weekends & bank holidays).
Facilities ⊗ �🏌 & 🖳 (ex Mon) ⬛ ♀ ♨ 🏠 ⎝
Location Elmfield Rd (N side of town on A691)
Hotel ★★69% Lord Crewe Arms Hotel,
BLANCHLAND ☎ (0434675) 251
8⇌ ☞ Annexe10⇌ ☞

CROOK
Map 12 NZ13

Crook ☎ Bishop Auckland (0388) 762429
Meadowland/parkland course in elevated position with
natural hazards, varied holes and terrain. Panoramic views
over Durham and Cleveland Hills.
18 holes, 6079yds, Par 68, SSS 69.
Club membership 430.
Visitors welcome, but limited availability on weekends.
Societies must telephone in advance.
Green Fees £12 per day (£20 weekends).
Facilities ⊗ ⏳ 🖳 ⬛ (no catering Mon) ♀ ♨
Location Low Jobs Hill (0.5m E off A690)
Hotel ★★★63% Park Head Hotel, New Coundon,
BISHOP AUCKLAND ☎ (0388) 661727
8⇌ ☞ Annexe7⇌

DARLINGTON
Map 08 NZ21

Blackwell Grange ☎ (0325) 464464
Pleasant parkland course with good views, easy walking.
18 holes, 5621yds, Par 68, SSS 67.
Club membership 950.
Visitors restricted Wed & Sun.
Societies must contact in writing.
Green Fees £18 per day (£20 per round weekends).
Facilities ⊗ ⏳ 🖳 ⬛ ♀ ♨ 🏠 ⚑ ⎝ Ralph Givens.
Location Briar Close (1m SW off A66)
Hotel ★★★65% Swallow King's Head Hotel,
Priestgate, DARLINGTON
☎ (0325) 380222 86⇌ ☞

Darlington ☎ (0325) 463936
Fairly flat parkland course with tree-lined fairways, and large
first-class greens. Championship standard.
18 holes, 6032yds, Par 70, SSS 72, Course record 64.
Club membership 750.
Visitors restricted weekends, bank holidays &
competition days. Must contact in advance and
have an introduction from own club.
Societies must contact in advance.
Green Fees not confirmed.
Facilities ⊗ & ⏳ by prior arrangement (ex Mon)
🖳 ⬛ ♀ ♨ 🏠 ⎝ Ian Todd.
Leisure snooker.
Location Haughton Grange (N side of town centre off
A1150)
Hotel ★★★♨♨67% Headlam Hall Hotel, Headlam,
Gainford, DARLINGTON
☎ (0325) 730238 17⇌ ☞ Annexe8⇌ ☞

Stressholme ☎ (0325) 461002
Picturesque municipal parkland course, long but wide, with
98 bunkers and a Par 3 hole played over a river.
18 holes, 6511yds, Par 71, SSS 71.
Club membership 650.
Visitors must contact in advance.
Societies apply to the steward or professional.
Green Fees not confirmed.
Facilities ⊗ 🖳 ⬛ ♀ ♨ 🏠 ⚑ ⎝ Tim Jenkins.
Location Snipe Ln (SW side of town centre on A67)
Hotel ★★★65% Swallow King's Head Hotel,
Priestgate, DARLINGTON
☎ (0325) 380222 86⇌ ☞

DURHAM
Map 12 NZ24

Brancepeth Castle ☎ 091-378 0075
Parkland course overlooked at the 9th hole by beautiful
Brancepeth Castle.
18 holes, 6300yds, Par 70, SSS 70.
Club membership 780.
Visitors may be restrictions at weekends for parties.
Societies must contact in advance.
Green Fees £23 (£30 weekends & bank holidays).
Facilities ⊗ ⏳ 🖳 ⬛ ♀ ♨ 🏠 ⚑ 🏊 ⎝ D C Howdon.
Location Brancepeth Village (4.5m SW on A690)
Hotel ★★★★68% Royal County Hotel, Old Elvet,
DURHAM
☎ 091-386 6821 150⇌ ☞

Durham City ☎ 091-378 0806
Undulating parkland course bordered on several holes by the
River Browney.
18 holes, 6326yds, Par 71, SSS 70.
Club membership 700.
Visitors   restricted on competition days.
Societies   must contact in advance.
Green Fees £18 per day (£24 weekends & bank holidays).
Facilities   ⊗ ⅷ ⅃ ⍟ ♀ ♧ ⌂ ℂ Steve Corbally.
Leisure   pool table.
Location   Littleburn, Langley Moor (1.5m S off A1050)
Hotel   ★★★68% Three Tuns Hotel, New Elvet,
                      DURHAM ☎ 091-386 4326 47⇌ ⋒

Mount Oswald ☎ 091-386 7527
Flat, wooded parkland course with Georgian clubhouse.
18 holes, 6101yds, Par 71, SSS 69, Course record 64.
Club membership 150.
Visitors   must contact in advance but may not play before
                      10am on Sun.
Societies   must contact in advance.
Green Fees £10 per round (£12 weekends & bank holidays).
Facilities   ⊗ ⅷ ⅃ ⍟ ♀ ♧ ⌂ ℾ
Location   Mount Oswald Manor, South Rd (1m S off
                      A1050)
Hotel   ★★64% Bridge Toby Hotel, Croxdale,
                      DURHAM ☎ 091-378 0524 46⇌ ⋒

MIDDLETON ST GEORGE   Map 08 NZ31

Dinsdale Spa ☎ Dinsdale (0325) 332297
A mainly flat, parkland course on high land above the
River Tees with views of the Cleveland Hills. Water
hazards front the 8th, 9th and 18th tees and the prevailing
west wind affects the later holes. There is a practice area
by the clubhouse.
18 holes, 6022yds, Par 70, SSS 69, Course record 64.
Club membership 850.
Visitors   restricted Tue & weekends. Must contact in
                      advance and have an introduction from own
                      club.
Societies   must contact in advance.
Green Fees not confirmed.
Facilities   ⊗ ⅷ ⅃ ⍟ ♀ ♧ ⌂ ℾ ℂ D N Dodds.
Location   1.5m SW
Hotel   ★★★64% St George Hotel, Middleton St
                      George, TEES-SIDE AIRPORT
                      ☎ (0325) 332631 59⇌ ⋒

NEWTON AYCLIFFE   Map 08 NZ22

Aycliffe ☎ Aycliffe (0325) 310820
A parkland course in a country setting.
18 holes, 5430yds, Par 68, SSS 66.
Visitors   must contact in advance.
Societies   apply in writing.
Green Fees not confirmed.
Facilities   ⅃ ⍟ ♀ ♧ ⌂ ℾ ℂ Robert Lister.
Leisure   indoor bowls, badminton, indoor cricket.
Location   Oakleaf Sports Complex, School Aycliffe Ln
                      (6m N of Darlington, off A6072)
Hotel   ★★★★71% Redworth Hall Hotel & Country
                      Club, REDWORTH
                      ☎ (0388) 772442 100⇌ ⋒

SEAHAM   Map 12 NZ44

Seaham ☎ 091-581 2354
Links course.
18 holes, 6017yds, Par 70, SSS 69, Course record 64.
Club membership 550.
Visitors   with member only weekends until 3.30pm.
Societies   must apply in writing.
Green Fees not confirmed.
Facilities   ⊗ & ⅷ by prior arrangement ⅃ ⍟ ♀ ♧ ⌂
Leisure   snooker.
Location   Dawdon (S side of town centre)
Hotel   ★★★71% Swallow Hotel, Queen's Pde,
                      Seaburn, SUNDERLAND
                      ☎ 091-529 2041 66⇌ ⋒

STANLEY   Map 12 NZ15

South Moor ☎ (0207) 232848
Moorland course with natural hazards.
18 holes, 6445yds, Par 72, SSS 71, Course record 66.
Club membership 650.
Visitors   must contact in advance but may not play
                      competition days.
Societies   must telephone in advance.
Green Fees £21 per day; £14 per round (£25 per day/round
                      weekends & bank holidays).
Facilities   ⊗ ⅷ by prior arrangement ⅃ ⍟ ♀ ♧ ⌂ ℾ ℂ
                      Shaun Cowell.
Leisure   snooker.
Location   The Middles, Craghead (1.5m SE on B6313)
Hotel   ★★★64% Beamish Park Hotel, Beamish Burn
                      Rd, MARLEY HILL ☎ (0207) 230666 47⇌ ⋒

EAST SUSSEX

BEXHILL   Map 05 TQ70

Cooden Beach ☎ Cooden (04243) 2040
The course is close by the sea, but is not real links in
character. Despite that, it is dry and plays well
throughout the year. There are some excellent holes such
as the 4th, played to a built-up green, the short 12th, and
three good holes to finish.
18 holes, 6450yds, Par 72, SSS 71, Course record 65.
Club membership 730.
Visitors   must have a handicap certificate. Restricted
                      at weekends. Must contact in advance and
                      have an introduction from own club.
Societies   must contact in advance.
Green Fees not confirmed.
Facilities   ⊗ ⅷ by prior arrangement
                      ⅃ ⍟ ♀ ♧ ⌂ ℾ ℂ Jeffrey Sim.
Leisure   snooker, bridge room.
Location   Cooden Sea Rd (2m W on A259)
Hotel   ★★★64% Cooden Resort Hotel, COODEN
                      BEACH ☎ (04243) 2281 40⇌ ⋒

Highwoods ☎ Bexhill-on-Sea (0424) 212625
Undulating course.
18 holes, 6218yds, Par 70, SSS 70, Course record 66.
Club membership 820.
Visitors	must play with member on Sun. Must contact in advance and have an introduction from own club.
Societies	must contact 6 months in advance.
Green Fees	not confirmed.
Facilities	⊗ (Sun only) ⓛ (Mon-Sat 10am-2pm) ♥ ♀ ♨ ⌂ ⌁ M Andrews.
Leisure	snooker.
Location	Ellerslie Ln (1.5m NW)
Hotel	★★★60% Granville Hotel, Sea Rd, BEXHILL-ON-SEA ☎ (0424) 215437 50⇆🐾

BRIGHTON & HOVE   Map 04 TQ30

Brighton & Hove ☎ Brighton (0273) 556482
Downland course with sea views.
18 holes, 5722yds, Par 68, SSS 68.
Club membership 320.
Visitors	must contact in advance and may not play Sun mornings.
Societies	must contact in advance.
Green Fees	not confirmed.
Facilities	⊗ ⓛ ♥ ♀ ♨ ⌁
Leisure	snooker.
Location	Dyke Rd (4m NW)
Hotel	★★60% St Catherines Lodge Hotel, Seafront, Kingsway, HOVE ☎ (0273) 778181 50rm(40⇆🐾)

Dyke ☎ Brighton (0273) 857296
This downland course has some glorious views both towards the sea and inland. The best hole on the course is probably the 17th; it is one of those teasing short holes of just over 200 yards, and is played across a gully to a high green.
18 holes, 6611yds, Par 72, SSS 72.
Club membership 700.
Visitors	restricted before noon on Sun.
Societies	must contact in advance.
Green Fees	£31 per day: £21 per round (£31 per round weekends).
Facilities	⊗ ⍟ by prior arrangement ⓛ ♥ ♀ ♨ ⌂ ⌁ ⌁ Paul Longmore.
Leisure	snooker.
Location	Dyke Rd (4m N between A23 & A27)
Hotel	★★60% St Catherines Lodge Hotel, Seafront, Kingsway, HOVE ☎ (0273) 778181 50rm(40⇆🐾)

East Brighton ☎ Brighton (0273) 604838
Undulating downland course, overlooking the sea. Windy.
18 holes, 6346yds, Par 72, SSS 70, Course record 68.
Club membership 700.
Visitors	must contact in advance & have handicap certificate, but may not play before 9am on weekdays.
Societies	must contact at least 1 month in advance.
Green Fees	£21 per day; £16 per round (£30 per day weekends).
Facilities	⊗ ⍟ ⓛ ♥ ♀ ♨ ⌂ ⌁ Wally Street.
Leisure	snooker.

Location	Roedean Rd (E side of town centre on B2118)
Hotel	★★★62% Norfolk Resort, 149 Kings Rd, BRIGHTON ☎ (0273) 738201 121⇆🐾

Hollingbury Park ☎ Brighton (0273) 552010
Municipal course in hilly situation on the Downs, overlooking the sea.
18 holes, 6500yds, Par 72, SSS 71.
Club membership 400.
Visitors	no restrictions
Societies	must book 1 month in advance
Green Fees	£11 weekday(£14 weekends & bank holidays).
Facilities	⊗ ⓛ ♥ ♀ ♨ ⌂ ⌁ ⌁ P Brown.
Location	Ditchling Rd (2m N of town centre)
Hotel	★★★62% Norfolk Resort, 149 Kings Rd, BRIGHTON ☎ (0273) 738201 121⇆🐾

Waterhall ☎ Brighton (0273) 508658
Hilly downland course with hard walking and open to the wind. Private club playing over municipal course.
18 holes, 5775yds, Par 69, SSS 68, Course record 66.
Club membership 420.
Visitors	may not play on competition days & before 10.30am at weekends.
Societies	must contact the secretary in writing.
Green Fees	not confirmed.
Facilities	⊗ by prior arrangement ⓛ ♥ ♀ ♨ ⌂ ⌁ ⌁ Paul Charman.
Location	Seddlescombe Rd, (Off Devils Dyke Road) (3m N off A27)
Hotel	★★60% St Catherines Lodge Hotel, Seafront, Kingsway, HOVE ☎ (0273) 778181 50rm(40⇆🐾)

West Hove ☎ Brighton (0273) 419738 & 413411
A downland course designed by Hawtree & Sons.
18 holes, 6252yds, Par 72, SSS 70.
Club membership 500.
Visitors	tee times by arrangement.
Societies	by arrangement.
Green Fees	£20 per day; £15 per round (£20 weekends).
Facilities	⊗ ⍟ by prior arrangement ⓛ ♥ ♀ ♨ ⌂ ⌁ ⌁ David Mills.
Leisure	snooker.
Location	Church Farm, Hangleton
Hotel	★★60% St Catherines Lodge Hotel, Seafront, Kingsway, HOVE ☎ (0273) 778181 50rm(40⇆🐾)

CROWBOROUGH   Map 05 TQ53

Crowborough Beacon ☎ (0892) 661511
A picturesque course in pleasant heathland. Though most fairways are wide and open, one or two are distinctly tight where a wayward shot results in a lost ball. By no means an easy course, with testing holes at the 2nd, 6th and 16th.
18 holes, 6318yds, Par 71, SSS 70.
Club membership 700.
Visitors	must contact in advance & have handicap certificate but may not play at weekends & bank holidays.
Societies	telephone in advance.
Green Fees	£34 per day; £22.50 per round.
Facilities	⊗ ⍟ ⓛ ♥ ♀ ♨ ⌂ ⌁ Dennis Newnham.

Location	Beacon Rd (1m SW on A26)
Hotel	★★★76% Spa Hotel, Mount Ephraim,
	TUNBRIDGE WELLS
	☎ (0892) 520331 76⇆ ↟

Dewlands Manor ☎ Rotherfield (0892) 852266 & 853308
A pretty, moderately hilly, Pay and Play parkland course with water features.
9 holes, 3186yds, Par 36, Course record 33.

Visitors	must contact in advance.
Societies	apply in writing.
Green Fees	£23 per 18 hole; £14.50 per 9 hole (£29/£17.50 weekends and bank holidays).
Facilities	⊗ ⅄ ☞ ♀⅄ 🖻 ⫶
Location	Cottage Hill, Rotherfield (0.5m S of Rotherfield)
Hotel	★★⅄68% Spindlewood Country House Hotel & Restaurant, Wallcrouch, WADHURST ☎ (0580) 200430 9⇆ ↟

EASTBOURNE   Map 05 TV69

Eastbourne Downs ☎ (0323) 720827
Downland/seaside course.
18 holes, 6635yds, Par 72, SSS 72.
Club membership 730.

Visitors	restricted after 1pm Sat & Sun.
Societies	must contact in advance.
Green Fees	not confirmed.
Facilities	⊗ ⅄ & ☞ (Wed-Sun) ♀⅄ 🖻 ⫶ ⫶
Location	East Dean Rd (1m W of town centre on A259)
Hotel	★★★58% Cavendish Hotel, Grand Pde, EASTBOURNE ☎ (0323) 410222 114⇆ ↟

Royal Eastbourne ☎ (0323) 729738
A famous club which celebrated its centenary in 1987.
The course plays longer than it measures. Testing holes
are the 8th, a par 3 played to a high green and the 16th, a
par 5 right-hand dog-leg.
Long Course: 18 holes, 6109yds, Par 70, SSS 69, Course record 62.
Short Course: 9 holes, 2147yds, Par 32, SSS 32.
Club membership 890.

Visitors	must have a handicap certificate for Long Course.
Societies	must telephone in advance.
Green Fees	on application.
Facilities	⊗ ⅄ ☞ (ex Mon) ▆ ♀⅄ 🖻 ⫶ ⫶ Richard Wooller.
Leisure	snooker.
Location	Paradise Dr (0.5m W of town centre)
Hotel	★★★74% Lansdowne Hotel, King Edward's Pde, EASTBOURNE ☎ (0323) 25174 due to change to 725174 127⇆ ↟

Willingdon ☎ (0323) 410981
Unique, hilly downland course set in oyster-shaped
amphitheatre.
18 holes, 6049yds, Par 69, SSS 69.
Club membership 550.

Visitors	by application.
Societies	Mon-Fri only. Must contact in advance by telephone.
Green Fees	£24 per day/round (£27 weekends & bank holidays).

Facilities	⊗ ⅄ by prior arrangement ☞ ▆ (no catering Mon) ♀⅄ 🖻 ⫶ ⫶ James Debenham.
Location	Southdown Rd (0.5m N of town centre off A22)
Hotel	★★★63% The Wish Tower, King Edward's Pde, EASTBOURNE ☎ (0323) 22676 65rm(57⇆)

FOREST ROW   Map 05 TQ43

Ashdown Forest Hotel ☎ (0342) 824866
Natural heathland and woodland course cut out of the
Ashdown Forest. The hotel specialises in catering for golf
breaks and societies.
18 holes, 5510yds, Par 68, SSS 67, Course record 62.
Club membership 150.

Visitors	are advised to contact in advance.
Societies	apply in advance.
Green Fees	not confirmed.
Facilities	⊗ ⅄ ☞ ▆ ♀⅄ 🖻 ⊠ ⫶ Martyn Landsborough.
Leisure	pool, darts.
Location	Chapel Ln (4m S of East Grinstead off A22 & B2110)

Royal Ashdown Forest ☎ (0342) 822018
Undulating heathland course. Long carries off the tees
and magnificent views over the Forest. Not a course for
the high handicapper.
Old Course: 18 holes, 6477yds, Par 72, SSS 71.
Club membership 450. ▶

Visitors	restricted weekends & Tue. Must have a handicap certificate.
Societies	must contact in advance.
Green Fees	£35 per day; £27 per round (£40/£32 weekends & bank holidays).
Facilities	⊗ ⓑ 🍺 ♀ (closes 8pm) 🔥 🏠 ⚐ (Martin Landsborough.
Location	Chapel Ln (SE side of village)
Hotel	★★★63% Woodbury House Hotel, Lewes Rd, EAST GRINSTEAD ☎ (0342) 313657 13⇄ ☞ Annexe1 ☞

HASTINGS & ST LEONARDS   Map 05 TQ80

Beauport Park ☎ Hastings (0424) 852977
Played over Hastings Public Course. Undulating parkland with stream and fine views.
18 holes, 6033yds, Par 70, SSS 70.
Club membership 290.

Visitors	no restrictions.
Societies	must contact in writing.
Green Fees	not confirmed.
Facilities	♀ 🔥 🏠 ⚐ (
Location	St Leonards-on-Sea (3m N of Hastings on A2100)
Hotel	★★★69% Beauport Park Hotel, Battle Rd, HASTINGS ☎ (0424) 851222 23⇄ ☞

LEWES   Map 05 TQ41

Lewes ☎ (0273) 473245
Downland course. Fine views.
18 holes, 5951yds, Par 71, SSS 69, Course record 67.
Club membership 720.

Visitors	may not play at weekends after 2pm. Must contact in advance.
Societies	must contact in advance.
Green Fees	not confirmed.
Facilities	⊗ 🎱 ⓑ 🍺 ♀ 🔥 🏠 (Paul Dobson.
Location	Chapel Hill (E side of town centre off A26)
Hotel	★★58% White Hart Hotel, 55 High St, LEWES ☎ (0273) 474676 & 476694 19rm(14⇄ ☞) Annexe21⇄ ☞

NEWHAVEN   Map 05 TQ40

Peacehaven ☎ (02739) 514049
Downland course, sometimes windy. Testing holes: 1st (par 3), 4th (par 4), 9th (par 3), 10th (par 3), 18th (par 3).
9 holes, 5305yds, Par 69, SSS 66.
Club membership 200.

Visitors	no restrictions.
Societies	telephone in advance
Green Fees	£18 per day; £12 per round (£16 weekends).
Facilities	⊗ ⓑ 🍺 ♀ 🔥 🏠 ⚐ (G Williams.
Location	Brighton Rd (0.75m W on A259)
Hotel	★★★67% The Star, ALFRISTON ☎ (0323) 870495 34⇄ ☞

RYE   Map 05 TQ92

Rye ☎ (0797) 225241
Typical links course with superb greens and views.
Old Course: 18 holes, 6317yds, Par 68, SSS 71, Course record 64.
Jubilee Course: 9 holes, 6141yds, Par 71, SSS 70.
Club membership 1000.

Visitors	must be invited/introduced by a member.
Green Fees	£52.50 per day; £34.50 per round (£57/£37.50 weekends).
Facilities	⊗ ⓑ 🍺 ♀ 🔥 🏠 (Peter Marsh.
Location	Camber (2.75m SE off A259)
Hotel	★★69% George Hotel, High St, RYE ☎ (0797) 222114 22⇄ ☞

SEAFORD   Map 05 TV49

Seaford ☎ (0323) 892442
The great H. Taylor did not perhaps design as many courses as his friend and rival, James Braid, but Seaford's original design was Taylor's. It is a splendid downland course with magnificent views and some fine holes.
18 holes, 6233yds, Par 69, SSS 70.
Club membership 800.

Visitors	must contact in advance, may play on weekdays only after 9.30am (ex Tue).
Societies	must contact in advance.
Green Fees	not confirmed.
Facilities	⊗ 🎱 ⓑ 🍺 ♀ 🔥 🏠 🍴 (
Leisure	snooker.

Location	Firle Rd, East Blatchington (1m N)
Hotel	★★★67% The Star, ALFRISTON
	☎ (0323) 870495 34 ⇌ 🐾

TICEHURST   Map 05 TQ63

Dale Hill ☎ (0580) 200112
Picturesque course with woodland, water and gently
undulating fairways. Hotel and leisure centre within grounds.
18 holes, 6066yds, Par 69, SSS 69.
Club membership 550.
Visitors   restricted mornings & must play after 10am
                  weekends.
Societies   must contact in writing.
Green Fees £20 per round (£25 weekends).
Facilities   ⊗ 🎏 🖢 ♥ ♀ 🛆 🖴 ⛽ 🐾 ⏄ Alan Gillard.
Leisure   heated indoor swimming pool, fishing, snooker,
                  sauna, solarium, gymnasium.
Location   N side of town off B2087
Hotel   ★★67% Tudor Court Hotel, Rye Rd,
                  HAWKHURST ☎ (0580) 752312 18 ⇌ 🐾

UCKFIELD   Map 05 TQ42

East Sussex National ☎ (0825) 750577
Created with a £30 million budget, the East Sussex
National, which runs round the elegant Horsted Place
Hotel, is a wonderful creation for golfers and is planned
to be one of the most luxurious golf clubs in the world.
Its two courses have been created with tournaments in
mind and the 18th green has been designed so that 50,000
spectators can see.
East Course: 18 holes, 7081yds, Par 72, SSS 74, Course
record 67.
West Course: 18 holes, 7154yds, Par 72, SSS 74, Course
record 64.
Club membership 250.
Visitors   must contact in advance and may require a
                  handicap certificate. Must accompany a
                  member on West Course.
Societies   must contact the Corporate Hospitality Dept.
Green Fees £65 per round (£75 weekends).
Facilities   ⊗ 🎏 by prior arrangement
                  🖢 ♥ ♀ 🛆 🖴 ⛽ 🐾 ⏄ Greg Dukart.
Leisure   hard tennis courts, heated indoor swimming
                  pool, riding, sauna, croquet.
Location   Little Horsted (S on A22)
Hotel   ★★★(red)⚜ Horsted Place Hotel, Little
                  Horsted, UCKFIELD
                  ☎ (0825) 750581 17 ⇌ 🐾

Piltdown ☎ (0825) 722033
Natural heathland course with much heather and gorse. No
bunkers, easy walking, fine views.
18 holes, 6070yds, Par 69, SSS 68, Course record 67.
Club membership 400.
Visitors   must telephone for details of restricted times.
Societies   must contact in writing.
Green Fees £27.50 per day/round.
Facilities   ⊗ 🎏 by prior arrangement
                  🖢 ♥ ♀ 🛆 🖴 ⛽ ⏄ John Amos.
Location   3m NW off A272
Hotel   ★★66% Halland Forge Hotel, HALLAND
                  ☎ (0825) 840456 Annexe20 ⇌ 🐾

Horsted Place

★★★
(Red)
❀❀❀

A splendid Victorian mansion, just off the A26
south of Uckfield, set in 23 acres of stunning
Sussex countryside. Part of the 1,100 acre estate
of East Sussex National Golf Club, Horsted Place
is the obvious choice of golfers. For the non-
golfers there is an indoor heated swimming pool,
tennis and croquet. All rooms have been
individually and stylishly decorated, 15 of the 17
bedrooms being suites, Chef Allan Garth,
renowned for his eclectic style of cooking,
guarantees a range of innovative menus making
full use of the local produce. Two elegantly
decorated rooms provide meeting and dining
facilities. Helicopter Pad for the high-flyers!

General Manager: Jonathan W. Ritchie.

For information please write to:
Little Horsted, Near Uckfield, East Sussex TN22 5TS
Tel: 0825 750581   Fax: 0825 750459

ESSEX

ABRIDGE   Map 05 TQ49

Abridge Golf and Country Club
☎ Stapleford (0708) 688396
A parkland course with easy walking. The quick drying
course is by no means easy to play. This has been the
venue of several professional tournaments. Abridge is a
Golf and Country Club and has all the attendant facilities.
18 holes, 6703yds, Par 72, SSS 72.
Club membership 600.
Visitors   must contact in advance. Play with member
                  only at weekends.
Societies   Mon & Wed only; must contact in advance.
Green Fees not confirmed.
Facilities   ⊗ (ex Fri) 🖢 ♥ ♀ (ex Fri)
                  🛆 🖴 ⏄ Mike Herbert.
Leisure   heated outdoor swimming pool, snooker,
                  sauna.
Location   Epping Ln, Stapleford Tawney (1.75m NE)
Hotel   ★★★62% Forte Posthouse, High Rd, Bell
                  Common, EPPING
                  ☎ (0992) 573137 Annexe79 ⇌ 🐾

BASILDON

Map 05 TQ78

Basildon ☎ (0268) 533297
Undulating municipal parkland course. Testing 13th hole (par 4).
18 holes, 6122yds, Par 70, SSS 69, Course record 59.
Club membership 300.
Visitors   no restrictions.
Societies   must contact in advance.
Green Fees £13.50 (£14.50 weekends).
Facilities   🏌 💪 ♀ ⚒ ☎ ⛳ ❬ Graham Hill.
Location   Clay Hill Ln, Kingswood (1m S off A176)
Hotel   ★★★64% Forte Posthouse, Cranes
Farm Rd, BASILDON
☎ (0268) 533955 110⇄ 🐾

Pipps Hill Country Club ☎ (0268) 523456
Flat course with ditches and pond.
9 holes, 2829yds, Par 34, SSS 34.
Club membership 400.
Visitors   no restrictions.
Societies   must contact in advance.
Green Fees not confirmed.
Facilities   ♀ ⚒
Location   Cranes Farm Rd (N side of town centre off A127)
Hotel   ★★★64% Forte Posthouse, Cranes Farm Rd, BASILDON
☎ (0268) 533955 110⇄ 🐾

BENFLEET

Map 05 TQ78

Boyce Hill ☎ (0268) 793625
Hilly parkland course with good views.
18 holes, 5377yds, Par 68, SSS 68.
Club membership 600.
Visitors   must have a handicap certificate. May only play with member at weekends.
Societies   Thu only.
Green Fees £20 per round; £35 per day.
Facilities   ⊗ 🏌 💪 ♀ ⚒ ☎ ⛳ ❬ Graham Burroughs.
Location   Vicarage Hill, South Benfleet (0.75m NE of Benfleet Station)
Hotel   ★★★64% Forte Posthouse, Cranes Farm Rd, BASILDON
☎ (0268) 533955 110⇄ 🐾

BRAINTREE

Map 05 TL72

Braintree ☎ (0376) 346079
Parkland course with many rare trees.
18 holes, 6161yds, Par 70, SSS 69, Course record 65.
Club membership 750.
Visitors   may not play on Sun mornings. With member only Sat, Sun afternoon and bank holidays. Must contact in advance and have a handicap certificate.
Societies   must contact in advance.
Green Fees £25 per day/round (£40 weekends).
Facilities   ⊗ 🍽 🏌 💪 ♀ ⚒ ☎ ❬ Tony Parcell.
Location   Kings Ln, Stisted (1m W off A120)
Hotel   ★★59% The Saracen's Head, High St, GREAT DUNMOW
☎ (0371) 873901 24⇄

Towerlands ☎ (0376) 326802
Undulating, grassland course. Driving range and sportshall.
9 holes, 2703yds, Par 34, SSS 66.
Club membership 300.
Visitors   must not play before 12.30pm weekends.
Societies   must contact in advance by telephone.
Green Fees 9 holes: £8.50 Mon-Fri only; 18 holes £12.50 daily.
Facilities   ⊗ 🍽 🏌 💪 ♀ ⚒ ☎ ⛳ ❬ Andrew Boulter.
Leisure   squash, sports hall, indoor bowls, driving range.
Location   Panfield Rd (On B1053)
Hotel   ★★69% White Hart Hotel, Bocking End, BRAINTREE
☎ (0376) 321401 31⇄ 🐾

BRENTWOOD

Map 05 TQ59

Bentley ☎ Coxtie Green (0277) 373179
Parkland course with water hazards.
18 holes, 6709yds, Par 72, SSS 72.
Club membership 550.
Visitors   may only play after 11am on bank holidays. Must contact in advance and have a handicap certificate.
Societies   must contact in advance.
Green Fees £26 per day; £20 per round.
Facilities   ⊗ 🍽 by prior arrangement 🏌 💪 ♀ ⚒ ☎ ❬ Keith Bridges.
Location   Ongar Rd (3m NW on A128)
Hotel   ★★★67% Forte Posthouse, Brook St, BRENTWOOD
☎ (0277) 260260 111⇄

Hartswood ☎ (0277) 218850
Municipal parkland course, easy walking.
18 holes, 6160yds, Par 70, SSS 69, Course record 69.
Club membership 800.
Visitors   must contact in advance.
Societies   must contact in advance.
Green Fees not confirmed.
Facilities   Catering at the club by prior arrangement ♀ ⚒ ☎ ⛳ ❬ John Stanion.
Location   King George's Playing Fields, Ingrave Rd (0.75m SE on A128)
Hotel   ★★★67% Forte Posthouse, Brook St, BRENTWOOD
☎ (0277) 260260 111⇄

Warley Park ☎ (0277) 224891
Parkland course with reasonable walking. Numerous water hazards. There is also a golf-practice ground.
27 holes, 3240yds, Par 36, SSS 71.
Club membership 650.
Visitors   must contact in advance and have an introduction from own club.
Societies   must contact in advance.
Green Fees not confirmed.
Facilities   ⊗ 🍽 🏌 💪 ♀ ⚒ ☎ ⛳ ❬ P O'Connor.
Location   Magpie Ln, Little Warley (2.5m S off B186)
Hotel   ★★★67% Forte Posthouse, Brook St, BRENTWOOD
☎ (0277) 260260 111⇄

BULPHAN
Map 05 TQ68

Langdon Hills Hotel & Golf Complex
☎ Basildon (0268) 548444
The complex is the base of the European School of Golf. The 18-hole course is of championship standard and, since the summer of 1992, there is also a 9-hole public course. Practice facilities include a 22-bay covered floodlit driving range, short game practice area with greens and bunkers and three hole practice course.
Langdon: 18 holes, 6485yds, Par 72, SSS 71.
Horndon: 9 holes, 2861yds, Par 36, SSS 68.
Club membership 700.

Visitors	must have a handicap certificate & must contact the club in advance.
Societies	must book in advance.
Green Fees	Langdon £26.50 per day; £18.50 per round (£25 per round weekends). Horndon £6 per 18holes; £4 per 9 holes (£7.50 per 18 holes weekends).
Facilities	⊗ ⅏ ㊉ ☘ ♀ ♨ 🖻 ☂ 🎗 (
Leisure	22 bay floodlit covered driving range.
Location	Lower Dunton Rd
Hotel	★★★★65% Brentwood Moat House, London Rd, BRENTWOOD ☎ (0277) 225252 3⇄ 🐾 Annexe30⇄ 🐾

BURNHAM-ON-CROUCH
Map 05 TQ99

Burnham-on-Crouch ☎ (0621) 782282 & 785508
Undulating meadowland course, easy walking, windy.
9 holes, 5918yds, Par 68, SSS 68.
Club membership 400.

Visitors	may only play Mon-Wed & Fri 9.30am-2pm, Thu noon-2pm. Must contact in advance.
Societies	Tue only. Must contact in writing.
Green Fees	£20.
Facilities	⊗ ㊉ ♀ ♨ 🖻
Location	Ferry Rd, Creeksea (1.25m W off B1010)
Hotel	★★63% Blue Boar Hotel, Silver St, MALDON ☎ (0621) 852681 21⇄ 🐾 Annexe8⇄ 🐾

CANEWDON
Map 05 TQ99

Ballards Gore ☎ Southend (0702) 258917 & 258924
A parkland course with several lakes.
18 holes, 7062yds, Par 73, SSS 74.
Club membership 750.

Visitors	may not play at weekends.
Societies	apply in advance.
Green Fees	£20 per day.
Facilities	⊗ ㊉ ♀ ♨ 🖻 (Ian Marshall.
Leisure	snooker.
Location	Gore Rooad (2m NE of Rochford)
Hotel	★★★66% Hotel Renouf, Bradley Way, ROCHFORD ☎ (0702) 541334 24⇄ 🐾

CANVEY ISLAND
Map 05 TQ78

Castle Point ☎ (0268) 510830
A flat seaside links course with water hazards.
18 holes, 6176yds, Par 71, SSS 69, Course record 72.
Club membership 320.

Visitors	must book for weekends.
Societies	by prior arrangement.
Green Fees	£8.75 per round (£13 weekends).
Facilities	⊗ ⅏ ㊉ ♀ ♨ 🖻 ☂ 🎗 (John Hudson.
Location	Somnes Av (SE of Basildon, A130 to Canvey Island)
Hotel	★★★63% Chichester Hotel, Old London Rd, Wickford, BASILDON ☎ (0268) 560555 2⇄ Annexe32⇄

CHELMSFORD
Map 05 TL70

Channels ☎ (0245) 440005
Built on land from reclaimed gravel pits, 18 very exciting holes with plenty of lakes providing an excellent test of golf.
18 holes, 5636yds, Par 69, SSS 68 or 9 holes, 2971yds, Par 35.
Club membership 750.

Visitors	must contact in advance & play with member at weekends.
Societies	must contact in advance.
Green Fees	£28 per day.
Facilities	⊗ ⅏ ㊉ ♀ ♨ 🖻 (Ian Sinclair.
Leisure	fishing.
Location	Belstead Farm Ln, Little Waltham (3.5m NE off A130)
Hotel	★★★54% South Lodge Hotel, 196 New London Rd, CHELMSFORD ☎ (0245) 264564 24⇄ 🐾 Annexe17⇄

Chelmsford ☎ (0245) 256483
An undulating parkland course, hilly in parts, with 3 holes in woods and four difficult par 4's. From the reconstructed clubhouse there are fine views over the course and the wooded hills beyond.
18 holes, 5944yds, Par 68, SSS 68.
Club membership 650.

Visitors	must contact in advance & have handicap certificate. With member only at weekends.
Societies	must contact 9 months in advance.
Green Fees	£33 per day; £23 per round.
Facilities	⊗ ⅏ (weekends only) ㊉ ♀ ♨ 🖻 (D Bailey.
Location	Widford (1.5m S of town centre off A12)
Hotel	★★★54% South Lodge Hotel, 196 New London Rd, CHELMSFORD ☎ (0245) 264564 24⇄ 🐾 Annexe17⇄

CHIGWELL
Map 05 TQ49

Chigwell ☎ 081-500 2059
A course of high quality, mixing meadowland with parkland. For those who believe 'all Essex is flat' the undulating nature of Chigwell will be a refreshing surprise. The greens are excellent and the fairways tight with mature trees.
18 holes, 6279yds, Par 71, SSS 70, Course record 66.
Club membership 657.

Visitors	must contact in advance & have handicap certificate, but must be accompanied by member at weekends.
Societies	must contact in writing
Green Fees	£35 per day; £28 per round.
Facilities	⊗ ⅏ ㊉ ♀ ♨ 🖻 ☂ 🎗 (▶

| Location | High Rd (0.5m S on A113) |
| Hotel | ★★59% Roebuck Hotel, North End, BUCKHURST HILL ☎ 081-505 4636 29⇄ 🛏 |

CHIGWELL ROW
Map 05 TQ49

Hainault Forest ☎ 081-500 0385
Club playing over Borough of Redbridge public courses; hilly parkland subject to wind. Two courses, driving range.
No 1 Course: 18 holes, 5744yds, Par 70, SSS 67, Course record 65.
No 2 Course: 18 holes, 6600yds, Par 71, SSS 71.
Club membership 600.

Visitors	no restrictions
Societies	must contact in writing
Green Fees	not confirmed.
Facilities	⊗ ㅸ 🍺 🏌 ♀ ♨ 🏠 ⛳ 🛈 T Dungate.
Location	Romford Rd, Chigwell Row (0.5m S on A113)
Hotel	★★★60% Woodford Bridge Hotel, Milton Damerel, HOLSWORTHY ☎ (040926) 481 12⇄ 🛏

CLACTON-ON-SEA
Map 05 TM11

Clacton ☎ (0255) 421919
Windy, seaside course.
18 holes, 6244yds, Par 70, SSS 68.
Club membership 650.

Visitors	must contact in advance.
Societies	must contact in writing.
Green Fees	not confirmed.
Facilities	♨ 🏠 🛈
Location	West Rd (1.25m SW of town centre)
Hotel	★★65% Maplin Hotel, Esplanade, FRINTON-ON-SEA ☎ (0255) 673832 12rm(9⇄1 🛏)

COLCHESTER
Map 05 TL92

Birch Grove ☎ (0206) 734276
A pretty, undulating course surrounded by woodland - small but challenging with excellent greens.
9 holes, 4038yds, Par 62, SSS 60, Course record 61.
Club membership 250.

Visitors	restricted Sun mornings.
Societies	must contact in advance.
Green Fees	£10 (£12 weekends & bank holidays).
Facilities	⊗ ㅸ 🍺 🏌 ♀ ♨ 🏠
Location	Layer Rd, Kingsford (2.5m S on B1026)
Hotel	★★68% Kings Ford Park Hotel, Layer Rd, Layer De La Haye, COLCHESTER ☎ (0206) 734301 13⇄ 🛏

Colchester ☎ (0206) 853396
A fairly flat parkland course.
18 holes, 6319yds, Par 70, SSS 70.
Club membership 800.

Visitors	must contact in advance & have handicap certificate. With member only at weekends.
Societies	must contact in advance.
Green Fees	£22 per day.
Facilities	⊗ ㅸ by prior arrangement 🍺 🏌 ♀ ♨ 🏠 🛈 Mark Angel.

| Location | Braiswick (1.5m NW of town centre on B1508) |
| Hotel | ★★★60% George Hotel, 116 High St, COLCHESTER ☎ (0206) 578494 47⇄ 🛏 |

Stoke-by-Nayland ☎ Nayland (0206) 262836
Two undulating courses (Gainsborough and Constable) situated in Dedham Vale. Some water hazards and hedges. On Gainsborough the 10th (par 4) takes 2 shots over a lake; very testing par 3 at 11th.
Gainsborough Course: 18 holes, 6516yds, Par 72, SSS 71.
Constable Course: 18 holes, 6544yds, Par 72, SSS 71.
Club membership 1460.

Visitors	restricted at weekends.
Societies	weekdays only . Must contact in advance.
Green Fees	£22 per 18 holes, £28 per 36 holes (£30 weekends).
Facilities	⊗ ㅸ 🍺 🏌 ♀ ♨ 🏠 ⛳ 🛈 Kevin Lovelock.
Leisure	squash, fishing, sauna, laser shoot, clay shoot.
Location	Keepers Ln, Leavenheath (1.5m NW of Stoke-by-Nayland on B1068)
Hotel	★★★61% Broadway Hotel, The Green, BROADWAY ☎ (0386) 852401 20⇄ 🛏

EARLS COLNE
Map 05 TL82

Colne Valley ☎ Halstead (0787) 224233
An 18-hole course along the valley of the River Colne. Opened in May 1991.
18 holes, 6272yds, Par 71, SSS 70.
Club membership 350.

Visitors	only after 10am at weekends, must dress correctly,no sharing of clubs.
Societies	apply in writing,minimum of 12.
Green Fees	£22 per day; £18 per round (£22 per round weekends after 10am).
Facilities	⊗ ㅸ 🍺 🏌 ♀ ♨ 🏠 🛈 Kimberley Hurley.
Location	Station Rd
Hotel	★★★67% White Hart Hotel, Market End, COGGESHALL ☎ (0376) 561654 18⇄ 🛏

Earls Colne Golf & Leisure Centre ☎ (0787) 224466
Created on the site of a World War II airfield, this challenging public course contains 14 lakes. Also 9-hole course and 4-hole instruction course as well as a variety of leisure facilities.
18 holes, 6900yds, Par 73, SSS 72, Course record 71.
Club membership 500.

Visitors	no restrictions.
Societies	must telephone in advance.
Green Fees	not confirmed.
Facilities	⊗ ㅸ (Wed-Sat) 🍺 🏌 ♀ ♨ 🏠 🛈 Owen Mckenna.
Leisure	hard tennis courts, heated indoor swimming pool, fishing, sauna, solarium, gymnasium.
Hotel	★★★67% White Hart Hotel, Market End, COGGESHALL ☎ (0376) 561654 18⇄ 🛏

FRINTON-ON-SEA
Map 05 TM22

Frinton ☎ (0255) 674618
Flat seaside links course, easy walking, windy. Also a short course.
Long Course: 18 holes, 6259yds, Par 71, SSS 70.
Short Course: 18 holes, 2508yds, Par 66.
Club membership 800.

Visitors	must have a handicap certificate for Long course.
Societies	must contact in writing.
Green Fees	£22 per day; £7.50 per day Short Course.
Facilities	⊗ 〗 by prior arrangement ⓘ ⌣ ♀ ⌂ 🕿 ⌁ (Peter Taggart.
Leisure	snooker.
Location	1 The Esplanade (SW side of town centre)
Hotel	★★65% Maplin Hotel, Esplanade, FRINTON-ON-SEA 🕿 (0255) 673832 12rm(9⇄1 ↾)

GOSFIELD   Map 05 TL72

Gosfield Lake 🕿 Halstead (0787) 474747
Parkland course with bunkers, lake and water hazards.
Designed by Sir Henry Cotton/Mr Howard Swan and opened
in 1988. Also 9-hole course.
Lakes Course: 18 holes, 6512yds, Par 72, SSS 71.
Meadows Course: 9 holes, 4037yds, Par 66.
Club membership 850.

Visitors	a handicap certificate is required for Lakes Course. With member only at weekends from noon.
Societies	apply in writing.
Green Fees	Lakes: £20 per day. Meadows: £10 per day.
Facilities	⊗ 〗 by prior arrangement ⓘ ⌣ ♀ ⌂ 🕿 (
Leisure	sauna.
Location	The Manor House, Hall Dr
Hotel	★★69% White Hart Hotel, Bocking End, BRAINTREE 🕿 (0376) 321401 31⇄ ↾

HARLOW   Map 05 TL40

Canons Brook 🕿 (0279) 421482
Parkland course designed by Henry Cotton.
18 holes, 6728yds, Par 73, SSS 73.
Club membership 800.

Visitors	may not play at weekends.
Societies	must contact in advance.
Green Fees	£25 per day/round.
Facilities	⊗ 〗 ⓘ ⌣ (no catering Mon) ♀ ⌂ 🕿 ⌁ (Alan McGinn.
Location	Elizabeth Way (3m S of M11)
Hotel	★★★67% Churchgate Manor Hotel, Churchgate St, Old Harlow, HARLOW 🕿 (0279) 420246 85⇄

North Weald 🕿 Epping (0992) 522118
Although only opened in November 1993, the blend of lakes
and meadowland give this testing course an air of maturity.
18 holes, 6239yds, Par 71.
Club membership 780.

Visitors	must contact in advance and have handicap certificate, limited at weekends.
Societies	contact in advance.
Green Fees	£20 (£25 weekends & bank holidays).
Facilities	⊗ 〗 ⓘ ⌣ ♀ ⌂ 🕿 ⌁ (
Leisure	sauna.
Location	North Weald Bassett, Epping (M11 exit 7,off A414 towards Chipping Ongar)
Hotel	★★★62% Harlow Moat House, Southern Way, HARLOW 🕿 (0279) 422441 120⇄ ↾

HARWICH   Map 05 TM23

Harwich & Dovercourt 🕿 (0255) 503616
Flat moorland course with easy walking.
9 holes, 5742yds, SSS 68.
Club membership 420.

Visitors	with member only at weekends. Must contact in advance and have an introduction from own club.
Societies	must contact in writing.
Green Fees	not confirmed.
Facilities	⊗ 〗 ⓘ & ⌣ by prior arrangement ♀ ⌂ 🕿
Location	Station Rd, Parkeston, Dovercourt (W side 0.25m from docks on A120)
Hotel	★★55% Cliff Hotel, Marine Pde, Dovercourt, HARWICH 🕿 (0255) 503345 & 507373 28⇄ ↾

INGRAVE   Map 05 TQ69

Thorndon Park 🕿 Brentwood (0277) 811666
Among the best of the Essex courses with a fine new
purpose-built clubhouse and a lake. The springy turf is
easy on the feet. Many newly planted young trees now
replace the famous old oaks that were such a feature of
this course.
18 holes, 6481yds, Par 71, SSS 71.
Club membership 680.

Visitors	must contact in advance and play with member at weekends.
Societies	must contact in advance.
Green Fees	£40 per day; £25 per round.
Facilities	⊗ ⓘ ⌣ ♀ ⌂ 🕿 ⌁ (Brian White.
Location	Ingrave Rd (W side of village on A128)
Hotel	★★★67% Forte Posthouse, Brook St, BRENTWOOD 🕿 (0277) 260260 111⇄

LOUGHTON   Map 05 TQ49

Loughton 🕿 081-502 2923
Hilly 9-hole parkland course on the edge of Epping Forest.
9 holes, 4700yds, Par 64, SSS 63, Course record 65.
Club membership 350.

Visitors	must contact in advance.
Societies	telephone in advance.
Green Fees	£8 per 18 holes; £5 per 9 holes (£10/£6 weekends).
Facilities	ⓘ ⌣ ♀ ⌂ 🕿 ⌁ (S Layton.
Location	Clays Ln, Debden Green (1.5m SE of Theydon Bois)
Hotel	★★★62% Forte Posthouse, High Rd, Bell Common, EPPING 🕿 (0992) 573137 Annexe79⇄ ↾

MALDON   Map 05 TL80

Forrester Park 🕿 (0621) 891406
Tight, undulating parkland course with tree-lined fairways
and good views over the Blackwater estuary. Easy walking.
Attractive 16th-century clubhouse.
18 holes, 6073yds, Par 71, SSS 69.
Club membership 1200.

▶

Visitors	must contact in advance but may not play before 9.30am Tue & Wed or before 12.30pm weekends & bank holidays.
Societies	must apply in writing.
Green Fees	£20 per day; £14 per round (£20 per round weekends & bank holidays).
Facilities	⊗ 🍴 💺 ♀ 🏔 🏠 (Gary Pike.
Leisure	hard tennis courts, practice ground.
Location	Beckingham Rd, Great Totham (3m SE of Witham on A12)
Hotel	★★63% Blue Boar Hotel, Silver St, MALDON ☎ (0621) 852681 21⇌ ⋔ Annexe8⇌ ⋔

Maldon ☎ (0621) 853212
Flat, parkland course in a triangle of land by the River Chelmer, the Blackwater Canal and an old railway embankment. Alternate tees on 2nd 9 holes.
9 holes, 6197yds, Par 71, SSS 69.
Club membership 480.

Visitors	may play after 2pm and at weekends only with member.
Societies	may play Mon & Thu. Must apply in writing.
Green Fees	£15 per round (Mon-Fri).
Facilities	🍴 💺 ♀ 🏔 🏠
Location	Beeleigh, Langford (1m NW off B1018)
Hotel	★★63% Blue Boar Hotel, Silver St, MALDON ☎ (0621) 852681 21⇌ ⋔Annexe8⇌ ⋔

ORSETT

Map 05 TQ68

Orsett ☎ Grays Thurrock (0375) 891352
A very good test of golf - this heathland course with its sandy soil is quick drying and provides easy walking. Close to the Thames estuary it is seldom calm and the main hazards are the prevailing wind and thick gorse. Any slight deviation can be exaggerated by the wind and a lost ball in the gorse results. The clubhouse has been modernised.
18 holes, 6614yds, Par 72, SSS 72, Course record 68.
Club membership 900.

Visitors	restricted weekends & bank holidays. Must contact in advance and have a handicap certificate.
Societies	must contact in advance.
Green Fees	£30 per day.
Facilities	⊗ 🍴 by prior arrangement 🍴 💺 ♀ 🏔 🏠 ⋔ (Robert Newberry.
Leisure	snooker.
Location	Brentwood Rd (1.5m SE off A128)
Hotel	★★★64% Forte Posthouse, Cranes Farm Rd, BASILDON ☎ (0268) 533955 110⇌ ⋔

PURLEIGH

Map 05 TL80

Three Rivers ☎ Maldon (0621) 828631
Parkland course.
Kings Course: 18 holes, 6348yds, Par 73, SSS 70.
Queens Course: 9 holes, 1071yds, Par 27.

Visitors	must contact in advance & have handicap certificate but may not play at weekends & bank holidays.
Societies	Tue-Fri only; must contact in advance.
Green Fees	not confirmed.
Facilities	⊗ 🍴 🍴 💺 ♀ 🏔 🏠 🏁 (Graham Packer.

Leisure	hard tennis courts, heated outdoor swimming pool, squash, snooker, solarium.
Location	Stow Rd (1m from Purleigh on B1012)
Hotel	★★63% Blue Boar Hotel, Silver St, MALDON ☎ (0621) 852681 21⇌ ⋔Annexe8⇌ ⋔

ROCHFORD

Map 05 TQ89

Rochford Hundred ☎ (0702) 544302
Parkland course with ponds and ditches as natural hazards.
18 holes, 6292yds, Par 72, SSS 70.
Club membership 800.

Visitors	no restrictions.
Societies	must contact in writing.
Green Fees	not confirmed.
Facilities	♀ 🏔 🏠 (
Location	Hall Rd (W on B1013)
Hotel	★69% Balmoral Hotel, 34 Valkyrie Rd, Westcliffe-on-Sea, SOUTHEND-ON-SEA ☎ (0702) 342947 22⇌ ⋔

SAFFRON WALDEN

Map 05 TL53

Saffron Walden ☎ (0799) 522786
Undulating parkland course, beautiful views.
18 holes, 6609yds, Par 72, SSS 72 or 6371yds, Par 72, SSS 71.
Club membership 1000.

Visitors	with member only at weekends. Must contact in advance and have a handicap certificate.
Societies	must contact in advance.
Green Fees	£28 per day/round.
Facilities	⊗ 🍴 💺 ♀ 🏔 🏠 (Philip Davis.
Location	Windmill Hill (NW side of town centre off B184)
Hotel	★★65% Saffron Hotel, 10-18 High St, SAFFRON WALDEN ☎ (0799) 522676 21rm(8⇌8 ⋔)

SOUTHEND-ON-SEA

Map 05 TQ88

Belfairs ☎ (0702) 525345
Municipal parkland course run by the Borough Council. Tight second half through thick woods, easy walking.
18 holes, 5795yds, Par 70, SSS 68.
Club membership 300.

Visitors	restricted weekends & bank holidays.
Green Fees	not confirmed.
Facilities	🏠 ⋔ (
Leisure	hard tennis courts.
Location	Eastwood Rd North, Leigh on Sea (3m W, N of A13)
Hotel	★69% Balmoral Hotel, 34 Valkyrie Rd, Westcliffe-on-Sea, SOUTHEND-ON-SEA ☎ (0702) 342947 22⇌ ⋔

Thorpe Hall ☎ (0702) 582205
Parkland course.
18 holes, 6286yds, Par 71, SSS 71, Course record 67.
Club membership 1000.

Visitors	must contact in advance & have handicap certificate. With member only weekends & bank holidays.
Societies	must contact one year in advance.
Green Fees	£29 per day/round.

Facilities ⊗ & ♨ (ex Mon) ♨ ⚲ ⚱ 🏠 (Gary Harvey.
Leisure squash, snooker, sauna.
Location Thorpe Hall Av, Thorpe Bay (2m E off A13)
Hotel ★69% Balmoral Hotel, 34 Valkyrie Rd,
Westcliffe-on-Sea, SOUTHEND-ON-SEA
☎ (0702) 342947 22⇆ ♞

SOUTH OCKENDON · Map 05 TQ58

Belhus Park Municipal ☎ (0708) 854260
Municipal parkland type course with easy walking.
18 holes, 5450yds, Par 68, SSS 67, Course record 63.
Club membership 250.
Visitors no restrictions. Must have proper golf shoes and
shirts to be worn at all times.
Societies must contact in writing.
Green Fees not confirmed.
Facilities ♨ ♨ ⚲ ⚱ 🏠 ⛳ (Gary Lunn.
Leisure heated indoor swimming pool, squash, sauna,
solarium, gymnasium, 11 bay floodlit driving range.
Location Belhus Park (2m SW off B1335)
Hotel ★★★64% Forte Posthouse, Cranes Farm Rd,
BASILDON ☎ (0268) 533955 110⇆ ♞

STAPLEFORD ABBOTTS · Map 05 TQ59

Stapleford Abbotts ☎ (04023) 81108
Two championship 18-hole courses and a 9-hole par 3. Many
lakes on each course.
Abbotts Course: 18 holes, 6431yds, Par 72, SSS 71.
Friars Course: 9 holes, 1140yds, Par 27.
Priors Course: 18 holes, 5771yds, Par 69, SSS 65.
Club membership 800.
Visitors restricted at weekends. Must contact in advance.
Societies by arrangement.
Green Fees not confirmed.
Facilities ⚱ 🏠 ⛳ (
Leisure sauna, gymnasium.
Location Horsemanside, Tysea Hill (1m E off B175)
Hotel ★★59% Roebuck Hotel, North End,
BUCKHURST HILL ☎ 081-505 4636 29⇆ ♞

THEYDON BOIS · Map 05 TQ49

Theydon Bois ☎ (0992) 813054
The course was originally a nine-hole built into Epping
Forest. It was later extended to 18-holes which were
well-planned and well-bunkered but are situated out in
the open on the hillside. The old nine in the Forest are
short and have three bunkers among them, but even so a
wayward shot can be among the trees. The autumn
colours here are truly magnificent.
18 holes, 5472yds, Par 68, SSS 68, Course record 64.
Club membership 625.
Visitors must contact in advance and have a
handicap certificate.
Societies Mon & Tue only. Must contact in advance.
Green Fees £23 per day (£34 weekends & bank holidays).
Facilities ⊗ �🍽 by prior arrangement ♨ ♨ ⚲ 🏠
⛳ (Robert Joyce.
Location Theydon Rd (1m N)
Hotel ★★★62% Forte Posthouse, High Rd, Bell
Common, EPPING
☎ (0992) 573137 Annexe79⇆ ♞

TOLLESHUNT D'ARCY · Map 05 TL91

Quietwaters ☎ Maldon (0621) 860410
Two 18-hole courses. The Links is a seaside course with a
number of greenside ponds and strategically placed bunkers,
while the Lakes is a championship course with large water
features and mounding between fairways.
Links Course: 18 holes, 6194yds, Par 71, SSS 70.
*Lakes Course: 18 holes, 6767yds, Par 72, SSS 72, Course
record 67.*
Club membership 600.
Visitors restricted at weekends. Must contact in advance.
Societies must contact in advance.
Green Fees not confirmed.
Facilities ⊗ ♨ ♨ ⚲ ⚱ 🏠 ⛴ (Denis Pugh.
Leisure hard tennis courts, heated indoor swimming
pool, squash, fishing, snooker, sauna, solarium,
gymnasium, 8 international bowling rinks.
Location Colchester Rd (1.75m NE on B1026)
Hotel ★★68% Kings Ford Park Hotel, Layer Rd,
Layer De La Haye, COLCHESTER
☎ (0206) 734301 13⇆ ♞

TOOT HILL · Map 05 TL50

Toot Hill ☎ Ongar (0277) 365523
Pleasant course with several water hazards and sand greens.
18 holes, 6053yds, Par 70, SSS 69, Course record 70.
Club membership 400.
Visitors welcome but may not play at weekends.
Societies by prior arrangement.
Green Fees £25 per round.
Facilities ⊗ ♨ ♨ ⚲ ⚱ 🏠 (Geoff Bacon.
Location School Rd (7m SE of Harlow, off A414)
Hotel ★★★62% Forte Posthouse, High Rd, Bell
Common, EPPING
☎ (0992) 573137 Annexe79⇆ ♞

WITHAM · Map 05 TL81

Braxted Park Estate ☎ Maldon (0621) 892305
A Pay and Play course in ancient parkland, surrounded by
lakes and extremely pretty countryside. Suitable for beginners
and average players.
9 holes, 1980yds, Par 30.
Visitors may play week days only.
Societies apply in writing 8 weeks prior to visit.
Green Fees £11 per 18 holes; £8 per 9 holes.
Facilities ⛴
Leisure hard tennis courts, heated indoor swimming
pool, fishing, snooker, sauna.
Location 7m SE of Braintree

WOODHAM WALTER · Map 05 TL80

Bunsay Downs ☎ Danbury (0245) 222648
Attractive 9-hole public course. Also par 3.
9 holes, 5864yds, Par 70, SSS 68.
Badgers: 9 holes, 2638yds, Par 54.
Club membership 600.
Visitors no restrictions.
Societies Mon & Tue only. Must contact in advance.
Green Fees 9 holes: £7.50-£8. 18 holes £9.50-£10. ▶

Facilities ⊗ 〣 (Wed-Sat only) ⓫ ▆ ♀ ⚂ 🏠 ⛏ 🥢
M Walker.
Location Little Baddow Rd
Hotel ★★63% Blue Boar Hotel, Silver St, MALDON
☎ (0621) 852681 21⇄ ☞Annexe8⇄ ☞

Warren ☎ Danbury (0245) 223258
Attractive parkland course with natural hazards and good views.
18 holes, 6229yds, Par 70, SSS 70, Course record 65.
Club membership 840.
Visitors must play with club member at weekends before 3pm. Must have a handicap certificate.
Societies must contact in advance.
Green Fees £34 per day; £26 per round.
Facilities ⊗(Sun) ⓫ ▆ ♀ ⚂ 🏠 🥢 Miss Mickey Walker.
Leisure snooker.
Location 0.5m SW
Hotel ★★63% Blue Boar Hotel, Silver St, MALDON
☎ (0621) 852681 21⇄ ☞Annexe8⇄ ☞

GLOUCESTERSHIRE

CHELTENHAM   Map 03 SO92

Cotswold Hills ☎ (0242) 515264
A gently undulating course with open aspects and views of the Cotswolds.
18 holes, 6345yds, Par 70, SSS 72.
Club membership 750.
Visitors no restrictions.
Societies must apply in writing.
Green Fees £26 per day; £21 per round (£31/£26 weekends).
Facilities ⊗ 〣 ⓫ ▆ ♀ ⚂ 🏠 🥢 Noel Boland.
Location Ullenwood (3m S off A436)
Hotel ★★★68% Forte Crest Hotel, Crest Way, Barnwood, GLOUCESTER
☎ (0452) 613311 123⇄ ☞

Lilley Brook ☎ (0242) 526785
Undulating parkland course. Magnificent views over Cheltenham and surrounding coutryside.
18 holes, 6226yds, Par 69, SSS 70, Course record 63.
Club membership 800.
Visitors must contact in advance and have handicap certificate. With member only at weekends.
Societies by prior arrangement, except Tue.
Green Fees £20 per day/round.
Facilities ⊗ 〣 ⓫ ▆ (catering weekdays) ♀ ⚂ 🏠 ⛏ 🥢 Forbes Hadden.
Location Cirencester Rd, Charlton Kings (3m S on A435)
Hotel ★★★★52% The Queen's, Promenade, CHELTENHAM ☎ (0242) 514724 74⇄ ☞

CIRENCESTER   Map 04 SP00

Cirencester ☎ (0285) 652465
Undulating Cotswold course.
18 holes, 6002yds, Par 70, SSS 69, Course record 64.
Club membership 750.
Visitors may not play on competition days. Must contact in advance and have a handicap certificate.

Societies must contact in writing.
Green Fees £20 per day (£25 weekends & bank holidays).
Facilities ⊗ 〣 by prior arrangement ⓫ ▆ ♀ ⚂ 🏠 ⛏ 🥢 Geoff Robbins.
Location Cheltenham Rd, Bagendon (1.5m N on A435)
Hotel ★★★65% Stratton House Hotel, Gloucester Rd, CIRENCESTER ☎ (0285) 651761 41⇄ ☞

CLEEVE HILL   Map 03 SO92

Cleeve Hill ☎ (024267) 2025
Undulating heathland course.
18 holes, 6217yds, Par 69, SSS 70.
Club membership 650.
Visitors must contact in advance. Some restrictions weekends.
Societies must contact in advance.
Green Fees £7 (£8 weekends & bank holidays).
Facilities ⊗ 〣 (Fri & Sat other times by prior arrangement) ⓫ ▆ ♀ ⚂ 🏠 ⛏ 🥢 David Finch.
Leisure skittle alley.
Location nr Prestbury (1m NE on A46)
Hotel ★★★61% Hotel De La Bere, Southam, CHELTENHAM ☎ (0242) 237771 32⇄ ☞Annexe25⇄

COLEFORD   Map 03 SO51

Forest Hills ☎ (0594) 810620
A parkland course on a plateau with panoramic views of Coleford and Forest of Dean. Some testing holes with the Par-5 13th hole sitting tight on a water hazard.
18 holes, 5600yds, Par 68, SSS 67, Course record 66.
Visitors no restrictions Mon-Sat, Sun by arrangement.
Societies contact in advance.
Green Fees £13 per 18 holes (£15 weekends).
Facilities ⊗ 〣 ⓫ ▆ ♀ ⚂ 🏠
Location Mile End Rd
Hotel ★★71% The Speech House, Forest of Dean, COLEFORD ☎ (0594) 822607 14⇄ ☞

Royal Forest of Dean ☎ Dean (0594) 832583
Established in 1973 and now matured into an extremely pleasant parkland course.
18 holes, 5459yds, Par 69, SSS 66.
Club membership 500.
Visitors are required to give Tee-off times.
Societies welcome Mon-Thu, must telephone in advance.
Green Fees £14 per day (£16 weekends & bank holidays).
Facilities ⊗ 〣 ⓫ ▆ ♀ ⚂ 🏠 ⛏ 🥢 John Nicol.
Leisure hard tennis courts, outdoor swimming pool, bowling green.
Location Lords Hill (Off M5/M50 4m from Monmouth)
Hotel ★★71% The Speech House, Forest of Dean, COLEFORD ☎ (0594) 822607 14⇄ ☞

DURSLEY   Map 03 ST79

Stinchcombe Hill ☎ (0453) 542015
High on the hill with splendid views of the Cotswolds, the River Severn and the Welsh hills. A downland course with good turf, some trees and an interesting variety of greens.
18 holes, 5723yds, Par 68, SSS 68, Course record 63.
Club membership 500.

Visitors	restricted at weekends. Must contact in advance.
Societies	must apply in writing.
Green Fees	£20 per day; £15 per round (£25 per day/round weekends & bank holidays).
Facilities	⊗ � ⅃ ♥ ♀ ♨ ⚐ ✆ Brendan Wynne.
Leisure	pool table.
Location	Stinchcombe Hill (1m W off A4135)
Hotel	★★63% The Old Schoolhouse Hotel, Canonbury St, BERKELEY ☎ (0453) 811711 7⇄ ↾

GLOUCESTER

Map 03 SO81

Gloucester Hotel & Country Club ☎ (0452) 411331
Undulating, wooded course, built around a hill with superb views over Gloucester and the Cotswolds. The 12th is a drive straight up a hill, nicknamed 'Coronary Hill'.
18 holes, 5613yds, Par 70, SSS 69.
Club membership 550.

Visitors	must book at weekends. Handicap certificate required.
Societies	weekends only, by arrangement.
Green Fees	not confirmed.
Facilities	⊗ & �Ⅲ by prior arrangement ♥ ♥ ♀ ♨ ⚐ ✆ ↾ ✆
Leisure	hard tennis courts, heated indoor swimming pool, squash, snooker, sauna, solarium, gymnasium, table tennis, skittles, dry ski slope.
Location	Matson Ln, Robinswood Hill (2m SW off M5)
Hotel	★★★69% Bowden Hall Resort Hotel, Bondend Ln, Upton St Leonards, GLOUCESTER ☎ (0452) 614121 72⇄ ↾

LYDNEY

Map 03 SO60

Lydney ☎ Dean (0594) 842614 & 841561
Flat parkland/meadowland course with prevailing wind along fairways.
9 holes, 5329yds, Par 66, SSS 66.
Club membership 350.

Visitors	with member only at weekends & bank holidays.
Societies	must telephone in advance.
Green Fees	£12 per day.
Facilities	♥ ♥ ♀ ♨
Location	Lakeside Av (SE side of town centre)
Hotel	★★71% The Speech House, Forest of Dean, COLEFORD ☎ (0594) 822607 14⇄ ↾

MINCHINHAMPTON

Map 03 SO80

Minchinhampton (New Course)
☎ Nailsworth (0453) 833866
The course is on an upland Costwold plateau. It is level and open in design. Very good golf is needed to achieve par of 72.
New Course: 18 holes, 6675yds, Par 72, SSS 72.
Club membership 1600.

Visitors	must contact in advance & have handicap certificate.
Societies	must contact by telephone.

Green Fees	£24 per day; (£30 weekends & bank holidays).
Facilities	⊗ ⅢⅢ by prior arrangement ♥ ♥ ♀ ♨ ⚐ ✆ ↾ Chris Steele.
Leisure	snooker.
Location	New Course (2m E)
Hotel	★★★♣65% Burleigh Court, Minchinhampton, STROUD ☎ (0453) 883804 11⇄ ↾Annexe6⇄ ↾

Minchinhampton (Old Course) ☎ Nailsworth (0453) 832642
Old Course: 18 holes, 6295yds, Par 71, SSS 70.
Club membership 1600.

Visitors	must contact in advance.
Societies	must contact by telephone.
Green Fees	£10 per day (£13 weekends).
Facilities	⊗ ⅢⅢ by prior arrangement ♥ ♥ ♀ ♨ ⚐ ✆ ↾ Chris Steele.
Leisure	snooker.
Location	Old Course (1.5m W)
Hotel	★★★♣65% Burleigh Court, Minchinhampton, STROUD ☎ (0453) 883804 11⇄ ↾Annexe6⇄ ↾

PAINSWICK

Map 03 SO80

Painswick ☎ (0452) 812180
Downland course set on Cotswold Hills at Painswick Beacon, with fine views. Short course more than compensated by natural hazards and tight fairways.
18 holes, 4895yds, Par 67, SSS 64.
Club membership 420.

Visitors	with member only on Sun.
Societies	must apply in writing.
Green Fees	£10 per round (£15 weekend).
Facilities	⊗ ⅢⅢ ♥ ♥ ♀ ♨ ⚐
Location	1m N on A46
Hotel	★★★58% Bear of Rodborough Hotel, Rodborough Common, STROUD ☎ (0453) 878522 47⇄ ↾

TEWKESBURY

Map 03 SO83

Tewkesbury Park Hotel Golf & Country Club
☎ (0684) 295405
A parkland course in a sheltered situation beside the River Severn. The par 3, 5th is an exacting hole calling for accurate distance judgment. The hotel and country club offer many sports facilities.
18 holes, 6197yds, Par 73, SSS 70, Course record 68.
Club membership 553.

Visitors	must contact in advance and have an introduction from own club.
Societies	apply in writing.
Green Fees	not confirmed.
Facilities	⊗ ⅢⅢ ♥ ♥ ♀ ♨ ⚐ ✆ ↾ ✆ Robert Taylor.
Leisure	hard tennis courts, heated indoor swimming pool, squash, snooker, sauna, solarium, gymnasium.
Location	Lincoln Green Ln (1m SW off A38)
Hotel	★★★66% Tewkesbury Park Hotel Golf & Country Club, Lincoln Green Ln, TEWKESBURY ☎ (0684) 295405 78⇄ ↾

WESTONBIRT
Map 03 ST88

Westonbirt ☎ (066688) 242 & 333
A parkland course with good views.
9 holes, 4504yds, Par 64, SSS 64.
Club membership 150.
Visitors no restrictions.
Societies must apply in writing.
Green Fees not confirmed.
Facilities 🍺 (in summer) 🏌
Location Westonbirt School (E side of village off A433)
Hotel ★★★64% Hare & Hounds Hotel, Westonbirt,
TETBURY ☎ (0666) 880233
22⇌ ⬥Annexe8⇌ ⬥

WOTTON-UNDER-EDGE
Map 03 ST79

Cotswold Edge ☎ Dursley (0453) 844167 & 844398
Meadowland course situated in a quiet Cotswold valley. First
half flat and open, second half more varied.
18 holes, 5816yds, Par 71, SSS 68, Course record 68.
Club membership 800.
Visitors preferable to contact in advance, at weekends
may only play with member.
Societies must contact in writing.
Green Fees £15 per day/round.
Facilities ⊗ 🏌 by prior arrangement 🍺 ⬥ ⬥ 🏌
David Gosling.
Location Upper Rushmire (N of town on B4058 Wotton-
Tetbury road)
Hotel ★★63% The Old Schoolhouse Hotel,
Canonbury St, BERKELEY
☎ (0453) 811711 7⇌ ⬥

GREATER LONDON

Those courses which fall within the confines of the London
Postal District area (ie have London postcodes - W1, SW1
etc) are listed under the county heading of **London** in the
gazetteer (see page 133).

ADDINGTON
Map 05 TQ36

Addington Court ☎ 081-657 0281
Challenging, well-drained courses designed by F. Hawtree.
Two 18-hole courses, 9-hole course and a pitch-and-putt
course.
Old: 18 holes, 5577yds, Par 67, SSS 67, Course record 63.
New Falconwood: 18 holes, 5360yds, Par 66, SSS 66.
Club membership 350.
Visitors no restrictions.
Societies must telephone in advance.
Green Fees not confirmed.
Facilities ⊗ 🏌 by prior arrangement 🍺 ⬥ ⬥ 🏌
Geoffrey A Cotton.
Location Featherbed Ln (1m S off A2022)
Hotel ★★★★62% Selsdon Park Hotel, Sanderstead,
CROYDON ☎ 081-657 8811 170⇌ ⬥

> This guide is up-dated annually – make sure
> you use the up-to-date edition

Addington Palace ☎ 081-654 3061
Hard-walking parkland course, with two (par 4) testing holes
(2nd and 10th).
18 holes, 6262yds, Par 71, SSS 71.
Club membership 600.
Visitors must play with member at weekends & bank
holidays.
Societies Tue, Wed & Fri only.
Green Fees not confirmed.
Facilities ⊗ (Tue-Fri and Sun) 🏌 by prior arrangement
🍺 ⬥ ⬥ 🏌 M Pilkington.
Location Gravel Hill (0.5m SW on A212)
Hotel ★★★★62% Selsdon Park Hotel, Sanderstead,
CROYDON ☎ 081-657 8811 170⇌ ⬥

BARNEHURST
Map 05 TQ57

Barnehurst ☎ (0322) 523746
Parkland course, easy walking.
9 holes, 5320yds, Par 66, SSS 66.
Club membership 300.
Visitors restricted Tue, Thu, Sat (pm) & Sun.
Societies by arrangement.
Green Fees not confirmed.
Facilities ⊗ 🍺 ⬥ ⬥ 🏌 B Finch.
Location Mayplace Rd East (.75m NW of Crayford off
A2000)
Hotel ★★★71% Forte Posthouse, Black Prince
Interchange, Southwold Rd, BEXLEY
☎ (0322) 526900 102⇌ ⬥

BARNET
Map 04 TQ29

Arkley ☎ 081-449 0394
Wooded parkland course situated on highest spot in
Hertfordshire with fine views.
9 holes, 6045yds, Par 69, SSS 69.
Club membership 400.
Visitors with member only at weekends.
Societies Wed, Thu, Fri, by arrangement.
Green Fees £25 per day; £20 per round.
Facilities ⊗ 🏌 🍺 ⬥ ⬥ 🏌 Mark Squire.
Location Rowley Green Rd (2m W off A411)
Hotel ★★★67% Edgwarebury Hotel, Barnet Ln,
ELSTREE ☎ 081-953 8227 50⇌ ⬥

Dyrham Park Country Club ☎ 081-440 3361
Parkland course.
18 holes, 6369yds, Par 71, SSS 70, Course record 65.
Club membership 1200.
Visitors must be guest of member.
Societies Wed only, must book in advance.
Green Fees £18.50 per day (£26 weekends).
Facilities ⊗ 🏌 🍺 ⬥ (all day) ⬥ 🏌 Bill Large.
Leisure hard tennis courts, heated outdoor swimming
pool, fishing, snooker.
Location Galley Ln (3m NW off A1081)
Hotel ★★★64% Forte Posthouse, Bignells Corner,
SOUTH MIMMS ☎ (0707) 43311 120⇌ ⬥

Old Fold Manor ☎ 081-440 9185
Heathland course, good test of golf.
18 holes, 6471yds, Par 71, SSS 71.
Club membership 522.

Visitors with member only weekends & bank holidays. Handicap certificate/letter of introduction required.
Societies must apply in writing.
Green Fees £27 per round.
Facilities ⊗ ☷ by prior arrangement ⬓ ☗ (no catering Mon & Wed) ♀ (ex Mon & Wed) ⚄ ☎ ⴲ ໄ Peter Jones.
Leisure snooker.
Location Old Fold Ln, Hadley Green (N side of town centre on A1000)
Hotel ★★59% Holtwhites Hotel, 92 Chase Side, ENFIELD ☎ 081-363 0124 30rm(28⇄ ⋔)

BECKENHAM   Map 05 TQ36

Beckenham Place ☎ 081-658 5374
Picturesque course in the grounds of a public park. The course is played over by the Braeside Golf Club.
18 holes, 5722yds, Par 68, SSS 68.
Club membership 200.
Visitors no restrictions.
Societies must contact in advance.
Green Fees not confirmed.
Facilities ♀ ⚄ ☎ ⴲ ໄ
Location The Mansion (0.5m N on B2015)
Hotel ★★★58% Bromley Court Hotel, Bromley Hill, BROMLEY ☎ 081-464 5011 120⇄ ⋔

Langley Park ☎ 081-658 6849
This is a pleasant, but difficult, well-wooded, parkland course with natural hazards including a lake at the 18th hole.
18 holes, 6488yds, Par 69, SSS 71, Course record 65.
Club membership 650.
Visitors may not play at weekends. Must contact in advance & have handicap certificate.
Societies Wed & Thu only, must apply in writing.
Green Fees £35 per day/round.
Facilities ⊗ ⬓ ☗ ♀ ⚄ ☎ ⴲ ໄ George Ritchie.
Location Barnfield Wood Rd (0.5 N on B2015)
Hotel ★★★58% Bromley Court Hotel, Bromley Hill, BROMLEY ☎ 081-464 5011 120⇄ ⋔

BEXLEYHEATH   Map 05 TQ47

Bexleyheath ☎ 081-303 6951
Undulating course.
9 holes, 5239yds, Par 66, SSS 66.
Club membership 350.
Visitors may not play weekends & bank holidays.
Societies by arrangement.
Green Fees £20 per day.
Facilities ⊗ ☷ ⬓ ☗ ♀ ⚄
Location Mount Dr, Mount Rd (1m SW)
Hotel ★★★71% Forte Posthouse, Black Prince Interchange, Southwold Rd, BEXLEY ☎ (0322) 526900 102⇄ ⋔

BIGGIN HILL   Map 05 TQ45

Cherry Lodge ☎ (0959) 572250 & 576712
Undulating parkland course with good views.
18 holes, 6652yds, Par 72, SSS 72, Course record 69.
Club membership 850.

Visitors must contact in advance but may not play at weekends.
Societies must telephone in advance.
Green Fees £32 per day; £23 per round.
Facilities ⊗ ☷ (Fri & Sat only) ⬓ ☗ ♀ ⚄ ☎ ໄ Nigel Child.
Leisure sauna.
Location Jail Ln (1m E)
Hotel ★★★65% Kings Arms Hotel, Market Square, WESTERHAM ☎ (0959) 562990 16⇄ ⋔

BROMLEY   Map 05 TQ46

Magpie Hall Lane ☎ 081-462 7014
Flat course, ideal for beginners.
9 holes, 2745yds, Par 70, SSS 67.
Club membership 100.
Visitors no restrictions.
Societies must contact in advance.
Green Fees not confirmed.
Facilities ♀ ☎ ⴲ ໄ
Location Magpie Hall Ln (2m SE off A21)
Hotel ★★★58% Bromley Court Hotel, Bromley Hill, BROMLEY ☎ 081-464 5011 120⇄ ⋔

Shortlands ☎ 081-460 2471
Easy walking parkland course with a brook as a natural hazard.
9 holes, 5261yds, Par 65, SSS 66, Course record 59.
Club membership 410.
Visitors must be guest of member.
Green Fees £10 with member.
Facilities ⚄ ☎ ໄ Jamie Bates.
Location Meadow Rd, Shortlands (0.75m W off A222)
Hotel ★★★58% Bromley Court Hotel, Bromley Hill, BROMLEY ☎ 081-464 5011 120⇄ ⋔

Sundridge Park ☎ 081-460 0278
The East course is longer than the West but many think the shorter of the two courses is the more difficult. The East is surrounded by trees while the West is more hilly, with good views. Both are certainly a good test of golf.
East Course: 18 holes, 6467yds, Par 70, SSS 71, Course record 65.
West Course: 18 holes, 6007yds, Par 68, SSS 69, Course record 67.
Club membership 1200.
Visitors may only play on weekdays. Must contact in advance and must have a handicap certificate.
Societies must contact in advance.
Green Fees £36 per day.
Facilities ⊗ ☷ ⬓ ☗ ♀ ⚄ ☎ ໄ Bob Cameron.
Location Garden Rd (N side of town centre off A2212)
Hotel ★★★58% Bromley Court Hotel, Bromley Hill, BROMLEY ☎ 081-464 5011 120⇄ ⋔

We make every effort to ensure that our information is accurate but details may change after we go to print

CARSHALTON
Map 04 TQ26

Oaks Sports Centre ☎ 081-643 8363
Public parkland course with floodlit, covered driving range.
18 holes, 6033yds, Par 70, SSS 69 or 9 holes, 1443yds, Par 28, SSS 28.
Club membership 750.
Visitors no restrictions.
Societies must apply in writing.
Green Fees £9 per round (£11 weekends). 9 hole: £4.25 per round (£5.20 weekends).
Facilities ⊗ ⊪ ⅃ 🍴 ☕ ♀ ﹠ 🏠 ⅂ ⅂ G Horley, P Rees, P Congdon.
Leisure squash.
Location Woodmansterne Rd (0.5m S on B278)
Hotel ★★★66% Forte Posthouse, Purley Way, CROYDON ☎ 081-688 5185 83⇄

CHESSINGTON
Map 04 TQ16

Chessington ☎ 081-391 0948
Tree-lined parkland course designed by Patrick Tallack.
9 holes, 1400yds, Par 27, SSS 28.
Club membership 250.
Visitors must book 7.30am-noon weekends only.
Societies must telephone 1 month in advance.
Green Fees not confirmed.
Facilities ⊗ ⅃ ⊪ ☕ ♀ ﹠ 🏠 ⅂ ⅂ R Cornwell.
Location Garrison Ln (Opp Chessington South Station nr Zoo)
Hotel ★★62% Heathside Hotel, Brighton Rd, BURGH HEATH ☎ (0737) 353355 73⇄ 🐾

CHISLEHURST
Map 05 TQ47

Chislehurst ☎ 081-467 2782
Pleasantly wooded undulating parkland/heathland course.
Magnificent clubhouse with historical associations.
18 holes, 5128yds, Par 66, SSS 65.
Club membership 800.
Visitors must contact in advance. With member only weekends.
Societies must contact in writing.
Green Fees not confirmed.
Facilities ⊗ ⊪ ☕ ♀ ﹠ 🏠 ⅂ ⅂
Leisure snooker.
Location Camden, Park Rd
Hotel ★★★58% Bromley Court Hotel, Bromley Hill, BROMLEY ☎ 081-464 5011 120⇄ 🐾

COULSDON
Map 04 TQ25

Coulsdon Court ☎ 081-660 0468 & 081-668 0414
A public parkland course with good views. Clubhouse formerly owned by the Byron family.
18 holes, 6037yds, Par 70, SSS 69.
Visitors must book mid-week for weekends.
Societies by arrangement.
Green Fees £11 per round (£13.75 weekends).
Facilities ⊗ ⅃ ⊪ ☕ ♀ ﹠ 🏠 ⅂ ⊫ ⅂
Leisure hard tennis courts, squash, solarium, gymnasium.
Location Coulsdon Rd (0.75m E off A23 on B2030)
Hotel ★★★★62% Selsdon Park Hotel, Sanderstead, CROYDON ☎ 081-657 8811 170⇄ 🐾

Woodcote Park ☎ 081-668 2788
Slightly undulating parkland course.
18 holes, 6337yds, Par 71, SSS 70.
Club membership 700.
Visitors must contact in advance & have handicap certificate but may not play at weekends.
Societies must contact in advance.
Green Fees not confirmed.
Facilities ⊗ ⅃ by prior arrangement ⊪ ☕ ♀ ﹠ 🏠 ⅂ D Hudspith.
Leisure snooker.
Location Meadow Hill, Bridle Way (1m N of town centre off A237)
Hotel ★★★66% Forte Posthouse, Purley Way, CROYDON ☎ 081-688 5185 83⇄

CROYDON
Map 05 TQ36

Croham Hurst ☎ 081-657 5581
Parkland course with tree-lined fairways and bounded by wooded hills. Easy walking.
18 holes, 6274yds, Par 70, SSS 70.
Club membership 800.
Visitors must contact in advance & have handicap certificate. With member only weekends & bank holidays.
Societies must book 1 year in advance.
Green Fees £32 per day/round (£42 weekends & bank holidays).
Facilities ⊗ ⅃ by prior arrangement ⊪ ☕ ♀ ﹠ 🏠 ⅂ ⅂ Eric Stillwell.
Location Croham Rd (1.5m SE)
Hotel ★★★★62% Selsdon Park Hotel, Sanderstead, CROYDON ☎ 081-657 8811 170⇄ 🐾

Selsdon Park ☎ 081-657 8811
Parkland course. Full use of hotel's sporting facilities by residents.
18 holes, 6402yds, Par 71, SSS 69.
Visitors restrictions at weekends for non-residents.
Societies must contact in advance.
Green Fees £20 per round (£35 weekends).
Facilities ⊗ ⅃ ⊪ ☕ ♀ ﹠ 🏠 ⅂ ⊨ ⅂
Leisure hard and grass tennis courts, outdoor and indoor heated swimming pools, squash, snooker, sauna, solarium, gymnasium, croquet & boule.
Location Addington Rd, Sanderstead (3m S on A2022)
Hotel ★★★★62% Selsdon Park Hotel, Sanderstead, CROYDON ☎ 081-657 8811 170⇄ 🐾

Shirley Park ☎ 081-654 1143
This parkland course lies amid fine woodland with good views of Shirley Hills. The more testing holes come in the middle section of the course. The remarkable 7th hole calls for a 187-yard iron or wood shot diagonally across a narrow valley to a shelved green set right-handed into a ridge.
18 holes, 6210yds, Par 71, SSS 70.
Club membership 1000.
Visitors must contact in advance & have handicap certificate. With member only at weekends.
Societies by arrangement.
Green Fees £26 per day/round.
Facilities ⊗ ⅃ ⊪ ☕ ♀ ﹠ 🏠 ⅂ ⅂ Hogan Stott.
Leisure snooker.

Location	Addiscombe Rd (E side of town centre on A232)
Hotel	★★★★64% Croydon Park Hotel, 7 Altyre Rd, CROYDON ☎ 081-680 9200 214 ⇄ ♖

DOWNE   Map 05 TQ46

High Elms ☎ (0689) 858175
Municipal parkland course. Very tight 13th, 230 yds (par 3).
18 holes, 6340yds, Par 71, SSS 70.
Club membership 570.
Visitors no restrictions.
Green Fees not confirmed.
Facilities ⊗ ⅢⅠ ╚ ♥ ♀ ⚐ ⚑
Location High Elms Rd (1.5m NE)
Hotel ★★★58% Bromley Court Hotel, Bromley Hill, BROMLEY ☎ 081-464 5011 120⇄ ♖

West Kent ☎ Orpington (0689) 851323
Partly hilly downland course.
18 holes, 6399yds, Par 70, SSS 70.
Club membership 750.
Visitors with member only at weekends. Must contact in advance and have a handicap certificate.
Societies must apply in writing.
Green Fees not confirmed.
Facilities ⊗ ╚ ♥ ♀ ⚐ ⚑ ⚑ Roger Fidler.
Location West Hill (0.75m SW)
Hotel ★★★58% Bromley Court Hotel, Bromley Hill, BROMLEY ☎ 081-464 5011 120⇄ ♖

ENFIELD   Map 05 TQ39

Crews Hill ☎ 081-363 6674
Parkland course in country surroundings.
18 holes, 6230yds, Par 70, SSS 70.
Club membership 548.
Visitors Mon-Fri before 9am. Handicap certificate required.
Societies must apply in writing.
Green Fees not confirmed.
Facilities ⊗ ⅢⅠ ╚ (no catering Mon) ♥ ♀ ⚐ ⚑ J Reynolds.
Location Cattlegate Rd, Crews Hill (3m NW off A1005)
Hotel ★★59% Holtwhites Hotel, 92 Chase Side, ENFIELD ☎ 081-363 0124 30rm(28⇄ ♖)

Enfield ☎ 081-363 3970
Public parkland course. Salmons Brook crosses 7 holes.
18 holes, 6137yds, Par 72, SSS 70 or 5924yds, Par 69, SSS 68.
Club membership 625.
Visitors must contact in advance & have handicap certificate. With member only at weekends.
Societies Mon, Wed & Fri, must contact in advance.
Green Fees £30 per day; £20 per round.
Facilities ⊗ ⅢⅠ ╚ ♥ ♀ ⚐ ⚑ Lee Fickling.
Location Old Park Rd South (W side of town centre off A110)
Hotel ★★59% Holtwhites Hotel, 92 Chase Side, ENFIELD ☎ 081-363 0124 30rm(28⇄ ♖)

Enfield Municipal ☎ 081-363 4454
Flat wooded parkland course. 9th hole is a left-hand dog-leg with second shot over a brook.
18 holes, 5755yds, Par 68, SSS 68.
Club membership 350.
Visitors must play with member.
Societies must apply in writing to the secretary.
Green Fees not confirmed.
Facilities ⊗ ⅢⅠ ♥ ⚐ ⚑ ⚑ David Lewis.
Location Beggars Hollow, Clay Hill (N side of town centre)
Hotel ★★59% Holtwhites Hotel, 92 Chase Side, ENFIELD ☎ 081-363 0124 30rm(28⇄ ♖)

GREENFORD   Map 04 TQ18

Ealing ☎ 081-997 0937
Flat, parkland course relying on natural hazards; trees, tight fairways, and the River Brent which affects 9 holes.
18 holes, 6216yds, Par 70, SSS 70.
Club membership 700.
Visitors Mon-Fri only on application to pro shop.
Societies Mon, Wed & Thu only by arrangement.
Green Fees £30 per day/round.
Facilities ⊗ ╚ ♥ ♀ ⚐ ╚ ⚑ Arnold Stickley.
Location Perivale Ln
Hotel ★★57% Osterley Hotel, 764 Great West Rd, OSTERLEY ☎ 081-568 9981 57⇄ ♖Annexe5rm

Horsenden Hill ☎ 081-902 4555
A well-kept, tree-lined short course.
9 holes, 1618yds, Par 28, SSS 28.
Club membership 135.
Visitors no restrictions.
Societies telephone for details.
Green Fees £3.95 per 9 holes (£5.95 weekends).
Facilities ⊗ ╚ ♥ ♀ ╚ ⚐ ⚑ ⚑ Anthony Ferrier.
Location Whitten Av, Woodland Rise (3m NE on A4090)
Hotel ★★★62% Master Brewer Hotel, Western Av, HILLINGDON ☎ (0895) 251199 106⇄ ♖

Perivale Park ☎ 081-575 7116
Parkland course.
9 holes, 2600yds, Par 68, SSS 65.
Club membership 180.
Visitors no restrictions.
Green Fees £3.95 per 9 holes (£5.95 weekends and bank holidays).
Facilities ╚ ♥ ♀ ⚐ ⚑ ⚑ Peter Bryant.
Location Stockdove Way (E side of town centre, off A40)
Hotel ★★★67% Carnarvon Hotel, Ealing Common, LONDON ☎ 081-992 5399 145 ⇄ ♖

HADLEY WOOD   Map 04 TQ29

Hadley Wood ☎ 081-449 4328
A parkland course on the northwest edge of London. The gently undulating fairways have a friendly width inviting the player to open his shoulders, though the thick rough can be very punishing to the unwary. The course is pleasantly wooded and there are some admirable views.
18 holes, 6473yds, Par 72, SSS 71, Course record 67.
Club membership 600.
▶

Visitors	may not play Tue mornings & Sat. Must book in advance Sun.
Societies	by arrangement.
Green Fees	£40 per day; £30 per round.
Facilities	⊗ (Mon-Fri only) ▥ by prior arrangement ▤ (Mon-Fri only) ▀ ♀ ⚲ 🏠 ✆ Peter Jones.
Leisure	snooker.
Location	Beech Hill (E side of village)
Hotel	★★★★60% West Lodge Park Hotel, Cockfosters Rd, HADLEY WOOD ☎ 081-440 8311 48⇔ ♠Annexe2⇔ ♠

HAMPTON
Map 04 TQ17

Fulwell ☎ 081-977 3844
Championship-length parkland course with easy walking. The 575-yd, 17th, is notable.
18 holes, 6544yds, Par 71, SSS 71.
Club membership 650.

Visitors	may not play weekends. Must contact in advance and have a handicap certificate.
Societies	must apply in writing.
Green Fees	not confirmed.
Facilities	⊗ ▥ by prior arrangement ▤ ▀ ♀ ⚲ 🏠 ✆ David Haslam.
Location	Wellington Rd, Hampton Hill (1.5m N on A311)
Hotel	★★★64% Richmond Hill, 146-150 Richmond Hill, RICHMOND ☎ 081-940 2247 & 081-940 5466 124⇔ ♠

HAMPTON WICK
Map 04 TQ16

Home Park ☎ 081-977 2658
Flat, parkland course with easy walking.
18 holes, 6218yds, Par 71, SSS 71.
Club membership 573.

Visitors	no restrictions.
Societies	must contact in advance.
Green Fees	£15 per day (£20 weekends).
Facilities	⊗ ▥ ▤ ▀ ♀ ⚲ 🏠 ✆ Len Roberts.
Location	Off A308 on W side of Kingston Bridge
Hotel	★★★64% Richmond Hill, 146-150 Richmond Hill, RICHMOND ☎ 081-940 2247 & 081-940 5466 124⇔ ♠

HILLINGDON
Map 04 TQ08

Hillingdon ☎ (0895) 233956
Parkland course west of London.
9 holes, 5490yds, Par 68, SSS 67.
Club membership 400.

Visitors	may not play Thu, weekends, or bank holidays. Must have an introduction from own club.
Societies	must apply in writing.
Green Fees	not confirmed.
Facilities	⊗ ▥ by prior arrangement ▤ ▀ ♀ ⚲ 🏠 ✆
Location	Dorset Way, Vine Ln (W side of town off A4020)
Hotel	★★★62% Master Brewer Hotel, Western Av, HILLINGDON ☎ (0895) 251199 106⇔ ♠

HOUNSLOW
Map 04 TQ17

Airlinks ☎ 081-561 1418
Meadowland/parkland course designed by P. Allis and D. Thomas.
18 holes, 5885yds, Par 71, SSS 68, Course record 65.
Club membership 500.

Visitors	may not play before noon at weekends.
Societies	must apply in writing.
Green Fees	not confirmed.
Facilities	⊗ ▥ by prior arrangement in winter ▤ ▀ ♀ ⚲ 🏠 ✆ Ken Wyckham.
Leisure	36 bay flood lit driving range.
Location	Southall Ln (W of Hounslow off M4 junc 3)
Hotel	★★★62% Master Robert Hotel, Great West Rd, HOUNSLOW ☎ 081-570 6261 100⇔ ♠

Hounslow Heath Municipal ☎ 081-570 5271
Parkland course in a conservation area, planted with an attractive variety of trees. The 15th hole lies between the fork of two rivers.
18 holes, 5820yds, Par 69, SSS 68.
Club membership 300.

Visitors	may not play at weekends.
Societies	must telephone in advance.
Green Fees	not confirmed.
Facilities	⚲ 🏠 ✆
Location	Staines Rd
Hotel	★★★★62% Forte Crest, Sipson Road, West Drayton, WEST DRAYTON ☎ 081-759 2323 569⇔ ♠

ILFORD
Map 05 TQ48

Ilford ☎ 081-554 2930
Fairly flat parkland course intersected five times by a river.
18 holes, 5702yds, Par 68, SSS 68.
Club membership 592.

Visitors	must contact in advance, restricted weekends & bank holidays.
Societies	must contact in advance.
Green Fees	£13.50 per round (£16 weekends).
Facilities	⊗ ▀ ♀ ⚲ 🏠 ✆
Location	Wanstead Park Rd (NW side of town centre off A12)
Hotel	★★★68% Woodford Moat House, Oak Hill, WOODFORD GREEN ☎ 081-505 4511 99⇔ ♠

ISLEWORTH
Map 04 TQ17

Wyke Green ☎ 081-560 8777
Fairly flat parkland course.
18 holes, 6242yds, Par 69, SSS 70, Course record 64.
Club membership 730.

Visitors	restricted weekends & bank holidays. Must contact in advance and a handicap certificate required.
Societies	must apply in writing.
Green Fees	£28 per day (£42 weekends).
Facilities	⊗ ▥ ▤ ▀ ♀ ⚲ 🏠 ✆ David Holmes.
Leisure	snooker.
Location	Syon Ln (1.5m N on B454 off A4)
Hotel	★★★62% Master Robert Hotel, Great West Rd, HOUNSLOW ☎ 081-570 6261 100⇔ ♠

KINGSTON UPON THAMES   Map 04 TQ16

Coombe Hill ☎ 081-942 2284
A splendid course in wooded terrain. The undulations
and trees make it an especially interesting course of great
charm. And there is a lovely display of rhododendrons in
May and June.
18 holes, 6303yds, Par 71, SSS 71.
Club membership 550.
Visitors   must contact in advance & have handicap
               certificate. With member only at weekends.
Societies   must book in advance.
Green Fees £45 per day.
Facilities   ⊗ ⓑ ➤ ♀ ⚘ 🏠 ⛳ 𝄞 Craig Defoy.
Leisure   snooker, sauna.
Location   Golf Club Dr, Coombe Ln West (1.75m E
               on A238)
Hotel   ★★★★★73% Hyatt Carlton Tower Hotel,
               Cadogan Place, LONDON
               ☎ 071-235 5411 224 ⇆ 🐾

Coombe Wood ☎ 081-942 0388
Parkland course.
18 holes, 5210yds, Par 66, SSS 66.
Club membership 650.
Visitors   must contact in advance & play with member at
               weekends.
Societies   Wed, Thu & Fri; must contact in advance.
Green Fees not confirmed.
Facilities   ⊗ ⓑ ➤ ♀ ⚘ 🏠 ⛳ 𝄞 David Butler.
Location   George Rd (1.25m NE on A308)
Hotel   ★★63% Haven Hotel, Portsmouth Rd, ESHER
               ☎ 081-398 0023   16⇆ 🐾Annexe4⇆ 🐾

MITCHAM   Map 04 TQ26

Mitcham ☎ 081-648 4197 & 081-648 4280
A wooded heathland course on a gravel base.
18 holes, 5935yds, Par 69, SSS 68.
Club membership 500.
Visitors   must telephone & book in advance.
Societies   must phone in advance.
Green Fees £10 per round.
Facilities   ⊗ ⓑ ➤ ♀ ⚘ 🏠 𝄞 Jeff Godfrey.
Location   Carshalton Rd (1m S)
Hotel   ★★★66% Forte Posthouse, Purley Way,
               CROYDON ☎ 081-688 5185   83⇆

NEW MALDEN   Map 04 TQ26

Malden ☎ 081-942 0654
Parkland course with the hazard of the Beverley Brook which
affects 4 holes (3rd, 7th, 8th and 12th).
18 holes, 6201yds, Par 71, SSS 70, Course record 65.
Club membership 800.
Visitors   restricted weekends. Must contact in advance.
Societies   must apply in writing.
Green Fees not confirmed.
Facilities   ⊗ ⓑ ➤ ♀ ⚘ 🏠 𝄞 Robert Hunter.
Location   Traps Ln (N side of town centre off B283)
Hotel   ★★★64% Kingston Lodge Hotel, Kingston Hill,
               KINGSTON UPON THAMES
               ☎ 081-541 4481   62⇆ 🐾

NORTHWOOD   Map 04 TQ09

Haste Hill ☎ (0923) 822877
Parkland course with stream running through. Excellent
views.
18 holes, 5787yds, Par 68, SSS 68.
Club membership 350.
Visitors   no restrictions.
Societies   must apply in writing 2 months in advance.
Green Fees not confirmed.
Facilities   ⊗ ⓑ ➤ ♀ ⚘ 🏠 ⛳ 𝄞 Philip Howard.
Location   The Drive (0.5m S off A404)
Hotel   ★★67% Harrow Hotel, Roxborough Bridge,
               12-22 Pinner Rd, HARROW
               ☎ 081-427 3435   76⇆ 🐾

Northwood ☎ (0923) 821384
A very old club to which, it is said, golfers used to drive
from London by horse-carriage. They would find their
golf interesting as present-day players do. The course is
relatively flat although there are some undulations, and
trees and whins add not only to the beauty of the course
but also to the test of golf.
18 holes, 6493yds, Par 71, SSS 71.
Club membership 800.
Visitors   with member only weekends.
Societies   Mon, Thu & Fri only, by arrangement.
Green Fees £30 per day; £20 per round.
Facilities   ⚘ 🏠 ⛳ 𝄞 C J Holdsworth.
Location   Rickmansworth Rd (SW side of village off
               A404)
Hotel   ★★67% Harrow Hotel, Roxborough Bridge,
               12-22 Pinner Rd, HARROW
               ☎ 081-427 3435   76⇆ 🐾

Sandy Lodge ☎ (0923) 825429
A links-type, very sandy, heathland course.
18 holes, 6081yds, Par 70, SSS 70, Course record 64.
Club membership 750.
Visitors   must contact in advance & have handicap
               certificate. Not permitted weekends & bank
               holidays.
Societies   must apply in writing.
Green Fees £26 per round.
Facilities   ⊗ 🍴 ⓑ ➤ ♀ ⚘ 🏠 𝄞
Location   Sandy Lodge Ln (N side of town centre
               off A4125)
Hotel   ★★★64% Bedford Arms Thistle Hotel,
               CHENIES ☎ (0923) 283301   10⇆ 🐾

ORPINGTON   Map 05 TQ46

Cray Valley ☎ (0689) 39677 & 31927
An open parkland course with two man-made lakes and open
ditches.
18 holes, 5400yds, Par 70, SSS 67.
Club membership 640.
Visitors   no restrictions.
Societies   by arrangement.
Green Fees £11 per day (£17 weekends).
Facilities   ⊗ ⓑ ➤ ♀ ⚘ 🏠 𝄞 John Gregory.
Location   Sandy Ln (1m off A20)
Hotel   ★★★58% Bromley Court Hotel, Bromley Hill,
               BROMLEY ☎ 081-464 5011   120⇆ 🐾

Lullingstone Park ☎ (0959) 34542
Popular 27-hole public course set in 690 acres of undulating parkland. Championship length 18-holes, plus 9-hole course and a further 9-hole pitch and putt.
18 holes, 6759yds, Par 72, SSS 72, Course record 71 or 9 holes, 2432yds, Par 33.
Club membership 400.
Visitors   welcome.
Societies   must telephone in advance.
Green Fees   not confirmed.
Facilities   ⊗ ㉐ ♨ ♀ ⚘ 🏠 ⅋ ℓ David Cornford.
Location   Parkgate, Chelsfield (Leave M25 junct 4 and take Well Hill turn)
Hotel   ★★★58% Bromley Court Hotel, Bromley Hill, BROMLEY ☎ 081-464 5011 120⇄ ℝ

Ruxley Park Golf Centre ☎ (0689) 871490
Parkland course with public, floodlit driving range. Difficult 6th hole, par 4. Easy walking and good views.
18 holes, 5892yds, Par 71, SSS 68.
Club membership 500.
Visitors   may not play mornings on weekends & bank holidays. Must contact in advance.
Societies   must telephone two weeks in advance.
Green Fees   not confirmed.
Facilities   ⊗ ㉐ ♨ ♀ ⚘ 🏠 ℓ Mark Woodman.
Leisure   driving range, covered bays (floodlit).
Location   Sandy Ln, St Paul's Cray (2m NE on A223)
Hotel   ★★★58% Bromley Court Hotel, Bromley Hill, BROMLEY ☎ 081-464 5011 120⇄ ℝ

PINNER

Map 04 TQ18

Grims Dyke ☎ 081-428 4539
Pleasant, undulating parkland course.
18 holes, 5600yds, Par 69, SSS 67, Course record 64.
Club membership 590.
Visitors   with member only at weekends.
Societies   must apply in writing.
Green Fees   £25 per day; £20 per round.
Facilities   ⊗ ㉐ ♨ ♀ ⚘ 🏠 ℓ John Rule.
Location   Oxhey Ln, Hatch End (3m N on A4008)
Hotel   ★★67% Harrow Hotel, Roxborough Bridge, 12-22 Pinner Rd, HARROW ☎ 081-427 3435 76⇄ ℝ

Pinner Hill ☎ 081-866 0963
A hilly, wooded parkland course.
18 holes, 6280yds, Par 72, SSS 70, Course record 63.
Club membership 770.
Visitors   are required to have handicap certificate on Mon, Tue & Fri, Wed & Thu are public days. Contact in advance.
Societies   Mon, Tue & Fri only, by arrangement.
Green Fees   £25 per day (£32 weekends). Wed & Thu £8.10 per round.
Facilities   ⊗ & 🕯 by prior arrangement ㉐ ♨ ♀ ⚘ 🏠 ⅋ ℓ Mark Grieve.
Location   Southview Rd, Pinner Hill (2m NW off A404)
Hotel   ★★67% Harrow Hotel, Roxborough Bridge, 12-22 Pinner Rd, HARROW ☎ 081-427 3435 76⇄ ℝ

PURLEY

Map 05 TQ36

Purley Downs ☎ 081-657 8347
Hilly downland course. Notable holes are 6th and 12th.
18 holes, 6020yds, Par 70, SSS 69, Course record 65.
Club membership 700.
Visitors   must have a handicap certificate, & play on weekdays only.
Societies   must contact in advance.
Green Fees   £28 per day/round.
Facilities   ⊗ ㉐ ♨ ♀ ⚘ 🏠 ℓ Graham Wilson.
Leisure   snooker.
Location   106 Purley Downs Rd (E side of town centre off A235)
Hotel   ★★★66% Forte Posthouse, Purley Way, CROYDON ☎ 081-688 5185 83⇄

RICHMOND UPON THAMES

Map 04 TQ17

Richmond ☎ 081-940-4351
A beautiful and historic wooded, parkland course on the edge of Richmond Park, with six par-3 holes. The 4th is often described as the best short hole in the south of England. Low scores are uncommon because cunningly sited trees call for great accuracy. The clubhouse is one of the most distinguished small Georgian mansions in England.
18 holes, 5780yds, Par 70, SSS 69.
Club membership 700.
Visitors   may not play weekends.
Societies   must apply in writing.
Green Fees   £32 per day.
Facilities   ⊗ ㉐ ♨ ♀ ⚘ 🏠 ⅋ ℓ Nick Job.
Location   Sudbrook Park, Petersham (1.5m S off A307)
Hotel   ★★★64% Richmond Hill, 146-150 Richmond Hill, RICHMOND ☎ 081-940 2247 & 081-940 5466 124⇄ ℝ

Royal Mid-Surrey ☎ 081-940 1894
A long playing parkland course. The flat fairways are cleverly bunkered. The 18th provides an exceptionally good par 4 finish with a huge bunker before the green to catch the not quite perfect long second.
Outer Course: 18 holes, 6343yds, Par 69, SSS 70, Course record 64.
Inner Course: 18 holes, 5544yds, Par 68, SSS 67, Course record 70.
Club membership 1200.
Visitors   may not play at weekends. Must contact in advance and be introduced by member or another club.
Societies   must apply in writing.
Green Fees   not confirmed.
Facilities   ⊗ ㉐ ♨ ♀ ⚘ 🏠 ⅋ ℓ David Talbot.
Leisure   snooker.
Location   Old Deer Park (0.5m N of Richmond upon Thames off A316)
Hotel   ★★★64% Richmond Hill, 146-150 Richmond Hill, RICHMOND ☎ 081-940 2247 & 081-940 5466 124⇄ ℝ

ROMFORD   Map 05 TQ58

Maylands Golf Club & Country Park
☎ Ingrebourne (0708) 342055
Picturesque undulating parkland course.
18 holes, 6351yds, Par 71, SSS 70.
Club membership 700.
Visitors   with member only at weekends.
Societies   Mon, Wed & Fri only, by arrangement.
Green Fees £30 per day; £20 per round (£40/£30 weekends).
Facilities ⊗ �🏛 (Mon, Wed & Fri only, Apr-Oct)
                🛒 ☕ ♀ ⚲ 🏌 ⟨ John Hopkin.
Location   Colchester Rd, Harold Park
Hotel   ★★★67% Forte Posthouse, Brook St,
                BRENTWOOD ☎ (0277) 260260 111⇥

Romford ☎ (0708) 740986
A many-bunkered parkland course with easy walking. It
is said there are as many bunkers as there are days in the
year. The ground is quick drying making a good course
for winter play when other courses might be too wet.
18 holes, 6374yds, Par 72, SSS 70.
Club membership 693.
Visitors   with member only weekends & bank
                holidays. Must contact in advance & have
                handicap certificate.
Societies   must telephone in advance.
Green Fees £30 per day; £23 per round.
Facilities ⊗ �🏛 (weekends only) 🛒 ☕ ♀ ⚲ 🏌 ⟨
                Harry Flatman.
Location   Heath Dr, Gidea Park (1m NE on A118)
Hotel   ★★★67% Forte Posthouse, Brook St,
                BRENTWOOD ☎ (0277) 260260 111⇥

RUISLIP   Map 04 TQ08

Ruislip ☎ (08956) 32004
Municipal parkland course. Many trees.
18 holes, 5703yds, Par 69, SSS 68, Course record 65.
Club membership 450.
Visitors   no restrictions.
Societies   must telephone in advance.
Green Fees not confirmed.
Facilities ⊗ �🏛 🛒 ☕ ♀ ⚲ 🏌 ⟨ Derek Nash.
Leisure   snooker, 40 booth driving range.
Location   Ickenham Rd (0.5m SW on B466)
Hotel   ★★★62% Master Brewer Hotel, Western Av,
                HILLINGDON ☎ (0895) 251199 106⇥ ☏

SIDCUP   Map 05 TQ47

Sidcup ☎ 081-300 2150
Easy walking parkland course with natural water hazards.
9 holes, 2861yds, Par 68, SSS 68, Course record 65.
Club membership 400.
Visitors   with member only weekends & bank holidays.
                Must contact in advance and have an
                introduction from own club.
Societies   must apply in writing.
Green Fees not confirmed.
Facilities ⊗ ⁋ by prior arrangement 🛒 ☕ ♀ ⚲ 🏌 ⟨
                Ross V Taylor.
Leisure   snooker.

Location   7 Hurst Rd (N side of town centre off A222)
Hotel   ★★★58% Bromley Court Hotel, Bromley Hill,
                BROMLEY ☎ 081-464 5011 120⇥ ☏

SOUTHALL   Map 04 TQ17

West Middlesex ☎ 081-574 3450
Gently undulating parkland course.
18 holes, 6242yds, Par 69, SSS 70.
Club membership 500.
Visitors   restricted weekends & bank holidays.
Societies   apply in writing.
Green Fees not confirmed.
Facilities ⚲ 🏌 ⟨
Location   Greenford Rd (W side of town centre on A4127
                off A4020)
Hotel   ★★★62% Master Robert Hotel, Great West Rd,
                HOUNSLOW ☎ 081-570 6261 100⇥ ☏

STANMORE   Map 04 TQ19

Stanmore ☎ 081-954 2599
North London parkland course.
18 holes, 5884yds, Par 68, SSS 68.
Club membership 600.
Visitors   must contact in advance & have handicap
                certificate. With member only at weekends &
                bank holidays.
Societies   Wed & Thu only, by arrangement.
Green Fees Mon & Fri £8.10 per round. Tue-Thu £25 per
                round.
Facilities ⊗ ⁋ 🛒 ☕ ♀ ⚲ 🏌 ⟨ V Law.
Location   29 Gordon Av (S side of town centre)
Hotel   ★★67% Harrow Hotel, Roxborough Bridge, 12-
                22 Pinner Rd, HARROW
                ☎ 081-427 3435 76⇥ ☏

SURBITON   Map 04 TQ16

Surbiton ☎ 081-398 3101
Parkland course with easy walking.
18 holes, 6211yds, Par 70, SSS 70.
Club membership 750.
Visitors   with member only at weekends & bank holidays.
                Must contact in advance and have a handicap
                certificate.
Societies   must apply in writing.
Green Fees not confirmed.
Facilities ⊗ ⁋ & 🛒 (in season) ☕ ♀ ⚲ 🏌 ⟨ Paul
                Milton.
Location   Woodstock Ln (2m S off A3)
Hotel   ★★★64% Richmond Hill, 146-150 Richmond
                Hill, RICHMOND ☎ 081-940 2247 &
                081-940 5466 124⇥ ☏

TWICKENHAM   Map 04 TQ17

Strawberry Hill ☎ 081-894 0165
Parkland course with easy walking.
9 holes, 2381yds, Par 64, SSS 62, Course record 59.
Club membership 350.
Visitors   with member only at weekends.
Societies   must apply in writing.
Green Fees not confirmed.

▶

Facilities ⊗ 🍽 by prior arrangement 🔼 🍺 ♀ ⛳ 🏠 (Peter Buchan.
Location Wellesley Rd (S side of town centre off A311)
Hotel ★★★64% Richmond Hill, 146-150 Richmond Hill, RICHMOND ☎ 081-940 2247 & 081-940 5466 124⇌ ✎

Twickenham ☎ 081-783 1748 & 1698
Municipal commonland course.
9 holes, 3180yds, Par 72, SSS 71.
Club membership 200.
Visitors no restrictions.
Societies apply in advance
Green Fees £5 (£6 weekends).
Facilities ⊗ 🍽 🔼 🍺 ♀ ⛳ 🏠 (Steve Lloyd.
Leisure floodlit driving range.
Location Staines Rd (2m W on A305)
Hotel ★★★64% Richmond Hill, 146-150 Richmond Hill, RICHMOND ☎ 081-940 2247 & 081-940 5466 124⇌ ✎

UPMINSTER Map 05 TQ58

Upminster ☎ (0708) 222788
Parkland course adjacent to river.
18 holes, 5951yds, Par 68, SSS 69.
Club membership 800.
Visitors with member only at weekends. Must have an introduction from own club.
Societies apply in writing.
Green Fees not confirmed.
Facilities ♀ ⛳ 🏠 (
Location 114 Hall Ln (N side of town centre)
Hotel ★★★67% Forte Posthouse, Brook St, BRENTWOOD ☎ (0277) 260260 111⇌

UXBRIDGE Map 04 TQ08

Uxbridge ☎ (0895) 237287
Municipal parkland course, undulating and tricky.
18 holes, 5750yds, Par 68, SSS 68, Course record 64.
Club membership 700.
Visitors no restrictions.
Societies Thu by arrangment.
Green Fees not confirmed.
Facilities ⊗ 🍽 by prior arrangement 🔼 🍺 ♀ ⛳ 🏠 ⛴ (Phil Howard.
Leisure snooker.
Location The Drive, Harefield Place (2m N off B467)
Hotel ★★★62% Master Brewer Hotel, Western Av, HILLINGDON ☎ (0895) 251199 106⇌ ✎

WEMBLEY Map 04 TQ18

Sudbury ☎ 081-902 3713
Undulating parkland course very near centre of London.
18 holes, 6282yds, Par 69, SSS 70.
Club membership 650.
Visitors must have handicap certificate. With member only at weekends.
Societies must apply in writing.
Green Fees not confirmed.
Facilities ⊗ 🍽 by prior arrangement 🔼 🍺 ♀ ⛳ 🏠 (Neil Jordan.

Leisure snooker.
Location Bridgewater Rd (SW side of town centre on A4090)
Hotel ★★67% Harrow Hotel, Roxborough Bridge, 12-22 Pinner Rd, HARROW ☎ 081-427 3435 76⇌ ✎

WEST DRAYTON Map 04 TQ07

Holiday ☎ (0895) 444232
Fairly large, testing, hilly par 3 course suitable both for beginners and scratch players.
9 holes, 1618yds, Par 28, Course record 50.
Club membership 120.
Visitors restricted Sun morning.
Societies by arrangement.
Green Fees £5.25 per round (£6.50 weekends).
Facilities catering facilities available at hotel ♀ ⛳ 🏠 ⛴ 🛏
Leisure heated indoor swimming pool, sauna, solarium, gymnasium.
Location Stockley Rd (1m SE off A408)
Hotel ★★★★59% Holiday Inn Crowne Plaza, Stockley Rd, West Drayton, WEST DRAYTON ☎ (0895) 445555 380⇌

WOODFORD GREEN Map 05 TQ49

Woodford ☎ 081-504 0553 & 081-504 4254
Forest land course on the edge of Epping Forest. Views over the Lea Valley to the London skyline.
9 holes, 5806yds, Par 70, SSS 68.
Club membership 400.
Visitors must contact in advance. With member only Tue/Thu mornings, weekends & bank holidays.
Societies must contact in advance.
Green Fees not confirmed.
Facilities ⊗ (ex Mon) 🔼 🍺 ♀ ⛳ 🏠 (Ashley Johns.
Location Sunset Av (NW side of town centre off A104)
Hotel ★★★68% Woodford Moat House, Oak Hill, WOODFORD GREEN ☎ 081-505 4511 99⇌ ✎

GREATER MANCHESTER

ALTRINCHAM Map 07 SJ78

Altrincham ☎ 061-928 0761
Municipal parkland course with easy walking, water on many holes, rolling contours and many trees. Driving range in grounds.
18 holes, 6162yds, Par 71, SSS 69.
Club membership 350.
Visitors must book in advance.
Societies by prior arrangement.
Green Fees £6 per round (£7 weekends & bank holidays).
Facilities ⛳ 🏠 ⛴ (John Jackson.
Leisure driving range.
Location Stockport Rd (0.75 E of Altrincham on A560)
Hotel ★★★65% Cresta Court Hotel, Church St, ALTRINCHAM ☎ 061-927 7272 139⇌ ✎

Dunham Forest ☎ 061-928 2605
Attractive parkland course cut through magnificent beech woods.
18 holes, 6636yds, Par 72, SSS 72.
Club membership 600.
Visitors   may not play weekends & bank holidays.
Societies   telephone for availability.
Green Fees £27 per round (£32 weekends).
Facilities   ⊗ ⅏ by prior arrangement ⅃ ⬛ ♀ ⚲ 🏠 ⚲�‍ Ian Wrigley.
Leisure   hard tennis courts, squash, snooker.
Location   Oldfield Ln (1.5m W off A56)
Hotel   ★★★66% Bowdon Hotel, Langham Rd, Bowdon, ALTRINCHAM
                     ☎ 061-928 7121 82⇥

Ringway ☎ 061-904 9609
Parkland course, with interesting natural hazards. Easy walking, good views.
18 holes, 6307yds, Par 71, SSS 70.
Club membership 720.
Visitors   may not play before 9.30am or between 1-2pm. Must have handicap certificate.
Societies   Thu only May-Sep.
Green Fees not confirmed.
Facilities   ⊗ ⬛ ♀ ⚲ 🏠 ⚲ Nick Ryan.
Leisure   snooker.
Location   Hale Mount, Hale Barns (2.5m SE on A538)
Hotel   ★★★65% Cresta Court Hotel, Church St, ALTRINCHAM ☎ 061-927 7272 139⇥ 🐾

ASHTON-IN-MAKERFIELD   Map 07 SJ59

Ashton-in-Makerfield ☎ (0942) 727267 & 719330
Well-wooded parkland course. Easy walking.
18 holes, 6250yds, Par 70, SSS 70.
Club membership 800.
Visitors   restricted Sat & bank holidays. With member only on Sun. No visitors Wed.
Societies   apply in writing.
Green Fees £21.
Facilities   ⊗ ⅏ ⅃ ⬛ ♀ ⚲ 🏠 ⚲⚲ Peter Allan.
Leisure   snooker.
Location   Garswood Park, Liverpool Rd (0.5m W of M6 (Junc 24) on A58)
Hotel   ★★★67% Forte Posthouse, Lodge Ln, Newton-Le-Willows, HAYDOCK
                     ☎ (0942) 717878 136⇥

ASHTON-UNDER-LYNE   Map 07 SJ99

Ashton-under-Lyne ☎ 061-330 1537
A testing, varied moorland course, with large greens. Easy walking. Three new holes have improved the course.
18 holes, 6300yds, Par 70, SSS 70, Course record 69.
Club membership 650.
Visitors   with member only weekends & bank holidays.
Societies   telephone in advance.
Green Fees not confirmed.
Facilities   ⊗ ⅏ ⅃ ⬛ ♀ ⚲ 🏠 ⚲ Colin Boyle.
Leisure   snooker.
Location   Gorsey Way, Higher Hurst (1.5m NE)
Hotel   ★★71% York House Hotel, York Place, Richmond St, ASHTON-UNDER-LYNE
                     ☎ 061-330 5899 24⇥ 🐾Annexe10⇥

Dukinfield ☎ 061-338 2340
Recently extended, tricky hillside course with several difficult Par 3s and a very long par 5.
18 holes, 5400yds, Par 67, SSS 67.
Club membership 400.
Visitors   may not play on Wed afternoons & must play with member at weekends. Must contact in advance.
Societies   must contact in advance.
Green Fees £16.50 per round.
Facilities   ⊗ ⅏ by prior arrangement ⅃ by prior arrangement ⬛ ♀ ⚲ 🏠 ⚲ Colin Boyle.
Location   Lyne Edge, Yew Tree Ln (S off B6175)
Hotel   ★★71% York House Hotel, York Place, Richmond St, ASHTON-UNDER-LYNE
                     ☎ 061-330 5899 24⇥ 🐾Annexe10⇥

BOLTON   Map 07 SD70

Bolton ☎ (0204) 843067
This well maintained heathland course is always a pleasure to visit. The 12th hole should be treated with respect and so too should the final four holes which have ruined many a card.
18 holes, 6300yds, Par 70, SSS 70.
Club membership 600.
Visitors   restricted at weekends.
Societies   welcome Mon, Thu & Fri, apply in writing.
Green Fees £30-£32 per day; £25-£28 per round.
Facilities   ⊗ ⅏ by prior arrangement ⅃ ⬛ ♀ ⚲ 🏠 ⚲ R Longworth.
Leisure   snooker.
Location   Lostock Park, Chorley New Rd (3m W on A673)
Hotel   ★★★60% Pack Horse Hotel, Bradshawgate, Nelson Square, BOLTON
                     ☎ (0204) 27261 72⇥ 🐾

Bolton Municipal ☎ (0204) 842336
A parkland course.
18 holes, 6336yds, Par 71, SSS 69, Course record 68.
Club membership 300.
Visitors   no restrictions
Societies   telephone in advance.
Green Fees not confirmed.
Facilities   ⊗ ⅏ by prior arrangement ⅃ ⬛ ♀ ⚲ 🏠 ⚲⚲ A K Holland.
Location   Links Rd (3m W on A673)
Hotel   ★★★62% Forte Posthouse, Beaumont Rd, BOLTON ☎ (0204) 651511 96⇥ 🐾

Breightmet ☎ (0204) 27381
Long parkland course.
9 holes, 6416yds, Par 72, SSS 71.
Club membership 350.
Visitors   may not play weekends.
Societies   welcome Tue & Thu only, apply in advance in writing.
Green Fees £15 per round (£18 weekends & bank holidays).
Facilities   ⊗ ⅏ ⅃ ⬛ ♀ ⚲
Leisure   snooker.
Location   Red Bridge, Ainsworth (E side of town centre off A58)
Hotel   ★★★60% Pack Horse Hotel, Bradshawgate, Nelson Square, BOLTON
                     ☎ (0204) 27261 72⇥ 🐾

Deane ☎ (0204) 61944 & 651808
Undulating parkland course with small ravines on approaches to some holes.
18 holes, 5583yds, Par 68, SSS 67, Course record 64.
Club membership 500.
Visitors must be a member of a golf club.
Societies must apply in writing.
Green Fees £17.50 per day (£22.50 weekened and bank holidays).
Facilities ⊗ ⍟ by prior arrangement 🄇 ☕ ♀ ⚐ 📷 (David Martindale.
Leisure snooker.
Location Broadford Rd, Deane
Hotel ★★★62% Forte Posthouse, Beaumont Rd, BOLTON ☎ (0204) 651511 96⇄ 🐾

Dunscar ☎ (0204) 303321 & 301090
A scenic moorland course with panoramic views. A warm friendly club.
18 holes, 6085yds, Par 71, SSS 69, Course record 64.
Club membership 600.
Visitors may normally play after 9.30am & 1.30pm; some restrictions at weekends.
Societies must telephone in advance.
Green Fees £20 per day (£30 weekends).
Facilities ⊗ ⍟ 🄇 ☕ ♀ ⚐ 📷 ⛳ (Gary Treadgold.
Leisure snooker.
Location Longworth Ln, Bromley Cross (3m N off A666)
Hotel ★★★64% Egerton House Hotel, Blackburn Rd, Egerton, BOLTON ☎ (0204) 307171 32⇄ 🐾

Great Lever & Farnworth ☎ (0204) 656137
Downland course with easy walking.
18 holes, 5859yds, Par 70, SSS 69, Course record 67.
Club membership 600.
Visitors must contact in advance.
Societies contact in advance.
Green Fees £12 per day (£19 weekends).
Facilities ⊗ ⍟ 🄇 ☕ ♀ ⚐ 📷 (Donald Stirling.
Leisure snooker.
Location Lever Edge Ln (SW side of town centre off A575)
Hotel ★★★60% Pack Horse Hotel, Bradshawgate, Nelson Square, BOLTON ☎ (0204) 27261 72⇄ 🐾

Harwood ☎ (0204) 22878
Mainly flat parkland course.
9 holes, 5993yds, Par 71, SSS 69, Course record 67.
Club membership 410.
Visitors with member only weekends.
Societies contact in writing.
Green Fees not confirmed.
Facilities 🄇 ☕ ♀ ⚐
Leisure snooker.
Location Springfield, Roading Brook Rd, Harwood (2.5m NE off B6196)
Hotel ★★★64% Egerton House Hotel, Blackburn Rd, Egerton, BOLTON ☎ (0204) 307171 32⇄ 🐾

Old Links ☎ (0204) 842307
Championship moorland course.
18 holes, 6408yds, Par 72, SSS 72, Course record 64.
Club membership 750.

Visitors welcome except championship days & Sat until 4pm.
Societies apply by letter.
Green Fees £25 per day (£30 weekends).
Facilities ⊗ ⍟ 🄇 ☕ ♀ ⚐ 📷 (Paul Horridge.
Leisure snooker.
Location Chorley Old Rd (NW of town centre on B6226)
Hotel ★★★60% Pack Horse Hotel, Bradshawgate, Nelson Square, BOLTON ☎ (0204) 27261 72⇄ 🐾

Regent Park ☎ (0204) 844170
Parkland course.
18 holes, 6069yds, Par 70, SSS 69.
Club membership 230.
Visitors no restrictions.
Societies must telephone in advance.
Green Fees not confirmed.
Facilities ⚐ 📷 ⛳ (
Location Links Rd, Chorley New Rd (3.5m W off A673)
Hotel ★★★62% Forte Posthouse, Beaumont Rd, BOLTON ☎ (0204) 651511 96⇄ 🐾

BRAMHALL   Map 07 SJ88

Bramall Park ☎ 061-485 3199
Well-wooded parkland course with splendid views of the Pennines.
18 holes, 6043yds, Par 70, SSS 69.
Club membership 600.
Visitors must contact in advance.
Societies apply in writing.
Green Fees not confirmed.
Facilities ⊗ ⍟ 🄇 ☕ ♀ ⚐ 📷 (M Proffitt.
Leisure snooker.
Location 20 Manor Rd (NW side of town centre off B5149)
Hotel ★★★68% Bramhall Moat House, Bramhall Ln South, BRAMHALL ☎ 061-439 8116 65⇄ 🐾

Bramhall ☎ 061-439 4057
Undulating parkland course, easy walking.
18 holes, 6293yds, Par 70, SSS 70.
Club membership 720.
Visitors welcome except Thu & Sat. Must contact in advance.
Societies Wed only, apply in writing.
Green Fees £25 per day (£35 Fri, Sun & bank holidays).
Facilities ⚐ 📷 (Brian Nield.
Leisure snooker.
Location Ladythorn Rd (E side of town centre off A5102)
Hotel ★★★68% Bramhall Moat House, Bramhall Ln South, BRAMHALL ☎ 061-439 8116 65⇄ 🐾

BROMLEY CROSS   Map 07 SD71

Turton ☎ Bolton (0204) 852235
Moorland course.
9 holes, 5584yds, Par 68, SSS 67.
Club membership 325.
Visitors with member only at weekends and bank holidays. May not play Wed before 3pm.
Societies must contact in writing.

Green Fees £15 per day.
Facilities (catering by prior arrangement) ♀ ⚑
Location Wood End Farm, Chapeltown Rd
(3m N on A676)
Hotel ★★★64% Egerton House Hotel, Blackburn Rd,
Egerton, BOLTON ☎ (0204) 307171 32⇄ ♠

BURY
Map 07 SD81

Bury ☎ 061-766 4897
Hard walking on hilly moorland course.
18 holes, 5961yds, Par 69, SSS 69, Course record 65.
Club membership 650.
Visitors must have a handicap certificate but may not
play at weekends.
Societies contact in advance.
Green Fees £18 (£26 weekends).
Facilities ⊗ ⋔ ⓑ ▆ ♀ ⚑ ⌂ (M Peel.
Leisure snooker.
Location Unsworth Hall, Blackford Bridge (2m S on A56)
Hotel ★58% Woolfield House Hotel, Wash Ln, BURY
☎ 061-797 9775 16rm(3⇄7 ♠)

Lowes Park ☎ 061-764 1231
Moorland course, with easy walking. Usually windy.
9 holes, 6009yds, Par 70, SSS 69.
Club membership 250.
Visitors may not play Wed & Sat, by appointment Sun.
Must contact in advance.
Societies contact in advance.
Green Fees not confirmed.
Facilities ⊗ ⋔ ⓑ ▆ (no catering Mon) ♀ (ex Mon)
Location Hill Top, Walmersley (N side of town centre
off A56)
Hotel ★58% Woolfield House Hotel, Wash Ln, BURY
☎ 061-797 9775 16rm(3⇄7 ♠)

Walmersley ☎ 061-764 1429
Moorland hillside course, with wide fairways, large greens
and extensive views. Testing holes: 2nd (484 yds) par 5; 4th
(444 yds) par 4.
9 holes, 6114yds, Par 72, SSS 70, Course record 64.
Club membership 450.
Visitors must contact in advance & have handicap
certificate. Restricted at weekends.
Societies telephone one month in advance.
Green Fees £12 per day.
Facilities ⊗ ⋔ ⓑ ▆ (no catering Mon) ♀ (ex Mon) ⚑
Location Garretts Close, Walmersley (3m N off A56)
Hotel ★★★62% Old Mill Hotel, Springwood,
RAMSBOTTOM ☎ (0706) 822991 36⇄

CHEADLE
Map 07 SJ88

Cheadle ☎ 061-491 4452
Parkland course with hazards on every hole, from sand
bunkers and copses to a stream across six of the fairways.
9 holes, 5006yds, Par 64, SSS 65.
Club membership 446.
Visitors may not play Tue & Sat. Must contact in
advance and have a handicap certificate.
Societies apply in writing.
Green Fees £12 per round (£23 Sun & bank holidays).
Facilities ⊗ ⋔ by prior arrangement ⓑ ▆ ♀ ⚑ ⌂(
Andrew Collins.

Leisure snooker.
Location Cheadle Rd (S side of village off A5149)
Hotel ★★63% Wycliffe, 74 Edgeley Rd, Edgeley,
STOCKPORT ☎ 061-477 5395 20⇄ ♠

DENTON
Map 07 SJ99

Denton ☎ 061-336 3218
Easy, flat parkland course with brook running through.
Notable hole is one called 'Death and Glory'.
18 holes, 6290yds, Par 72, SSS 70.
Club membership 600.
Visitors may not play at weekends. Must contact in
advance.
Green Fees not confirmed.
Facilities ♀ ⚑ ⌂(
Location Manchester Rd (1.5m W on A57)
Hotel ★★71% York House Hotel, York Place,
Richmond St, ASHTON-UNDER-LYNE
☎ 061-330 5899 24⇄ ♠Annexe10⇄

FAILSWORTH
Map 07 SD80

Brookdale ☎ 061-681 4534
Undulating parkland course, with river crossed 5 times in
play. Hard walking.
18 holes, 6040yds, Par 68, SSS 68.
Club membership 600.
Visitors restricted Sun and Tue (ladies day). Must contact
in advance and have a handicap certificate.
Societies must contact in writing.
Green Fees £18 per day (£22 weekends).
Facilities ⊗ & ⋔ by prior arrangement
ⓑ ▆ ♀ ⚑ ⌂ ⫟(Jason Spibey.
Leisure snooker.
Location Ashbridge, Woodhouses (N side of Manchester)
Hotel ★★61% Midway Hotel, Manchester Rd,
Castleton, ROCHDALE
☎ (0706) 32881 24⇄ ♠

FLIXTON
Map 07 SJ79

William Wroe Municipal ☎ 061-748 8680
Parkland course, with easy walking.
18 holes, 4395yds, Par 64, SSS 61, Course record 60.
Club membership 225.
Visitors restricted weekends. Must contact in advance.
Green Fees not confirmed.
Facilities ⚑ ⌂ ⫟(Roland West.
Location Pennybridge Ln (E side of village off B5158)
Hotel ★63% Beaucliffe Hotel, 254 Eccles Old Rd,
Pendleton, SALFORD
☎ 061-789 5092 21rm(2⇄15 ♠)

GATLEY
Map 07 SJ88

Gatley ☎ 061-437 2091
Parkland course. Moderately testing.
9 holes, 5934yds, Par 68, SSS 68.
Club membership 400.
Visitors may not play Tue & Sat. With member only
weekends.
Societies apply in writing.
Green Fees £18 per day.

►

Facilities ⊗ ⅏ ⓛ & ▆ by prior arrangement ♀ ⚐ 🛏 ℓ
Leisure squash, snooker.
Location Waterfall Farm, Styal Rd, Heald Green (S side of village off B5166)
Hotel ★★★★60% Belfry Hotel, Stanley Rd, HANDFORTH ☎ 061-437 0511 81⇄

HALE

Map 07 SJ78

Hale ☎ 061-980 4225
Beautiful, undulating parkland course, with the River Bollin winding round fairways.
9 holes, 5780yds, Par 70, SSS 68.
Club membership 300.
Visitors may not play before 4.30pm Thu; with member only weekends.
Societies apply in writing.
Green Fees £25 per day; £20 per round.
Facilities ⚐ 🛏 ℓ Joy Jackson.
Location Rappax Rd (1.25m SE)
Hotel ★★★66% Bowdon Hotel, Langham Rd, Bowdon, ALTRINCHAM ☎ 061-928 7121 82⇄

HAZEL GROVE

Map 05 SJ98

Hazel Grove ☎ 061-483 3978
Parkland course.
18 holes, 6300yds, Par 71, SSS 70, Course record 65.
Club membership 550.
Visitors must contact in advance and have a handicap certificate.
Societies must apply in writing.
Green Fees £22.50 per round (£27.50 weekends).
Facilities ⊗ ⅏ ⓛ ▆ ♀ ⚐ 🛏 ⚑ℓ M E Hill.
Leisure snooker.
Location Buxton Rd (1m E off A6)
Hotel ★★★68% Bramhall Moat House, Bramhall Ln South, BRAMHALL ☎ 061-439 8116 65⇄ ☍

HINDLEY

Map 07 SD60

Hindley Hall ☎ Wigan (0942) 55131
Parkland course with mostly easy walking.
18 holes, 5840yds, Par 69, SSS 68, Course record 63.
Club membership 500.
Visitors restricted Wed and weekends. Must contact in advance and have an introduction from own club.
Societies apply in writing.
Green Fees not confirmed.
Facilities ⊗ ⅏ by prior arrangement ⓛ ▆ (no catering Mon) ♀ ⚐ 🛏 ℓ N Brazell.
Leisure snooker.
Location Hall Ln (1m N off A58)
Hotel ★★61% Brocket Arms Hotel, Mesnes Rd, WIGAN ☎ (0942) 46283 27⇄ ☍

HORWICH

Map 07 SD61

Horwich ☎ (0204) 696980
Parkland course with natural hazards and generally windy. Hard walking.
9 holes, 5286yds, Par 67, SSS 67, Course record 64.
Club membership 300.

Visitors must be accompanied by member.
Societies must contact in writing.
Green Fees not confirmed.
Facilities ♀ ⚐
Location Victoria Rd (SE side of village A673)
Hotel ★★★62% Forte Posthouse, Beaumont Rd, BOLTON ☎ (0204) 651511 96⇄ ☍

HYDE

Map 07 SJ99

Werneth Low ☎ 061-368 2503
Hard walking but good views from this moorland course. Exposed to wind.
9 holes, 5734yds, Par 70, SSS 68.
Club membership 350.
Visitors may not play Tue mornings, weekends & bank holidays.
Societies must contact in advance.
Green Fees not confirmed.
Facilities ⊗ ⅏ by prior arrangement ⓛ ▆ ♀ ⚐ 🛏 ℓ Tony Bacchus.
Location Werneth Low (2m S of town centre)
Hotel ★★70% Red Lion Inn, 112 Buxton Rd, High Ln, STOCKPORT ☎ (0663) 765227 6⇄ ☍

LEIGH

Map 07 SD60

Pennington ☎ (0942) 682852
Municipal parkland course, with natural hazards of brooks, ponds and trees, and easy walking.
9 holes, 2919yds, Par 35, SSS 34.
Club membership 150.
Visitors no restrictions.
Societies must contact in advance.
Green Fees not confirmed.
Facilities ▆ 🛏 ⚑ℓ
Location St Helen's Rd (SW side of town centre off A572)
Hotel ★★63% Kirkfield Hotel, 2/4 Church St, NEWTON LE WILLOWS ☎ (0925) 228196 17⇄ ☍

LITTLEBOROUGH

Map 07 SD91

Whittaker ☎ (0706) 378310
Moorland 9-hole course.
9 holes, 5632yds, Par 68, SSS 67, Course record 61.
Club membership 150.
Visitors welcome except for Tue pm and Sun.
Societies apply to Secretary.
Green Fees £10 per day (£12 weekends).
Facilities catering by arrangement only. ⚐
Location Whittaker Ln (3m NE of Rochdale, along A58)
Hotel ★★★68% Norton Grange Hotel, Manchester Rd, Castleton, ROCHDALE ☎ (0706) 30788 50⇄ ☍

MANCHESTER

Map 07 SJ89

Blackley ☎ 061-643 2980
Parkland course. Course crossed by footpath.
18 holes, 6237yds, Par 70, SSS 70, Course record 65.
Club membership 670.

Visitors with member only Thu & weekends.
Societies apply in advance.
Green Fees £17.
Facilities ⊗ ⋕ ⅃ ⬛ ♀ ⚼ 🍴 ₹ Mike Barton.
Location Victoria Ave East, Blackley (4m N of city centre, on Rochdale Rd)
Hotel ★★★62% The Bower Hotel, Hollinwood Av, Chadderton, OLDHAM
☎ 061-682 7254 66⊨ 🐦

Chorlton ☎ 061-881 5830 & 061-881 3139
Meadowland course with trees, stream and several ditches.
18 holes, 6004yds, Par 70, SSS 69, Course record 63.
Club membership 780.
Visitors handicap certificate required.
Societies on Thu only by prior booking.
Green Fees £20 per day (£25 weekends).
Facilities ⊗ ⋕ ⅃ ⬛ (no catering Mon, times vary seasonally) ♀ ⚼ 🍴 ⚲ ₹ David Screeton.
Leisure snooker, practice area.
Location Barlow Hall, Barlow Hall Rd, Chorlton-cum-Hardy (4m S of Manchester A5103/A5145)
Hotel ★★★58% Willow Bank Hotel, 340-342 Wilmslow Rd, Fallowfield, MANCHESTER
☎ 061-224 0461 116⊨ 🐦

Davyhulme Park ☎ 061-748 2260
Parkland course.
18 holes, 6237yds, Par 72, SSS 70, Course record 67.
Club membership 500.
Visitors may not play on Wed & Sat; must play with member on Sun. Must have an introduction from own club.
Societies must contact in advance.
Green Fees not confirmed.
Facilities ⊗ ⋕ by prior arrangement ⅃ ⬛ ♀ ⚼ 🍴 ⚲ ₹ Hugh Lewis.
Leisure snooker.
Location Gleneagles Rd, Davyhulme (8m S adj to Park Hospital)
Hotel ★63% Beaucliffe Hotel, 254 Eccles Old Rd, Pendleton, SALFORD
☎ 061-789 5092 21rm(2⊨15 🐦)

Didsbury ☎ 061-998 9278
Parkland course.
18 holes, 6273yds, Par 70, SSS 70, Course record 64.
Club membership 700.
Visitors restricted Tue, Wed & weekends.
Societies must contact in advance.
Green Fees £22 per day (£25 weekends).
Facilities ⊗ ⋕ ⅃ ⬛ ♀ ⚼ 🍴 ⚲ ₹ Peter Barber.
Leisure snooker.
Location Ford Ln, Northenden (6m S of city centre off A5145)
Hotel ★★★62% Forte Posthouse, Palatine Rd, Northenden, MANCHESTER
☎ 061-998 7090 190⊨ 🐦

Fairfield ☎ 061-370 1641 & 061-370 2292
Parkland course set around a reservoir. Course demands particularly accurate placing of shots.
18 holes, 5654yds, Par 70, SSS 68.
Club membership 400.

Visitors may not play mornings at weekends & may be restricted on Wed & Thu.
Societies apply in writing to Secretary.
Green Fees £16 per round (£20 weekends & bank holidays).
Facilities ♀ ⚼ 🍴 ₹
Leisure snooker.
Location Booth Rd, Audenshaw (1.5m W of Audenshaw off A635)
Hotel ★★71% York House Hotel, York Place, Richmond St, ASHTON-UNDER-LYNE
☎ 061-330 5899 24⊨ 🐦Annexe10⊨

Houldsworth ☎ 061-224 5055
Flat parkland course, tree-lined and with water hazards. Testing holes 9th (par 5) and 13th (par 5).
18 holes, 5819yds, Par 70, SSS 68.
Club membership 520.
Visitors may not play weekends & bank holidays. Must contact in advance.
Societies by prior arrangement.
Green Fees not confirmed.
Facilities ⊗ & ⋕ by prior arrangement ⅃ ⬛ ♀ ⚼ 🍴 ₹ David Naylor.
Leisure snooker.
Location Wingate House, Higher Levenshulme (4m SE of city centre off A6)
Hotel ★★★58% Willow Bank Hotel, 340-342 Wilmslow Rd, Fallowfield, MANCHESTER
☎ 061-224 0461 116⊨ 🐦

Northenden ☎ 061-998 4738
Parkland course surrounded by the River Mersey.
18 holes, 6469yds, Par 72, SSS 71.
Club membership 600.
Visitors Must contact in advance. Tee reserved for members 8.30-9.15am & 12.30-1.15pm.
Societies Tue & Fri only, telephone in advance.
Green Fees £25 per day (£27.50 weekends).
Facilities ⊗ ⋕ ⅃ ⬛ ♀ ⚼ 🍴 ₹ Bill McColl.
Leisure snooker.
Location Palatine Rd (6.5m S of city centre on B1567 off A5103)
Hotel ★★★62% Forte Posthouse, Palatine Rd, Northenden, MANCHESTER
☎ 061-998 7090 190⊨ 🐦

Pike Fold ☎ 061-740 1136
Picturesque, hilly course. Good test of golf.
9 holes, 5785yds, Par 70, SSS 68, Course record 66.
Club membership 200.
Visitors may not play Sun. Must be with member Sat & bank holidays.
Societies apply in writing.
Green Fees £12 per day.
Facilities ⊗ & ⋕ by prior arrangement ⅃ ⬛ ♀ ⚼
Leisure snooker.
Location Cooper Ln, Victoria Av, Blackley (4m N of city centre off Rochdale Rd)
Hotel ★★★62% The Bower Hotel, Hollinwood Av, Chadderton, OLDHAM
☎ 061-682 7254 66⊨ 🐦

Withington ☎ 061-445 9544
Flat parkland course.
18 holes, 6410yds, Par 71, SSS 71.
Club membership 600.

▶

Visitors welcome except Thu, must contact in advance, restricted at weekends.
Societies welcome except Thu, Sat & Sun.
Green Fees £24 per day; £22 per round (£30/£28 weekends).
Facilities ⊗ ⊤ by prior arrangement ▐ ☻ ♀ ♨ 🏠 ℓ R J Ling.
Leisure snooker.
Location 243 Palatine Rd, West Didsbury (4m SW of city centre off B5167)
Hotel ★★★62% Forte Posthouse, Palatine Rd, Northenden, MANCHESTER
☎ 061-998 7090 190⇄ ♠

Worsley ☎ 061-789 4202
Well-wooded parkland course.
18 holes, 6220yds, Par 72, SSS 70, Course record 66.
Club membership 700.
Visitors no restrictions.
Societies Mon, Wed & Thu only.
Green Fees £25 per day; £20 per round.
Facilities ⊗ ⊤ ▐ ☻ ♀ ♨ 🏠 ⊤ ℓ Ceri Cousins.
Leisure snooker.
Location Stableford Av, Monton Green, Eccles (6.5m NW of city centre off A572)
Hotel ★★★57% Novotel Manchester West Hotel, Worsley Brow, WORSLEY
☎ 061-799 3535 119⇄ ♠

MELLOR
Map 07 SJ98

Mellor & Townscliffe ☎ 061-427 2208
Scenic parkland and moorland course, undulating with some hard walking. Good views. Testing 200 yd, 9th hole, par 3.
18 holes, 5925yds, Par 70, SSS 69, Course record 64..
Club membership 650.
Visitors with member only Sun.
Societies apply by letter.
Green Fees £18 per day (£25 weekends & bank holidays).
Facilities ⊗ ⊤ ▐ ☻ ♀ ♨ 🏠 ℓ Michael J Williams.
Location Gibb Ln, Tarden (0.5m S)
Hotel ★74% Springfield Hotel, Station Rd, MARPLE
☎ 061-449 0721 6⇄ ♠

MIDDLETON
Map 07 SD80

Manchester ☎ 061-643 3202
Moorland golf of unique character over a spaciously laid out course with generous fairways sweeping along to large greens. A wide variety of holes will challenge the golfer's technique, particularly the testing last three holes.
18 holes, 6464yds, Par 72, SSS 72.
Club membership 700.
Visitors must contact in advance, restricted weekends.
Societies apply in writing.
Green Fees £25 per day/round (£30 weekends & bank holidays).
Facilities ⊗ & ⊤ by prior arrangement ▐ ☻ ♀ ♨ 🏠 ℓ Brian Connor.
Leisure snooker, driving range.
Location Hopwood Cottage, Rochdale Rd (2.5m N off A664)
Hotel ★★61% Midway Hotel, Manchester Rd, Castleton, ROCHDALE
☎ (0706) 32881 24⇄ ♠

North Manchester ☎ 061-643 9033
A long, tight heathland course with natural water hazards. Excellent views of the Yorkshire Wolds.
18 holes, 6527yds, Par 72, SSS 72, Course record 66.
Club membership 800.
Visitors no restrictions.
Societies telephone in advance.
Green Fees not confirmed.
Facilities ⊗ ⊤ by prior arrangement ▐ ☻ ♀ ♨ 🏠 ⊤ ℓ
Leisure snooker.
Location Rhodes House, Manchester Old Rd (W side of town centre off A576)
Hotel ★★★62% The Bower Hotel, Hollinwood Av, Chadderton, OLDHAM
☎ 061-682 7254 66⇄ ♠

MILNROW
Map 07 SD91

Tunshill ☎ (0706) 342095
Testing moorland course, particularly 6th and 15th (par 5's).
9 holes, 5804yds, Par 70, SSS 68.
Club membership 275.
Visitors must contact in advance, restricted weekends & evenings.
Societies apply in writing.
Green Fees not confirmed.
Facilities ▐ & ☻ (ex Mon) ♀ ♨
Leisure snooker, pool table.
Location Kiln Ln (1m NE M62 exit junc 21 off B6225)
Hotel ★★★68% Norton Grange Hotel, Manchester Rd, Castleton, ROCHDALE
☎ (0706) 30788 50⇄ ♠

OLDHAM
Map 07 SD90

Crompton & Royton ☎ 061-624 2154
Undulating moorland course.
18 holes, 6222yds, Par 70, SSS 70, Course record 65.
Club membership 721.
Visitors must contact in advance and may not play at weekends, Tue or Wed.
Societies apply in writing or telephone 061-624 2154
Green Fees £24 (£30 weekends).
Facilities ⊗ ⊤ ▐ ☻ ♀ ♨ 🏠 ℓ David Melling.
Leisure snooker.
Location Highbarn (0.5m NE of Royton)
Hotel ★★★62% The Bower Hotel, Hollinwood Av, Chadderton, OLDHAM
☎ 061-682 7254 66⇄ ♠

Oldham ☎ 061-624 4986
Moorland course, with hard walking.
18 holes, 5045yds, Par 66, SSS 65.
Club membership 300.
Visitors must contact in advance.
Societies must contact in advance.
Green Fees not confirmed.
Facilities ⊗ (ex Mon) ⊤ (ex Mon) ▐ (ex Mon) ☻ (ex Mon) ♀ ♨ 🏠 ℓ
Location Lees New Rd (2.5m E off A669)
Hotel ★★71% York House Hotel, York Place, Richmond St, ASHTON-UNDER-LYNE
☎ 061-330 5899 24⇄ ♠ Annexe10⇄

Werneth ☎ 061-624 1190
Semi-moorland course, with a deep gulley and stream
crossing eight fairways. Testing hole: 3rd (par 3).
18 holes, 5363yds, Par 68, SSS 66, Course record 63.
Club membership 460.
Visitors   may not play on Tue or Thu and weekends. Must
              contact in advance.
Societies   must contact in advance.
Green Fees   £16 per round.
Facilities   ⊗ ⅏ ⅃ 🍺 ♀ ⚑ 🏠 ℓ
Leisure   snooker.
Location   Green Ln, Garden Suburb (S side of town centre
              off A627)
Hotel   ★★71% York House Hotel, York Place,
              Richmond St, ASHTON-UNDER-LYNE
              ☎ 061-330 5899 24⇆ ℟Annexe10⇆

PRESTWICH   Map 07 SD80

Prestwich ☎ 061-773 2544
Parkland course, near to Manchester city centre.
18 holes, 4712yds, Par 64, SSS 63.
Club membership 450.
Visitors   with member only at weekends.
Societies   apply in writing.
Green Fees   £16 per weekday.
Facilities   ⊗ ⅏ ⅃ 🍺 (no catering Mon) ♀ ⚑ 🏠 ℓ
              G P Coope.
Leisure   snooker.
Location   Hilton Ln (N side of town centre on A6044)
Hotel   ★63% Beaucliffe Hotel, 254 Eccles Old Rd,
              Pendleton, SALFORD
              ☎ 061-789 5092 21rm(2⇆15 ℟)

ROCHDALE   Map 07 SD81

Castle Hawk ☎ (0706) 40841
Two parkland courses, with challenging par 3s, and a driving
range.
New: 9 holes, 5398yds, Par 68, SSS 68, Course record 67.
Old: 18 holes, 3158yds, Par 55, Course record 53.
Club membership 160.
Visitors   no restrictions.
Societies   must contact in advance.
Green Fees   £6 (£7.50 weekends).
Facilities   ⊗ ⅏ ⅃ 🍺 ♀ ⚑ 🏠 ⚑ℓ Mike Vipond.
Leisure   fishing, driving range.
Location   Chadwick Ln, Castleton (S of Rochdale, nr junc
              20 (M62))
Hotel   ★★★68% Norton Grange Hotel, Manchester
              Rd, Castleton, ROCHDALE
              ☎ (0706) 30788 50⇆ ℟

Rochdale ☎ (0706) 43818
Parkland course with enjoyable golf and easy walking.
18 holes, 5780yds, Par 71, SSS 68.
Club membership 700.
Visitors   must contact in advance for details of restricted
              times.
Societies   apply in writing.

For an explanation of symbols and
abbreviations, see page 11

Green Fees £20 (£24 weekends & bank holidays).
Facilities   ⊗ ⅏ ⅃ 🍺 ♀ ⚑ 🏠 ℓ Andrew Laverty.
Leisure   snooker.
Location   Edenfield Rd, Bagslate (1.75m W on A680)
Hotel   ★★61% Midway Hotel, Manchester Rd,
              Castleton, ROCHDALE
              ☎ (0706) 32881 24⇆ ℟

Springfield Park ☎ (0706) 56401 (weekend only)
Parkland-moorland course situated in a valley. The River
Roch adds an extra hazard to the course.
18 holes, 5237yds, Par 67, SSS 66, Course record 67.
Club membership 270.
Visitors   must book for weekends.
Societies   telephone in advance.
Green Fees   not confirmed.
Facilities   🏠 ⚑ℓ David Wills.
Location   Springfield Park, Bolton Rd (1.5m SW off A58)
Hotel   ★★61% Midway Hotel, Manchester Rd,
              Castleton, ROCHDALE
              ☎ (0706) 32881 24⇆ ℟

ROMILEY   Map 07 SJ99

Romiley ☎ 061-430 2392
Parkland course, well-wooded.
18 holes, 6421yds, Par 70, SSS 71.
Club membership 700.
Visitors   must contact in advance.
Societies   apply in writing.
Green Fees   £28 per day; £22 per round (£44/£33 weekends
              & bank holidays).
Facilities   ⚑ 🏠 ⚑ℓ Gary Butler.
Leisure   snooker.
Location   Goose House Green (E side of town centre off
              B6104)
Hotel   ★★70% Red Lion Inn, 112 Buxton Rd, High
              Ln, STOCKPORT ☎ (0663) 765227 6⇆ ℟

SALE   Map 07 SJ79

Ashton on Mersey ☎ 061-973 3220
Parkland course with easy walking.
9 holes, 6146yds, Par 72, SSS 69.
Club membership 360.
Visitors   with member only Sun & bank holidays, not Sat.
Green Fees   not confirmed.
Facilities   ⊗ ⅏ ⅃ 🍺 ♀ ⚑ 🏠 ℓ Paul Wagstaff.
Location   Church Ln (1m W of M63 junc 7)
Hotel   ★★★65% Cresta Court Hotel, Church St,
              ALTRINCHAM ☎ 061-927 7272 139⇆ ℟

Sale ☎ 061-973 1638
Parkland course.
18 holes, 6346yds, Par 71, SSS 70, Course record 66.
Club membership 600.
Visitors   dress regulations in club house & on course.
Societies   apply by letter.
Green Fees   on application.
Facilities   ⊗ ⅏ ⅃ 🍺 ♀ ⚑ 🏠 ⚑ℓ Mike Stewart.
Leisure   snooker.
Location   Golf Rd (NW side of town centre off A6144)
Hotel   ★★★65% Cresta Court Hotel, Church St,
              ALTRINCHAM
              ☎ 061-927 7272 139⇆ ℟

SHEVINGTON
Map 07 SD50

Gathurst ☎ Appley Bridge (0257) 252861
Testing parkland course, slightly hilly.
9 holes, 6282yds, Par 72, SSS 70.
Club membership 350.
Visitors after 5pm, with member only Wed, weekends & bank holidays.
Societies apply in writing.
Green Fees £20 per day/round.
Facilities ⊗ ℳ ɫ ☔ ♀ ⚘ 🏠 ℓ
Leisure snooker.
Location 62 Miles Ln (W side of village B5375 off junc 27 of M6)
Hotel ★★★64% Almond Brook Moat House, Almond Brook Rd, STANDISH ☎ (0257) 425588 126⇄ ℾ

STALYBRIDGE
Map 07 SJ99

Stamford ☎ (0457) 832126
Undulating moorland course.
18 holes, 5701yds, Par 70, SSS 68.
Club membership 450.
Visitors must telephone in advance.
Societies must contact in writing 1 month in advance.
Green Fees not confirmed.
Facilities ⊗ ℳ ɫ ☔ (no catering Mon) ♀ ⚘ 🏠
Leisure snooker.
Location Huddersfield Rd (2m NE off A635)
Hotel ★★71% York House Hotel, York Place, Richmond St, ASHTON-UNDER-LYNE ☎ 061-330 5899 24⇄ ℾAnnexe10⇄

STOCKPORT
Map 07 SJ89

Heaton Moor ☎ 061-432 2134
Parkland course, easy walking.
18 holes, 5907yds, Par 70, SSS 69, Course record 66.
Club membership 400.
Visitors restricted Tue & bank holidays.
Societies apply in writing.
Green Fees not confirmed.
Facilities ⊗ ℳ by prior arrangement ɫ ☔ ♀ ⚘ 🏠 ℾℓ C Loydall.
Location Heaton Mersey (N of town centre off B5169)
Hotel ★★66% Saxon Holme Hotel, 230 Wellington Rd, STOCKPORT ☎ 061-432 2335 30⇄ ℾ

Marple ☎ 061-427 2311
Parkland course.
18 holes, 5475yds, Par 68, SSS 67, Course record 65.
Club membership 500.
Visitors restricted Thu afternoon & weekend competition days.
Societies must contact in advance.
Green Fees £20 per day (£30 weekends & bank holidays).
Facilities ⊗ (ex Mon) ℳ by prior arrangement ɫ (ex Mon in winter) ☔ ♀ ⚘ 🏠 ℓ Nick Hamilton.
Location Barnsfold Rd, Hawk Green, Marple (S side of town centre)
Hotel ★★70% Red Lion Inn, 112 Buxton Rd, High Ln, STOCKPORT ☎ (0663) 765227 6⇄ ℾ

Reddish Vale ☎ 061-480 2359
Undulating heathland course designed by Dr. A Mackenzie and situated in the River Thame valley.
18 holes, 6100yds, Par 69, SSS 69, Course record 64.
Club membership 550.
Visitors must play with member at weekends.
Societies must contact in writing.
Green Fees £22.
Facilities ⊗ ɫ ☔ ♀ ⚘ 🏠 ℓ Richard Brown.
Leisure snooker.
Location Southcliffe Rd, Reddish (1.5m N off Reddish road)
Hotel ★★63% Wycliffe, 74 Edgeley Rd, Edgeley, STOCKPORT ☎ 061-477 5395 20⇄ ℾ

Stockport ☎ 061-427 2001 & 061-427 2421
A beautifully situated course in wide open countryside. It is not too long but requires that the player plays all the shots, to excellent greens.
18 holes, 6326yds, Par 71, SSS 71.
Club membership 500.
Visitors must contact in advance, restricted Ladies Day (Tue) and weekends.
Societies Wed & Thu only, apply in writing.
Green Fees £35 per day; £25 per round (£35 per round weekends).
Facilities ⊗ ℳ by prior arrangement ɫ ☔ by prior arrangement ♀ ⚘ 🏠 ℙ ℓ T Le Brocq.
Leisure snooker.
Location Offerton Rd, Offerton (4m SE on A627)
Hotel ★★70% Red Lion Inn, 112 Buxton Rd, High Ln, STOCKPORT ☎ (0663) 765227 6⇄ ℾ

SWINTON
Map 07 SD70

Swinton Park ☎ 061-794 1785
One of Lancashire's longest inland courses. Clubhouse extensions have greatly improved the facilities.
18 holes, 6712yds, Par 73, SSS 72.
Club membership 600.
Visitors restricted at weekends. Must contact in advance and have handicap certificate.
Societies by letter.
Green Fees not confirmed.
Facilities ⊗ ℳ ɫ ☔ ♀ ⚘ 🏠 ℓ James Wilson.
Leisure snooker.
Location East Lancashire Rd (1m W off A580)
Hotel ★63% Beaucliffe Hotel, 254 Eccles Old Rd, Pendleton, SALFORD ☎ 061-789 5092 21rm(2⇄15 ℾ)

UPPERMILL
Map 07 SD90

Saddleworth ☎ Saddleworth (0457) 873653
Moorland course, with superb views of Pennines.
18 holes, 5976yds, Par 71, SSS 69.
Club membership 743.
Visitors must contact in advance, restricted at weekends.
Societies apply in writing.
Green Fees £22 per day (£25 weekends).
Facilities ⊗ ℳ ɫ ☔ (no catering Mon) ♀ ⚘ 🏠 ℓ E T Shard.
Leisure snooker.
Location Mountain Ash, Ladcastle Rd, Oldham (E side of town centre off A670)

Hotel   ★★71% York House Hotel, York Place,
               Richmond St, ASHTON-UNDER-LYNE
               ☎ 061-330 5899 24⊷ 🐾Annexe10⊷

URMSTON   Map 07 SJ79

Flixton ☎ 061-748 2116
Meadowland course bounded by River Mersey.
9 holes, 6410yds, Par 71, SSS 71.
Club membership 450.
Visitors   with member only weekends & bank holidays.
Societies   apply by letter to Steward.
Green Fees   weekdays £17.50.
Facilities   ⊗ ⅻ by prior arrangement ⮂ 🍺 ♀ ⚿ 📷 🐾
                 R Ling.
Leisure   snooker.
Location   Church Rd, Flixton (S side of town centre on
                 B5213)
Hotel   ★★★58% Ashley Hotel, Ashley Rd, Hale,
                 ALTRINCHAM ☎ 061-928 3794 47⊷ 🐾

WALKDEN   Map 07 SD70

Brackley Municipal ☎ 061-790 6076
Mostly flat course.
9 holes, 3003yds, Par 35, SSS 69.
Visitors   no restrictions.
Green Fees   not confirmed.
Facilities   📷 🐾
Location   2m NW on A6
Hotel   ★63% Beaucliffe Hotel, 254 Eccles Old Rd,
                 Pendleton, SALFORD
                 ☎ 061-789 5092 21rm(2⊷15 🐾)

WESTHOUGHTON   Map 07 SD60

Westhoughton ☎ (0942) 811085
Compact downland course.
9 holes, 2886yds, Par 35, SSS 68.
Club membership 280.
Visitors   with member only at weekends.
Societies   must apply in writing.
Green Fees   £15 per day.
Facilities   ⊗ & ⅻ by prior arrangement ⮂ 🍺 ♀ ⚿ 📷 🐾
                 P Wesselingh.
Leisure   snooker, pool table.
Location   Long Island (0.5m NW off A58)
Hotel   ★★★62% Forte Posthouse, Beaumont Rd,
                 BOLTON ☎ (0204) 651511 96⊷ 🐾

WHITEFIELD   Map 07 SD80

Stand ☎ 061-766 2388
A semi-parkland course with five moorland holes. A fine test
of golf with a very demanding finish.
18 holes, 6426yds, Par 72, SSS 71.
Club membership 680.
Visitors   must contact in advance but may not play on Tue
                 or weekends.
Societies   must apply in writing.
Green Fees   £20 per day (£25 weekends).
Facilities   ⊗ ⅻ by prior arrangement ⮂ 🍺 ♀ ⚿ 📷 🐾

Leisure   snooker.
Location   The Dales, Ashbourne Grove (1m W off A667)
Hotel   ★58% Woolfield House Hotel, Wash Ln, BURY
                 ☎ 061-797 9775 16rm(3⊷7 🐾)

Whitefield ☎ 061-766 3096
Fine sporting parkland course with well-watered greens.
18 holes, 6041yds, Par 69.
Club membership 500.
Visitors   must contact in advance and have an
                 introduction from own club.
Societies   must contact in advance.
Green Fees   not confirmed.
Facilities   Catering on request ♀ ⚿ 📷 🐾 🐾 Paul Reeves.
Leisure   hard tennis courts, snooker.
Location   Higher Ln (N side of town centre on A665)
Hotel   ★★★★50% Portland Thistle Hotel, 3/5 Portland
                 St, Piccadilly Gdns, MANCHESTER
                 ☎ 061-228 3400 205 ⊷ 🐾

WIGAN   Map 07 SD50

Haigh Hall ☎ (0942) 831107
Municipal parkland course, with hard walking, and a canal
forms the west boundary. Adjacent to 'Haigh Country Park'
with many facilities.
18 holes, 6423yds, Par 70, SSS 71, Course record 66.
Club membership 150.
Visitors   no restrictions.
Green Fees   not confirmed.
Facilities   ⊗ ⅻ 🍺 ♀ (weekend afternoons) ⚿ 📷 🐾 🐾
                 Ian Lee.
Location   Haigh Country Park, Haigh (2m NE off B5238)
Hotel   ★★61% Brocket Arms Hotel, Mesnes Rd,
                 WIGAN ☎ (0942) 46283 27⊷ 🐾

Wigan ☎ Standish (0257) 421360
Among the best of Lancashire's 9-hole courses. The fine old
clubhouse is the original Arley Hall, and is surrounded by a
moat.
9 holes, 6058yds, Par 70, SSS 69, Course record 64.
Club membership 320.
Visitors   welcome except Tue. Must contact in advance.
Societies   apply in writing.
Green Fees   not confirmed.
Facilities   ⊗ ⅻ ⮂ 🍺 ♀ ⚿
Leisure   snooker.
Location   Arley Hall, Haigh (3m NE off B5238)
Hotel   ★★★64% Almond Brook Moat House, Almond
                 Brook Rd, STANDISH
                 ☎ (0257) 425588 126⊷ 🐾

WOODFORD   Map 07 SJ88

Avro ☎ 061-439 2709
An attractive, tight and challenging 9-hole course.
9 holes, 5735yds, Par 69, SSS 68.
Club membership 400.
Visitors   must be accompanied by member.
Green Fees   not confirmed.
Facilities   🍺 ⚿
Location   Old Hall Ln (W side of village on A5102)
Hotel   ★★★68% Bramhall Moat House, Bramhall Ln
                 South, BRAMHALL ☎ 061-439 8116 65⊷ 🐾

WORSLEY Map 07 SD70

Ellesmere ☎ 061-790 2122
Parkland course with natural hazards. Testing holes: 3rd (par 5), 9th (par 3), 13th (par 4). Hard walking.
18 holes, 5954yds, Par 69, SSS 69.
Club membership 550.
Visitors welcome except club competition days & bank holidays. Must contact in advance & have handicap certificate.
Societies Mon-Wed only, contact in advance.
Green Fees £24 per day; £18 per round (£25 per day/round weekends).
Facilities ⊗ ✗Ⅲ ⅼ ▆ ♀ ⚑ 🛆 ⛿ ⛿ Terry Morley.
Leisure snooker.
Location Old Clough Ln (N side of village off A580)
Hotel ★63% Beaucliffe Hotel, 254 Eccles Old Rd, Pendleton, SALFORD ☎ 061-789 5092 21rm(2⇄15 ⋒)

HAMPSHIRE

ALDERSHOT Map 04 SU85

Army ☎ (0252) 540638
Picturesque heathland course with three par 3's, over 200 yds.
18 holes, 6550yds, Par 71, SSS 71.
Club membership 800.
Visitors must contact in advance & have handicap certificate.
Societies Mon & Thu only.
Green Fees not confirmed.
Facilities ⊗ ✗Ⅲ by prior arrangement ⅼ ▆ ♀ 🛆 ⚑ ⛿ N Turner.
Location Laffans Rd (1.5m N of town centre off A323/A325)
Hotel ★★★67% Forte Crest, Lynchford Rd, FARNBOROUGH ☎ (0252) 545051 110⇄ ⋒

ALRESFORD Map 04 SU53

Alresford ☎ (0962) 733746
A testing downland course on well drained chalk. Now expanded to 18 holes, incorporating the original 12, but changing direction of play to give two starting points and two closing greens near clubhouse.
12 holes, 6038yds, Par 70, SSS 69.
Club membership 600.
Visitors must contact in advance but may not play before noon on weekends & bank holidays.
Societies must telephone in advance.
Green Fees £23 per day; £18 per round (£30 per round weekends & bank holidays).
Facilities ⊗ ✗Ⅲ ⅼ ▆ ♀ 🛆 ⚑ ⛿ ⛿ Malcolm Scott.
Location Cheriton Rd, Tichborne Down (1m S on B3046)
Hotel ★★65% Grange Hotel, 17 London Rd, Holybourne, ALTON ☎ (0420) 86565 26⇄ ⋒Annexe4 ⇄ ⋒

ALTON Map 04 SU73

Alton ☎ (0420) 82042
Undulating meadowland course.
9 holes, 5744yds, Par 68, SSS 68.
Club membership 340.
Visitors must have a handicap of 18 or less to play at weekends & bank holidays, or be accompanied by a member.
Societies weekdays only.
Green Fees not confirmed.
Facilities ♀ 🛆 ⚑ ⛿
Location Old Odiham Rd (2m N off A32)
Hotel ★★★61% Alton House Hotel, Normandy St, ALTON ☎ (0420) 80033 38⇄ ⋒

AMPFIELD Map 04 SU42

Ampfield Par Three ☎ Braishfield (0794) 68480
Pretty parkland course designed by Henry Cotton in 1963. Well-bunkered greens.
18 holes, 2478yds, Par 54, SSS 53, Course record 49.
Club membership 510.
Visitors must contact in advance & have a handicap certificate to play at weekends & bank holidays. Golf shoes must be worn & no club sharing.
Societies must contact in writing.
Green Fees £15 per day; £9 per round (£15.50 per round weekends & bank holidays).
Facilities ⊗ ⅼ ▆ ♀ 🛆 ⚑ ⛿ ⛿ Richard Benfield.
Location Winchester Rd (4m NE of Romsey on A31)
Hotel ★★★68% Potters Heron Hotel, AMPFIELD ☎ (0703) 266611 54⇄

ANDOVER Map 04 SU34

Andover ☎ (0264) 358040
Hilly downland course, fine views.
9 holes, 5933yds, Par 69, SSS 68.
Club membership 500.
Visitors restricted mornings at weekends and bank holidays.
Societies must contact in writing.
Green Fees £12 per round; (£22 Sun & bank holidays).
Facilities ⊗ (ex Wed) ✗Ⅲ (ex Wed & Sun) ⅼ ▆ ♀ 🛆 ⚑ ⛿ ⛿ Andrea Timms.
Location 51 Winchester Rd (1m S on A3057)
Hotel ★★60% Danebury Hotel, High St, ANDOVER ☎ (0264) 323332 24⇄ ⋒

BARTON-ON-SEA Map 04 SZ29

Barton-on-Sea ☎ New Milton (0425) 615308
Though not strictly a links course, it is right on a cliff edge with views over the Isle of Wight and Christchurch Bay. On a still day there is nothing much to it - but when it blows the course undergoes a complete change in character. At present in process of reconstruction to 27 holes which should be in play from September 1993.
18 holes, 5737yds, Par 69, SSS 68.
Club membership 700.
Visitors after 8.30am Mon-Fri & 11.15am weekends & bank holidays. Must contact in advance and have a handicap certificate.
Societies Wed & Fri only. Must book well in advance.

Green Fees not confirmed.
Facilities ⊗ ⓑ ■ ♀ ☂ 🏠 ☂ᶠ ʟ P Coombs.
Location Milford Rd (B3058 E side of town)
Hotel ★★★★★(red)😂 Chewton Glen Hotel,
Christchurch Rd, NEW MILTON
☎ (0425) 275341 58🛏 ♜

BASINGSTOKE Map 04 SU65

Basingstoke ☎ (0256) 465990
A well-maintained parkland course with wide and
inviting fairways. You are inclined to expect longer
drives than are actually achieved - partly on account of
the trees. There are many two-hundred-year-old beech
trees, since the course was built on an old deer park.
18 holes, 6239yds, Par 70, SSS 70.
Club membership 700.
Visitors must have a handicap certificate and play
with member at weekends.
Societies Wed & Thu only.
Green Fees £30 per day; £22 per round.
Facilities ⊗ & 🎢 (ex Mon) ⓑ ■ ♀ ☂ 🏠 ʟ
Ian Hayes.
Location Kempshott Park (3.5m SW on A30 M3 exit 7)
Hotel ★★★61% Forte Posthouse, Grove Rd,
BASINGSTOKE ☎ (0256) 468181 84🛏 ♜

Dummer ☎ (0256) 397888
Due to open in July 1993 and designed by Peter Alliss/Clive
Clark to consist of two 9-hole loops with water hazards. Gentle
terrain makes the course suitable for players of all ages.
18 holes, 6556yds, Par 72.
Club membership 830.
Visitors must contact in advance, handicap card required,
limited at weekends.
Societies contact in advance.
Green Fees £20 (£25 weekends & bank holidays).
Facilities ⊗ 🎢 ⓑ ■ ♀ ☂ 🏠 ☂ᶠ ʟ
Leisure sauna.
Location Nr Basingstoke (off junc 7 of M3 towards
Dummer village)
Hotel ★★68% Wheatsheaf Hotel, NORTH WALTHAM
☎ (0256) 398282 28🛏 ♜

BORDON Map 04 SU73

Blackmoor ☎ (0420) 472775
A first-class moorland course with a great variety of
holes. Fine greens and wide pine tree-lined fairways are a
distinguishing feature. The ground is mainly flat and
walking easy.
18 holes, 6200yds, Par 69, SSS 70, Course record 65.
Club membership 700.
Visitors must have a letter of introduction from their
club or a handicap certificate; must be
accompanied by a member at weekends.
Must contact in advance.
Societies must telephone in advance.
Green Fees not confirmed.
Facilities ⊗ 🎢 ⓑ ■ ♀ ☂ 🏠 ☂ᶠ ʟ Andrew Hall.
Leisure practice ground & nets.
Location Whitehill
Hotel ★★★62% Bush Hotel, The Borough,
FARNHAM ☎ (0252) 715237 66🛏 ♜

BOTLEY Map 04 SU51

Botley Park Hotel & Country Club ☎ (0489) 780888
Pleasantly undulating course with water hazards. Driving
range and country club facilities.
18 holes, 6026yds, Par 70, SSS 70.
Club membership 750.
Visitors must contact in advance & have handicap
certificate.
Societies contact in advance.
Green Fees £23 per round (£30 weekends).
Facilities ⊗ 🎢 ⓑ ■ ♀ ☂ 🏠 ☂ᶠ ʟ Tim Barter.
Leisure hard tennis courts, heated indoor swimming
pool, squash, snooker, sauna, solarium,
gymnasium, croquet lawn & petanque.
Location Winchester Rd, Boorley Green (1m NW of
Botley on B3354)
Hotel ★★★★71% Botley Park Hotel & Country Club,
Winchester Rd, Boorley Green, BOTLEY
☎ (0489) 780888 100🛏 ♜

BROCKENHURST Map 04 SU20

Brokenhurst Manor ☎ Lymington (0590) 23332
An attractive woodland/heathland course set at the edge
of the New Forest, with the unusual feature of three loops
of six holes each to complete the round. Fascinating holes
include the short 5th and 12th, and the 4th and 17th, both
dog-legged. A stream also features on seven of the holes.
18 holes, 6222yds, Par 70, SSS 70, Course record 64.
Club membership 800. ▶

Visitors	must contact in advance and have a handicap certificate (maximum, men 24 and ladies 32).
Societies	Thu only. Apply in writing
Green Fees	£35 per day; £25 per round (£40 weekends & bank holidays).
Facilities	⊗ ⅏ ⅃ ⚑ ♀ ♨ 🏠 ℓ Brian Plucknett.
Location	Sway Rd (1m S on B3055)
Hotel	★★★63% Balmer Lawn Hotel, Lyndhurst Rd, BROCKENHURST ☎ (0590) 23116 58 ⇆ ℟
Additional Hotel	★★61% Watersplash Hotel, The Rise, BROCKENHURST ☎ (0590) 22344 23⇆ ℟

BURLEY
Map 04 SU20

Burley ☎ (0425) 402431
Undulating heather and gorseland. The 7th requires an accurately placed tee shot to obtain par 4. Played off different tees on second nine.
9 holes, 6149yds, Par 71, SSS 69, Course record 68.
Club membership 520.

Visitors	must contact in advance & have a handicap certificate. May not play before 4pm Sat.
Green Fees	£13 per day (£14 weekends & bank holidays).
Facilities	⅃ ⚑ ♀ ♨
Location	E side of village
Hotel	★★72% Struan Hotel & Restaurant, Horton Rd, Ashley Heath, RINGWOOD ☎ (0425) 473553 & 473029 10⇆ ℟

CORHAMPTON
Map 04 SU62

Corhampton ☎ Droxford (0489) 877279
Downland course.
18 holes, 6444yds, Par 71, SSS 71.
Club membership 650.

Visitors	must contact in advance & must play with member at weekends & bank holidays.
Societies	Mon & Thu only . Must telephone in advance.
Green Fees	£28 per day; £20 per round.
Facilities	♨ 🏠 ⚐ ℓ Garry Stubbington.
Location	Sheep's Pond Ln (1m W off B3055)
Hotel	★★73% Old House Hotel, The Square, WICKHAM ☎ (0329) 833049 9⇆ ℟Annexe3⇆ ℟

CRONDALL
Map 04 SU74

Oak Park ☎ Aldershot (0252) 850880
Gently undulating course overlooking pretty village. 16-bay floodlit driving range, practice green and practice bunker.
18 holes, 6437yds, Par 72, SSS 71.
Club membership 400.

Visitors	no restrictions.
Societies	must telephone in advance.
Green Fees	£16 per round (£22.50 weekends & public holidays).
Facilities	⊗ ⅏ (ex Sun & Mon) ⅃ ⚑ ♀ ♨ 🏠 ⚐ ℓ Simon Coaker & Anthony Dillon.
Leisure	practice green & covered driving range.
Location	Heath Ln (0.5m E of village off A287)
Hotel	★★★62% Bush Hotel, The Borough, FARNHAM ☎ (0252) 715237 66⇆ ℟

DIBDEN
Map 04 SU40

Dibden ☎ Southampton (0703) 207508
Municipal parkland course with views over Southampton Water. A pond guards the green at the par 5, 3rd hole. Twenty-bay driving range.
Course 1: 18 holes, 6206yds, Par 71, SSS 70.
Course 2: 9 holes, 1520yds, Par 29.
Club membership 600.

Visitors	no restrictions.
Societies	must contact in writing.
Green Fees	not confirmed.
Facilities	⊗ ⅏ ⅃ ⚑ ♀ ♨ 🏠 ⚐ ℓ Alan Bridge.
Location	Main Rd (2m NW of Dibden Purlieu)
Hotel	★★★60% Forest Lodge Hotel, Pikes Hill, Romsey Rd, LYNDHURST ☎ (0703) 283677 23⇆ ℟

EASTLEIGH
Map 04 SU41

Fleming Park ☎ (0703) 612797
Parkland course with stream-'Monks Brook'-running through.
18 holes, 4436yds, Par 65, SSS 62, Course record 62.
Club membership 300.

Visitors	no restrictions.
Societies	must contact in advance.
Green Fees	not confirmed.
Facilities	⊗ ⅏ ⅃ ⚑ ♀ ♨ 🏠 ⚐ ℓ Chris Strickett.
Location	Magpie Ln (E side of town centre)
Hotel	★★★63% Southampton Park Hotel, Cumberland Place, SOUTHAMPTON ☎ (0703) 223467 72⇆ ℟

EAST WELLOW
Map 04 SU32

Wellow ☎ Romsey (0794) 22872 & 23833
Parkland course around lake. Plenty of established and new trees.
18 holes, 5902yds, Par 70, SSS 68.
Club membership 400.

Visitors	must contact in advance.
Societies	apply in advance.
Green Fees	£15 per day (£20 weekends).
Facilities	⊗ ⅏ ⅃ ⚑ ♀ ♨ 🏠 ⚐ ℓ Jonathan Simpson.
Location	Ryedown Ln (3m SW of Romsey)
Hotel	★★★60% White Horse Hotel, Market Place, ROMSEY ☎ (0794) 512431 33⇆ ℟

FAREHAM
Map 04 SU50

Cams Hall ☎ (0329) 827222
Two Peter Alliss/Clive Clark designed golf courses opened in 1993.The Historic is in parkland and the Coastal has lakes and undulating hills.
Coastal: 18 holes, 6180yds, Par 71.
Historic: 9 holes, 3326yds, Par 36.
Club membership 1125.

> If visiting a brand new course, be sure to telephone before your visit to confirm the course information is correct

Visitors must contact in advance,and have handicap
certificate, restricted at weekends.
Societies must contact in advance.
Green Fees £20 per 18 holes; £12 per 9 holes (£25/£15
weekends and bank holidays).
Facilities ⊗ ⫘ ⮾ ⯅ ♟ ♨ ⮾ ⚑ { Jason Neves.
Leisure sauna.
Location M27 exit 11 to A27
Hotel ★★★67% Lysses House Hotel & Conference
Centre, 51 High St, FAREHAM
☎ (0329) 822622 21⇥ ⚑

FARNBOROUGH   Map 04 SU85

Southwood ☎ (0252) 548700
Municipal parkland course with stream running through.
18 holes, 5738yds, Par 69, SSS 68, Course record 67.
Club membership 700.
Visitors must contact in advance.
Societies must contact in advance.
Green Fees not confirmed.
Facilities ⊗ ⫘ by prior arrangement ⮾ ⯅ ♟ ⯅ ⚑ ⮾ ⚑ {
Bob Hammond.
Location Ively Rd (0.5m W)
Hotel ★★★67% Forte Crest, Lynchford Rd,
FARNBOROUGH ☎ (0252) 545051 110⇥ ⚑

FLEET   Map 04 SU85

North Hants ☎ (0252) 616443
Picturesque tree-lined course with much heather and
gorse close to the fairways. A comparatively easy par-4
first hole may lull the golfer into a false sense of security,
only to be rudely awakened at the testing holes which
follow. The ground is rather undulating and, though not
tiring, does offer some excellent 'blind' shots, and more
than a few surprises in judging distance.
18 holes, 6257yds, Par 69, SSS 70, Course record 67.
Club membership 700.
Visitors must contact in advance & have handicap
certificate. Must play with member at
weekends.
Societies Tue & Wed only.
Green Fees £23 per round (£28 weekends).
Facilities ⊗ ⫘ ⮾ ⯅ ♟ ⯅ ⚑ { Steve Porter.
Location Minley Rd (0.25m N of Fleet station on
B3013)
Hotel ★★★60% Lismoyne Hotel, Church Rd,
FLEET ☎ (0252) 628555 42⇥ ⚑

GOSPORT   Map 04 SZ69

Gosport & Stokes Bay ☎ (0705) 527941
A testing links course overlooking the Solent, with plenty of
gorse and short rough. Changing winds.
9 holes, 5856yds, Par 72, SSS 69, Course record 65.
Club membership 500.
Visitors may not play at weekends & Thu.
Societies must telephone in advance.
Green Fees £15 per day (varies in winter).
Facilities ⊗ by prior arrangement ⮾ ⯅ ♟ ⯅ ⚑ ⮾
Location Off Fort Rd, Haslar (S side of town centre)
Hotel ★★59% Anglesey Hotel, Crescent Rd,
Alverstoke, GOSPORT
☎ (0705) 582157 & 523932 18⇥ ⚑

HARTLEY WINTNEY   Map 04 SU75

Hartley Wintney ☎ (025126) 2214
Easy walking, parkland course in pleasant countryside.
Played off different tees on back nine, with testing par 4s at
4th and 13th.
9 holes, 6096yds, Par 70, SSS 69.
Club membership 400.
Visitors must contact in advance.
Societies Tue & Thu only.
Green Fees not confirmed.
Facilities ⯅ ⚑ {
Location London Rd (NE side of village on A30)
Hotel ★★★60% Lismoyne Hotel, Church Rd, FLEET
☎ (0252) 628555 42⇥ ⚑

HAYLING ISLAND   Map 04 SU70

Hayling ☎ (0705) 464446
A delightful links course among the dunes offering fine
sea-scapes and views across to the Isle of Wight. Varying
sea breezes and sometimes strong winds ensure that the
course seldom plays the same two days running. Testing
holes at the 12th and 13th, both par 4. Club selection is
important.
18 holes, 6489yds, Par 71, SSS 71.
Club membership 850.
Visitors must contact in advance and have a
handicap certificate.
Societies welcome Tue & Wed, apply in writing.
Green Fees £25 (£31 weekends).
Facilities ⊗ by prior arrangement ⮾ ⯅ ⯅ ⚑ ⮾ {
Location Links Ln (SW side of island at West Town)
Hotel ★★★65% Forte Posthouse, Northney Rd,
HAYLING ISLAND
☎ (0705) 465011 92⇥ ⚑

KINGSCLERE   Map 04 SU55

Sandford Springs ☎ (0635) 297881
The course has unique variety in beautiful surroundings
and offers three distinctive loops of 9 holes. There are
water hazards, woodlands and gradients to negotiate,
providing a challenge for all playing categories. From its
highest point there are extensive views.
The Park: 9 holes, 2963yds, Par 35, SSS 34.
The Lakes: 9 holes, 3180yds, Par 35, SSS 34.
The Wood: 9 holes, 3042yds, Par 36, SSS 35.
Club membership 600.
Visitors must contact in advance. Must play with
member at weekends.
Societies must contact in advance.
Green Fees £21 per 18 holes.
Facilities ⊗ ⫘ ⮾ ⯅ ♟ ⯅ ⚑ ⮾ ⚑ { Kim Brake &
Gary Edmunds.
Location Wolverton (on A339)
Hotel ★★★65% Millwaters, London Rd,
NEWBURY ☎ (0635) 528838 32⇥ ⚑

Remember – replace all divots, and repair
ball-marks or damage by spikes on
completion of the hole

KINGSLEY

Map 04 SU73

Dean Farm ☎ Bordon (0420) 489478
Undulating downland course.
9 holes, 1350yds, Par 27.
Visitors no restrictions.
Green Fees not confirmed.
Facilities ⓑ ☕
Leisure hard tennis courts.
Location W side of village off B3004
Hotel ★★65% Grange Hotel, 17 London Rd,
Holybourne, ALTON
☎ (0420) 86565 26⇥ ⋔Annexe4⇥ ⋔

LECKFORD

Map 04 SU33

Leckford ☎ (0264) 810320
A testing downland course with good views.
9 holes, 6444yds, Par 70, SSS 71.
Club membership 200.
Visitors must be accompanied by member and contact in
advance.
Green Fees not confirmed.
Facilities ⌂
Location 1m SW off A3057
Hotel ★★★61% Grosvenor Hotel, High St,
STOCKBRIDGE
☎ (0264) 810606 25⇥

LEE-ON-SOLENT

Map 04 SU50

Lee-on-Solent ☎ (0705) 551170
A modest parkland/heathland course, yet a testing one. The
five short holes always demand a high standard of play and
the 13th is rated one of the best in the country.
18 holes, 5959yds, Par 69, SSS 69, Course record 66.
Club membership 700.
Visitors must play with member at weekends. Must
contact in advance.
Societies must contact in advance.
Green Fees not confirmed.
Facilities ⊗ ⊪ ⓑ ☕ ♀ ⌂ 🏠ℓ John Richardson.
Location Brune Ln (1m N off B3385)
Hotel ★★★63% Red Lion Hotel, East St, FAREHAM
☎ (0329) 822640 44⇥

LIPHOOK

Map 04 SU83

Liphook ☎ (0428) 723271
Heathland course with easy walking and fine views.
18 holes, 6250yds, Par 70, SSS 70, Course record 67.
Club membership 800.
Visitors must contact in advance, may not play
Sunday mornings, and must have a handicap
certificate.
Societies must contact in advance.
Green Fees £33 per day; £24 per round (£45/£35 Sat,
£40 per round Sun).
Facilities ⊗ ⓑ ☕ ♀ ⌂ 🏠 ⍑ℓ Ian Large.
Location Wheatsheaf Enclosure (1.5m SW off A3)
Hotel ★★★72% Lythe Hill Hotel, Petworth Rd,
HASLEMERE
☎ (0428) 651251 40⇥ ⋔

Old Thorns London Kosaido ☎ (0428) 724555
A challenging 18-hole championship-standard course
designed around magnificent oaks, beeches and Scots pine.
18 holes, 6041yds, Par 72, SSS 70.
Visitors must contact in advance.
Societies must telephone in advance.
Green Fees not confirmed.
Facilities ⊗ ⍰ ⓑ ☕ ♀ ⌂ 🏠 ⍑ ⍱ℓ Philip Loxley.
Leisure hard tennis courts, heated indoor swimming
pool, sauna, solarium.
Location Longmoor Rd (1m W on B2131)
Hotel ★★★72% Lythe Hill Hotel, Petworth Rd,
HASLEMERE ☎ (0428) 651251 40⇥ ⋔

LYNDHURST

Map 04 SU20

Bramshaw ☎ Southampton (0703) 813433
Two 18-hole courses. The Manor Course is landscaped
parkland with excellent greens, and features mature trees
and streams. The Forest course is set amidst beautiful
open forest. Easy walking. The Bell Inn Hotel, attached to
the club, provides fine accommodation just a wedge shot
from the first tee, and reserved tee times for its guests.
*Manor Course: 18 holes, 6233yds, Par 71, SSS 70,
Course record 66.*
*Forest Course: 18 holes, 5774yds, Par 69, SSS 68,
Course record 66.*
Club membership 1200.
Visitors must contact in advance & be accompanied
by member at weekends.
Societies may not play at weekends. Must telephone
in advance.
Green Fees £30 per day (£20 in winter).
Facilities ⊗ ⍰ ⓑ ☕ ♀ ⌂ 🏠 ⍑ℓ Clive Bonner.
Location Brook (On B3079 1m W of M27 junc 1)
Hotel ★★★65% Bell Inn, BROOK
☎ (0703) 812214 22⇥
(See advertisement on page 56)

New Forest ☎ (0703) 282450
This picturesque heathland course is laid out in a typical
stretch of the New Forest on high ground a little above
the village of Lyndhurst. Natural hazards include the
inevitable forest ponies. The first two holes are somewhat
teasing, as is the 485-yard (par 5) 9th. Walking is easy.
18 holes, 5742yds, Par 69, SSS 68, Course record 66.
Club membership 900.
Visitors must contact in advance.
Societies must contact in advance.
Green Fees £12 per day/round (£14 weekends & bank
holidays).
Facilities ⊗ ⓑ ☕ (not Sun) ♀ ⌂ 🏠ℓ Ken Gilhespy.
Location Southampton Rd (0.5m NE off A35)
Hotel ★★★70% Crown Hotel, High St,
LYNDHURST ☎ (0703) 282922 40⇥ ⋔

OVERTON

Map 04 SU54

Test Valley ☎ Basingstoke (0256) 771737
A new inland links course with featured bunkering and
ponds, superbly drained with fine greens. Playable from 6000
to 6850 yds.
18 holes, 6811yds, Par 72, SSS 73.
Club membership 600.

Visitors advisable to ring in advance.
Societies apply in writing or telephone in advance.
Green Fees £22 per day; £14 per 18 holes (£32/£20 weekends).
Facilities ⊗ ⏝ ⅊ ♣ 🏠 ⚑ (Terry Notley.
Location Micheldever Rd (6m S of Kingsclere)
Hotel ★★68% Wheatsheaf Hotel, NORTH WALTHAM
☎ (0256) 398282 28⇄ ♛

PETERSFIELD   Map 04 SU72

Petersfield ☎ (0730) 62386
Part-heath, parkland course with a lake, and good views.
18 holes, 5603yds, Par 69, SSS 67, Course record 65.
Club membership 650.
Visitors restricted weekends & bank holidays.
Societies must contact in writing.
Green Fees £15-£21 (£21-£30 weekends & bank holidays).
Facilities ⊗ ⏝ by prior arrangement ♣ ⅊ ♣ 🏠 (
Stephen Clay.
Location Heath Rd (E side of town centre off A3)
Hotel ★★★68% Spread Eagle Hotel, South St,
MIDHURST ☎ (0730) 816911
37⇄ ♛Annexe4 ♛

PORTSMOUTH & SOUTHSEA   Map 04 SU60

Great Salterns Public Course
☎ Portsmouth (0705) 664549 & 699519
Easy walking, seaside course with open fairways and testing shots onto well-guarded, small greens. Testing 13th hole, par 4, requiring 130yd shot across a lake.
18 holes, 5610yds, Par 69, SSS 66, Course record 64.
Club membership 700.
Visitors no restrictions.
Societies must contact in advance.
Green Fees £9.40 per round (£6.90 winter).
Facilities ⊗ ⏝ ♣ ⅊ ♀ 🏠 ⚑ 🏌 (Terry Healy.
Location Eastern Rd (NE of town centre on A2030)
Hotel ★★★60% Hospitality Inn, St Helens Pde,
SOUTHSEA ☎ (0705) 731281
115⇄ ♛

Southsea ☎ Portsmouth (0705) 660945
Municipal, meadowland course.
18 holes, 5900yds, Par 72, SSS 68, Course record 64.
Club membership 650.
Visitors no restrictions.
Societies must contact in advance.
Green Fees not confirmed.
Facilities 🏠 ⚑ (Terry Healy.
Location The Mansion, Great Salterns, Eastern Rd
(0.5m off M27)
Hotel ★★★60% Hospitality Inn, St Helens Pde,
SOUTHSEA ☎ (0705) 731281
115⇄ ♛

ROMSEY   Map 04 SU32

Dunwood Manor ☎ Lockerley (0794) 40549
Undulating parkland course with fine views. Testing 1st hole: Reynolds Leap (par 4).
18 holes, 5885yds, Par 69, SSS 69.
Club membership 800.

Visitors must contact in advance & have handicap certificate, restricted weekends.
Societies must contact in advance.
Green Fees £30 per day; £20 per round (£30 per round weekends).
Facilities ⊗ ⏝ by prior arrangement ♣ ⅊ ♣ 🏠 ⚑ (
Richard Pilbury.
Leisure snooker.
Location Shootash Hill (4m W off A27)
Hotel ★★★68% Potters Heron Hotel, AMPFIELD
☎ (0703) 266611 54⇄

Romsey ☎ Southampton (0703) 734637
Parkland/woodland course with narrow tree-lined fairways.
Six holes are undulating, rest are sloping. There are superb views over the Test valley.
18 holes, 5851yds, Par 69, SSS 68.
Club membership 700.
Visitors must play with member at weekends.
Societies Mon, Tue & Thu, must contact in advance.
Green Fees £24 per day; £19.50 per round.
Facilities ⊗ ⏝ by prior arrangement ♣ ⅊ ♣ 🏠 (
Mark Desmond.
Location Romsey Rd, Nursling (3m S on A3057)
Hotel ★★★60% Hospitality Inn, St Helens Pde,
SOUTHSEA ☎ (0705) 731281
115⇄ ♛

ROTHERWICK   Map 04 SU75

Tylney Park ☎ Hook (0256) 762079
Parkland course. Practice area.
18 holes, 6109yds, Par 70, SSS 69.
Club membership 700.
Visitors must be with member at weekends or have a handicap certificate.
Societies must apply by phone in advance.
Green Fees £20 per day (£28 per round weekends).
Facilities ⊗ ⏝ by prior arrangement ♣ ⅊ ♣ 🏠 (
C De Bruin/M Kimberley.
Location 0.5m SW
Hotel ★★★★(red)♨ Tylney Hall Hotel,
ROTHERWICK ☎ (0256) 764881
35⇄Annexe56⇄

ROWLANDS CASTLE   Map 04 SU71

Rowlands Castle ☎ Portsmouth (0705) 412784
Exceptionally dry in winter, the flat parkland course is a testing one with a number of tricky dog-legs and bunkers much in evidence. The 7th, at 522yds, is the longest hole on the course and leads to a well-guarded armchair green.
18 holes, 6381yds, Par 72, SSS 70.
Club membership 850.
Visitors must play with member Sat; restricted Sun.
Must contact in advance.
Societies Tue & Thu only; must contact in writing.
Green Fees not confirmed.
Facilities ⊗ ♣ ⅊ ♣ 🏠 (
Location Links Ln (W side of village off B2149)
Hotel ★★★65% Forte Posthouse, Northney Rd,
HAYLING ISLAND
☎ (0705) 465011 92 ⇄ ♛

SHEDFIELD
Map 04 SU51

Meon Valley Hotel Golf & Country Club ☎
Wickham (0329) 833455
It has been said that a golf course architect is as good as
the ground on which he has to work. Here Hamilton Stutt
had magnificent terrain at his disposal and a very good
and lovely parkland course is the result. There are three
holes over water. The hotel provides many sports
facilities.
*Meon Course: 18 holes, 6519yds, Par 71, SSS 71, Course
record 67.*
Valley Course: 9 holes, 5770yds, Par 70, SSS 68.
Club membership 700.

Visitors may book up to seven days in advance.
Societies must contact in writing.
Green Fees Meon Course: £36 per day; £24 per round
(£30 per round weekends & bank holidays).
Valley Course: £10 per round (£15
weekends & bank holidays).
Facilities ⊗ ℳ ⓑ ♥ ♀ ♨ 🏌 ⚑ ⚔ (John Stirling.
Leisure hard tennis courts, heated indoor swimming
pool, squash, snooker, sauna, solarium,
gymnasium, health & beauty salon.
Location Sandy Ln (off A334 between Botley and
Wickham)
Hotel ★★73% Old House Hotel, The Square,
WICKHAM ☎ (0329) 833049
9⇨ ⋔Annexe3⇨ ⋔

SOUTHAMPTON
Map 04 SU41

Chilworth ☎ (0703) 733166 & 740544
A 9-hole course with a restricted booking system to allow
undisturbed play.
Manor Golf Course: 9 holes, 2347yds, Par 32, SSS 63.
Club membership 300.
Visitors must book in advance.
Societies must contact in advance.
Green Fees £5 per 9 holes (£7.50 weekends & bank
holidays).
Facilities ⊗ ℳ by prior arrangement ⓑ ♥ 🏌 ⚑ (
Martin Butcher.
Leisure floodlit driving range with 31 bays.
Location Main Rd, Chilworth (A27 towards Romsey)
Hotel ★★★60% Southampton Moat House, Highfield
Ln, Portswood, SOUTHAMPTON
☎ (0703) 559555 66⇨ ⋔

Southampton ☎ (0703) 760478
This beautiful municipal parkland course always ensures a
good game, fast in summer, slow in winter. Three par 4's
over 450 yds.
18 holes, 6213yds, Par 69, SSS 70.
Club membership 500.
Visitors no restrictions.
Societies welcome.
Green Fees not confirmed.
Facilities ♀ ♨ 🏌 ⚑ (
Location Golf Course Rd, Bassett (4m N of city centre off
A33)
Hotel ★★63% Star Hotel, High St, SOUTHAMPTON
☎ (0703) 339939 45rm(38⇨ ⋔)

Stoneham ☎ (0703) 769272
A hilly, heather course with sand or peat sub-soil; the
fairways are separated by belts of woodland and gorse to
present a varied terrain. The interesting 4th is a difficult
par 4 and the fine 11th has cross-bunkers about 150 yards
from the tee.
18 holes, 6310yds, Par 72, SSS 70.
Club membership 800.
Visitors restricted at weekends. Must contact in
advance.
Societies must apply to secretary.
Green Fees £27 per day/round (£30 weekends & bank
holidays).
Facilities ⊗ ℳ by prior arrangement ⓑ ♥ ♀ (all day)
♨ 🏌 (Ian Young.
Location Bassett Green Rd, Bassett (4m N of city
centre off A27)
Hotel ★★★60% Polygon Hotel, Cumberland
Place, SOUTHAMPTON
☎ (0703) 330055 119⇨ ⋔

SOUTHWICK
Map 04 SU60

Southwick Park Naval Recreation Centre
☎ Cosham (0705) 370683
Set in 100 acres of parkland.
18 holes, 5972yds, Par 69, SSS 69, Course record 64.
Club membership 700.
Visitors must contact in advance and may play weekday
mornings only.
Societies Tue only, telephone in advance.
Green Fees on application.
Facilities ⓑ ♥ ♀ ♨ 🏌 ⚑ (John Green.
Leisure pitch & putt, skittle alley.
Location Pinsley Dr (0.5m SE off B2177)
Hotel ★★73% Old House Hotel, The Square,
WICKHAM
☎ (0329) 833049 9⇨ ⋔Annexe3⇨ ⋔

TADLEY
Map 04 SU66

Bishopswood ☎ (0734) 815213 & 812200
Wooded course, fairly tight, with stream and natural water
hazards.
9 holes, 6474yds, Par 72, SSS 71, Course record 68.
Club membership 500.
Visitors must contact in advance. No play weekends.
Societies must contact by telephone.
Green Fees 9 holes £8; 18 holes £13.
Facilities ♨ 🏌 (Steve Ward.
Leisure floodlit driving range.
Location Bishopswood Ln (1m W off A340)
Hotel ★★★64% Romans Hotel, Little London Rd,
SILCHESTER ☎ (0734) 700421
11⇨Annexe13⇨ ⋔

> A golf course name printed in **bold italics**
> means we have been unable to verify
> information with the club's management for
> the current year

TIDWORTH

Map 04 SU24

Tidworth Garrison ☎ Stonehenge (0980) 42301
A breezy, dry downland course with lovely turf, fine
trees and views over Salisbury Plain and the surrounding
area. The 3rd and 12th holes are notable. The 564-yard
13th, going down towards the clubhouse, gives the big
hitter a chance to let fly.
18 holes, 6075yds, Par 69, SSS 69, Course record 64.
Club membership 850.
Visitors must contact in advance but may not play
before 3.30pm summer weekends & bank
holidays.
Societies must contact in writing.
Green Fees £18 per day.
Facilities ⊗ Ⅲ ⅃ ♥ ♀ ♤ ⌂ ⱺ ⱡ Terry Gosden.
Leisure practice area putting & chipping greens.
Location Bulford Rd (W side of village off A338)
Hotel ★★★61% Ashley Court, Micheldever Rd,
ANDOVER ☎ (0264) 357344
9⇆ ⟋Annexe26⇆ ⟋

WATERLOOVILLE

Map 04 SU60

Portsmouth ☎ (0705) 372210 & 372299
Hilly, challenging course subject to wind. Good views of
Portsmouth Harbour.
18 holes, 6139yds, Par 69, SSS 69, Course record 64.
Club membership 600.
Visitors must book in advance.
Societies must book in advance, booking fee £11.60.
Green Fees £14 per day; £9.40 per 18 holes; £5.30 per 9
holes.
Facilities ⊗ Ⅲ by prior arrangement ⅃ ♥ ♀ ♤ ⌂ ⱺ ⱡ
Ian Roper.
Location Crookhorn Ln, Purbrook (2m S, off A3)
Hotel ★★★57% The Bear Hotel, East St, HAVANT
☎ (0705) 486501 42⇆

Waterlooville ☎ Portsmouth (0705) 263388
Parkland course, easy walking.
18 holes, 6647yds, Par 72, SSS 72.
Club membership 800.
Visitors must contact in advance & may only play on
weekdays.
Societies Thu only; apply by letter.
Green Fees £30 per day; £20 per round.
Facilities ⊗ ⅃ ♥ ♀ ♤ ⌂ ⱡ John Hay.
Location Cherry Tree Av, Cowplain (NE side of town
centre off A3)
Hotel ★★★65% Forte Posthouse, Northney Rd,
HAYLING ISLAND
☎ (0705) 465011 92⇆ ⟋

WINCHESTER

Map 04 SU42

Hockley ☎ Twyford (0962) 713165
High downland course with good views.
18 holes, 6279yds, Par 71, SSS 70.
Club membership 700.
Visitors must play with member at weekends.
Societies must contact in writing.
Green Fees not confirmed.

Facilities ⊗ & Ⅲ (ex Mon) ⅃ ♥ ♀ ♤ ⌂ ⱺ ⱡ Terry
Lane.
Location Twyford (2m S on A333)
Hotel ★★★★64% Forte Crest, Paternoster Row,
WINCHESTER
☎ (0962) 861611 94⇆ ⟋

Royal Winchester ☎ (0962) 852462
The Royal Winchester Club must be included in any list
of notable clubs, because of its age (it dates from 1888)
and also because the club was involved in one of the very
first professional matches. Today it still flourishes on its
present sporting, downland course. Hilly in places.
18 holes, 6212yds, Par 71, SSS 70, Course record 67.
Club membership 700.
Visitors must play with member at weekends. Must
contact in advance and have a handicap
certificate.
Societies must contact in writing.
Green Fees £26 per day weekdays.
Facilities ⊗ Ⅲ ⅃ ♥ ♀ ♤ ⌂ ⱺ ⱡ Steven Hunter.
Location Sarum Rd (1.5m W off A3090)
Hotel ★★★★♨74% Lainston House Hotel,
Sparsholt, WINCHESTER
☎ (0962) 863588 38rm(37⇆ ⟋)

South Winchester ☎ (0962) 877800
Due to open in September 1993, this Peter Alliss/Clive Clark
course incorporates downland and meadows.
18 holes, 6688yds, Par 72.
Club membership 850.
Visitors must contact in advance and have handicap
certificate, limited at weekends.
Societies must contact in advance.
Green Fees £20 (£25 weekends and bank holidays).
Facilities ⊗ Ⅲ ⅃ ♥ ♀ ♤ ⌂ ⱺ ⱡ Richard Adams.
Leisure sauna.
Location Pitt (off A3090)
Hotel ★★★65% Royal Hotel, Saint Peter St,
WINCHESTER ☎ (0962) 840840
75⇆ ⟋

HEREFORD & WORCESTER

ALVECHURCH

Map 07 SP07

Kings Norton ☎ Wythall (0564) 826706
An old club with three, 9-hole courses; the Blue, Red and
Yellow. Parkland with some exacting water hazards, it
has housed important events. There is also a 12-hole, par
3 course.
27 holes, 7064yds, Par 72, SSS 74, Course record 65.
Club membership 984.
Visitors may not play at weekends.
Societies must telephone in advance.
Green Fees £29.50 per day; £27 per 18 holes.
Facilities ⊗ Ⅲ ⅃ ♥ ♀ ♤ ⌂
Leisure snooker, practice area.
Location Brockhill Ln, Weatheroak (3m NE)
Hotel ★★★67% Forte Crest Leeds/Bradford,
Leeds Rd, BRAMHOPE
☎ (0532) 842911 126⇆ ⟋

BEWDLEY

Map 07 SO77

Little Lakes Golf and Country Club ☎ (0299) 266385
A testing 9-hole undulating parkland course offering alternative tees for the second nine and some pleasing views.
9 holes, 6247yds, Par 73, SSS 72, Course record 70.
Club membership 500.

Visitors	must contact in advance but may not play at weekends.
Societies	must telephone in advance.
Green Fees	£10 per round.
Facilities	⊗ ⅢⅢ ⓛ ▄ ♀ ♨ 🏠 ⌇ Mark A Laing.
Leisure	hard tennis courts, outdoor swimming pool, fishing.
Location	Lye Head (2.25m W off A456)
Hotel	★★★67% Stourport Moat House, 35 Hartlebury Rd, STOURPORT-ON-SEVERN ☎ (0299) 827733 68⇄ ℟

Wharton Park ☎ (0299) 405222 & 405163
18-hole championship-standard course with some long Par 5s on the 6th (577yds) and the 9th (525yds).
18 holes, 6600yds, Par 73, SSS 72, Course record 67.
Club membership 600.

Visitors	advisable to telephone in advance.
Societies	apply in writing.
Green Fees	£30 per 36 holes; £20 per 18 holes (£35/£25 weekends).
Facilities	⊗ ⅢⅢ ⓛ ▄ ♀ ♨ 🏠 ⌇ Angus Hoare.
Leisure	fishing, snooker.
Location	Longbank
Hotel	★★★67% Stourport Moat House, 35 Hartlebury Rd, STOURPORT-ON-SEVERN ☎ (0299) 827733 68⇄ ℟

BISHAMPTON

Map 03 SO95

Vale Golf & Country Club ☎ (038682) 781
Opened in 1991 this course offers an American-style layout, with large greens, trees and bunkers and several water hazards. Its rolling fairways provide a testing round, as well as superb views of the Malvern Hills. Picturesque and peaceful. Also 9-hole course and 20-bay driving range.
International: 18 holes, 7041yds, Par 73, SSS 73.
Lenches: 9 holes, 2980yds, Par 35, SSS 35.
Club membership 700.

Visitors	may be restricted at peak times weekends. Booking preferred.
Societies	must apply in advance.
Green Fees	not confirmed.
Facilities	⊗ ⅢⅢ ⓛ ▄ ♀ ♨ 🏠 ⌇ Caroline Griffiths.
Leisure	tennis courts, fishing, riding, clay pigeon shooting.
Location	Hill Furze Rd
Hotel	★★58% The Chequers Inn, Chequers Ln, FLADBURY ☎ (0386) 860276 & 860527 8⇄ ℟

BLAKEDOWN

Map 07 SO87

Churchill and Blakedown ☎ (0562) 700200
Pleasant course on hilltop with extensive views.
9 holes, 6472yds, Par 72, SSS 71.
Club membership 365.

Visitors	with member only weekends & bank holidays.
Societies	Mon-Fri, by arrangement.
Green Fees	not confirmed.
Facilities	⊗ ⅢⅢ ⓛ ▄ (ex Mon) ♀ ♨ 🏠 ⌇ K M Wheeler.
Location	Churchill Ln (W side of village off A456)
Hotel	★★70% Gainsborough House Hotel, Bewdley Hill, KIDDERMINSTER ☎ (0562) 820041 42⇄ ℟

BROADWAY

Map 04 SP03

Broadway ☎ (0386) 853683
At the edge of the Cotswolds this downland course lies at an altitude of 900 ft above sea level, with extensive views.
18 holes, 6216yds, Par 72, SSS 69, Course record 65.
Club membership 850.

Visitors	must play with member Sat before 3pm. No ladies Sun (am). Must contact in advance.
Societies	must contact in advance.
Green Fees	£28 per day; £23 per round (£27 per round weekends & bank holidays).
Facilities	⊗ ⅢⅢ by prior arrangement ⓛ ▄ (no catering Mon) ♀ ♨ 🏠 ⌇ Martyn Freeman.
Location	Willersey Hill (2m NE)
Hotel	★★★70% Dormy House Hotel, Willersey Hill, BROADWAY ☎ (0386) 852711 26⇄ ℟Annexe23⇄

BROMSGROVE

Map 07 SO97

Blackwell ☎ 021-445 1994
Pleasantly undulating parkland with a variety of trees. Laid out in two 9-hole loops.
18 holes, 6202Yds, Par 70, SSS 71, Course record 68.

Visitors	must contact in advance, must have handicap certificate.
Societies	must contact in advance.
Green Fees	£36 per day.
Facilities	⊗ by prior arrangement ⅢⅢ ⓛ ▄ ♀ ♨ 🏠 ⌇ Nigel Blake.
Location	Blackwell (2m W of Alvechurch)
Hotel	★★★71% Pine Lodge Hotel, Kidderminster Rd, BROMSGROVE ☎ (0527) 576600 118⇄ ℟

Bromsgrove Golf Centre ☎ (0527) 575886 & 570505
A Pay and Play, Hawtree-designed 9-hole course. Also 41 bay floodlit driving range and floodlit practice bunker.
9 holes, 3159yds, Par 35, SSS 70.
Club membership 300.

Visitors	no restrictions.
Societies	weekdays only, apply in writing.
Green Fees	£10 per 18 holes; £6 per 9 holes (£12/£7 weekends).
Facilities	▄ ♨ 🏠 ⌇ Graeme Long, Steve Fanning.
Location	Stratford Rd (E side of Bromsgrove, 6m W of Alvechurch)
Hotel	★★★★65% Stakis Birmingham-Bromsgrove County Court Hot, Birmingham Rd, BROMSGROVE ☎ 021-447 7888 141⇄ ℟

DROITWICH
Map 03 SO86

Droitwich ☎ (0905) 774344
Undulating parkland course.
18 holes, 6040yds, Par 70, SSS 69, Course record 63.
Club membership 785.
Visitors   Mon-Fri handicap certificate required, with
              member only weekends & bank holidays.
Societies must apply by telephone or letter.
Green Fees £24 per day.
Facilities ⊗ ⅲ ⓛ ▆ ♀ (Tue-Sat) ♨ ⌂ ⓕ C Thompson.
Leisure   snooker.
Location   Ford Ln (1.5m N off A38)
Hotel   ★★★★70% Chateau Impney Hotel,
              DROITWICH ☎ (0905) 774411 67⇄ ↾

Ombersley ☎ Worcester (0905) 620747
Undulating course in beautiful countryside high above the
edge of the Severn Valley. Covered driving range and putting
green.
18 holes, 6289yard, Par 72, SSS 68.
Club membership 600.
Visitors   suitable dress expected, no jeans.
Societies telephone in advance.
Green Fees £9.60 per 18 holes (£12.80 weekends).
Facilities ⊗ ⅲ ⓛ ▆ ♀ ♨ ⌂ ⓕ ↾ Graham Glenister.
Leisure   covered driving range, putting green.
Location   Bishops Wood Rd, Lineholt, Ombersley (3m W
              of Droitwich)
Hotel   ★★★★57% Raven Hotel, DROITWICH
              ☎ (0905) 772224 72⇄ ↾

FLADBURY
Map 03 SO94

Evesham ☎ Evesham (0386) 860395
Parkland, heavily wooded, with the River Avon running
alongside 5th and 14th holes. Good views. Nine greens
played from eighteen different tees.
9 holes, 6418yds, Par 72, SSS 71, Course record 69.
Club membership 400.
Visitors   except Tue & competition days. With members
              only at weekends. Handicap certificate required.
              Must be a member of a E.G.U. affiliated club.
Societies must apply by letter.
Green Fees £15 per day/round.
Facilities ⊗ & ⅲ by prior arrangement
              ⓛ ▆ ♀ ♨ ⌂ ↾ ↾ Charles Haynes.
Location   Craycombe Links, Old Worcester Rd (0.75m N
              on B4084)
Hotel   ★★★69% The Evesham Hotel, Coopers Ln, off
              Waterside, EVESHAM
              ☎ (0386) 765566 40⇄ ↾

HEREFORD
Map 03 SO53

Belmont Golf Hotel ☎ (0432) 352666
Partly wooded course, the second half of which is on the
banks of the River Wye.
18 holes, 6480yds, Par 71, SSS 71, Course record 70.
Club membership 500.
Visitors   advised to contact in advance at weekends.
Societies must contact in writing.
Green Fees £24 per day; £14 per round (£28/£18 weekends
              & bank holidays).

Facilities ⅲ & ⓛ (ex Sun) ▆ ♀ ♨ ⌂ ⊶ ↾ Mike Welsh.
Leisure   hard tennis courts, fishing, snooker, bowling
              green.
Location   Belmont House, Belmont (2m S on A4654)
Hotel   ★★★67% Hereford Moat House, Belmont Rd,
              HEREFORD ☎ (0432) 354301
              28⇄ ↾Annexe32⇄ ↾

HOLLYWOOD
Map 07 SP07

Gay Hill ☎ 021-474 6001
A meadowland course, some 7m from Birmingham.
18 holes, 6532yds, Par 72, SSS 71.
Club membership 715.
Visitors   must play with member at weekends.
Societies must contact in writing.
Green Fees not confirmed.
Facilities ♀ ♨ ⌂ ↾ ↾
Leisure   snooker.
Location   Alcester Rd (N side of village)
Hotel   ★★★67% Regency Hotel, Stratford Rd, Shirley,
              SOLIHULL ☎ 021-745 6119 112⇄ ↾

KIDDERMINSTER
Map 07 SO87

Habberley ☎ (0562) 745756
Very hilly, wooded parkland course.
9 holes, 5400yds, Par 69, SSS 68.
Club membership 300.
Visitors   except competition days. Must contact in
              advance.
Societies must apply in writing.
Green Fees not confirmed.
Facilities ⊗ ⅲ ⓛ ▆ ♀ ♨ ⌂
Location   2m NW
Hotel   ★★70% Gainsborough House Hotel, Bewdley
              Hill, KIDDERMINSTER
              ☎ (0562) 820041 42⇄ ↾

Kidderminster ☎ (0562) 822303
Parkland course with natural hazards and some easy walking.
18 holes, 6405yds, Par 72, SSS 71, Course record 67.
Club membership 700.
Visitors   must have a handicap, with member only
              weekends & bank holidays.
Societies must apply by letter.
Green Fees £22 per day.
Facilities ⊗ (ex Mon) ⅲ (ex Sun & Mon)
              ⓛ ▆ ♀ ♨ ⌂ ↾ ↾ Nick Underwood.
Location   Russell Rd (0.5m SE of town centre)
Hotel   ★★70% Gainsborough House Hotel, Bewdley
              Hill, KIDDERMINSTER
              ☎ (0562) 820041 42⇄ ↾

KINGTON
Map 03 SO25

Kington ☎ (0544) 230340 & 231320
The highest 18-hole course in England, with magnificent
views over seven counties. A natural heathland course
with easy walking on mountain turf cropped by sheep.
There is bracken to catch any really bad shots but no sand
traps.
18 holes, 5840yds, Par 70, SSS 68.
Club membership 600.
►

Visitors	except weekends 10.15am-noon & 1.45-2.45pm & competition days.
Societies	must telephone in advance
Green Fees	not confirmed.
Facilities	⊗ ⅷ by prior arrangement ⅊ ⬛ ♀ ⌂ ⌂ (Dean Oliver.
Location	Bradnor Hill (.5m N off B4355)
Hotel	★★★57% Talbot Hotel, West St, LEOMINSTER ☎ (0568) 616347 20⇄ ⬚

LEOMINSTER   Map 03 SO45

Leominster ☎ (0568) 611402
Sheltered parkland course alongside River Lugg with undulating land for nine holes.
18 holes, 6045yds, Par 69, SSS 69, Course record 69.
Club membership 600.

Visitors	must contact in advance, may not play Sun morning.
Societies	must apply in advance.
Green Fees	£17 per day (£21 weekends & bank holidays).
Facilities	⊗ ⅷ ⅊ (ex Mon) ⬛ ♀ ⌂ ⌂ ⌐ (Gareth Bebb.
Leisure	fishing.
Location	Ford Bridge (3m S on A49)
Hotel	★★56% Royal Oak Hotel, South St, LEOMINSTER ☎ (0568) 612610 17 ⇄ ⬚Annexe1 ⇄ ⬚
Additional Hotel	★★★57% Talbot Hotel, West St, LEOMINSTER ☎ (0568) 616347 20⇄ ⬚

★★★

West Street – Leominster – Herefordshire – HR6 8EP

A coaching inn originating from the 15th century, oak beams, log fire and traditional hospitality. Leominster lies in an 'undiscovered' corner of England – memorable for its beautiful countryside, black and white villages and wealth of antique shops – an easy drive to Wye Valley, Malvern Hills, Welsh Marches and Ironbridge, home of the industrial revolution.

* * * * * * * * * * * *

The Talbot Hotel Offers A Two Day Golfing Break
Dinner, Bed and Breakfast PLUS two days golf at Leominster 18 hole course – £114 to £122 per person
OR
Golf at Kington Golf Course (two days price on request)
Enquiries, Hotel Brochure and Further Information
Telephone 0568 616347

MALVERN WELLS   Map 03 SO74

Worcestershire ☎ Malvern (0684) 575992
Fairly easy walking on windy downland course with trees, ditches and other natural hazards. Outstanding views of Malvern Hills and Severn Valley. 17th hole (par 5) is approached over small lake.
18 holes, 6449yds, Par 71, SSS 71.
Club membership 800.

Visitors	only after 10am at weekends or with a member. Must contact in advance & have handicap certificate.
Societies	must apply in writing.
Green Fees	£25 per day/round (£30 weekends & bank holidays).
Facilities	⊗ ⅷ by prior arrangement ⅊ ⬛ ♀ ⌂ ⌂ (
Leisure	snooker.
Location	Wood Farm, Hanley Rd (2m S of Gt Malvern on B4209)
Hotel	★★★58% Foley Arms Hotel, Worcester Rd, MALVERN ☎ (0684) 573397 26⇄ ⬚Annexe2⇄ ⬚

REDDITCH   Map 07 SP06

Abbey Park Golf & Country Club ☎ (0527) 68006
Young parkland course opened in 1985, with rolling fairways. A 'Site of Special Scientific Interest', the course includes two fly-fishing lakes and is pleasant to play.
18 holes, 6411yds, Par 71, SSS 71, Course record 69.
Club membership 1400.

Visitors	with member only weekends (am).
Societies	must apply in writing.
Green Fees	£10 per round (£12.50 weekends).
Facilities	⊗ ⅷ ⅊ ⬛ ♀ ⌂ ⌂ ⌐ ⋈ (R K Cameron.
Leisure	heated indoor swimming pool, fishing, snooker, sauna, solarium, gymnasium.
Location	Dagnell End Rd (1.25m N off A441 on B4101)
Hotel	★★★60% Southcrest Hotel, Pool Bank, Southcrest, REDDITCH ☎ (0527) 541511 58⇄ ⬚

Pitcheroak ☎ (0257) 541054 & 541043
Woodland course, hilly in places.
9 holes, 4527yds, Par 66, SSS 62.
Club membership 350.

Visitors	no restrictions.
Societies	welcome.
Green Fees	not confirmed.
Facilities	⊗ ⅷ ⅊ ⬛ ♀ ⌂ ⌂ ⌐ (David Stewart.
Leisure	putting green & practice ground.
Location	Plymouth Rd (SW side of town centre off A448)
Hotel	★★★60% Southcrest Hotel, Pool Bank, Southcrest, REDDITCH ☎ (0527) 541511 58⇄ ⬚

Redditch ☎ (0527) 543309
Parkland course, the hazards including woods, ditches and large ponds. The par 4, 14th is a testing hole.
18 holes, 6671yds, Par 72, SSS 72, Course record 68.
Club membership 873.

Visitors	with member only weekends & bank holidays.
Societies	must apply in writing.
Green Fees	£27.50 per day; £20 per round.

Facilities ⊗ 〗⊪ ⅃ (ex Sun & Mon) 🍺 ♀ 🏖 🏠 ▎
F Powell.
Leisure snooker.
Location Lower Grinsty Ln, Callow Hill (2m SW)
Hotel ★★★60% Southcrest Hotel, Pool Bank, Southcrest, REDDITCH
☎ (0527) 541511 58⇄ ▮

ROSS-ON-WYE
Map 03 SO62

Ross-on-Wye ☎ Gorsley (098982) 267
The undulating, parkland course has been cut out of a silver birch forest; the fairways being well-screened from each other. The fairways are tight, the greens good.
18 holes, 6500yds, Par 72, SSS 73, Course record 70.
Club membership 750.
Visitors must contact in advance, restricted at weekends.
Societies must telephone in advance.
Green Fees £25 per day (£30 weekends).
Facilities ⊗ 〗⊪ ⅃ 🍺 ♀ 🏖 🏠 ▎
Leisure snooker.
Location Two Park, Gorsley (on B4221 N side of M50 junc 3)
Hotel ★★(red) Wharton Lodge Country House Hotel, Weston-under-Penyard, ROSS-ON-WYE ☎ (0989) 81795 9⇄ ▮

UPPER SAPEY
Map 03 SO66

Sapey ☎ (08867) 288
Parkland course with views of the Malvern Hills. Trees, lakes and water hazards. Not too strenuous a walk.
18 holes, 5900yds, Par 69, SSS 68.
Club membership 623.
Visitors no restrictions.
Societies must contact in advance.
Green Fees £15 (£20 per round weekends).
Facilities ⊗ 〗⊪ ⅃ 🍺 ♀ 🏖 🏠 ☂ 🏮 ▎
Leisure fishing.
Location B4203 Bromyard/Whitley Rd
Hotel ★★★🏌78% Elms Hotel, ABBERLEY
☎ (0299) 896666 16⇄ ▮Annexe9⇄ ▮

WORCESTER
Map 03 SO85

Tolladine ☎ (0905) 21074
Parkland course, hilly and very tight, but with excellent views of the surrounding hills and Worcester city.
9 holes, 2813yds, Par 68, SSS 67.
Club membership 350.
Visitors with member only weekend & bank holidays.
Societies must apply in writing.
Green Fees £12.
Facilities 🍺 ♀ 🏖 🏠
Location Tolladine Rd (1.5m E)
Hotel ★★★58% Giffard Hotel, High St, WORCESTER
☎ (0905) 726262 103⇄ ▮

Worcester Golf & Country Club ☎ (0905) 422555
Fine parkland course with many trees, a lake, and views of the Malvern Hills.
18 holes, 5658yds, Par 67, SSS 67, Course record 67.
Club membership 1100.

Visitors with member only weekends. Must contact in advance and have a handicap certificate.
Societies must apply in advance.
Green Fees not confirmed.
Facilities ⊗ 〗⊪ 🍺 ♀ 🏖 🏠 ▎
Leisure hard and grass tennis courts, squash, snooker.
Location Boughton Park (SW side of city centre off A4103)
Hotel ★★★58% Giffard Hotel, High St, WORCESTER
☎ (0905) 726262 103⇄ ▮

WORMSLEY
Map 03 SO44

Herefordshire ☎ Canon Pyon (0432) 830219
Undulating parkland course with expansive views.
18 holes, 6100yds, Par 70, SSS 69.
Club membership 800.
Visitors must contact in advance.
Societies must apply in advance.
Green Fees £20 per day; £14 per round (£26/£18 weekends & bank holidays).
Facilities ⊗ 〗⊪ 🍺 ♀ 🏖 🏠 🏮 ▎ David Hemming.
Location Ravens Causeway (E side of village)
Hotel ★★★62% The Green Dragon, Broad St, HEREFORD ☎ (0432) 272506 88⇄

WYTHALL
Map 07 SP07

Fulford Heath ☎ (0564) 824758 & 822806
A mature parkland course encompassing two classic par threes. The 11th, a mere 149 yards, shoots from an elevated tee through a channel of trees to a well protected green. The 16th, a 166 yard par 3, elevated green, demands a 140 yard carry over an imposing lake.
18 holes, 5971yds, Par 70, SSS 69.
Club membership 700.
Visitors with member only weekend & bank holidays. Must contact in advance and have a handicap certificate.
Societies must apply in writing.
Green Fees £25 weekdays.
Facilities ⊗ 〗⊪ 🍺 ♀ 🏖 🏠 ▎
Leisure snooker.
Location Tanners Green Ln (1m SE off A435)
Hotel ★★★63% St John's Swallow Hotel, 651 Warwick Rd, SOLIHULL
☎ 021-711 3000 177⇄ ▮

HERTFORDSHIRE

ALDENHAM
Map 04 TQ19

Aldenham Golf and Country Club
☎ Watford (0923) 853929
Undulating parkland course.
Old Course: 18 holes, 6455yds, Par 70, SSS 71.
New Course: 9 holes, 2403yds, Par 33.
Club membership 550.
Visitors Old Course restricted weekends before 1pm. New Course no restrictions.
Societies must contact in advance.
▶

Green Fees Old Course: £20 per day (£28 weekends & bank
holidays). New Course: £10 per day.
Facilities ⊗ ⅷ by prior arrangement ⅊ ▼ ♀ ⚑ ⌂ ⚐ ⌇
Alistair McKay.
Location Church Ln (W side of village)
Hotel ★★★59% Dean Park Hotel, 30-40 St Albans
Rd, WATFORD
☎ (0923) 229212 90⇥ ☏

BERKHAMSTED   Map 04 SP90

Berkhamsted ☎ (0442) 865832
There are no sand bunkers on this Championship
heathland course but this does not make it any easier to
play. The natural hazards will test the skill of the most
able players, with a particularly testing hole at the 11th,
568 yards, par 5. Fine Greens, long carries and heather
and gorse. The clubhouse is very comfortable.
18 holes, 6605yds, Par 71, SSS 72.
Club membership 750.
Visitors must have handicap certificate.
Societies Wed & Fri only, by arrangement.
Green Fees 36 holes £35, 18 holes £20
(£35 weekends after 11am).
Facilities ⊗ ⅷ (ex Mon & Tue) ⅊ ▼ ♀ ⚑ ⌂ ⚐ ⌇
Basil Proudfoot.
Location The Common (1.5m E)
Hotel ★★★★59% Pendley Manor, Cow Ln,
TRING ☎ (0442) 891891 71⇥ ☏

BISHOP'S STORTFORD   Map 05 TL42

Bishop's Stortford ☎ (0279) 654715
Parkland course, fairly flat.
18 holes, 6440yds, Par 71, SSS 71.
Club membership 700.
Visitors must contact in advance & have handicap
certificate but may not play weekends & bank
holidays.
Societies must contact in advance.
Green Fees £21 per day.
Facilities ⊗ ⅷ ⅊ ▼ ♀ ⚑ ⌂ ⌇ Vince Duncan.
Leisure snooker.
Location Dunmow Rd (1m W of M11 junc 8 on A1250)
Hotel ★★59% The Saracen's Head, High St, GREAT
DUNMOW ☎ (0371) 873901 24⇥

BRICKENDON   Map 05 TL30

Brickendon Grange ☎ Bayford (0992) 511258
Parkland course.
18 holes, 6349yds, Par 71, SSS 70.
Club membership 650.
Visitors must have handicap certificate. With member
only at weekends & bank holidays.
Societies by arrangement.
Green Fees £30 per day; £24 per round.
Facilities ⊗ ⅷ by prior arrangement ⅊ ▼ ♀ ⚑ ⌂ ⌇
John Hamilton.
Location W side of village
Hotel ★★★62% White Horse, Hertingfordbury,
HERTFORD ☎ (0992) 586791 42⇥

BROOKMANS PARK   Map 04 TL20

Brookmans Park ☎ Potters Bar (0707) 652487
Brookman's Park is an undulating parkland course, with
several cleverly constructed holes. But it is a fair course,
although it can play long. The 11th, par 3, is a testing
hole which plays across a lake.
18 holes, 6454yds, Par 71, SSS 71.
Club membership 750.
Visitors must contact in advance and have a
handicap certificate; must play with member
at weekends & bank holidays.
Societies Wed & Thu only; must telephone in
advance.
Green Fees £32 per day; £27 per round.
Facilities ⊗ ⅊ ▼ ♀ ⚑ ⌂ ⌇
Ian Jelley/Mike Plumbridge.
Leisure fishing, snooker.
Location Golf Club Rd (N side of village off A1000)
Hotel ★★★64% Forte Posthouse, Bignells
Corner, SOUTH MIMMS
☎ (0707) 43311 120⇥ ☏

BUNTINGFORD   Map 05 TL32

East Herts ☎ Ware (0920) 821978
An attractive undulating parkland course with magnificent
specimen trees.
18 holes, 6185yds, Par 71, SSS 71.
Club membership 700.
Visitors must contact in advance & have handicap
certificate, but may not play on Wed &
weekends.
Societies must contact in advance.
Green Fees not confirmed.
Facilities ⊗ ⅷ by prior arrangement ⅊ ▼ ♀ ⚑ ⌂ ⌇
Jim Hamilton.
Location Hamels Park (1m N of Puckeridge off A10)
Hotel ★★★65% Ware Moat House, Baldock St,
WARE ☎ (0920) 465011 50rm(43⇥6 ☏)

BUSHEY   Map 04 TQ19

Bushey Hall ☎ (0923) 225802
Parkland course.
18 holes, 6099yds, Par 70, SSS 69, Course record 66.
Club membership 620.
Visitors must contact in advance and have handicap
certificate. With member only at weekends.
Societies must contact in writing.
Green Fees £29.50 per day/£21 per round (£10 per round
Mon-Tue).
Facilities ⊗ ⅊ ▼ ♀ ⚑ ⌂ ⌇ D Fitzsimmons.
Location Bushey Hall Dr (1.5m NW on A4008)
Hotel ★★★59% Dean Park Hotel, 30-40 St Albans
Rd, WATFORD ☎ (0923) 229212 90⇥ ☏

> A golf course name printed in ***bold italics***
> means we have been unable to verify
> information with the club's management for
> the current year

Hartsbourne Golf & Country Club ☎ 081-950 1133
Parkland course with good views.
18 holes, 6305yds, Par 71, SSS 70, Course record 62 or 9 holes, 4968yds, Par 68, SSS 66.
Club membership 750.
Visitors   must be guest of a member.
Societies   must apply in writing.
Green Fees not confirmed.
Facilities   ⊗ �𝍤 by prior arrangement ⬚ ⬛ ♀ ♨ 🏠 (Geoff Hunt.
Location   Hartsbourne Ave (S off A4140)
Hotel   ★★★59% Dean Park Hotel, 30-40 St Albans Rd, WATFORD ☎ (0923) 229212 90⇌ ⻊

CHESHUNT   Map 05 TL30

Cheshunt ☎ (0992) 29777 & 24009
Municipal parkland course, well-bunkered with ponds, easy walking.
18 holes, 6613yds, Par 71, SSS 71, Course record 65.
Club membership 510.
Visitors   must book Tee-times through Pro shop.
Societies   must apply in writing.
Green Fees £8 per round (£10.50 weekends & bank holidays).
Facilities   ⊗ ⬛ ♀ ♨ 🏠 (Chris Newton.
Location   Cheshunt Park, Park Ln (1.5m NW off B156)
Hotel   ★★★62% Forte Posthouse, High Rd, Bell Common, EPPING
☎ (0992) 573137 Annexe79⇌ ⻊

CHORLEYWOOD   Map 04 TQ09

Chorleywood ☎ (0923) 282009
Heathland course with natural hazards and good views.
9 holes, 5676yds, Par 68, SSS 67.
Club membership 300.
Visitors   must contact in advance, restricted Tue & Thu mornings & weekends.
Societies   must apply in writing.
Green Fees not confirmed.
Facilities   ⊗ �𝍤 & ⬚ by prior arrangement ⬛ ♀ ♨ 🏠
Leisure   snooker.
Location   Common Rd (E side of village off A404)
Hotel   ★★★64% Bedford Arms Thistle Hotel, CHENIES ☎ (0923) 283301 10⇌ ⻊

ELSTREE   Map 04 TQ19

Elstree ☎ 081-953 6115
Parkland course.
18 holes, 6603yds, Par 73, SSS 72.
Club membership 650.
Visitors   advisable to contact in advance, no restrictions weekdays, may not play until after 2pm weekends.
Societies   telephone in advance.
Green Fees £30 per day (£40 weekends).
Facilities   ⊗ ⟨⬛ by prior arrangement ⬚ ⬛ ♀ ♨ (M Warwick, M Wood, M Kierstenson.
Leisure   driving range, golf simulator room.
Location   Watling St (E of Bushey, on A5)
Hotel   ★★★67% Edgwarebury Hotel, Barnet Ln, ELSTREE ☎ 081-953 8227 50⇌ ⻊

ESSENDON   Map 04 TL20

Hatfield London Country Club ☎ Potters Bar (0707) 642624
Parkland course with many varied hazards, including ponds, a stream and a ditch. 19th-century manor clubhouse. 9-hole pitch and putt.
18 holes, 6854yds, Par 72, SSS 73.
Visitors   must contact in advance
Societies   must apply in writing.
Green Fees not confirmed.
Facilities   ⊗ ⬚ ⬛ ♀ ♨ 🏠 ⌇ (Norman Greer.
Leisure   hard tennis courts.
Location   Bedwell Park (1m S)
Hotel   ★★★61% Hazel Grove Hotel, Roehyde Way, HATFIELD ☎ (0707) 275701 76⇌ ⻊

GRAVELEY   Map 04 TL22

Chesterfield Downs Family Golf Centre ☎ Letchworth (0462) 482929
A revolutionary new golf course with the emphasis on facilities for the entire family. Its undulating, open downland course has an inland links feel. There is a 25-bay floodlit, covered driving range, a 9-hole Par 3 and many other facilities.
Chesterfield Downs: 18 holes, 6630yds, Par 71, SSS 72, Course record 69.
Lannock Links: 9 holes, 975yds, Par 27, SSS 27.
Club membership 700.
Visitors   no restrictions.
Societies   must telephone in advance.
Green Fees £12.75 per round (£17.50 weekends).
Facilities   ⊗ �𝍤 ⬚ ⬛ ♀ ♨ 🏠 ⌇ (B Huke, M Isaacs, Jane Fernley.
Leisure   25 bay floodlit covered driving range.
Location   Jack's Hill
Hotel   ★★★60% Hertfordpark Hotel, Danestrete, STEVENAGE ☎ (0438) 350661 100⇌ ⻊

HARPENDEN   Map 04 TL11

Harpenden ☎ (0582) 712580
Gently undulating parkland course, easy walking.
18 holes, 6037yds, Par 70, SSS 70.
Club membership 800.
Visitors   must contact in advance. May not play Thu & weekends.
Societies   must apply in writing.
Green Fees £28 per day; £19 per round.
Facilities   ⊗ ⟨⬛ ⬚ ⬛ ♀ ♨ 🏠 ⌇ (D Smith.
Location   Hammonds End, Redbourn Ln (1m S on B487)
Hotel   ★★★68% Harpenden Moat House Hotel, 18 Southdown Rd, HARPENDEN ☎ (0582) 764111 18⇌ ⻊Annexe35⇌ ⻊

Harpenden Common ☎ (0582) 715959
Flat, easy walking, good greens, typical common course.
18 holes, 5651yds, Par 68, SSS 67.
Club membership 820.
Visitors   must have handicap certificate. With member only at weekends. Must contact in advance.
Societies   Thu & Fri only, by arrangement.
Green Fees £25 per day; £20 per round.

►

Facilities ⊗ ▥ ⓛ ♥ ⦶ ⛌ 🏠 ⛳ ⛴ Barney Puttick.
Location Cravells Rd, East Common (1m S on A1081)
Hotel ★★★65% Glen Eagle Hotel, 1 Luton Rd, HARPENDEN ☎ (0582) 760271 50🛏 ⋔

HEMEL HEMPSTEAD

Map 04 TL00

Boxmoor ☎ (0442) 242434
Challenging, very hilly, moorland course with sloping fairways divided by trees. Fine views. Testing holes: 3rd (par 3), 4th (par 4).
9 holes, 4302yds, Par 62, SSS 64.
Club membership 250.
Visitors may not play on Sun.
Societies must telephone in advance.
Green Fees £10 per day (£15 weekends).
Facilities ⊗ ▥ ⓛ ♥ (catering by arrangement) ⦶ ⛌
Location 18 Box Ln, Boxmoor (2m SW on B4505)
Hotel ★★66% The Two Brewers Inn, The Common, CHIPPERFIELD ☎ (0923) 265266 20🛏 ⋔

Little Hay ☎ (0442) 833798
Semi-parkland, inland links.
18 holes, 6678yds, Par 72, SSS 72.
Visitors no restrictions.
Societies must contact in advance.
Green Fees not confirmed.
Facilities ⛌ 🏠 ⛳ ⛴
Leisure floodlit golf range, 9 hole pitch & putt.
Location Box Ln, Bovingdon (1.5m SW on B4505 off A41)
Hotel Forte Posthouse, Breakspear Way, HEMEL HEMPSTEAD ☎ (0442) 51122 147🛏 ⋔

Shendish House ☎ (0442) 232220
A hilly course with plenty of trees and good greens. A tough course for any golfer.
9 holes, 6076yds, Par 70, SSS 69, Course record 70.
Visitors must contact club in advance, a handicap certificate is required Mon-Fri. Only with a member at weekends.
Societies must apply in writing.
Green Fees £25 per day: £18 per 18 holes.
Facilities ⊗ ▥ by prior arrangement ⓛ ♥ ⦶ ⛌ 🏠
Leisure hard and grass tennis courts, snooker, pitch & putt.
Location London Rd, Apsley
Hotel ★★★58% Aubrey Park Hotel, Hemel Hempstead Rd, REDBOURN ☎ (0582) 792105 119🛏 ⋔

KNEBWORTH

Map 04 TL22

Knebworth ☎ Stevenage (0438) 812752
Parkland course, easy walking.
18 holes, 6492yds, Par 71, SSS 71, Course record 69.
Club membership 900.
Visitors must have handicap certificate , but may not play at weekends.
Societies by arrangement.
Green Fees £27 per day/round.
Facilities ⊗ ▥ ⓛ ♥ ⦶ ⛌ 🏠 ⛴ Bobby Mitchell.
Location Deards End Ln (N side of village off B197)
Hotel ★★★62% Forte Posthouse, Old London Rd, Broadwater, STEVENAGE ☎ (0438) 365444 54🛏 ⋔

LETCHWORTH

Map 04 TL23

Letchworth ☎ (0462) 683203
Planned more than 50 years ago by Harry Vardon, this adventurous, parkland course is set in a peaceful corner of 'Norman' England. To its variety of natural and artificial hazards is added an unpredictable wind.
18 holes, 6181yds, Par 70, SSS 69.
Club membership 1000.
Visitors with member only at weekends. Must contact in advance and have a handicap certificate.
Societies Wed, Thu & Fri only, must telephone in advance.
Green Fees £23.50 per round; £32.50 per day.
Facilities ⓛ ♥ ⦶ ⛌ 🏠 ⛴
Location Letchworth Ln (S side of town centre off A505)
Hotel ★★★59% Blakemore Thistle, Little Wymondley, HITCHIN ☎ (0438) 355821 83🛏 ⋔

LITTLE GADDESDEN

Map 04 SP91

Ashridge ☎ (0442) 842244
Good parkland course, challenging but fair. Good clubhouse facilities.
18 holes, 6217yds, Par 72, SSS 70.
Club membership 730.
Visitors must contact in advance & have handicap certificate but may not play Thu, weekends & bank holidays.
Societies weekdays except Thu (Mar-Oct), by arrangement.
Green Fees £50 per day; £34 per round.
Facilities ⊗ ▥ ♥ ⦶ ⛌ 🏠 ⛳ ⛴ Geoff J Pook.
Hotel ★★★(red) Bell Inn, ASTON CLINTON ☎ (0296) 630252 6🛏 ⋔Annexe15🛏 ⋔

POTTERS BAR

Map 04 TL20

Potters Bar ☎ (0707) 652020
Undulating parkland course with water in play on many holes.
18 holes, 6273yds, Par 71, SSS 70, Course record 65.
Club membership 520.
Visitors must contact in advance & have handicap certificate. With member only at weekends.
Societies Mon-Fri only, by arrangement.
Green Fees £27.50 per day; £18 per round.
Facilities ⊗ ▥ by prior arrangement ⓛ ♥ ⦶ ⛌ 🏠 ⛴ Kevin Hughes.
Location Darkes Ln (N side of town centre)
Hotel ★★★64% Forte Posthouse, Bignells Corner, SOUTH MIMMS ☎ (0707) 43311 120🛏 ⋔

RADLETT

Map 04 TL10

Porters Park ☎ (0923) 854127
A splendid, undulating parkland course with fine trees and lush grass. The holes are all different and interesting - on many accuracy of shot to the green is of paramount importance.
18 holes, 6313yds, Par 70, SSS 70, Course record 65.
Club membership 800.

Visitors	must have handicap certificate. With member only on Fri afternoons & weekends.
Societies	Wed & Thu only, must telephone in advance.
Green Fees	£42 per day; £28 per round.
Facilities	⊗ & Ⅲ by prior arrangement ⅃ ⬤ ♀ ♈ 🏠 ⚐ (David Gleeson.
Location	Shenley Hill (NE side of village off A5183)
Hotel	★★★73% Noke Thistle Hotel, Watford Rd, ST ALBANS ☎ (0727) 54252 111⇨ ⌀

REDBOURN
Map 04 TL11

Redbourn ☎ (0582) 792150
Testing parkland course (Five par 4's over 400 yds). Also 9-hole par 3 course.
18 holes, 6407yds, Par 70, SSS 71 or 9 holes, 2722yds, Par 27.

Visitors	must play with member at weekends & bank holidays until 3pm.
Societies	must telephone in advance.
Green Fees	18 hole: £14 per round (£18 weekends & bank holidays). 9 hole: £4.20 per round.
Facilities	⊗ Ⅲ by prior arrangement ⅃ ⬤ ♀ ♈ 🏠 ⚐ (
Leisure	driving range.
Location	Kinsbourne Green Ln (1m N off A5183)
Hotel	★★★68% Harpenden Moat House Hotel, 18 Southdown Rd, HARPENDEN ☎ (0582) 764111 18⇨ ⌀Annexe35⇨ ⌀

RICKMANSWORTH
Map 04 TQ09

Moor Park ☎ (0923) 773146
Two parkland courses.
High Golf Course: 18 holes, 6713yds, Par 72, SSS 72.
West Golf Course: 18 holes, 5815yds, Par 69, SSS 68.
Club membership 1800.

Visitors	must contact in advance but may not play at weekends, bank holidays or before 10am on Tue & Thu.
Societies	must apply in writing.
Green Fees	High: £30 per round. West: £25 per round.
Facilities	⊗ (ex Sat) ⅃ ⬤ ♀ ♈ 🏠 (L Farmer.
Location	1.5m SE off A4145
Hotel	★★★59% Dean Park Hotel, 30-40 St Albans Rd, WATFORD ☎ (0923) 229212 90⇨ ⌀

Rickmansworth Public Course ☎ (0923) 775278
Undulating, municipal parkland course.
18 holes, 4492yds, Par 63, SSS 62, Course record 63.
Club membership 300.

Visitors	must contact the club in advance for weekend play.
Societies	must contact in advance.
Green Fees	£8 per round (£11.50 weekends).
Facilities	⊗ Ⅲ⅃ ⬤ ♀ ♈ 🏠 ⚐ (Iain Duncan.
Leisure	pool table.
Location	Moor Ln (2m S of town off A4145)
Hotel	★★★59% Dean Park Hotel, 30-40 St Albans Rd, WATFORD ☎ (0923) 229212 90⇨ ⌀

ROYSTON
Map 05 TL34

Royston ☎ (0763) 242696
Heathland course on undulating terrain and fine fairways.
18 holes, 6032yds, Par 70, SSS 67, Course record 65.
Club membership 650.

Visitors	with member only at weekends. Must contact in advance.
Societies	by arrangement.
Green Fees	not confirmed.
Facilities	⊗ Ⅲ⅃ ⬤ (no catering Sun) ♀ ♈ 🏠 (
Leisure	snooker.
Location	Baldock Rd (0.5m W of town centre)
Hotel	★★★59% Blakemore Thistle, Little Wymondley, HITCHIN ☎ (0438) 355821 83⇨ ⌀

ST ALBANS
Map 04 TL10

Batchwood Hall ☎ (0727) 833349 & 844250
Municipal parkland course designed by J H Taylor and opened in 1935.
18 holes, 6489yds, Par 71, SSS 71.
Club membership 425.

Visitors	may not play on Sat & Sun mornings.
Green Fees	£7.50 per round (£10 weekends).
Facilities	⅃ ⬤ ♀ ♈ 🏠 ⚐ (Jimmy Thompson.
Leisure	hard tennis courts, squash, solarium, gymnasium.
Location	Batchwood Dr (1m NW off A5183)
Hotel	★★★65% St Michael's Manor Hotel, Fishpool St, ST ALBANS ☎ (0727) 864444 22⇨

Verulam ☎ (0727) 853327
Parkland course with fourteen holes having out-of-bounds. Water affects the 5th, 6th and 7th holes. Samuel Ryder was Captain here in 1927 when he began the now celebrated Ryder Cup Competition.
18 holes, 6457yds, Par 72, SSS 71.
Club membership 650.

Visitors	must contact in advance & have handicap certificate. With member only at weekends.
Societies	must contact one year in advance.
Green Fees	Mon: £11 per round. Tue-Fri: £20 per round.
Facilities	⊗ Ⅲ by prior arrangement ⅃ ⬤ ♀ ♈ 🏠 ⚐ (Nick Burch.
Leisure	practice nets.
Location	London Rd (1m from junc 22 of M25 off A1081)
Hotel	★★★★72% Sopwell House Hotel & Country Club, Cottonmill Ln, Sopwell, ST ALBANS ☎ (0727) 864477 92⇨ ⌀

STEVENAGE
Map 04 TL22

Stevenage Golf Centre ☎ (0438) 880424
Municipal course designed by John Jacobs, with natural water hazards and some wooded areas.
18 holes, 6451yds, Par 72, SSS 71, Course record 65.

Visitors	no restrictions.
Societies	must contact 1 week in advance. Deposit required.
Green Fees	£7.80 per round (£9.50 weekends).

▶

Facilities ⊗ ⬛ 🍺 ♀(all day) 🏌 🏠 ⛳ ⁎ Keith Bond.
Leisure floodlit driving range.
Location Aston Ln (4m SE off B5169)
Hotel ★★★62% Forte Posthouse, Old London Rd, Broadwater, STEVENAGE
☎ (0438) 365444 54⇨ 🅿

WARE
Map 05 TL31

Chadwell Springs ☎ (0920) 461447
Quick drying moorland course on high plateau subject to wind. The first two holes are par 5 and notable.
9 holes, 6042yds, Par 72, SSS 69.
Club membership 400.
Visitors with member only at weekends.
Societies apply in writing,
Green Fees not confirmed.
Facilities ⊗ ⽱ by prior arrangement ⬛ 🍺 ♀🏠 ⁎ A N Shearn.
Location Hertford Rd (0.75m W on A119)
Hotel ★★★65% Ware Moat House, Baldock St, WARE ☎ (0920) 465011 50rm(43⇨6 🅿)

Hanbury Manor Golf & Country Club ☎ (0920) 487722
Superb parkland course designed by Jack Nicklaus II. Large oval tees, watered fairways and undulating greens make up the first 9 holes. Attractive lakes and deep-faced bunkers are strategically sited. Second 9 holes offer open panoramas and challenging holes.
18 holes, 6663yds, Par 72, SSS 72, Course record 70.
Club membership 500.
Visitors with handicap certificate, members guest and hotel residents welcome.
Green Fees on application.
Facilities ⊗ ⽱ ⬛ 🍺 ♀🏌🏠 ⛳ ⁎ Peter Blaze.
Leisure hard tennis courts, heated indoor swimming pool, squash, snooker, sauna, solarium, gymnasium, jacuzzi & steam room.
Hotel ★★★★★78% Hanbury Manor, Thundridge, WARE ☎ (0920) 487722 69⇨ 🅿 Annexe27⇨ 🅿

WATFORD
Map 04 TQ19

West Herts ☎ (0923) 236484
Another of the many clubs that were inaugurated in the 1890's when the game of golf was being given a tremendous boost by the performances of the first star professionals, Braid, Vardon and Taylor. The West Herts course is close to Watford but it's tree-lined setting is beautiful and tranquil. Set out on a plateau the course is exceedingly dry. It also has a very severe finish with the 17th, a hole of 378 yards, the toughest on the course. The last hole measures over 480 yards.
18 holes, 6488yds, Par 72, SSS 71.
Club membership 752.
Visitors must contact in advance & have handicap certificate. No play at weekends.
Societies Wed & Fri only, must apply in writing.
Green Fees £20 per round.
Facilities ⊗ ⽱ by prior arrangement ⬛ 🍺 ♀🏠 ⛳ ⁎
Location Cassiobury Park (W side of town centre off A412)

Hotel ★★★59% Dean Park Hotel, 30-40 St Albans Rd, WATFORD
☎ (0923) 229212 90⇨ 🅿

WELWYN GARDEN CITY
Map 04 TL21

Mill Green ☎ Welwyn Garden (0707) 276900
Due to open in September 1993, the 18-hole, Peter Alliss/Clive Clark designed, Mill Green course makes use of woodland and meadows. The par 3 9-hole gives a good test for improving the short game.
18 holes, 6470yds, Par 72.
Club membership 830.
Visitors must contact in advance and have handicap certificate, restricted at weekends.
Societies contact in advance.
Green Fees £20 (£25 weekends).
Facilities ⊗ ⽱ ⬛ 🍺 ♀🏠 ⛳ ⁎
Leisure sauna, par 3 course.
Location Mill Green (exit 4 of A1(M),A414 to Mill Green)
Hotel ★★★61% Hazel Grove Hotel, Roehyde Way, HATFIELD ☎ (0707) 275701 76⇨ 🅿

Panshanger Golf & Squash Complex ☎ (0707) 333350
Municipal parkland course overlooking Mimram Valley. Squash.
18 holes, 6638yds, Par 72, SSS 70.
Visitors no restrictions.
Societies apply in writing.
Green Fees not confirmed.
Facilities ⊗ ⽱ ⬛ 🍺 (catering by prior arrangement) ♀ 🏠 ⛳ ⁎
Leisure squash.
Location Herns Ln (N side of town centre off B1000)
Hotel ★★★57% Forte Crest Hotel, Homestead Ln, WELWYN GARDEN CITY
☎ (0707) 324336 58⇨ 🅿

Welwyn Garden City ☎ (0707) 325243
Undulating parkland course with a ravine. Course record holder is Nick Faldo.
18 holes, 6100yds, Par 70, SSS 69.
Club membership 820.
Visitors must contact in advance & have handicap certificate but may not play Sun.
Societies Wed & Thu only, by arrangement.
Green Fees £25 per round (£33 Sun).
Facilities ⊗ ⽱ ⬛ 🍺 ♀🏠 ⛳ ⁎ Simon Bishop.
Location Mannicotts (W side of city, exit 6 off A1)
Hotel ★★★57% Forte Crest Hotel, Homestead Ln, WELWYN GARDEN CITY
☎ (0707) 324336 58⇨ 🅿

WHEATHAMPSTEAD
Map 04 TL11

Mid Herts ☎ (058283) 2242
Commonland, wooded with heather and gorse-lined fairways.
18 holes, 6060yds, Par 69, SSS 69, Course record 63.
Club membership 600.
Visitors may not play Tue, Wed afternoons & weekends.
Societies must contact in writing.
Green Fees £31 per day; £21 per round.
Facilities ⊗ ⬛ ♀🏌🏠 ⁎

Location Gustard Wood (1m N on B651)
Hotel ★★★68% Harpenden Moat House Hotel, 18
Southdown Rd, HARPENDEN
☎ (0582) 764111 18⇄ ⌂Annexe35 ⇄ ⌗

HUMBERSIDE

BEVERLEY   Map 08 TA03

Beverley & East Riding ☎ (0482) 867190
Picturesque parkland course with some hard walking and
natural hazards - trees and gorse bushes. Also cattle and
sheep (spring to autumn); horse-riders are an occasional
hazard in the early morning.
18 holes, 5949yds, Par 68, SSS 68, Course record 62.
Club membership 460.
Visitors restricted weekends & bank holidays.
Societies telephone(0482) 868757 to arrange.
Green Fees not confirmed.
Facilities ⊗ ⅷ by prior arrangement ⅃ ▞ ♀ ⚐ ⌗
Ian Mackie.
Location The Westwood (1m SW on B1230)
Hotel ★★★66% Beverley Arms Hotel, North Bar
Within, BEVERLEY
☎ (0482) 869241 57⇄ ⌗

BRANDESBURTON   Map 08 TA14

Hainsworth Park ☎ Hornsea (0964) 542362
A parkland course with easy walking.
18 holes, 6003yds, Par 71, SSS 69.
Club membership 400.
Visitors welcome except competition days. Contact in
advance.
Societies apply in writing.
Green Fees £10 per round (£15 weekends & bank holidays).
Facilities ⊗ & ⅷ by prior arrangement ⅃ (ex Mon)
▞ ♀ ⚐ ⌗ ⌂
Leisure squash.
Location Burton Holme (SW side of village on A165)
Hotel ★★★63% Tickton Grange Hotel, Tickton,
BEVERLEY
☎ (0964) 543666 16⇄ ⌗

BRIDLINGTON   Map 08 TA16

Bridlington ☎ (0262) 606367
Clifftop, seaside course, windy at times, with hazards of
bunkers, ponds, ditches and trees.
18 holes, 6491yds, Par 71, SSS 71, Course record 68.
Club membership 620.
Visitors welcome except Sun until 11.15am and Wed 9-
11.30am.
Societies telephone secretary one week in advance.
Green Fees £15 per day; £10 per round (£20 weekends &
bank holidays).
Facilities ⊗ ⅷ ⅃ ▞ ♀ ⚐ ⌗ ⌂
Leisure snooker.
Location Belvedere Rd (1m S off A165)
Hotel ★★67% Monarch Hotel, South Marine Dr,
BRIDLINGTON
☎ (0262) 674447 40rm(36⇄ ⌗)

BROUGH   Map 08 SE92

Brough ☎ Hull (0482) 667291 & 667374
Parkland course.
18 holes, 6159yds, Par 68, SSS 69.
Club membership 800.
Visitors with member only at weekends. Must have
handicap certificate and contact in advance.
Societies apply by letter.
Green Fees £25 per day (£35 weekends).
Facilities ⊗ ⅷ ⅃ ▞ ♀ ⚐ ⌗ ⌂ Gordon Townhill.
Leisure snooker.
Location Cave Rd (0.5m N)
Hotel ★★★64% Forte Posthouse Hull, Ferriby High
Rd, NORTH FERRIBY
☎ (0482) 645212 97⇄ ⌗

CLEETHORPES   Map 08 TA30

Cleethorpes ☎ (0472) 814060
Flat meadowland seaside course intersected by large dykes.
18 holes, 6018yds, Par 70, SSS 69, Course record 64.
Club membership 760.
Visitors restricted Wed afternoons.
Societies Tue,Thu or Fri only. Must contact in advance.
Green Fees not confirmed.
Facilities ⊗ & ⅷ by prior arrangement ⅃ ▞ ♀ ⚐ ⌗ ⌂
Eric Sharp.
Location Kings Rd (1.5m S off A1031)
Hotel ★★★70% Kingsway Hotel, Kingsway,
CLEETHORPES ☎ (0472) 601122 50⇄ ⌗

DRIFFIELD, GREAT   Map 08 TA05

Driffield ☎ Driffield (0377) 43116
An easy walking, parkland course.
18 holes, 6199yds, Par 70, SSS 69.
Club membership 633.
Visitors no restrictions.
Societies
Green Fees £18 per day/round (£28 weekends).
Facilities ⊗ ⅷ by prior arrangement ⅃ ▞ ♀ ⚐
Location Sunderlandwick (2m S of off A164)
Hotel ★★♣57% Wold House Country Hotel,
Nafferton, DRIFFIELD
☎ (0377) 44242 10rm(7⇄ ⌗) Annexe1 ⌗

ELSHAM   Map 08 TA01

Elsham ☎ Barnetby (0652) 680291
Parkland course in country surroundings. Easy walking.
18 holes, 6411yds, Par 71, SSS 71.
Club membership 600.
Visitors ~~with member only weekends & bank holidays.~~
Societies must contact in advance.
Green Fees not confirmed.
Facilities ⊗ ⅷ ⅃ ▞ ♀ ⚐ ⌗ Stuart Brewer.
Location Barton Rd (2m SW on B1206)
Hotel ★★★65% Wortley House Hotel, Rowland Rd,
SCUNTHORPE
☎ (0724) 842223 38⇄ ⌗

FLAMBOROUGH

Map 08 TA27

Flamborough Head ☎ Bridlington (0262) 850333
Undulating seaside course.
18 holes, 5438yds, Par 66, SSS 66.
Club membership 500.
Visitors may not play before noon on Sun & must be member of recognised golf club.
Societies must contact in advance.
Green Fees £12 per day (£16 weekends & bank holidays).
Facilities ⊗ ⅷ ⅬⅬ ⅬⅬ (no catering Mon in winter) ⅬⅬ
Leisure snooker.
Location Lighthouse Rd (2m E off B1259)
Hotel ★64% Flaneburg Hotel, North Marine Rd, FLAMBOROUGH ☎ (0262) 850284 13rm(8 ⅬⅬ)

GRIMSBY

Map 08 TA21

Grimsby ☎ (0472) 342630
Parkland course with easy walking.
18 holes, 6058yds, Par 70, SSS 69, Course record 66.
Club membership 725.
Visitors restricted at weekends.
Societies welcome Mon-Fri only, telephone in advance.
Green Fees not confirmed.
Facilities ⅬⅬ ⅬⅬ ⅬⅬ
Leisure bowling green.
Location Littlecoates Rd (W side of town centre off A1136)
Hotel ★★★67% Forte Posthouse, Littlecoates Rd, GRIMSBY ☎ (0472) 350295 52 ⅬⅬ

HESSLE

Map 08 TA02

Hessle ☎ Hull (0482) 650171
Well-wooded downland course, easy walking, windy.
18 holes, 6290yds, Par 72, SSS 70, Course record 68 or 6638yds, Par 72, SSS 72.
Club membership 650.
Visitors must have a handicap certificate. Must contact in advance.
Societies must telephone in advance.
Green Fees not confirmed.
Facilities ⊗ ⅷ ⅬⅬ ⅬⅬ (all catering by prior arrangement) ⅬⅬ ⅬⅬ Grahame Fieldsend.
Leisure snooker.
Location Westfield Rd, Raywell (4m NW off A164)
Hotel ★★★64% Forte Posthouse Hull, Ferriby High Rd, NORTH FERRIBY ☎ (0482) 645212 97 ⅬⅬ

HORNSEA

Map 08 TA14

Hornsea ☎ (0964) 532020
Flat, parkland course with good greens.
18 holes, 6475yds, Par 71, SSS 71.
Club membership 600.
Visitors with member only at weekends & after 3pm. Must contact in advance.
Societies apply in writing.
Green Fees £24 per day; £17.50 per round (£25 weekends after 3pm).

Facilities ⊗ ⅷ by prior arrangement ⅬⅬ ⅬⅬ ⅬⅬ (all day) ⅬⅬ ⅬⅬ Brian Thompson.
Leisure snooker, practice area.
Location Rolston Rd (1m S of on B1242)
Hotel ★★★66% Beverley Arms Hotel, North Bar Within, BEVERLEY ☎ (0482) 869241 57 ⅬⅬ

HOWDEN

Map 08 SE72

Boothferry ☎ (0430) 430364
A heavily bunkered meadowland course with several dykes.
18 holes, 6600yds, Par 73, SSS 72, Course record 64.
Club membership 900.
Visitors must contact in advance.
Societies must contact for booking form.
Green Fees £7.50 per day (£11 weekends and bank holidays).
Facilities ⊗ ⅷ ⅬⅬ ⅬⅬ ⅬⅬ ⅬⅬ ⅬⅬ Stewart Wilkinson.
Location Spaldington Ln, Goole (2.5m N of Howden off B1228)
Hotel ★★61% Clifton Hotel, 1 Clifton Gardens, Boothferry Rd, GOOLE ☎ (0405) 761336 9rm(5 ⅬⅬ 3 ⅬⅬ)

HULL

Map 08 TA02

Ganstead Park ☎ (0482) 811121
Parkland course, easy walking.
18 holes, 6801yds, Par 72, SSS 73, Course record 67.
Club membership 700.
Visitors welcome except Sun & Wed mornings.
Societies must contact in advance.
Green Fees not confirmed.
Facilities ⊗ ⅷ ⅬⅬ ⅬⅬ (no catering Sun evenings or Mon) ⅬⅬ ⅬⅬ ⅬⅬ ⅬⅬ Michael J Smee.
Leisure snooker.
Location Longdales Ln, Coniston (6m NE off A165)
Hotel ★★65% Waterfront Hotel, Dagger Ln, HULL ☎ (0482) 227222 30 ⅬⅬ

Hull ☎ (0482) 658919
Parkland course.
18 holes, 6242yds, Par 70, SSS 70.
Club membership 750.
Visitors must contact in advance & have handicap certificate. With member only at weekends.
Societies apply in writing.
Green Fees £25 per day; £20 per round.
Facilities ⊗ ⅬⅬ ⅬⅬ ⅬⅬ ⅬⅬ ⅬⅬ David Jagger.
Leisure snooker.
Location The Hall, 27 Packman Ln (5m W of city centre off A164)
Hotel ★★★70% Willerby Manor Hotel, Well Ln, WILLERBY ☎ (0482) 652616 36 ⅬⅬ

Springhead Park ☎ (0482) 656309
Municipal parkland course with tight, tree-lined, undulating fairways.
18 holes, 6402yds, Par 71, SSS 71.
Club membership 667.
Visitors welcome ex Sun (tee reserved).
Green Fees not confirmed.
Facilities ⅬⅬ ⅬⅬ ⅬⅬ Barry Herrington.
Location Willerby Rd (5m W off A164)
Hotel ★★★70% Willerby Manor Hotel, Well Ln, WILLERBY ☎ (0482) 652616 36 ⅬⅬ

Sutton Park ☎ (0482) 74242
Municipal parkland course.
18 holes, 6251yds, Par 70, SSS 70.
Club membership 450.
Visitors no restrictions.
Societies apply to Hull Leisure Services, 79 Ferensway, Hull.
Green Fees £4.50 per round (£6.50 weekends).
Facilities 🝙 🍺 ♀ ♣ 🏠 🔧 ⟨ Paul Rushworth.
Leisure snooker.
Location Salthouse Rd (3m NE on B1237 off A165)
Hotel ★★65% Waterfront Hotel, Dagger Ln, HULL ☎ (0482) 227222 30⇥ 🏌

IMMINGHAM   Map 08 TA11

Immingham ☎ (0469) 575298
Parkland course with some water hazards and a public footpath across holes 1, 2 & 8.
18 holes, 6161yds, Par 71, SSS 69, Course record 70.
Club membership 650.
Visitors restricted Sat pm and Sun am.
Societies must telephone and confirm in writing.
Green Fees £20 per day; £14 per round (£20 weekend and bank holidays).
Facilities ⊗ 🝙 🍺 ♀ ♣ 🏠 🔧 ⟨ N Harding.
Location St Andrews Ln, off Church Ln (7m NW of Grimsby)
Hotel ★★63% Old Chapel Hotel & Restaurant, 50 Station Rd, IMMINGHAM ☎ (0469) 572377 14⇥ 🏌

NORMANBY   Map 08 SE81

Normanby Hall ☎ Scunthorpe (0724) 720226
Parkland course.
18 holes, 6548yds, Par 72, SSS 71, Course record 68.
Club membership 740.
Visitors no restrictions.
Societies may not play at weekends & bank holidays; must contact in advance.
Green Fees not confirmed.
Facilities ⊗ 🝙 🍺 ♀ ♣ 🏠 🔧 ⟨ C Mann.
Location Normanby Park (5m N of Scunthorpe adj to Normanby Hall)
Hotel ★★63% Royal Hotel, Doncaster Rd, SCUNTHORPE ☎ (0724) 282233 33⇥ 🏌

SCUNTHORPE   Map 08 SE81

Holme Hall ☎ (0724) 862078
Heathland course with sandy subsoil. Easy walking.
18 holes, 6475yds, Par 71, SSS 71, Course record 65.
Club membership 675.
Visitors ~~must play with member at weekends & bank~~ holidays. Must contact in advance.
Societies must contact in advance.
Green Fees £18 per round/day.
Facilities ⊗ 🍴 by prior arrangement 🝙 🍺 (no catering Mon) ♀ ♣ 🏠 🔧 ⟨ Richard McKiernan.
Leisure snooker.
Location Holme Ln, Bottesford (3m SE)
Hotel ★★63% Royal Hotel, Doncaster Rd, SCUNTHORPE ☎ (0724) 282233 33⇥ 🏌

Kingsway ☎ (0724) 840945
Parkland course with many par 3's.
9 holes, 1915yds, Par 30, SSS 29.
Visitors no restrictions.
apply giving one week's notice.
Green Fees not confirmed.
Facilities ♣ 🏠 🔧
Location Kingsway (W side of town centre off A18)
Hotel ★★63% Royal Hotel, Doncaster Rd, SCUNTHORPE ☎ (0724) 282233 33⇥ 🏌

Scunthorpe ☎ (0724) 866561
Very tight parkland course.
18 holes, 6028yds, Par 71, SSS 70, Course record 67.
Club membership 700.
Visitors may not play Sun. Handicap certificate required. Must contact in advance.
Societies apply in writing.
Green Fees £20 per round (£24 per 36 holes).
Facilities ⊗ 🍴 🝙 🍺 ♀ ♣ 🏠 ⟨ Andrew Lawson.
Leisure snooker.
Location Ashby Decoy, Burringham Rd (2.5m SW on B1450)
Hotel ★★63% Royal Hotel, Doncaster Rd, SCUNTHORPE ☎ (0724) 282233 33 ⇥ 🏌

WITHERNSEA   Map 08 TA32

Withernsea ☎ (0964) 612214
Exposed seaside links with narrow, undulating fairways, bunkers and small greens.
9 holes, 5112yds, Par 66, SSS 64, Course record 64.
Club membership 550.
Visitors with member only at weekends.
Societies apply in writing.
Green Fees £8 per day.
Facilities ♣ 🏠 ⟨ Graham Harrison.
Location Chesnut Av (S side of town centre off A1033)
Hotel ★★64% Pearson Park Hotel, Pearson Park, HULL ☎ (0482) 43043 32⇥ 🏌

KENT

ADDINGTON   Map 05 TQ65

West Malling ☎ (0732) 844785
Two 18-hole parkland courses.
Spitfire: 18 holes, 6142yds, Par 70, SSS 70, Course record 67.
Hurricane: 18 holes, 6011yds, Par 70, SSS 69, Course record 69.
Club membership 800.
Visitors may not play Spitfire course.
Societies must apply in writing.
Green Fees £30 per day; £20 per round.
Facilities ⊗ 🍴 by prior arrangement 🝙 🍺 ♀ ♣ 🏠 ⟨ Paul Foston.
Leisure squash, snooker, table tennis.
Location London Rd (1m S off A20)
Hotel ★★★63% Larkfield Priory Hotel, London Rd, LARKFIELD ☎ (0732) 846858 52⇥ 🏌

ASHFORD
Map 05 TR04

Ashford ☎ (0233) 622655
Parkland course with good views and easy walking. Narrow fairways and tightly bunkered greens ensure a challenging game.
18 holes, 6246yds, Par 71, SSS 70.
Club membership 650.

Visitors	must contact in advance & have handicap certificate.
Societies	Tue & Thu only, by arrangement.
Green Fees	£27.50 per day (Mon-Fri).
Facilities	⊗ ⅷ by prior arrangement ⅊ ☂ ♀ ⚘ 🏠 ⟮ Hugh Sherman.
Location	Sandyhurst Ln (1.5m NW off A20)
Hotel	★★★58% Master Spearpoint Hotel, Canterbury Rd, Kennington, ASHFORD ☎ (0233) 636863 36⇥ ▮

BARHAM
Map 05 TR25

Broome Park ☎ Canterbury (0227) 831701
Championship standard parkland course in a valley, with a 350-year-old mansion clubhouse.
18 holes, 6610yds, Par 72, SSS 72, Course record 66.
Club membership 400.

Visitors	must contact in advance & have handicap certificate, but may not play Sat/Sun mornings.
Societies	Mon-Fri only, by arrangement.
Green Fees	£30 per day; £25 per round (£37.50/£30 weekends & bank holidays).
Facilities	⊗ ⅷ ⅊ ☂ ♀ ⚘ 🏠 ⟮ Tienne Britz.
Leisure	hard tennis courts, heated outdoor swimming pool, squash, riding, snooker, sauna, solarium, gymnasium, clay pigeon shooting, croquet, putting.
Location	1.5m SE on A260
Hotel	★★★60% Chaucer Hotel, Ivy Ln, CANTERBURY ☎ (0227) 464427 42⇥ ▮

BEARSTED
Map 05 TQ85

Bearsted ☎ Maidstone (0622) 38198
Parkland course with fine views of the North Downs.
18 holes, 6278yds, Par 72, SSS 68.
Club membership 700.

Visitors	must be member of recognised golf club & have handicap certificate, but may not play at weekends.
Societies	must apply in writing one year in advance.
Green Fees	£30 per day; £22 per round.
Facilities	⊗ ⅷ ⅊ ☂ ♀ ⚘ 🏠 ⟮ Tim Simpson.
Location	Ware St (2.5m E of Maidstone off A20)
Hotel	★★★68% Tudor Park Hotel, Ashford Rd, Bearstead, MAIDSTONE ☎ (0622) 34334 due to change to 734334 119⇥ ▮

BOROUGH GREEN
Map 05 TQ65

Wrotham Heath ☎ (0732) 884800
Parkland course, hilly, good views.
9 holes, 5918yds, Par 69, SSS 68.
Club membership 376.

Visitors	with member only at weekends. Must contact in advance and have a handicap certificate.
Societies	Fri only, by arrangement.
Green Fees	not confirmed.
Facilities	⊗ ⅷ by prior arrangement ⅊ ☂ ♀ ⚘ 🏠 ⟮ Harry Dearden.
Location	Seven Mile Ln (2.25m E on B2016)
Hotel	★★★64% Hotel Riviera, West Cliff Gardens, BOURNEMOUTH ☎ (0202) 552845 34⇥ ▮

BROADSTAIRS
Map 05 TR36

North Foreland ☎ Thanet (0843) 862140
A picturesque course situated where the Thames Estuary widens towards the sea. North Foreland always seems to have a breath of tradition of golf's earlier days about it. Perhaps the ghost of one of its earlier professionals, the famous Abe Mitchell, still haunts the lovely turf of the fairways. Walking is easy and the wind is deceptive. The 8th and 17th, both par 4, are testing holes. There is also an approach and putting course.
18 holes, 6382yds, Par 71, SSS 71.
Short Course: 18 holes, 1760yds, Par 54.
Club membership 1000.

Visitors	for Main course are required to book in advance & have handicap certificate. Short course has no restrictions.
Societies	Wed & Fri only, by arrangement.
Green Fees	Main course £35 per day; £25 per round (£35 per round weekends). Short course £5.50/£6.50 per day.
Facilities	⊗ ⅷ ⅊ ☂ ♀ ⚘ 🏠 ⟮ Mike Lee.
Leisure	hard tennis courts.
Location	Convent Rd, Kingsgate (1.5m N off B2052)
Hotel	★★66% Royal Albion Hotel, Albion St, BROADSTAIRS ☎ (0843) 868071 19⇥ ▮

CANTERBURY
Map 05 TR15

Canterbury ☎ (0227) 453532
Undulating parkland course, densely wooded in places, with elevated trees and difficult drives on several holes.
18 holes, 6249yds, Par 70, SSS 70.
Club membership 700.

Visitors	may only play after 3pm weekends & bank holidays.
Societies	by arrangement.
Green Fees	£32 per day; £24 per round (£32 per round weekends).
Facilities	⊗ ⅊ ☂ ♀ ⚘ 🏠 ⟮ Paul Everard.
Location	Scotland Hills (1.5m E on A257)
Hotel	★★★60% Chaucer Hotel, Ivy Ln, CANTERBURY ☎ (0227) 464427 42⇥ ▮

CHART SUTTON
Map 05 TQ84

The Ridge ☎ Maidstone (0622) 844382
Opened in May 1993, the course was designed by Patrick Dawson around mature orchards to challenge all levels of player. The par 5, 18th has two lakes to negotiate.
18 holes, 6254yds, Par 71, SSS 70.
Club membership 650.

Visitors by arrangement only, must have handicap certificate.
Societies by arrangement.
Green Fees £25.
Facilities ⊗ ⊼ 🄻 🍺 ♀ ⚲ 🏠 ⚑ ꞁ Marc Boggia, Alan Robertson.
Location Chartway St, East Sutton (5m S of Bearsted, off A274)
Hotel ★★★68% Tudor Park Hotel, Ashford Rd, Bearstead, MAIDSTONE ☎ (0622) 34334 due to change to 734334 119⇥ 🐾

CRANBROOK
Map 05 TQ73

Cranbrook ☎ (0580) 712833
Scenic, parkland course with easy terrain, backed by Hemstead Forest and close to Sissinghurst Castle (1m) and Bodiam Castle (6m). testing hole at 12th (530 yds par 5). Venue for the County Championships.
18 holes, 6351yds, Par 70.
Club membership 500.
Visitors may not play at weekends before 11am.
Societies must apply in writing.
Green Fees £19 per round (£27.50 weekends).
Facilities ⊗ ⊼ 🄻 🍺 ♀ ⚲ 🏠
Location Benenden Rd (2m E)
Hotel ★★67% Hartley Mount Country House, Hartley Rd, CRANBROOK ☎ (0580) 712230 & 713099 6⇥ 🐾

DARTFORD
Map 05 TQ57

Birchwood Park ☎ Swanley (0322) 660554
18-hole course of two separate nines, reasonably demanding for good golfers. Last four holes very interesting. Additional 9-hole simple beginners/practice course and 38 bay floodlit driving range.
18 holes, 6364yds, Par 71, SSS 70.
Visitors advisable to contact in advance, restricted Sat & Sun mornings.
Societies apply in writing or telephone.
Green Fees £16 per 18 holes; £4 per 9 holes (£23/£5 weekends).
Facilities ⊗ 🄻 🍺 ♀ ⚲ 🏠 ⚑ ꞁ Martyn Hirst.
Leisure 38 bay floodlit driving range.
Location Birchwood Rd, Wilmington (B258 between Dartford & Swanley)
Hotel Swallow Hotel, 1 Broadway, Bexleyheath, BEXLEY ☎ Central Res 091-529 4666 122⇥ 🐾

Dartford ☎ (0322) 226455
Heathland course.
18 holes, 5914yds, Par 69, SSS 68, Course record 65.
Club membership 750.
Visitors may not play at weekends. Must have a handicap certificate.
Societies Mon & Fri only. Must telephone in advance.
Green Fees £28 per day.
Facilities ⊗ ⊼ by prior arrangement 🄻 🍺 ♀ ⚲ 🏠 ꞁ Gary Cooke.
Location Dartford Heath
Hotel ★★★71% Forte Posthouse, Black Prince Interchange, Southwold Rd, BEXLEY ☎ (0322) 526900 102⇥ 🐾

DEAL
Map 05 TR35

Royal Cinque Ports ☎ (0304) 374007
Famous championship seaside links, windy but with easy walking. Outward nine is generally considered the easier, inward nine is longer and includes the renowned 16th, perhaps the most difficult hole. On a fine day there are wonderful views across the Channel.
18 holes, 6785yds, Par 72, SSS 72, Course record 65.
Club membership 1200.
Visitors restricted Wed mornings, weekends & bank holidays. Must contact in advance and have a handicap certificate.
Societies must contact in advance.
Green Fees £45 per day.
Facilities ⊗ & ⊼ by prior arrangement 🄻 🍺 ♀ ⚲ 🏠 ⚑ ꞁ Andrew Reynolds.
Location Golf Rd (Along seafront at N end of Deal)
Hotel ★★★62% Forte Posthouse, Singledge Ln, Whitfield, DOVER ☎ (0304) 821222 67⇥ 🐾

EDENBRIDGE
Map 05 TQ44

Edenbridge Golf & Country Club ☎ (0732) 865097
Gently undulating course with a driving range.
18 holes, 6257yds, Par 73, SSS 72.
Skeynes: 18 holes, 5671yds, Par 67.
Club membership 820.
Visitors must contact in advance, restricted at weekends.
Societies must contact in advance.
Green Fees not confirmed.
Facilities ⊗ ⊼ by prior arrangement 🄻 🍺 ♀ ⚲ 🏠 ⚑ ꞁ Brian Hemsley.
Leisure solarium, gymnasium.
Location Crouch House Rd (1m W of town centre)
Hotel ★★★(red)▟ Gravetye Manor Hotel, EAST GRINSTEAD ☎ (0342) 810567 18⇥

EYNSFORD
Map 05 TQ56

Austin Lodge ☎ (0322) 868944
A well drained course in secluded rolling countryside. Over 7000 yds from the medal tees.
18 holes, 6600yds, Par 73, SSS 71, Course record 68.
Club membership 600.
Visitors must contact in advance, may not play until after 1pm on weekends and bank holidays.
Societies telephone for bookings.
Green Fees £17 per 18 holes; (£23 weekends).
Facilities ⊗ ⊼ 🄻 🍺 ♀ ⚲ 🏠 ꞁ Nigel Willis.
Location Eynsford Station (6m S of Dartford)
Hotel ★★★★59% Brands Hatch Thistle Hotel, BRANDS HATCH ☎ (0474) 854900 140⇥ 🐾

FAVERSHAM
Map 05 TR06

Faversham ☎ (0795) 890561
A beautiful inland course laid out over part of a large estate with pheasants walking the fairways quite tamely. Play follows two heavily wooded valleys but the trees affect only the loose shots going out of bounds. Fine views.
18 holes, 6030yds, Par 70, SSS 69, Course record 65.
Club membership 800. ▶

Visitors	must have handicap certificate. With member only at weekends. Contacting the club in advance is advisable.
Societies	must contact in advance.
Green Fees	£23 per round (£24 weekends).
Facilities	⊗ ⅢⅢ ᗺ ☕ ♀ ♟ 🏠 ⅼ Gordon Nixon.
Location	Belmont Park (3.5m S)
Hotel	★★★★(red)♨ Eastwell Manor Hotel, Eastwell Park, Boughton Lees, ASHFORD ☎ (0233) 635751 23⇥ 🐾

GILLINGHAM

Map 05 TQ76

Gillingham ☎ Medway (0634) 853017
Parkland course.
18 holes, 5879yds, Par 70, SSS 68, Course record 65.
Club membership 830.

Visitors	must be member of recognised golf club with a handicap certificate. Must contact in advance. With member only weekends & bank holidays.
Societies	must apply in writing.
Green Fees	£22 per day/round.
Facilities	⊗ & ⅢⅢ (ex Mon & Tue) ᗺ ☕ ♀ ♟ 🏠 ⅼ Brian Impett.
Location	Woodlands Rd (1.5m SE on A2)
Hotel	★★★65% Forte Posthouse, Maidstone Rd, ROCHESTER ☎ (0634) 687111 105⇥ 🐾

GRAVESEND

Map 05 TQ67

Mid Kent ☎ (0474) 568035
A well-maintained downland course with some easy walking and some excellent greens. The first hole is short, but nonetheless a real challenge. The slightest hook and the ball is out of bounds or lost.
18 holes, 6206yds, Par 70, SSS 70.
Club membership 1200.

Visitors	must contact in advance & have handicap certificate. With member only at weekends.
Societies	Tue only; must contact in advance.
Green Fees	£35 per day; £28 per round.
Facilities	⊗ ⅢⅢ by prior arrangement ᗺ ☕ ♀ ♟ 🏠 ⅼ Neil Hansen.
Location	Singlewell Rd (S side of town centre off A227)
Hotel	★★★★68% Bridgewood Manor Hotel, Bridgewood Roundabout, Maidstone Rd, ROCHESTER ☎ (0634) 201333 100⇥ 🐾

HAWKHURST

Map 05 TQ73

Hawkhurst ☎ (0580) 752396
Undulating parkland course.
9 holes, 5774yds, Par 72, SSS 68, Course record 70.
Club membership 480.

Visitors	must contact in advance and play with member at weekends.
Societies	must apply in writing.
Green Fees	not confirmed.
Facilities	⊗ ⅢⅢ ᗺ ☕ ♀ ♟ 🏠 ⅼ Tony Collins.
Leisure	squash.
Location	High St (W side of village off A268)
Hotel	★★67% Tudor Court Hotel, Rye Rd, HAWKHURST ☎ (0580) 752312 18⇥ 🐾

HERNE BAY

Map 05 TR16

Herne Bay ☎ (0227) 373964
Parkland course with bracing air.
18 holes, 5466yds, Par 68, SSS 67.
Club membership 350.

Visitors	may not play mornings at weekends.
Green Fees	not confirmed.
Facilities	♀ ♟ 🏠 ⅼ
Location	Thanet Way (1m S on A291)
Hotel	★★★61% Falstaff Hotel, St Dunstans St, CANTERBURY ☎ (0227) 462138 24⇥ 🐾

HOLTYE

Map 05 TQ43

Holtye ☎ Cowden (0342) 850635
Undulating forest/heathland course with tree-lined fairways providing testing golf. Difficult tees on back nine.
9 holes, 5289yds, Par 66, SSS 66, Course record 65.
Club membership 500.

Visitors	may not play weekend & Thu mornings. Must contact in advance.
Societies	Tue & Fri only, by arrangement.
Green Fees	not confirmed.
Facilities	⊗ ⅢⅢ ᗺ ☕ ♀ ♟ 🏠 ⅼ Kevin Hinton.
Location	N side of village on A264
Hotel	★★★(red)♨ Gravetye Manor Hotel, EAST GRINSTEAD ☎ (0342) 810567 18⇥

HOO

Map 05 TQ77

Deangate Ridge ☎ Medway (0634) 251180
Parkland, municipal course designed by Fred Hawtree. 18-hole pitch and putt.
18 holes, 6300yds, Par 71, SSS 70.
Club membership 950.

Visitors	no restrictions.
Societies	must apply in writing.
Green Fees	not confirmed.
Facilities	♟ 🏠 ᵀ ⅼ
Leisure	hard tennis courts.
Location	4m NE of Rochester off A228
Hotel	★★★65% Forte Posthouse, Maidstone Rd, ROCHESTER ☎ (0634) 687111 105⇥ 🐾

HYTHE

Map 05 TR13

Hythe Imperial ☎ (0303) 267554
A 9-hole links course played off alternative tees on the second nine. Flat but interesting and testing. Hotel provides many leisure and sports facilities.
9 holes, 5533yds, Par 68, SSS 67, Course record 65.
Club membership 440.

Visitors	must have handicap certificate, but may not play at weekends. Must contact in advance.
Societies	must apply in writing.
Green Fees	not confirmed.
Facilities	⊗ ⅢⅢ ᗺ ☕ ♀ ♟ 🏠 ᵀ ♨ ⅼ Gordon Ritchie.
Leisure	hard and grass tennis courts, heated indoor swimming pool, squash, snooker, sauna, solarium, gymnasium, bowling, croquet, putting.
Location	Princes Pde (SE side of town)
Hotel	★★★★71% The Hythe Imperial Hotel, Princes Pde, HYTHE ☎ (0303) 267441 100⇥ 🐾

Sene Valley ☎ (0303) 268513
A two-level downland course which provides interesting golf over an undulating landscape with sea views.
18 holes, 6276yds, Par 71, SSS 70.
Club membership 650.

Visitors	must contact in advance & be member of recognised golf club or have handicap certificate.
Societies	must contact in advance.
Green Fees	£25 per day/round.
Facilities	⊗ & ■ (ex Mon) ♀ ♨ 🛅 (Paul Moger.
Leisure	snooker.
Location	Sene (1m NE off B2065)
Hotel	★★★★71% The Hythe Imperial Hotel, Princes Pde, HYTHE ☎ (0303) 267441 100➪ ↟

KINGSDOWN   Map 05 TR34

Walmer & Kingsdown ☎ (0304) 373256
This course near Deal has through the years been overshadowed by its neighbours at Deal and Sandwich, yet it is a testing circuit with many undulations. The course is famous as being the one on which, in 1964, Assistant Professional, Roger Game became the first golfer in Britain to hole out in one at two successive holes; the 7th and 8th. The course is situated on top of the cliffs, with fine views.
18 holes, 6437yds, Par 72, SSS 71.
Club membership 600.

Visitors	must contact in advance & have handicap certificate but may not play before noon on weekends & bank holidays.
Societies	must contact in advance & give one month's notice.
Green Fees	£28 per day; £22 per round (£30/£24 weekends & bank holidays).
Facilities	⊗ ⓜ 🛅 ■ (catering during daylight hours only) ♀ ♨ 🛅 (Ian Coleman.
Location	The Leas (0.5m S off B2057)
Hotel	★★★62% Forte Posthouse, Singledge Ln, Whitfield, DOVER ☎ (0304) 821222 67➪ ↟

LAMBERHURST   Map 05 TQ63

Lamberhurst ☎ (0892) 890591
Parkland course crossing river twice. Fine views.
18 holes, 6232yds, Par 72, SSS 69, Course record 65.
Club membership 700.

Visitors	restricted weekend & bank holiday mornings. Handicap certificate required.
Societies	Tue, Wed & Thu only, by arrangement.
Green Fees	£30 per day; £20 per round (£36 weekends & bank holidays).
Facilities	⊗ ⓜ by prior arrangement 🛅 ■ ♀ ♨ 🛅 (Mike Travers.
Location	Church Rd (N side of village on A21)
Hotel	★★♨♨68% Spindlewood Country House Hotel & Restaurant, Wallcrouch, WADHURST ☎ (0580) 200430 9➪ ↟

For an explanation of symbols and abbreviations, see page 11

LITTLESTONE   Map 05 TR02

Littlestone ☎ New Romney (0679) 63355
Located in the Romney Marshes, this flattish seaside links course calls for every variety of shot. The 8th, 15th, 16th and 17th are regarded as classics by international golfers. Allowance for wind must always be made. Extensive practice area.
18 holes, 6460yds, Par 71, SSS 72, Course record 67.
Club membership 500.

Visitors	must contact in advance and have a handicap certificate. No visitors after 3pm weekends and bank holidays.
Societies	must contact one year in advance.
Green Fees	£35 per day; £25 per round (£30 per round weekends).
Facilities	⊗ 🛅 ■ ♀ ♨ 🛅 (Stephen Watkins.
Location	St Andrew's Rd (N side of village)
Hotel	★★★★71% The Hythe Imperial Hotel, Princes Pde, HYTHE ☎ (0303) 267441 100➪ ↟

Romney Warren ☎ New Romney (0679) 63355 & 62231
A traditional links course, newly developed alongside the course at Littlestone.
18 holes, 5126yds, Par 67, SSS 64.
Club membership 350.

Visitors	contact in advance to obtain times.
Societies	contact in advance.
Green Fees	£19 per 36 holes; £9.50 per 18 holes (£24/£12 weekends).
Facilities	⊗ ⓜ 🛅 ■ ♀ ♨ 🛅 (Stephen Watkins.
Location	St Andrews Rd (N side of Littlestone)
Hotel	★★★★71% The Hythe Imperial Hotel, Princes Pde, HYTHE ☎ (0303) 267441 100➪ ↟

MAIDSTONE   Map 05 TQ75

Cobtree Manor Park ☎ (0622) 681560
An undulating parkland course with some water hazards.
18 holes, 5716yds, Par 69, SSS 68, Course record 67.
Club membership 550.

Visitors	no restrictions.
Societies	Mon-Fri only, by arrangement.
Green Fees	not confirmed.
Facilities	⊗ ⓜ 🛅 ■ ♀ ♨ 🛅 (Martin Drew.
Location	Chatham Rd, Sandling (on A229 0.25m N of M20 junc 6)
Hotel	★★55% Boxley House Hotel, Boxley Rd, Boxley, MAIDSTONE ☎ (0622) 692269 11➪ ↟Annexe7➪ ↟

Leeds Castle ☎ (0622) 880467
Situated around Leeds Castle, this is one of the most picturesque courses in Britain. Re-designed in the 1980s by Neil Coles, it is a challenging 9-hole course with the added hazard of the Castle moat. 18-holes may be played on weekdays.
9 holes, 2880yds, Par 34, SSS 34, Course record 32.

Visitors	booking must be made. Bookings taken from 6 days in advance.
Societies	bookings taken up to 2yrs in advance.
Green Fees	£15 per 18 holes; £8.50 per 9 holes (£9.50 per 9 holes weekends). ▶

Facilities (Inn situated in shop car park) ⛳🏌🍴🏨
Chris Miller.
Location On A20, 4m outside Maidstone
Hotel ★★★68% Tudor Park Hotel, Ashford Rd,
Bearstead, MAIDSTONE ☎ (0622) 34334 due to
change to 734334 119🛏 🐾

RAMSGATE
Map 05 TR36

St Augustine's ☎ Thanet (0843) 590333
A comfortably flat course in this famous bracing
Championship area of Kent. Neither as long nor as
difficult as its lordly neighbours, St Augustine's will
nonetheless extend most golfers. Dykes run across the
course.
18 holes, 5197yds, Par 69, SSS 65, Course record 61.
Club membership 600.
Visitors must contact in advance and have a
handicap certificate.
Societies must contact in advance.
Green Fees £20 per day/round (£22 weekends and bank
holidays).
Facilities ⊗ ℍ by prior arrangement 🏌🍴♀⛳🏨 (
Derek Scott.
Location Cottington Rd, Cliffsend
Hotel ★★62% Marina Resort Hotel, Harbour Pde,
RAMSGATE ☎ (0843) 588276 59🛏 🐾

ROCHESTER
Map 05 TQ76

Rochester & Cobham Park ☎ Shorne (047 482) 3411
A first-rate course of challenging dimensions in
undulating parkland. All holes differ and each requires
accurate drive placing to derive the best advantage. The
clubhouse and course are situated a quarter of a mile
from the western end of the M2. The club was formed in
1891.
18 holes, 6440yds, Par 72, SSS 71, Course record 66.
Club membership 700.
Visitors must contact in advance & have handicap
certificate. No visitors weekends until after
4pm.
Societies Tue & Thu only, by arrangement.
Green Fees £36 per day; £26 per round.
Facilities ⊗ ℍ 🏌🍴♀⛳🏨(Matt Henderson.
Location Park Pale (2.5m W on A2)
Hotel ★★★★68% Bridgewood Manor Hotel,
Bridgewood Roundabout, Maidstone Rd,
ROCHESTER ☎ (0634) 201333 100🛏 🐾

SANDWICH
Map 05 TR35

Prince's ☎ (0304) 611118
Championship links of the highest calibre and
comparable to its near neighbours, Royal Cinque Ports.
Typical flat duneland running along the shore of
Sandwich Bay. The ball must be struck well to attain a
good score. 27 holes in three loops of nine which are
inter-connected to make up three 18 hole courses.
Dunes: 9 holes, 3343yds, Par 36, SSS 36.
Himalayas: 9 holes, 3163yds, Par 35, SSS 35.
Shore: 9 holes, 3347yds, Par 36, SSS 36.
Club membership 450.

Visitors must contact in advance and have a
handicap certificate.
Societies must contact in advance.
Green Fees £34 per day; £29.50 per round (£39-£44 per
day; £34 per round weekends & bank
holidays).
Facilities ⊗ ℍ 🏌🍴♀⛳🏨🍴(Philip Sparks.
Leisure snooker, pool table, games room.
Location Prince's Dr, Sandwich Bay (2m E via toll
road)
Hotel ★★59% The Bow Window Inn, High St,
LITTLEBOURNE ☎ (0227) 721264 8 🛏 🐾

ROYAL ST. GEORGE'S See page 117

SEVENOAKS
Map 05 TQ55

Knole Park ☎ (0732) 452150
The course is set in a majestic park with many fine trees
and deer running loose. It has a wiry turf seemingly
impervious to rain. Certainly a pleasure to play on.
Excellent views of Knole House and the North Downs.
Outstanding greens.
18 holes, 6249yds, Par 70, SSS 70.
Club membership 850.
Visitors must have handicap certificate, but may not
play at weekends or bank holidays. Must
contact in advance.
Societies must apply in writing one year in advance.
Green Fees £25.50 per round.
Facilities ⊗ 🏌🍴♀⛳🏨(P E Gill.
Leisure squash, snooker.
Location Seal Hollow Rd (SE side of town centre off
B2019)
Hotel ★★59% Sevenoaks Park Hotel, Seal
Hollow Rd, SEVENOAKS
☎ (0732) 454245 16rm(3🛏3 🐾)
Annexe10🛏 🐾

SHEERNESS
Map 05 TQ97

Sheerness ☎ (0795) 662585
Marshland/meadowland course, few bunkers, but many
ditches and water hazards. Often windy.
18 holes, 6460yds, Par 72, SSS 71, Course record 67.
Club membership 600.
Visitors with member only at weekends. A handicap
certificate is required.
Societies must apply in writing.
Green Fees not confirmed.
Facilities ⊗ ℍ by prior arrangement 🏌🍴♀⛳🏨(
Darran Clark.
Location Power Station Rd (1.5m E off A249)
Hotel ★★★★68% Bridgewood Manor Hotel,
Bridgewood Roundabout, Maidstone Rd,
ROCHESTER
☎ (0634) 201333 100🛏 🐾

If you know of a golf course that welcomes
visitors and is not already in this guide, we
should be grateful for information

Royal St. George's

Sandwich ☎(0304) 613090   **Map 05 TR35**

John Ingham writes: Sandwich is one of the most beautiful and unspoiled towns in southern England. Driving to this part of Kent is much like stepping back into history. The big golf course here, Royal St George's, is where Sandy Lyle won the Open Championship in 1985 by one shot from that colourful American, Payne Stewart.

Like the region, the clubhouse is old-fashioned and the seats near the window in the bar seem to have been there forever. The bar staff may know as much about fishing or lifeboats as they know about beer, and make a visit there a delight, providing you are not looking for modern sophistication.

The course itself is the truest links you will find in all England and the Royal & Ancient, in its wisdom, choose Royal St George's for major championships knowing it will find the pedigree player at the end of a week. Close to the sea, overlooking Pegwell Bay, any kind of wind can make this man-size test even tougher. The sweeping rough at the 1st can be daunting, so can the bunkers and the huge sandhills. But there are classic shots here.

Off-sea breezes can turn to incredible gales, and it is possible to find the course virtually unplayable. A smooth swing can be blown inside out and stories of three good woods to reach certain greens, into wind, are commonplace. Often the problem in high winds is simply to stand up and address the ball. Putting, too, can be almost impossible, with the ball blown off the surface and maybe into the sand. Christy O'Connor Jnr put together a 64 here, and no wonder it's the record!

Membership 675

Visitors must contact in advance. May not play at weekends

Societies must apply in writing

Green fees Midweek only £50 (18 holes); day £70

Facilities ⊗ ⓑ 🍺 ♀ ⚐ 🏠 ⚑ ⚐ (Niall Reynolds)

Location 1.5m E of town

18 holes, 6903yds, Par 70, SSS 74. Course record 64 (C. O'Connor Jnr)

WHERE TO STAY AND EAT NEARBY

HOTELS:

CANTERBURY
★★★ 61% Falstaff, St Dunstans St. ☎ (0227) 462138. 24 ⇌ ☜. English & Continental cuisine

DOVER
★★★ 62% Forte Posthouse, Singledge Ln, Whitfield (3m NW jct A2/A256). ☎ (0304) 821222. 67 ⇌ ☜

LITTLEBOURNE
★★ 59% The Bow Window Inn, High St. ☎ Canterbury (0227) 721264 8 ⇌ ☜. English & French cuisine

RAMSGATE
★★ 62% Marina Resort, Harbour Pde. ☎ Thanet (0843) 588276. 59 ⇌ ☜ English & continental cuisine

RESTAURANTS:

CANTERBURY
✕⊛ Ristorante Tuo e Mio, 16 The Borough. ☎ (0227) 761471 Italian cuisine

ST MARGARET'S AT CLIFFE
✕✕⊛⊛ Wallets Court, West Cliffe ☎ Dover (0304) 852424 English & French cuisine

SHOREHAM
Map 05 TQ56

Darenth Valley ☎ Otford (0959) 522944
Easy walking parkland course in beautiful valley. Testing
12th hole, par 4.
18 holes, 6356yds, Par 72, SSS 71, Course record 69.
Visitors	must book tees times through professional on (0959) 522922.
Societies	must contact in advance.
Green Fees	£11 (£15 weekends).
Facilities	⊗ & ▥ by prior arrangement ┗ ▜ ♀ ♋ ☎ ⛾ ⎰ Scott Fotheringham.
Leisure	putting greens, practice nets.
Location	Station Rd (1m E on A225)
Hotel	★★★67% Royal Oak Hotel, Upper High St, SEVENOAKS ☎ (0732) 451109 21⇆ ⋒Annexe16⇆ ⋒

SITTINGBOURNE
Map 05 TQ96

Sittingbourne & Milton Regis ☎ Newington (0795) 842261
A downland course with pleasant vistas. There are a few
uphill climbs, but the course is far from difficult. The 166-
yard, 2nd hole is a testing par 3.
18 holes, 6121yds, Par 70, SSS 69, Course record 66.
Club membership 714.
Visitors	may not play at weekends & are restricted Wed. Must contact in advance and have an introduction from own club.
Societies	must apply in writing.
Green Fees	not confirmed.
Facilities	⊗ ▥ ┗ ▜ ♀ ♋ ☎ ⛾ ⎰ John Hearn.
Location	Wormdale, Newington (3m W off A249)
Hotel	★★★★68% Bridgewood Manor Hotel, Bridgewood Roundabout, Maidstone Rd, ROCHESTER ☎ (0634) 201333 100⇆ ⋒

TENTERDEN
Map 05 TQ83

Tenterden ☎ (058) 763987
Attractive parkland course, last 3 holes are hilly.
18 holes, 6030yds, Par 70, SSS 69, Course record 65.
Club membership 650.
Visitors	restricted weekends & bank holidays. Must contact in advance.
Societies	must apply in writing.
Green Fees	£20 per day.
Facilities	⊗ ▥ by prior arrangement ┗ ▜ ♀ ♋ ☎ ⎰ Gary Potter.
Location	Woodchurch Rd (0.75m E on B2067)
Hotel	★★★56% White Lion Hotel, High St, TENTERDEN ☎ (05806) 5077 15⇆ ⋒

TONBRIDGE
Map 05 TQ54

Poultwood ☎ (0732) 364039
Public 'pay and play' woodland/parkland course. Easy but
varied walking, water hazards.
18 holes, 5569yds, Par 68, SSS 67.
Visitors	no restrictions.
Societies	must apply in writing.
Green Fees	£7.70 per round (£11.60 weekends).
Facilities	⊗ ▥ ┗ ▜ ♀ ♋ ☎ ⛾ ⎰ Ken Adwick.
Leisure	squash.

Location	Higham Ln
Hotel	★★★61% Rose & Crown Hotel, High St, TONBRIDGE ☎ (0732) 357966 50rm(49⇆ ⋒)

TUNBRIDGE WELLS (ROYAL)
Map 05 TQ53

Nevill ☎ (0892) 525818
Just within Sussex, the county boundary with Kent runs
along the northern perimeter of the course. Open
undulating ground, well-wooded with much heather and
gorse for the first half. The second nine holes slope away
from the clubhouse to a valley where a narrow stream
hazards two holes.
18 holes, 6336yds, Par 71, SSS 70.
Club membership 960.
Visitors	must contact in advance.
Societies	must apply in writing.
Green Fees	not confirmed.
Facilities	⊗ ▥ by prior arrangement ┗ ▜ ♀ ♋ ☎ ⛾ ⎰ Paul Huggett.
Location	Benhall Mill Rd
Hotel	★★★76% Spa Hotel, Mount Ephraim, TUNBRIDGE WELLS ☎ (0892) 520331 76⇆ ⋒

Tunbridge Wells ☎ (0892) 523034
Somewhat hilly, well-bunkered parkland course with lake;
trees form natural hazards.
9 holes, 4560yds, Par 65, SSS 62.
Club membership 600.
Visitors	must be members of an affiliated club and possess handicap certificate.
Societies	apply in writing.
Green Fees	£22 per round.
Facilities	⊗ ┗ ▜ ♀ ♋ ☎ ⎰ Keith Smithson.
Location	Langton Rd (1m W on A264)
Hotel	★★★76% Spa Hotel, Mount Ephraim, TUNBRIDGE WELLS ☎ (0892) 520331 76⇆ ⋒

WESTGATE ON SEA
Map 05 TR37

Westgate and Birchington ☎ Thanet (0843) 831115
Seaside course.
18 holes, 4926yds, Par 64, SSS 64, Course record 60.
Club membership 310.
Visitors	must contact in advance & have handicap certificate, restricted at weekends.
Societies	must contact three months in advance.
Green Fees	£12 per day (after 10am) (£15 after 11am weekends & bank holidays).
Facilities	⊗ by prior arrangement ┗ ▜ ♀ ♋ ☎ ⎰ Roger Game.
Location	176 Canterbury Rd (E side of town centre off A28)
Hotel	★★55% Ivyside Hotel, 25 Sea Rd, WESTGATE ON SEA ☎ (0843) 831082 67rm(65⇆ ⋒)

WEST KINGSDOWN
Map 05 TQ56

Woodlands Manor ☎ (0959) 523806
Interesting, undulating parkland course with testing 1st, 9th
and 15th holes.
18 holes, 5858yds, Par 69, SSS 68.
Club membership 550.

Visitors with member only weekend afternoons.
Societies apply in writing.
Green Fees not confirmed.
Facilities ♀ ⚲ 🖼 🏌 (
Location Woodlands (2m S off A20)
Hotel ★★59% Sevenoaks Park Hotel, Seal Hollow Rd,
SEVENOAKS ☎ (0732) 454245
16rm(3➪3 ⋔) Annexe10➪ ⋔

WHITSTABLE Map 05 TR16

Chestfield (Whitstable) ☎ Chestfield (022779) 4411
Parkland course with sea views.
18 holes, 6181yds, Par 70, SSS 70, Course record 66.
Club membership 730.
Visitors must contact in advance & have handicap
certificate but may not play at weekends.
Societies must apply in writing.
Green Fees £30 per day; £20 per round.
Facilities ⊗ ⬛ ♥ ♀ ⚲ 🖼 (John Brotherton.
Location 103 Chestfield Rd (2m SE off A299)
Hotel ★★★60% Chaucer Hotel, Ivy Ln,
CANTERBURY ☎ (0227) 464427 42➪ ⋔

Whitstable & Seasalter ☎ (0227) 272020
Links course.
9 holes, 5276yds, Par 65, SSS 63.
Club membership 300.
Visitors must play with member at weekends.
Societies apply for details
Green Fees £15 per round.
Facilities ⊗ & ⋔ by prior arrangement ⬛ ♥ ♀ ⚲ 🖼
Location Collingwood Rd (W side of town centre
off B2205)
Hotel ★★★60% Chaucer Hotel, Ivy Ln,
CANTERBURY ☎ (0227) 464427 42➪ ⋔

LANCASHIRE

ACCRINGTON Map 07 SD72

Accrington & District ☎ (0254) 232734
Moorland course with pleasant views of the Pennines and
surrounding areas.
18 holes, 5969yds, Par 70, SSS 69, Course record 64.
Club membership 600.
Visitors must contact in advance.
Societies contact in advance.
Green Fees £15 per day (£18 weekends).
Facilities ⊗ ⋔ ⬛ ♥ ♀ ⚲ 🖼 🏌 (Bill Harling.
Location Devon Av, Oswald Twistle (mid way between
Accrington & Blackburn)
Hotel ★★★64% Dunkenhalgh Hotel, Blackburn Rd,
Clayton le Moors, ACCRINGTON
☎ (0254) 398021 29➪ ⋔ Annexe51➪ ⋔

Baxenden & District ☎ (0254) 234555
Moorland course.
9 holes, 5740yds, SSS 68.
Visitors may not play Sat, Sun and bank holidays except
with member.
Societies must contact in advance.
Green Fees not confirmed.

Facilities ♀ ⚲
Location Top o' th' Meadow, Baxenden (1.5m SE off
A680)
Hotel ★★★64% Dunkenhalgh Hotel, Blackburn Rd,
Clayton le Moors, ACCRINGTON
☎ (0254) 398021 29➪ ⋔Annexe51➪ ⋔

Green Haworth ☎ (0254) 237580
Moorland course dominated by quarries and difficult in
windy conditions.
9 holes, 5556yds, Par 68, SSS 67, Course record 67.
Club membership 360.
Visitors may not play Sun, Mar-Oct.
Societies apply in writing. Weekdays only before 5pm.
Green Fees not confirmed.
Facilities ⊗ ⋔ ⬛ ♥ ♀ ⚲ 🖼
Leisure snooker.
Location Green Haworth (2m S off A680)
Hotel ★★★58% Blackburn Moat House, Preston New
Rd, BLACKBURN ☎ (0254) 264441 98➪ ⋔

BACUP Map 07 SD82

Bacup ☎ (0706) 873170
Moorland course, predominantly flat except climbs to 1st and
10th holes.
9 holes, 5652yds, Par 68, SSS 67.
Club membership 350.
Visitors must contact in advance.
Societies must contact in writing.
Green Fees not confirmed.
Facilities ⊗ ⋔ ⬛ ♥ ♀ ⚲
Location Bankside Ln (W side of town off A671)
Hotel ★★★61% Friendly Hotel, Keirby Walk,
BURNLEY ☎ (0282) 27611 49➪ ⋔

BARNOLDSWICK Map 07 SD84

Ghyll ☎ Earby (0282) 842466
Excellent, parkland course with outstanding views, especially
from the 8th tee where you can see the Three Peaks. Testing
3rd hole is an uphill par 4.
9 holes, 5422yds, Par 68, SSS 66, Course record 64.
Club membership 310.
Visitors may not play Tue mornings, Fri after 4.30pm &
Sun.
Societies must contact in writing.
Green Fees £14 per day (£18 weekends & bank holidays).
Facilities ⚲
Location Ghyll Brow (1m NE on B6252)
Hotel ★★★63% Stirk House Hotel, GISBURN
☎ (0200) 445581 36➪ ⋔ Annexe12➪

BLACKBURN Map 07 SD62

Blackburn ☎ (0254) 51122
Parkland course on a high plateau with stream and hills.
Superb views of Lancashire coast and the Pennines.
18 holes, 6147yds, Par 71, SSS 70.
Club membership 800.
Visitors restricted Tue & weekends.
Societies must contact in advance.
Green Fees £19 per day (£22 weekends & bank holidays).
Facilities ⊗ ⋔ ⬛ ♥ ♀ ⚲ 🖼 (Alan Rodwell. ▶
Leisure snooker.

Location	Beardwood Brow (1.25m NW of town centre off A677)
Hotel	★★★58% Blackburn Moat House, Preston New Rd, BLACKBURN ☎ (0254) 264441 98⇄ ⚑

BLACKPOOL   Map 07 SD33

Blackpool North Shore ☎ (0253) 52054
Undulating parkland course.
18 holes, 6400yds, Par 71, SSS 71.
Club membership 900.

Visitors	may not play Thu & Sat. Advisable to contact in advance.
Societies	must contact in advance.
Green Fees	£21 per day (£23 weekends).
Facilities	⊗ ≡ ⅃ ⚏ ♀ ♨ 🏠 ⚑ ℓ Brendan Ward.
Leisure	snooker.
Location	Devonshire Rd (On A587 N of town centre)
Hotel	★★71% Brabyns Hotel, Shaftesbury Av, North Shore, BLACKPOOL ☎ (0253) 54263 22⇄ ⚑ Annexe3⇄ ⚑

BURNLEY   Map 07 SD83

Burnley ☎ (0282) 21045
Moorland course with hilly surrounds.
18 holes, 5800yds, Par 69, SSS 69, Course record 65.
Club membership 600.

Visitors	may not play at weekends. Must contact in advance.
Societies	must contact in advance.
Green Fees	not confirmed.
Facilities	⊗ ≡ ⅃ ⚏ (no catering Mon) ♀ ♨ 🏠 ℓ William Tye.
Leisure	snooker.
Location	Glen View (1.5m S off A646)
Hotel	★★★61% Friendly Hotel, Keirby Walk, BURNLEY ☎ (0282) 27611 49⇄ ⚑

Towneley ☎ (0282) 38473
Parkland course, with other sporting facilities.
18 holes, 5812yds, Par 70, SSS 68, Course record 65.
Club membership 300.

Visitors	must contact in advance at weekends.
Societies	must contact in advance.
Green Fees	not confirmed.
Facilities	⊗ (ex Mon) ≡ by prior arrangement ⅃ (ex Mon) ⚏ ♀ ♨ 🏠 ⚑ ℓ
Location	Towneley Park, Todmorden Rd (1m SE of town centre on A671)
Hotel	★★★71% Oaks Hotel, Colne Rd, Reedley, BURNLEY ☎ (0282) 414141 58⇄ ⚑

CHORLEY   Map 07 SD51

Chorley ☎ (0257) 480263
A splendid moorland course with plenty of fresh air. The well-sited clubhouse affords some good views of the Lancashire coast and of Angelzarke, a local beauty spot. Beware of the short 3rd hole with its menacing out-of-bounds.
18 holes, 6295yds, Par 71, SSS 70.
Club membership 500.

Visitors	must contact in advance & have handicap certificate. Restricted Sat-Mon.
Societies	must contact in advance.
Green Fees	not confirmed.
Facilities	⊗ ≡ by prior arrangement ⅃ ⚏ ♀ ♨ 🏠 ℓ Paul Wesselingh.
Leisure	snooker, pool table, TV.
Location	Hall o' th' Hill, Heath Charnock (2.5m SE on A673)
Hotel	★★★67% Pines Hotel, CLAYTON-LE-WOODS ☎ (0772) 38551 39⇄ ⚑

Duxbury Jubilee Park ☎ (02572) 65380
Municipal parkland course.
18 holes, 6390yds, Par 71, SSS 70.
Club membership 225.

Visitors	must book 6 days in advance.
Societies	weekdays only. Must contact in advance.
Green Fees	not confirmed.
Facilities	⊗ ⅃ ⚏ ♀ ♨ 🏠 ⚑ ℓ David Clarke.
Location	Duxbury Park (2.5m S off A6)
Hotel	★★61% Welcome Lodge, Mill Ln, CHARNOCK RICHARD ☎ (0257) 791746 100⇄

Shaw Hill Hotel Golf & Country Club
☎ (02572) 69221
A fine course designed by one of Europe's most prominent golf architects and offering a considerable challenge as well as tranquillity and scenic charm. Seven lakes guard par 5 and long par 4 holes.
18 holes, 6467yds, Par 72, SSS 71.
Club membership 500.

Visitors	no restrictions.
Societies	must telephone in advance.
Green Fees	£30 per round (£40 weekends and bank holidays).
Facilities	⊗ (ex Sat) ≡ ⅃ ⚏ ♀ ♨ 🏠 ⚑ 🍴 ℓ David Clark.
Leisure	snooker, sauna, solarium.
Location	Preston Rd, Whittle-Le-Woods (On A6 1.5m N)
Hotel	★★★64% Shaw Hill Hotel Golf & Country Club, Preston Rd, Whittle-le-Woods, CHORLEY ☎ (0257) 269221 22⇄ ⚑

CLITHEROE   Map 07 SD74

Clitheroe ☎ (0200) 22292
One of the best inland courses in the country. Clitheroe is a parkland-type course with water hazards and good scenic views, particularly on towards Longridge, and Pendle Hill. The Club has been the venue for the Lancashire Amateur Championships, and for the 1991 County Championships Tournament.
18 holes, 6326yds, Par 71, SSS 71, Course record 67.
Club membership 720.

Visitors	must contact in advance.
Societies	must contact in writing.
Green Fees	£25 per day (£30 weekends & bank holidays).
Facilities	⊗ ≡ ⅃ ⚏ ♀ ♨ 🏠 ℓ John Twissell.
Location	Whalley Rd, Pendleton (2m S on A671)
Hotel	★★67% Shireburn Arms Hotel, HURST GREEN ☎ (025486) 518 15⇄ ⚑

COLNE   Map 07 SD84

Colne ☎ (0282) 863391
Moorland course.
9 holes, 5961yds, Par 70, SSS 69.
Club membership 300.
Visitors restricted Thu. Must contact in advance.
Societies must contact in advance.
Green Fees £12 per day (£16 weekends & bank holidays).
Facilities 🏌
Leisure snooker.
Location Law Farm, Skipton Old Rd (1m E off A56)
Hotel ★★★63% Stirk House Hotel, GISBURN
      ☎ (0200) 445581 36⇆ 🖊Annexe12⇆

DARWEN   Map 07 SD62

Darwen ☎ (0254) 701287
Moorland course.
18 holes, 5752yds, Par 68, SSS 68, Course record 64.
Club membership 600.
Visitors may not play on Sat.
Societies must telephone in advance.
Green Fees not confirmed.
Facilities ⊗ ⑩ ⓛ 🍺 (no catering Mon) ♀ (ex Mon) 🏌
       🏠 🥢 W Lennon.
Location Winter Hill (1m NW)
Hotel ★★★62% Whitehall Hotel, Springbank,
       Whitehall, DARWEN
       ☎ (0254) 701595 15⇆ 🖊

FLEETWOOD   Map 07 SD34

Fleetwood ☎ (0253) 873661
Championship length, flat seaside links where the player
must always be alert to changes of direction or strengh of
the wind.
18 holes, 6723yds, Par 72, SSS 72, Course record 64.
Club membership 600.
Visitors may not play on competition days.
Societies must contact in advance. A deposit of £5 per
       player is required.
Green Fees £20 per day (£25 weekends & bank
       holidays).
Facilities ⊗ ⑩ ⓛ 🍺 ♀ 🏌 🏠 🥢 Clive Thomas
       Burgess.
Leisure snooker.
Location Princes Way (W side of town centre)
Hotel ★★★65% North Euston Hotel, The
       Esplanade, FLEETWOOD
       ☎ (0253) 876525 56⇆ 🖊

HARWOOD, GREAT   Map 07 SD73

Great Harwood ☎ Blackburn (0254) 884391
Flat parkland course with fine views of the Pendle region.
9 holes, 6411yds, Par 73, SSS 71, Course record 68.
Club membership 325.
Visitors may not play on competition days. Must contact
       in advance.
Societies must contact in writing.
Green Fees not confirmed.
Facilities ⊗ ⑩ ⓛ & 🍺 (ex Mon) ♀ 🏌
Leisure snooker.

Location Harwood Bar, Whallwy Rd (E side of town
       centre on A680)
Hotel ★★67% Shireburn Arms Hotel, HURST GREEN
       ☎ (025486) 518 15⇆ 🖊

HASLINGDEN   Map 07 SD72

Rossendale ☎ Rossendale (0706) 831339
Testing, and usually windy meadowland course.
18 holes, 6267yds, Par 72, SSS 70.
Club membership 700.
Visitors restricted Sun. Must contact in advance.
Societies must telephone in advance & confirm in writing.
Green Fees £20 per day/round (£25 per round weekends).
Facilities ⊗ ⑩ ⓛ & 🍺 (Mon by prior arrangement only)
       ♀ (ex Mon lunchtime) 🏌 🏠 🥢 S J Nicholls.
Leisure snooker.
Location Ewood Ln Head (1.5m S off A56)
Hotel ★★★58% Blackburn Moat House, Preston New
       Rd, BLACKBURN ☎ (0254) 264441 98⇆ 🖊

HEYSHAM   Map 07 SD46

Heysham ☎ Lancaster (0524) 851011
Seaside parkland course.
18 holes, 6400yds, Par 69, SSS 70, Course record 65.
Club membership 900.
Visitors no restrictions.
Societies must contact in writing.
Green Fees £20 per day; £16 per round (£25 per day/round
       weekends & bank holidays).   ▶

Facilities ⊗ ⏻ (in season) 🛢 🍺 ♀ ♨ 🏠 ⛳ ℂ Simon
Fletcher.
Leisure snooker.
Location Trumacar Park, Middleton Rd (0.75m S off A589)
Hotel ★★60% Clarendon Hotel, Promenade, West End, MORECAMBE
☎ (0524) 410180 33rm(20⇄7 ♠)

KNOTT END-ON-SEA

Map 07 SD34

Knott End ☎ Blackpool (0253) 810576
Pleasant, undulating parkland course on banks of River Wyre.
Open to sea breezes.
18 holes, 5789yds, Par 69, SSS 68.
Club membership 700.
Visitors must contact one day in advance.
Societies must contact in writing.
Green Fees not confirmed.
Facilities ⊗ ⏻ 🛢 🍺 ♀ ♨ 🏠 ℂ Paul Walker.
Leisure snooker.
Location Wyre-Side (W side of village off B5377)
Hotel ★★★65% North Euston Hotel, The Esplanade, FLEETWOOD
☎ (0253) 876525 56⇄ ♠

LANCASTER

Map 07 SD46

Lancaster Golf & Country Club ☎ (0524) 751247
This course is unusual for parkland golf as it is exposed to the winds coming off the Irish Sea. It is situated on the Lune estuary and has some natural hazards and easy walking. There are however several fine holes among woods near the old clubhouse.
18 holes, 6282yds, Par 71, SSS 71.
Club membership 925.
Visitors restricted at weekends. Must contact in advance and have a handicap certificate.
Societies Mon-Fri only . Must contact in advance. Handicap certificate and letters of introduction required.
Green Fees £26 per day/round.
Facilities ⊗ ⏻ by prior arrangement
🛢 🍺 ♀ ♨ 🏠 ⋈ℂ David Sutcliffe.
Leisure snooker.
Location Ashton Hall, Ashton-with-Stodday (3m S on A588)
Hotel ★★★66% Strathmore Hotel, East Promenade, MORECAMBE
☎ (0524) 421234 51⇄ ♠

Lansil ☎ (0532) 685180
Parkland course.
9 holes, 5608yds, Par 70, SSS 67.
Club membership 375.
Visitors may not play before 1pm at weekends.
Societies weekdays only; must contact in writing.
Green Fees not confirmed.
Facilities ⊗ ⏻ 🛢 🍺 (catering eves & weekends only) ♀ (eves & weekends) ♨
Location Caton Rd (N side of town centre on A683)
Hotel ★★★64% Forte Posthouse, Waterside Park, Caton Rd, LANCASTER
☎ (0524) 65999 115⇄ ♠

LEYLAND

Map 07 SD52

Leyland ☎ (0772) 436457
Parkland course, fairly flat and usually breezy.
18 holes, 6123yds, Par 70, SSS 69.
Club membership 860.
Visitors restricted weekends & bank holidays. Must contact in advance.
Societies must contact in advance.
Green Fees not confirmed.
Facilities ⊗ ⏻ 🛢 🍺 ♀ ♨ 🏠 ℂ Colin Burgess.
Location Wigan Rd (E side of town centre on A49)
Hotel ★★★67% Pines Hotel, CLAYTON-LE-WOODS
☎ (0772) 38551 39⇄ ♠

LONGRIDGE

Map 07 SD63

Longridge ☎ (0772) 783291
Moorland course 850 ft high with views of the Ribble Valley, Trough of Bowland, The Fylde and Welsh Mountains.
18 holes, 5970yds, Par 70, SSS 68.
Club membership 600.
Visitors may not play 8-9.30am, noon-1pm, Sun 11am-12.15pm (winter) & weekends in summer.
Societies must contact in writing.
Green Fees £18 Mon-Thu per day (£21 Fri-Sun).
Facilities ⊗ ⏻ 🛢 🍺 ♀ ♨ 🏠 ℂ N S James.
Leisure snooker.
Location Fell Barn, Jeffrey Hill
Hotel ★★67% Shireburn Arms Hotel, HURST GREEN
☎ (025486) 518 15⇄ ♠

LYTHAM ST ANNES

Map 07 SD32

Fairhaven ☎ (0253) 736741
A flat, but interesting parkland links course of good standard.
There are natural hazards as well as numerous bunkers and players need to produce particularly accurate second shots.
18 holes, 6884yds, Par 74, SSS 73, Course record 65.
Club membership 950.
Visitors welcome, but may not play before 9am or between noon & 1.30pm.
Societies must contact in advance.
Green Fees £35 per day; £25 per round (£30 per round weekends & bank holidays).
Facilities ⊗ ⏻ 🛢 🍺 ♀ ♨ 🏠 ⛳ ℂ Ian Howieson.
Leisure snooker.
Location Lytham Hall Park, Ansdell (E side of town centre off B5261)
Hotel ★★★64% Bedford Hotel, 307-311 Clifton Dr South, LYTHAM ST ANNES
☎ (0253) 724636 36⇄ ♠

Lytham Green Drive ☎ (0253) 737390
Pleasant parkland course, ideal for holidaymakers.
18 holes, 6175yds, Par 70, SSS 69.
Club membership 780.
Visitors must contact in advance & have handicap certificate but may not play at weekends.
Societies must contact in advance.
Green Fees £24 per day; £19 per round (£31 per day weekends & bank holidays).
Facilities ⊗ & ⏻ by prior arrangement 🛢 🍺 ♀ ♨ 🏠 ℂ A Lancaster.

Leisure	snooker.
Location	Ballam Rd (E side of town centre off B5259)
Hotel	★★★★54% Clifton Arms, West Beach, Lytham, LYTHAM ST ANNES ☎ (0253) 739898 41⇆ ☛

ROYAL LYTHAM ST ANNES See page 125

St Annes Old Links ☎ (0253) 723597
Seaside links, qualifying course for open championship; compact and of very high standard, particularly greens. Windy, very long 5th, 17th and 18th holes. Famous hole: 9th (171 yds), par 3. Exceptional club facilities.
18 holes, 6616yds, par 72, SSS 72.
Club membership 950.

Visitors	may not play on Sat or before 9.15am & between noon-2pm. Sundays by prior arrangement only. handicap certificate requested.
Societies	must contact in advance.
Green fees	£25 per day (£30 weekends & bank holidays).
Facilities	⊗ ⍟ ⤋ ⬛ ♀ ⩙ 🖿 ℓ G G Hardiman.
Leisure	snooker.
Location	Highbury Rd (N side of town centre)
Hotel	★★★64% Bedford Hotel, 307-311 Clifton Dr South, LYTHAM ST ANNES ☎ (0253) 724636 36⇆ ☛

MORECAMBE   Map 07 SD46

Morecambe ☎ (0524) 412841
Holiday golf at its most enjoyable. The well-maintained, wind-affected seaside parkland course is not long but full of character. Even so the panoramic views across Morecambe Bay and to the Lake District and Pennines make concentration difficult. The 4th is a testing hole.
18 holes, 5770yds, Par 67, SSS 68.
Club membership 1200.

Visitors	may not play before 9.30am, noon-1.30pm Mon-Sat or before 11.15am Sun. Must have a handicap certificate.
Societies	must contact in advance.
Green Fees	£21 (£26 weekends).
Facilities	⊗ ⍟ ⤋ ⬛ ♀ ⩙ 🖿 ℓ P De Valle.
Leisure	snooker.
Location	Bare (N side of town centre on A5105)
Hotel	★★★64% Elms Hotel, Bare Village, MORECAMBE ☎ (0524) 411501 40⇆ ☛

NELSON   Map 07 SD83

Marsden Park ☎ (0282) 67525
Hilly, parkland course open to the wind.
18 holes, 5806yds, Par 70, SSS 68, Course record 66.
Club membership 320.

Visitors	must telephone in advance at weekends.
Societies	may not play on Sat. Must contact in writing.
Green Fees	not confirmed.

A golf course name printed in ***bold italics*** means we have been unable to verify information with the club's management for the current year

---

Facilities	⤋ & ⬛ (weekends or by prior arrangement) ♀ (weekends or by prior arrangement) ⩙ 🖿 ⇞ ℓ Nick Brown.
Location	Nelson Municipal Golf Course, Townhouse Rd (E side of town centre off A56)
Hotel	★★★71% Oaks Hotel, Colne Rd, Reedley, BURNLEY ☎ (0282) 414141 58⇆ ☛

Nelson ☎ (0282) 614583
Hilly moorland course, usually windy, with good views. Testing 8th hole, par 4.
18 holes, 5967yds, Par 70, SSS 69.
Club membership 600.

Visitors	may not play Thu afternoons & Sat Apr-Oct.
Societies	must contact in advance.
Green Fees	£18 per day (£20 weekends & bank holidays).
Facilities	⊗ (ex Mon) ⍟ (ex Mon & Fri) ⤋ (ex Mon) ⬛ ♀ ⩙ 🖿 ⇞ ℓ P Wiggins.
Location	King's Causeway, Brierfield (1.5m SE)
Hotel	★★★71% Oaks Hotel, Colne Rd, Reedley, BURNLEY ☎ (0282) 414141 58⇆ ☛

ORMSKIRK   Map 07 SD40

Ormskirk ☎ (0695) 72112
A pleasantly secluded, fairly flat, parkland course with much heath and silver birch. Accuracy from the tees will provide an interesting variety of second shots.
18 holes, 6358yds, Par 70, SSS 70.
Club membership 300.

Visitors	restricted Sat. Must contact in advance and have an introduction from own club.
Societies	must contact in writing.
Green Fees	not confirmed.
Facilities	⊗ ⍟ ⤋ ⬛ (no catering Mon) ♀ ⩙ 🖿 ℓ Jack Hammond.
Location	Cranes Ln, Lathom (1.5m NE)
Hotel	★★65% Bold Hotel, Lord St, SOUTHPORT ☎ (0704) 532578 23rm(15⇆7 ☛)

PLEASINGTON   Map 07 SD62

Pleasington ☎ Blackburn (0254) 202177
Plunging and rising across lovely moorland turf this course tests judgement of distance through the air to greens of widely differing levels. The 11th and 17th are testing holes.
18 holes, 6417yds, Par 71, SSS 71.
Club membership 605.

Visitors	may play Mon & Wed-Fri only.
Societies	must contact in advance.
Green Fees	£26 (£30 weekends & bank holidays).
Facilities	⊗ ⍟ ⤋ & ⬛ by prior arrangement ♀ ⩙ 🖿 ℓ Ged Furey.
Location	W side of village
Hotel	★★★58% Blackburn Moat House, Preston New Rd, BLACKBURN ☎ (0254) 264441 98 ⇆ ☛

POULTON-LE-FYLDE   Map 07 SD33

Poulton-le-Fylde ☎ (0253) 892444
Municipal parkland course, with easy walking.
9 holes, 5958yds, Par 70, SSS 69.
Club membership 300.

▶

Visitors no restrictions.
Societies apply in writing.
Green Fees £4.40 (£6 weekends & bank holidays).
Facilities ⊗ 🍴 ♥ ♀ ⚐ 🏌 ¶ (D Spencer.
Leisure heated indoor swimming pool, snooker.
Location Breck Rd (N side of town)
Hotel ★★★63% Savoy Hotel, Queens Promenade, North Shore, BLACKPOOL
🕿 (0253) 52561 147⇄ ♠

PRESTON
Map 07 SD52

Ashton & Lea 🕿 (0772) 726480 & 735282
Heathland/parkland course with pond and streams, offering pleasant walks and some testing holes.
18 holes, 6289yds, Par 71, SSS 70, Course record 65.
Club membership 825.
Visitors must contact in advance, restricted competition days & members tee times.
Societies weekdays only. Must contact in writing.
Green Fees Mon-Thu: £18 per day, Fri: £20 (£24 weekends & bank holidays).
Facilities ⊗ ⅏ 🍴 ♥ ♀ ⚐ (M Greenough.
Leisure snooker.
Location Tudor Av, Lea (3m W on A5085)
Hotel ★★★60% Forte Posthouse, The Ringway, PRESTON 🕿 (0772) 59411 126⇄ ♠

Fishwick Hall 🕿 (0772) 798300
Meadowland course overlooking River Ribble. Natural hazards.
18 holes, 6092yds, Par 70, SSS 69, Course record 66.
Club membership 650.
Visitors advisable to contact in advance.
Societies must contact in advance.
Green Fees £20 per day (£25 weekends & bank holidays).
Facilities ⊗ ⅏ 🍴 ♥ ♀ ⚐ (Stuart Bence.
Leisure snooker.
Location Glenluce Dr, Farringdon Park
Hotel ★★★60% Forte Posthouse, The Ringway, PRESTON 🕿 (0772) 59411 126⇄ ♠

Ingol 🕿 (0772) 734556
Long, high course with natural water hazards.
18 holes, 5868yds, Par 70, SSS 68.
Club membership 800.
Visitors must contact in advance but may not play on competition days.
Societies must contact in writing.
Green Fees on application.
Facilities ⊗ ⅏ 🍴 ♥ ♀ ⚐ (Mark Cartwright.
Leisure squash, snooker.
Location Tanterton Hall Rd, Ingol (2m NW junc 32 of M55 off B5411)
Hotel ★★★60% Forte Posthouse, The Ringway, PRESTON 🕿 (0772) 59411 126⇄ ♠

Penwortham 🕿 (0772) 744630
A progressive golf club set close to the banks of the River Ribble. The course has tree-lined fairways, excellent greens, and provides easy walking. Testing holes include the 178-yd, par 3 third, the 480-yd, par 5 sixth, and the 398-yd par 4 sixteenth.
18 holes, 5915yds, Par 69, SSS 68.
Club membership 870.

Visitors must contact in advance, restricted daily after 10am.
Societies Mon & Wed-Fri only. Must contact in advance.
Green Fees £25 per day (£28 weekends & bank holidays).
Facilities ⊗ ⅏ 🍴 ♥ ♀ ⚐ ⚐ (John Wright.
Leisure snooker.
Location Blundell Ln, Penwortham (1.5m W of town centre off A59)
Hotel ★★★65% Tickled Trout, Preston New Rd, Samlesbury, PRESTON
🕿 (0772) 877671 72⇄ ♠

Preston 🕿 (0772) 700011
Pleasant inland golf at this course set in very agreeable parkland. There is a well-balanced selection of holes, undulating amongst groups of trees, and not requiring great length.
18 holes, 6233yds, Par 71, SSS 70, Course record 63.
Club membership 600.
Visitors may play midweek only. Must contact in advance and have a handicap certificate.
Societies must contact in writing.
Green Fees £27 per day; £22 per round.
Facilities ⊗ ⅏ 🍴 ♥ ♀ ⚐ (P A Wells.
Leisure snooker.
Location Fulwood Hall Ln, Fulwood (N side of town centre)
Hotel ★★★69% Broughton Park Hotel & Country Club, Garstang Rd, Broughton, PRESTON
🕿 (0772) 864087 98⇄ ♠

RISHTON
Map 07 SD73

Rishton 🕿 Great Harwood (0254) 884442
Undulating moorland course.
9 holes, 6098yds, Par 70, SSS 69, Course record 66.
Club membership 250.
Visitors must play with member on weekends and bank holidays.
Societies must contact in advance.
Green Fees £12 per round.
Facilities ⊗ ⅏ 🍴 & ♥ by prior arrangement ♀ by arrangement ⚐
Location Eachill Links, Hawthorn Dr (S side of town off A678)
Hotel ★★★64% Dunkenhalgh Hotel, Blackburn Rd, Clayton le Moors, ACCRINGTON
🕿 (0254) 398021 29⇄ ♠ Annexe51⇄ ♠

SILVERDALE
Map 07 SD47

Silverdale 🕿 (0524) 701300
Difficult heathland course with rock outcrops. Excellent views.
9 holes, 5288yds, Par 70, SSS 67.
Club membership 500.
Visitors may only play on Sun in summer if accompanied by a member.
Societies must contact in writing.
Green Fees £12 per day (£17 weekends & bank holidays).
Facilities ⚐ ⚐ (S Sumner Roberts. ▶

Royal Lytham and St Annes

Lytham St Annes ☎ (0253) 724206   **Map 07 SD32**

John Ingham writes: Venue for many Open Championships, the most famous winner here was amateur Bobby Jones who, in 1926, put together a four-round total of 291 using wooden clubs and the old-fashioned ball. In the last round, when level with Al Watrous with two to play, Jones bunkered his teeshot at the 17th while Watrous hit a perfect drive and then a fine second on to the green. Jones climbed into the bunker, decided a 175-yard shot was needed if he had any chance, and hit a club similar to today's 4-iron. The shot was brilliant and finished, not only on the green, but nearer than his rival. Shaken, Watrous 3-putted, Jones got his four and finished with a perfect par while Watrous, rattled, had taken six. The club placed a plaque by the famous bunker and it's there to this day.

Since that time the course, which runs close to the railway but slightly inland from the sea, has staged other historic Opens. Bob Charles of New Zealand became the only left-hander to win the title while Tony Jacklin, in 1969, signalled the re-awakening of British golf by winning.

This huge links, not far from Blackpool, is not easy. When the wind gets up it can be a nightmare. And not everyone approves a championship course that starts with a par 3 hole and it is, in fact, a rare thing in Britain. Some object to the close proximity of red-bricked houses, and aren't keen on trains that rattle past. But it's a test full of history and deserves to be played.

Visitors	weekdays only. Must contact in advance, and have a letter of introduction from their own club with a handicap certificate
Societies	
Green fees	must apply to Secretary
Facilities	£60 per day; £45 per round ⊗ ⋔ (by arrangement) ⓛ ♖ ♀ ⋈ ⚘ ☎ ⸦ (E.Birchenough)
Leisure	snooker
Location	Links Gate (0.5m E of St Annes town)

18 holes, 6673 yds, Par 71, SSS 73, Course record 65 (Seve Ballesteros)

WHERE TO STAY AND EAT NEARBY

HOTELS:

LYTHAM ST ANNES

★★★★ 54% Clifton Arms, West Beach, Lytham. ☎(0253) 739898. 41⇌ ♠ English & French cuisine

★★★ 64% Bedford, 307-311 Clifton Drive South. ☎(0253) 724636. 36⇌ ♠ English & Continental cuisine

★★ 66% Chadwick, South Promenade. ☎(0253) 720061. 72⇌ ♠ English & French cuisine

★★ 66% St Ives, 7-9 South Promenade. ☎(0253) 720011. 71⇌ ♠ English & French cuisine

RESTAURANT:

THORNTON

✕ ✕ ⊛The Victorian House, ☎ Blackpool (025 3) 860619 French cuisine

Location   Red Bridge Ln (opposite Silverdale Station)
Hotel   ★62% Wheatsheaf Hotel, BEETHAM
            ☎ (05395) 62123 6⇥ ↿

UPHOLLAND   Map 07 SD50

Beacon Park ☎ (0695) 622700
Undulating/hilly parkland course, designed by Donald Steel,
with magnificent view of the Welsh hills and Blackpool
Tower. Twenty-four-bay floodlit driving range.
18 holes, 5996yds, Par 72, SSS 69, Course record 68.
Club membership 300.
Visitors   must contact at least 6 days in advance.
Societies   apply in writing
Green Fees not confirmed.
Facilities ⊗ ⅢⅢ ﯖ ♥ ♀ 스 ﹫ ⁤ ↿ Ray Peters.
Leisure   floodlit driving range.
Location   Beacon Ln (S of Ashurst Beacon Hill)
Hotel   ★★71% Holland Hall Hotel, 6 Lafford Ln,
            UPHOLLAND ☎ (0695) 624426
            28⇥ ↿Annexe6⇥ ↿

> *Dean Wood* ☎ (0695) 622219
> This parkland course has a varied terrain - flat front nine,
> undulating back nine. Beware the par 4, 11th and 17th
> holes, which has ruined many a card. If there were a prize
> for the best maintained course in Lancashire, Dean Wood
> would be a strong contender.
> *18 holes, 6137yds, Par 71, SSS 70, Course record 66.*
> *Club membership 850.*
> Visitors   restricted weekends, bank holidays &
>   competition days. Must contact in advance.
> Societies   must contact in writing.
> Green Fees not confirmed.
> Facilities ⊗ ⅢⅢ ﯖ ♥ ♀ 스 ﹫ ↿ Tony Coop.
> Leisure   snooker.
> Location   Lafford Ln (0.5m NE off A577)
> Hotel   ★★71% Holland Hall Hotel, 6 Lafford Ln,
>   UPHOLLAND ☎ (0695) 624426
>   28⇥ ↿Annexe6⇥ ↿

WHALLEY   Map 07 SD73

Whalley ☎ (0254) 822236
Parkland course on Pendle Hill, overlooking the Ribble
Valley. Superb views. Ninth hole over pond.
9 holes, 5900mtrs, Par 72, SSS 70.
Club membership 325.
Visitors   restricted Thu 12.30-4pm & Sat Apr-Sep.
Societies   must give 4 weeks notice Apr-Sep.
Green Fees £15 per day (£20 weekends & bank holidays).
Facilities ⊗ ⅢⅢ ﯖ ♥ ♀ 스 ﹫ ⁤ ↿ H Smith.
Location   Long Leese Barn, Portfield Ln
            (1m SE off A671)
Hotel   ★★★58% Blackburn Moat House, Preston New
            Rd, BLACKBURN
            ☎ (0254) 264441 98⇥ ↿

WHITWORTH   Map 07 SD81

Lobden ☎ Rochdale (0706) 343228
Moorland couse, with hard walking. Windy.
9 holes, 5750yds, Par 70, SSS 68.
Club membership 200.

Visitors   may not play Tue 3pm-7pm, Wed after 4pm or
            Sat.
Societies   must contact in writing.
Green Fees £10 per day (£12 weekends & bank holidays).
Facilities ⊗ ⅢⅢ ﯖ ♥ (catering by prior arrangement)
            ♀ 스
Leisure   snooker.
Location   Lobden Moor (E side of town centre off A671)
Hotel   ★★61% Midway Hotel, Manchester Rd,
            Castleton, ROCHDALE
            ☎ (0706) 32881 24⇥ ↿

WILPSHIRE   Map 07 SD63

Wilpshire ☎ Blackburn (0254) 248260
Semi-moorland course. Testing 17th hole (229 yds) par 3.
Extensive views of Ribble Valley, the coast and the
Yorkshire Dales.
18 holes, 5921yds, Par 69, SSS 68.
Club membership 794.
Visitors   may not play on competition days.
Societies   must contact in writing.
Green Fees not confirmed.
Facilities 스 ﹫ ↿
Hotel   ★★★58% Blackburn Moat House, Preston New
            Rd, BLACKBURN ☎ (0254) 264441 98⇥ ↿

● LEICESTERSHIRE ●

ASHBY-DE-LA-ZOUCH   Map 08 SK31

Willesley Park ☎ (0530) 414596
Undulating heathland and parkland course with quick
draining sandy sub-soil.
18 holes, 6304yds, Par 70, SSS 70.
Club membership 600.
Visitors   may not play before 9.30am on weekends &
            bank holidays. Must contact in advance and have
            a handicap certificate.
Societies   telephone to book, up to a year in advance.
Green Fees £25 per day (£30 weekends & bank holidays).
Facilities ⊗ ⅢⅢ ﯖ ♥ ♀ 스 ﹫ ↿ C J Hancock.
Leisure   snooker.
Location   Measham Rd (SW side of town centre on A453)
Hotel   ★★★65% Stanhope Hotel, Ashby Rd East,
            BRETBY ☎ (0283) 217954 28⇥ ↿

BIRSTALL   Map 04 SK50

Birstall ☎ Leicester (0533) 674322
Parkland course with trees, shrubs, ponds and ditches.
18 holes, 6222yds, Par 70, SSS 70.
Club membership 500.
Visitors   with member only Tue & weekends.
Societies   apply in writing.
Green Fees £25 per day.
Facilities ⊗ ⅢⅢ ﯖ ♥ ♀ 스 ﹫ ↿ D R Clarke.
Leisure   snooker, practise ground.
Location   Station Rd (SW side of town centre off A6)
Hotel   ★★★60% Hotel Saint James, Abbey St,
            LEICESTER ☎ (0533) 510666 72⇥ ↿

BOTCHESTON
Map 04 SK40

Leicestershire Forest Golf Centre ☎ Hinckley (0455) 824800
Parkland course with many trees, four Par 4s, but no steep gradients.
18 holes, 6111yds, Par 72, SSS 69, Course record 72.
Club membership 450.
Visitors must contact in advance for weekends.
Societies must telephone in advance.
Green Fees £15 per day; £10 per round (£10 per round after 11am).
Facilities ⊗ & ▥ by prior arrangement ⓑ ♥ ♀ ♨ 🏠 ⊣ ʔ Martin Wing.
Leisure driving range.
Location Markfield Ln
Hotel ★★★71% Fieldhead Hotel, Markfield Ln, MARKFIELD ☎ (0530) 245454 28⇄ ⨣

COSBY
Map 04 SP59

Cosby ☎ Leicester (0533) 864759
Undulating parkland course.
18 holes, 6418yds, Par 71, SSS 71, Course record 65.
Club membership 680.
Visitors before 4pm & with member only weekends & bank holidays. Must contact in advance and have handicap certificate.
Societies book with secretary.
Green Fees £22 per day; £20 per round.
Facilities ⊗ ▥ by prior arrangement ⓑ ♥ ♀ ♨ 🏠 ʔ David Bowring.
Leisure snooker.
Location Chapel Ln, Broughton Rd (S side of village off)
Hotel ★★★63% Forte Posthouse, Braunstone Ln East, LEICESTER ☎ (0533) 630500 172⇄ ⨣

GREETHAM
Map 08 SK91

Greetham Valley ☎ Empingham (078086) 666 & 444
Set in 200 acres, including mature woodland and water hazards, Greetham Valley was opened in spring 1992. The complex comprises an 18-hole course and clubhouse, a floodlit 9-hole Par 3 and a 21-bay floodlit driving range.
18 holes, 6656yds, Par 72.
Club membership 650.
Visitors must contact in advance.
Societies apply in writing.
Green Fees £15 (£25 weekends).
Facilities ⊗ ▥ ⓑ ♥ ♀ ♨ 🏠 ⊣ ʔ Mark Cunningham.
Location Off B668 in Greetham
Hotel ★★68% Ram Jam Inn, Great North Rd, STRETTON ☎ (0780) 410776 Annexe7⇄ ⨣

HINCKLEY
Map 04 SP49

Hinckley ☎ (0455) 615124
Rolling parkland with lake features, and lined fairways.
18 holes, 6517yds, Par 71, SSS 71.
Club membership 1000.

Visitors with member only weekends and bank holidays. Must contact in advance and have a handicap certificate.
Societies apply by letter.
Green Fees not confirmed.
Facilities ⊗ ▥ ⓑ ♥ ♀ ♨ 🏠 ʔ Richard Jones.
Leisure snooker.
Location Leicester Rd (1.5m NE on A47)
Hotel Longshoot Toby Hotel, Watling St, NUNEATON ☎ (0203) 329711 Annexe47⇄ ⨣

KETTON
Map 04 SK90

Luffenham Heath ☎ Stamford (0780) 720205
This undulating heathland course with low bushes, much gorse and many trees, lies in a conservation area for flora and fauna. From the higher part of the course there is a magnificent view across the Chater Valley.
18 holes, 6250yds, Par 70, SSS 70, Course record 64.
Club membership 555.
Visitors must contact in advance and a handicap certificate required.
Societies must telephone in advance
Green Fees £30 per day (£35 weekends & bank holidays).
Facilities ⊗ & ▥ by prior arrangement ⓑ ♥ ♀ ♨ 🏠 ʔ
Location Stamford (1.5m SW on A6121)
Hotel ★★★75% George of Stamford Hotel, St Martins, STAMFORD ☎ (0780) 55171 47⇄ ⨣

KIBWORTH
Map 04 SP69

Kibworth ☎ (0533) 792301
Parkland course with easy walking. A brook affects a number of fairways
18 holes, 6282yds, Par 71, SSS 70.
Club membership 700.
Visitors a handicap certificate is required. With member only weekends.
Societies must contact in advance.
Green Fees £21 per day/round.
Facilities ⊗ ▥ ⓑ ♥ ♀ ♨ 🏠 ⊣ ʔ Alan Strange.
Leisure snooker.
Location Weir Rd, Beauchamp (S side of village)
Hotel ★★★64% Three Swans Hotel, 21 High St, MARKET HARBOROUGH ☎ (0858) 466644 20⇄ ⨣Annexe16⇄ ⨣

KIRBY MUXLOE
Map 04 SK50

Kirby Muxloe ☎ Leicester (0533) 393457
Parkland course.
18 holes, 6303yds, Par 71, SSS 70.
Club membership 700.
Visitors must contact in advance and a handicap certificate is required. Restricted at weekends.
Societies must contact in advance.
Green Fees weekdays(ex Tue) £25 per day; £20 per round.
Facilities ⊗ ▥ ⓑ ♥ ♀ ♨ 🏠 ʔ R T Stephenson.
Leisure snooker, driving range.
Location Station Rd (S side of village off B5380)
Hotel ★★★★60% Holiday Inn, St Nicholas Circle, LEICESTER ☎ (0533) 531161 188⇄ ⨣

LEICESTER

Map 04 SK50

Humberstone Heights ☎ (0533) 764674
Municipal parkland course with 9 hole pitch and putt.
18 holes, 6300yds, Par 70, SSS 71, Course record 66.
Club membership 500.
Visitors   no restrictions.
Societies   must telephone in advance.
Green Fees   £6 per round (£7.50 weekends & bank holidays).
Facilities   ⊗ 🏠 ▬ ♀ 👥 🏠 ⛳ 🏌
Leisure   driving range & pitch & putt course.
Location   Gypsy Ln (2.5m NE of city centre)
Hotel   ★★★55% Park International Hotel,
                 Humberstone Rd, LEICESTER
                 ☎ (0533) 620471 220➪ ⋒

Leicestershire ☎ (0533) 738825
Pleasantly undulating parkland course.
18 holes, 6312yds, Par 68, SSS 70.
Club membership 750.
Visitors   must contact in advance & have handicap
                 certificate. Restricted Sat & Tue.
Societies   must telephone in advance.
Green Fees   £26 per day (£32 weekends & bank holidays).
Facilities   ⊗ 🍴 by prior arrangement 🏠 ▬ ♀ 👥 🏠 🏌
                 John R Turnbull.
Location   Evington Ln (2m E of city off A6030)
Hotel   ★★★67% Leicestershire Moat House, Wigston
                 Rd, Oadby, LEICESTER
                 ☎ (0533) 719441 57➪ ⋒

Western Park ☎ (0533) 872339
Pleasant, undulating parkland course with open aspect
fairways in two loops of nine holes.Not too difficult but a
good test of golf off the back tees. A driving range is due to
be completed by August 1993.
18 holes, 6561yds, Par 72, SSS 71.
Club membership 400.
Visitors   must contact in advance for availability etc.
Societies   may only play Mon-Thu. Must contact the
                 professional in advance.
Green Fees   £6 (£7.50 weekends).
Facilities   👥 🏠 ⛳ 🏌 Bruce Nicholas Whipham.
Location   Scudamore Rd, Braunstone Frith (1.5m W of
                 city centre off A47)
Hotel   ★★★63% Forte Posthouse, Braunstone Ln East,
                 LEICESTER ☎ (0533) 630500 172➪ ⋒

LOUGHBOROUGH

Map 08 SK51

Longcliffe ☎ (0509) 239129
A re-designed course of natural heathland with outcrops
of granite forming natural hazards especially on the 1st
and 15th. The course is heavily wooded and has much
bracken and gorse. There are a number of tight fairways
and one blind hole.
18 holes, 6551yds, Par 71, SSS 72.
Club membership 600.
Visitors   must contact in advance & have handicap
                 certificate. With member only at weekends.
Societies   by prior arrangement.
Green Fees   not confirmed.
Facilities   ⊗ 🍴 🏠 ▬ ♀ 👥 🏌 Ian D Bailey.
Location   Snell's Nook Ln, Nanpantan
                 (3m SW off B5350)

Hotel   ★★56% Great Central Hotel, Great Central
                 Rd, LOUGHBOROUGH
                 ☎ (0509) 263405 15➪ ⋒

LUTTERWORTH

Map 04 SP58

Lutterworth ☎ (0455) 552532
Hilly course with River Swift running through.
18 holes, 5570yds, Par 67, SSS 67.
Club membership 600.
Visitors   may not play at weekends.
Societies   Mon-Fri; must contact in advance.
Green Fees   not confirmed.
Facilities   ⊗ 🍴 🏠 ▬ ♀ 👥 🏠 🏌 Nick Melvin.
Location   Rugby Rd (0.5m S on A426)
Hotel   ★★★69% Denbigh Arms Hotel, High St,
                 LUTTERWORTH ☎ (0455) 553537 34➪ ⋒

MARKET HARBOROUGH

Map 04 SP78

Market Harborough ☎ (0858) 463684
A parkland course situated close to the town. There are wide-
ranging views over the surrounding countryside.
9 holes, 6080yds, Par 71, SSS 69.
Club membership 330.
Visitors   must play with member at weekends.
Societies   must telephone (0536) 771771 in advance.
Green Fees   not confirmed.
Facilities   ⊗ 🍴 🏠 ▬ ♀ 👥 🏠 ⛳ 🏌 Frazer Baxter.
Location   Oxendon Rd (1m S on A508)
Hotel   ★★★64% Three Swans Hotel, 21 High St,
                 MARKET HARBOROUGH
                 ☎ (0858) 466644 20➪ ⋒Annexe16➪ ⋒

MELTON MOWBRAY

Map 08 SK71

Melton Mowbray ☎ (0664) 62118
Downland but flat course providing easy walking. Open to
the wind.
18 holes, 5792yds, Par 70, SSS 70.
Club membership 447.
Visitors   no restrictions.
Societies   must contact in advance.
Green Fees   not confirmed.
Facilities   ▬ ♀ 👥
Location   Thorpe Arnold (2m NE on A607)
Hotel   ★★64% Sysonby Knoll Hotel, Asfordby Rd,
                 MELTON MOWBRAY ☎ (0664) 63563
                 23➪ ⋒Annexe1➪ ⋒

OADBY

Map 04 SK60

Glen Gorse ☎ Leicester (0533) 714159 & 713748
Fairly flat 18-hole parkland course with some mature trees,
new saplings and several water hazards.
18 holes, 6615yds, Par 72, SSS 72, Course record 65.
Club membership 700.
Visitors   unrestricted on weekdays, with member only Sat
                 & Sun.
Societies   by prior arrangement.
Green Fees   £25 per day; £22 per round.
Facilities   ⊗ 🍴 🏠 ▬ (catering Tue-Fri only) ♀ (Tue-Sat)
                 👥 🏠 ⛳ 🏌 Bob Larratt.

Leisure	riding, snooker.
Location	Glen Rd (on A6 trunk road between Oadby/Great Glen)
Hotel	★★★67% Leicestershire Moat House, Wigston Rd, Oadby, LEICESTER ☎ (0533) 719441 57⇄ ⁿ

Oadby ☎ (0533) 700326
Municipal parkland course.
18 holes, 6228yds, Par 71, SSS 69.
Club membership 400.

Visitors	no restrictions.
Societies	must contact in advance.
Green Fees	not confirmed.
Facilities	♀ ♨ 🏠 ⛳ (
Location	Leicester Rd (West side of town centre off A6)
Hotel	★★★67% Leicestershire Moat House, Wigston Rd, Oadby, LEICESTER ☎ (0533) 719441 57⇄ ⁿ

ROTHLEY   Map 08 SK51

Rothley Park ☎ (0533) 302809
Parkland course in picturesque situation.
18 holes, 6167yds, Par 70, SSS 69.
Club membership 600.

Visitors	restricted Tue, weekends & competitions. Must contact in advance and a handicap certificate required.
Societies	apply in writing.
Green Fees	£30 per day; £25 per round.
Facilities	⊗ & 𝕀𝕀𝕀 (ex Mon) ᴸ ♥ ♀ ♨ 🏠 (Peter Dolan.
Location	Westfield Ln (0.75m W on B5328)
Hotel	★★★70% Rothley Court Hotel, Westfield Ln, ROTHLEY ☎ (0533) 374141 15⇄ ⁿ Annexe21⇄ ⁿ

SCRAPTOFT   Map 04 SK60

Scraptoft ☎ (0533) 418863
Pleasant, inland country course.
18 holes, 6166yds, Par 69, SSS 69.
Club membership 550.

Visitors	with member only weekends. Handicap certificate required.
Societies	apply in writing.
Green Fees	not confirmed.
Facilities	⊗ 𝕀𝕀𝕀 ᴸ ♥ ♀ ♨ 🏠 ⛳ (Simon Sherratt.
Location	Beeby Rd (1m NE)
Hotel	★★★67% Leicestershire Moat House, Wigston Rd, Oadby, LEICESTER ☎ (0533) 719441 57⇄ ⁿ

ULLESTHORPE   Map 04 SP58

Ullesthorpe ☎ Leire (0455) 209023
Parkland course. Many leisure facilities.
18 holes, 6650yds, Par 72, SSS 72.
Club membership 640.

Visitors	may not play weekends. Must contact in advance.
Societies	contact in advance.
Green Fees	£19 per day.

Facilities	⊗ 𝕀𝕀𝕀 ᴸ ♥ ♀ ♨ 🏠 ⇄ (
Leisure	hard tennis courts, heated indoor swimming pool, snooker, sauna, solarium, gymnasium.
Location	Frolesworth Rd (0.5m N off B577)
Hotel	★★★69% Denbigh Arms Hotel, High St, LUTTERWORTH ☎ (0455) 553537 34⇄ ⁿ

WHETSTONE   Map 04 SP59

Whetstone ☎ (0533) 861424
Small and very flat parkland course adjacent to motorway.
18 holes, 5795yds, Par 68, SSS 68, Course record 64.
Club membership 500.

Visitors	limited times at weekends
Societies	must contact in advance.
Green Fees	£17.50 per day; £12.50 per round (£13.50 per roundweekends & bank holidays).
Facilities	⊗ & 𝕀𝕀𝕀 (ex weekends) ᴸ (ex Sun) ♥ ♀ ♨ 🏠 (David Raitt.
Location	Cambridge Rd, Cosby (1m S of village)
Hotel	★★★63% Forte Posthouse, Braunstone Ln East, LEICESTER ☎ (0533) 630500 172⇄ ⁿ

WOODHOUSE EAVES   Map 08 SK51

Charnwood Forest ☎ (0509) 890259
Hilly heathland course with hard walking, but no bunkers.
9 holes, 5960yds, Par 69, SSS 69, Course record 66.
Club membership 325.

Visitors	may be restricted Tue. Must contact in advance and have an introduction from own club.
Societies	apply in writing.
Green Fees	not confirmed.
Facilities	⊗ & 𝕀𝕀𝕀 by prior arrangement ᴸ ♥ ♀ ♨ 🏠 (Mark Lawrence.
Location	Breakback Ln (0.75m NW off B591)
Hotel	★★★★67% Quorn Country Hotel, Charwood House, Leicester Rd, QUORN ☎ (0509) 415050 19⇄ ⁿ

Lingdale ☎ (0509) 890703
Parkland course located in Charnwood Forest with some hard walking at some holes. The par 3, (3rd) and par 5, (8th) are testing holes. The 4th and 5th have water hazards.
18 holes, 6556yds, Par 71, SSS 71.
Club membership 583.

Visitors	restricted weekends & competition days.
Societies	must contact in writing.
Green Fees	£18 per day.
Facilities	⊗ 𝕀𝕀𝕀 by prior arrangement ᴸ ♥ ♀ ♨ 🏠 (Peter Sellears.
Leisure	practice ground, pool table.
Location	Joe Moore's Ln (1.5m S off B5330)
Hotel	★★★★67% Quorn Country Hotel, Charwood House, Leicester Rd, QUORN ☎ (0509) 415050 19⇄ ⁿ

For a full list of all the golf courses included in this guide, see the index at the end of the Directory

LINCOLNSHIRE

BELTON
Map 08 SK93

Belton Woods Hotel & Country Club
☎ Grantham (0476) 593200
Two challenging 18-hole courses, a 9-hole Par 3 and a
driving range. The Lancaster Course has 13 lakes, while the
Wellington boasts the third longest hole in Europe at 613
yards. Many leisure facilities.
*Lancaster: 18 holes, 7021yds, Par 73, SSS 74, Course record
69.*
Wellington: 18 holes, 6875yds, Par 72, SSS 73.
Spitfire: 9 holes, 1184yds, Par 27.
Club membership 900.
Visitors no advanced booking permitted.
Societies advance booking required.
Green Fees not confirmed.
Facilities ⊗ 洲 ⓑ ⬛ ♀ ⚘ 🏠 ⛳ ㅂ 𝄢 Dean Vannet.
Leisure hard tennis courts, heated indoor swimming
pool, squash, snooker, sauna, solarium,
gymnasium.
Location On A607, 2m N of Grantham
Hotel ★★★★66% Belton Woods Hotel & Country
Club, BELTON ☎ (0476) 593200 96⇌ ⋒

BLANKNEY
Map 08 TF06

Blankney ☎ Metheringham (0526) 320263
Open parkland course with mature trees; fairly flat.
18 holes, 6378yds, Par 71, SSS 71.
Club membership 630.
Visitors may not play Sun & winter weekends, restricted
Sat. Must contact in advance.
Societies contact in advance.
Green Fees £20 per day; £15 per round (£30/£20 weekends
& bank holidays).
Facilities ⊗ 洲 ⓑ ⬛ ♀ ⚘ 🏠 𝄢 Graham Bradley.
Leisure snooker.
Location 1m SW on B1188
Hotel ★★★57% Moor Lodge Hotel, Sleaford Rd,
BRANSTON ☎ (0522) 791366 25⇌ ⋒

BOSTON
Map 08 TF34

Boston ☎ (0205) 350589
Parkland course many water hazards in play on ten holes.
18 holes, 5825yds, Par 69, SSS 68, Course record 66.
Club membership 650.
Visitors welcome except weekends & bank holidays.
Must contact in advance.
Societies apply two weeks in advance.
Green Fees £15 per round; £20 per day (£20 per round; £30
per day weekends).
Facilities ⊗ 洲 ⓑ ⬛ ♀ ⚘ 🏠 ⛳ 𝄢 Terry Squires.
Location Cowbridge, Horncastle Rd (2m N off B1183)
Hotel ★★59% New England, 49 Wide Bargate,
BOSTON ☎ (0205) 365255 25⇌

> This guide is up-dated annually – make sure
> you use the up-to-date edition

BOURNE
Map 08 TF01

Toft Hotel ☎ Witham-on-the-Hill (077833) 614
Parkland course on the verge of the Lincoln Edge. Includes
lake and uses contours of the hills to full effect.
18 holes, 6486yds, Par 72, SSS 71, Course record 71.
Club membership 550.
Visitors advisable to book.
Societies apply in advance.
Green Fees £15 (£22 per day weekends).
Facilities ⊗ 洲 ⓑ ⬛ ♀ ⚘ 🏠 ⛳ ㅂ 𝄢 Mark Jackson.
Location Toft (15m SE of Spalding,on A6121
Bourne/Stamford)
Hotel ★★56% Angel Hotel, Market Place, BOURNE
☎ (0778) 422346 13⇌ ⋒

GAINSBOROUGH
Map 08 SK88

Gainsborough ☎ (0427) 613088
Scenic parkland course. Floodlit driving range.
18 holes, 6620yds, Par 73, SSS 72.
Club membership 600.
Visitors welcome weekdays. Must contact in advance.
Societies must telephone in advance.
Green Fees not confirmed.
Facilities ⊗ 洲 ⓑ ⬛ ♀ ⚘ 🏠 𝄢 Stephan Cooper.
Leisure snooker, driving range.
Location Thonock (1m N off A159)
Hotel ★★65% Hickman-Hill Hotel, Cox's Hill,
GAINSBOROUGH ☎ (0427) 613639
8rm(3⇌3 ⋒)

GEDNEY HILL
Map 09 TF31

Gedney Hill ☎ Holbeach (0406) 330922 & 330183
Flat parkland course similar to a links course. Made testing
by Fen winds and small greens. Also a 10-bay driving range.
18 holes, 5493yds, Par 70, SSS 66, Course record 67.
Club membership 300.
Visitors no restrictions.
Societies telephone in advance.
Green Fees £5.75 (£9.75 weekends and bank holidays).
Facilities ⊗ 洲 ⓑ ⬛ ♀ ⚘ 🏠 ⛳ 𝄢 David Creek.
Leisure snooker, 10 bay driving range.
Location West Drove (5m SE of Spalding)
Hotel ★★63% Queens Hotel, South Brink, WISBECH
☎ (0945) 583933 12⇌ ⋒Annexe6⇌

GRANTHAM
Map 08 SK93

Belton Park ☎ (0476) 67399
Parkland course, wooded, with water features, deer park and
Canadian Geese Reserve. Famous holes: 5th, 12th, 16th and
18th. 27-holes, with three 9-hole combinations.
18 holes, 6420yds, Par 71, SSS 71, Course record 65.
Ancaster: 18 holes, 6252yds, Par 70, SSS 70.
Belmont: 18 holes, 6016yds, Par 69, SSS 69.
Club membership 900.
Visitors no restrictions.
Societies apply in writing.
Green Fees £17 per round (£26 weekends & bank holidays).
Facilities ⊗ 洲 by prior arrangement ⓑ ⬛ ♀ ⚘ 🏠 ⛳ 𝄢
Brian McKee.
Leisure two practice fairways.

Location	Belton Ln, Londonthorpe Rd (1.5m NE off A607)
Hotel	★★★64% Angel & Royal Hotel, High St, GRANTHAM ☎ (0476) 65816 30⇄ ℟

Sudbrook Moor ☎ (0400) 50796 & 50876
A testing 9-hole parkland course in open countryside.
9 holes, 4566yds, Par 66, SSS 61, Course record 69.

Visitors	preferable to contact in advance.
Societies	prior application.
Green Fees	£5 per day (£7 weekends and bank holidays).
Facilities	⊗ ⅢⅢ ⓛ ♥ ♀ ♨ ⚑ ℣ ℟ Tim Hutton.
Location	Charity Ln, Carlton Scroop
Hotel	★★68% Kings Hotel, North Pde, GRANTHAM ☎ (0476) 590800 22rm(21⇄ ℟)

HORNCASTLE   Map 08 TF26

Horncastle ☎ (0507) 526800
Heathland course with many water hazards and bunkers; very challenging. There is a 25-bay floodlit driving range.
18 holes, 5782yds, Par 70, SSS 70, Course record 75.
Club membership 300.

Visitors	no jeans, T-shirts or tracksuits.
Societies	apply in writing.
Green Fees	not confirmed..
Facilities	⊗ ⅢⅢ ⓛ ♥ ♀ ⚑ ℣ E C Wright.
Leisure	fishing, floodlit driving range.
Location	West Ashby (1.5m N Horncastle)
Hotel	★★★67% Petwood House Hotel, Stixwould Rd, WOODHALL SPA ☎ (0526) 352411 46⇄ ℟

LINCOLN   Map 08 SK97

Canwick Park ☎ (0522) 522166 & 542912
Parkland course. Testing 14th hole (par 3).
18 holes, 6237yds, Par 70, SSS 70.
Club membership 576.

Visitors	restricted at weekends. Must contact in advance.
Societies	must contact 1 month in advance.
Green Fees	£20 per day; £13 per round (£22 per day, £14 per round weekends & bank holidays).
Facilities	⊗ ⅢⅢ & ⓛ (ex Mon) ♥ ♀ ♨ ⚑ ℣ ℟ S Williamson.
Location	Canwick Park, Washingborough Rd (2m SE on B1190)
Hotel	★★★63% Forte Posthouse, Eastgate, LINCOLN ☎ (0522) 520341 70⇄ ℟

Carholme ☎ (0522) 23725
Parkland course where prevailing west winds can add interest. Good views.
18 holes, 6114yds, Par 71, SSS 69.
Club membership 700.

Visitors	may not play Sat, Sun & bank holidays. Must contact in advance.
Societies	apply in writing.
Green Fees	not confirmed.
Facilities	ⓛ (ex Mon) ♥ ♀ ♨ ⚑ ℣ ℟ Gary Leslie.
Location	Carholme Rd (1m W of city centre on A57)
Hotel	★★★★63% The White Hart, Bailgate, LINCOLN ☎ (0522) 526222 50⇄

LOUTH   Map 08 TF38

Louth ☎ (0507) 603681
Undulating parkland course, fine views.
18 holes, 6477yds, Par 71, SSS 71, Course record 64.
Club membership 700.

Visitors	must contact in advance and have a handicap certificate.
Societies	must contact in advance.
Green Fees	£18 day; £15 per round (£20/18 weekends and bank holidays).
Facilities	⊗ ⅢⅢ by prior arrangement ⓛ ♥ ♀ ♨ ⚑ ℣ ℟ A Blundell.
Leisure	squash.
Location	Crowtree Ln (SE side of town centre off A157)
Hotel	★★65% Priory Hotel, Eastgate, LOUTH ☎ (0507) 602930 12rm(6⇄3 ℟)

MARKET RASEN   Map 08 TF18

Market Rasen & District ☎ (0673) 842416
Picturesque, well-wooded heathland course, easy walking, breezy with becks forming natural hazards. Good views of Lincolnshire Wolds.
18 holes, 6043yds, Par 70, SSS 69.
Club membership 550.

Visitors	must play with member at weekends and must contact in advance.
Societies	Tue & Fri only; must contact in advance.
Green Fees	not confirmed.
Facilities	♨ ⚑ ℣ A M Chester.
Location	Legsby Rd (2m SE)
Hotel	★★★63% Forte Posthouse, Eastgate, LINCOLN ☎ (0522) 520341 70⇄ ℟

SKEGNESS   Map 09 TF56

North Shore Hotel & Golf Club ☎ (0754) 763298
A half-links, half-parkland course designed by James Braid in 1910. Easy walking and good sea views.
18 holes, 6134yds, Par 71, SSS 71, Course record 68.
Club membership 400.

Visitors	must observe dress rules & must be competent golfers.
Societies	telephone in advance.
Green Fees	not confirmed.
Facilities	⊗ ⅢⅢ ⓛ ♥ ♀ ♨ ⚑ ℣
Leisure	hard tennis courts, snooker.
Location	North Shore Rd (1m N of town centre off A52)
Hotel	★★★58% Crown Hotel, Drummond Rd, Seacroft, SKEGNESS ☎ (0754) 610760 27⇄ ℟

Seacroft ☎ (0754) 763020
A typical seaside links with flattish fairways separated by low ridges and good greens. Easy to walk round. To the east are sandhills leading to the shore. Southward lies 'Gibraltar Point Nature Reserve'.
18 holes, 6501yds, Par 71, SSS 71, Course record 67.
Club membership 620.

Visitors	must contact in advance & have handicap certificate but may not play before 9.30am.
Societies	contact in advance. ▶

Green Fees £28 per day; £20 per round (£35/£25 weekends & bank holidays).
Facilities ⊗ ⅲ ⚐ ⬛ ♀ 🏠 (Robin Lawie.
Location Drummond Rd, Seacroft (S side of town centre)
Hotel ★★★58% Crown Hotel, Drummond Rd, Seacroft, SKEGNESS
☎ (0754) 610760 27⇄ ⟍

SLEAFORD
Map 08 TF04

Sleaford ☎ South Rauceby (05298) 273
Inland links-type course, moderately wooded and fairly flat.
18 holes, 6443yds, Par 72, SSS 71, Course record 65.
Club membership 650.
Visitors may not play Sun in winter. Must have a handicap certificate.
Societies apply in writing.
Green Fees £18 per day (£26 weekends & bank holidays).
Facilities ⊗ & ⅲ (ex Mon) ⚐ ⬛ (dinner by arrangement) ♀ 🏠 (J N Wilson.
Location South Rauceby (1m W off A153)
Hotel ★★★64% Angel & Royal Hotel, High St, GRANTHAM
☎ (0476) 65816 30⇄ ⟍

SPALDING
Map 08 TF22

Spalding ☎ (077585) 386 & 234
A pretty, well laid-out course in a fenland area. The River Glen runs beside the 1st and 2nd holes, and streams, ponds and new tree plantings add to the variety of this well-maintained course.
18 holes, 6450yds, Par 71, SSS 71.
Club membership 750.
Visitors are advised to contact in advance and must have a handicap certificate.
Societies must contact in advance.
Green Fees not confirmed.
Facilities 🏠 (John Spencer.
Location Surfleet (5m N off A16)
Hotel ★★59% New England, 49 Wide Bargate, BOSTON
☎ (0205) 365255 25⇄

STAMFORD
Map 04 TF00

Burghley Park ☎ (0780) 53789
Open parkland course with superb greens, many new trees, ponds and bunkers. Situated in the grounds of Burghley House.
18 holes, 6200yds, Par 70, SSS 70, Course record 64.
Club membership 950.
Visitors with member only weekends. Must contact in advance & have handicap certificate.
Societies apply in writing.
Green Fees £20 per day (half price after noon in winter months).
Facilities ⊗ ⅲ by prior arrangement (Apr-Sep) ⚐ ⬛ ♀ 🏠 (Glenn Davies.
Location St Martins (1m S of town on B1081)
Hotel ★★★75% George of Stamford Hotel, St Martins, STAMFORD
☎ (0780) 55171 47⇄ ⟍

STOKE ROCHFORD
Map 08 SK92

Stoke Rochford ☎ Great Ponton (047683) 275
Parkland course designed by C. Turner.
18 holes, 6251yds, Par 70, SSS 70, Course record 65.
Club membership 525.
Visitors must contact in advance, restricted to 9am weekdays, 10.30am weekends & bank holidays.
Societies contact one year in advance.
Green Fees £24 per day; £17 per round (£35/£26 weekends & bank holidays).
Facilities ⊗ & ⅲ by prior arrangement ⚐ ⬛ by prior arrangement ♀ 🏠 (Angus Dow.
Leisure snooker.
Location Off A1 5m S of Grantham
Hotel ★★68% Kings Hotel, North Pde, GRANTHAM
☎ (0476) 590800 22rm(21⇄ ⟍)

SUTTON BRIDGE
Map 09 TF42

Sutton Bridge ☎ Holbeach (0406) 350323
Parkland course.
9 holes, 5850yds, Par 70, SSS 68.
Club membership 350.
Visitors may not play competition days, weekends & bank holidays. Must contact in advance & have handicap certificate.
Societies telephone in advance.
Green Fees £15 per day/round.
Facilities ⊗ ⅲ ⚐ ⬛ (no catering Mon) ♀ (ex Mon) 🏠 ⌐(R Wood.
Location New Rd (E side of village off A17)
Hotel ★★★65% The Duke's Head, Tuesday Market Pl, KING'S LYNN
☎ (0553) 774996 71⇄ ⟍

SUTTON ON SEA
Map 09 TF58

Sandilands ☎ (0507) 441432
Flat links course on the sea shore.
18 holes, 5995yds, Par 70, SSS 69.
Club membership 300.
Visitors no restrictions.
Societies welcome weekdays only, telephone in advance.
Green Fees £18 per day; £12 per round (£18 per round weekends & bank holidays).
Facilities ⊗ ⚐ ⬛ ♀ 🏠
Location 1.5m S off A52
Hotel ★★69% Grange & Links Hotel, Sea Ln, Sandilands, MABLETHORPE
☎ (0507) 441334 23⇄ ⟍

TORKSEY
Map 08 SK87

Lincoln ☎ (042771) 210
A testing inland course with quick-drying sandy subsoil and easy walking.
18 holes, 6438yds, Par 71, SSS 71.
Club membership 700.
Visitors may not play between noon-1.30pm or on weekends & bank holidays. Must contact in advance and have a handicaps certificate.
Societies apply by letter.
Green Fees £23 per day; £18 per round.

Facilities ⊗ ⅏ ⅂ ♨ ♀ ⚮ 🕾 (A Carter.
Location SW side of village
Hotel ★★★★63% The White Hart, Bailgate,
LINCOLN ☎ (0522) 526222 50⊷

WOODHALL SPA — Map 08 TF16

Woodhall Spa ☎ (0526) 352511
One of the country's greatest and most beautiful
heathland courses, founded in 1905, and originally laid
out by Harry Vardon. It provides flat, easy walking
amongst heather and tree-lined fairways, and is renowned
for its vast bunkers and clubhouse atmosphere.
18 holes, 6907yds, Par 73, SSS 73.
Club membership 450.
Visitors must be a member of a golf club affiliated to
the appropriate Golf Union, maximum
handicap gentlemen 20-ladies 30, handicap
certificate must be produced.
Societies must book in advance.
Green Fees not confirmed.
Facilities ⊗ ⅏ ⅂ ♨ ♀ ⚮ 🕾 (P Fixter.
Location The Broadway (NE side of village
off B1191)
Hotel ★★★69% Fownes Resort Hotel, City Walls
Rd, WORCESTER
☎ (0905) 613151 61⊷ ⋔

WOODTHORPE — Map 09 TF48

Woodthorpe Hall ☎ Withern (0507) 450294
Parkland course.
18 holes, 4659yds, Par 64, SSS 63.
Club membership 400.
Visitors no restrictions.
Societies apply at least one month prior to visit.
Green Fees £8 per day.
Facilities ⊗ ⅏ ⅂ ♨ ♀ ⊷
Leisure fishing, snooker.
Location 8m due W of Sutton-on-Sea
Hotel ★★69% Grange & Links Hotel, Sea Ln,
Sandilands, MABLETHORPE
☎ (0507) 441334 23⊷ ⋔

● LONDON ●

**Courses within the London Postal District area (ie those
that have London Postcodes - W1, SW1 etc) are listed
here in postal district order commencing East then North,
South and West. Courses outside the London Postal area, but
within Greater London are to be found listed under the county
of Greater London in the gazetteer (see page 74).**

E4 CHINGFORD

Royal Epping Forest ☎ 081-529 2195 & 081-529 5708
Woodland course. 'Red' garments must be worn.
18 holes, 6620yds, Par 72, SSS 70.
Club membership 495.
Visitors booking system in operation.
Green Fees not confirmed..
Facilities ⚮ 🕾 (

Location Forest Approach, Chingford (300 yds S of
Chingford Station)
Hotel ★★★68% Woodford Moat House, Oak Hill,
WOODFORD GREEN ☎ 081-505 4511 99⊷ ⋔

West Essex ☎ 081-529 7558
Testing parkland course within Epping Forest. Notable holes
are 8th (par 4), 16th (par 4), 18th (par 5).
18 holes, 6289yds, Par 71, SSS 70, Course record 65.
Club membership 645.
Visitors must contact in advance & have handicap
certificate but may not play on Tue morning,
Thu afternoon & weekends.
Societies must contact in advance.
Green Fees £38 per day; £30 per round.
Facilities ⊗ ⅏ ⅂ ♨ (catering by arrangement) ♀ ⚮ 🕾 (
Charles Cox.
Leisure snooker.
Location Bury Rd, Sewardstonebury (off N Circular Rd at
Chingford on M25)
Hotel ★★59% Roebuck Hotel, North End,
BUCKHURST HILL ☎ 081-505 4636 29⊷ ⋔

E11 LEYTONSTONE

Wanstead ☎ 081-989 3938
A flat, picturesque parkland course with many trees and
shrubs and providing easy walking. The par 3, 16th, involves
driving across a lake.
18 holes, 6109yds, Par 69, SSS 69, Course record 61.
Club membership 500.
Visitors must contact in advance and may only play Mon,
Tue & Fri.
Societies by arrangement.
Green Fees not confirmed.
Facilities ⚮ 🕾 (
Leisure fishing.
Location Overton Dr, Wanstead (from central London
A11 NE to Wanstead)
Hotel ★★★68% Woodford Moat House, Oak Hill,
WOODFORD GREEN ☎ 081-505 4511 99⊷ ⋔

N2 EAST FINCHLEY

Hampstead ☎ 081-455 0203
Undulating parkland course.
9 holes, 5812yds, Par 68, SSS 68.
Club membership 500.
Visitors must contact in advance and a handicap
certificate is required.
Societies apply in writing.
Green Fees £23 per 18 holes (£30 per 18 holes weekends
and bank holidays).
Facilities ⅂ ♨ ♀ ⚮ 🕾 (Peter Brown.
Location Winnington Rd
Hotel ★★★62% Forte Posthouse, Haverstock Hill,
LONDON ☎ 071-794 8121 138⊷ ⋔

**A golf course name printed in *bold italics*
means we have been unable to verify
information with the club's management for
the current year**

N6 HIGHGATE

Highgate ☎ 081-340 1906
Parkland course.
18 holes, 5985yds, Par 69, SSS 69.
Club membership 705.
Visitors may not play Wed & weekends.
Societies by arrangement.
Green Fees £27 per round; £35 per 36 holes.
Facilities ⊗ ⅫⅠ by prior arrangement 🏌 ▆ ♀ ♨ 🏠 ʆ
Robin Turner.
Location Denewood Rd
Hotel ★★★★62% Regents Park Marriott, 128 King
Henry's Rd, Swiss Cottage, LONDON
071-722 7711 303⇄ ☜

N9 LOWER EDMONTON

Picketts Lock ☎ 081-803 3611
Tricky municipal parkland course with some narrow fairways
and the River Lea providing a natural hazard.
18 holes, 4902yds, Par 66, SSS 66.
Visitors no restrictions.
Green Fees not confirmed.
Facilities 🏌 ▆ ♀ ♨ 🏠 ʈ ʆ R Gerken.
Leisure heated indoor swimming pool, squash, snooker,
sauna, solarium, gymnasium.
Location Picketts Lock Sports Centre, Edmonton
Hotel ★★59% Holtwhites Hotel, 92 Chase Side,
ENFIELD ☎ 081-363 0124 30rm(28⇄ ☜)

N14 SOUTHGATE

Trent Park ☎ 081-366 7432 & 081-364 4450
Parkland course set in 150 acres of green belt area. Seven
holes played across Merryhills brook. Testing holes are 2nd
(423 yds) over brook, 190 yds from the tee, and up to plateau
green; 7th (463 yds) dog-leg, over brook, par 4.
18 holes, 6008yds, Par 69, SSS 69.
Club membership 950.
Visitors no restrictions.
Societies welcome Mon-Fri, must apply in advance.
Green Fees £10 (£12 weekends).
Facilities ⊗ ⅫⅠ by prior arrangement 🏌 ▆ ♀ ♨ 🏠 ʈ ʆ
Glynn Harris.
Location Bramley Rd, Southgate
Hotel ★★★★60% West Lodge Park Hotel,
Cockfosters Rd, HADLEY WOOD
☎ 081-440 8311 48⇄ ☜Annexe2⇄ ☜

N20 WHETSTONE

North Middlesex ☎ 081-445 1604
Short parkland course renowned for its tricky greens.
18 holes, 5625yds, Par 69, SSS 66, Course record 64.
Club membership 624.
Visitors must contact in advance and are advised to have
handicap certificate.
Societies must telephone in advance.
Green Fees £27.50 per day; £22 per round.
Facilities ⊗ ⅫⅠ 🏌 ▆ ♀ ♨ 🏠 ʆ Steve Roberts.
Location The Manor House, Friern Barnet Ln, Whetstone
Hotel ★★★67% Edgwarebury Hotel, Barnet Ln,
ELSTREE ☎ 081-953 8227 50⇄ ☜

South Herts ☎ 081-445 2035
An open undulating parkland course officially in
Hertfordshire, but now in a London postal area. It is,
perhaps, most famous for the fact that two of the greatest
of all British professionals, Harry Vardon and Dai Rees,
CBE were professionals at the club. The course is testing,
over rolling fairways, especially in the prevailing south-
west wind.
18 holes, 6432yds, Par 72, SSS 71.
Club membership 830.
Visitors must contact in advance & have handicap
certificate.
Societies Wed-Fri only, must apply in writing.
Green Fees not confirmed.
Facilities ♨ 🏠 ʈ ʆ
Location Links Dr, Totteridge
Hotel ★★★64% Forte Posthouse, Bignells
Corner, SOUTH MIMMS
☎ (0707) 43311 120⇄ ☜

N21 WINCHMORE

Bush Hill Park ☎ 081-360 5738
Pleasant parkland course surrounded by trees.
18 holes, 5809yds, Par 70, SSS 68.
Club membership 700.
Visitors may not play at weekends & bank holidays.
Must contact in advance and have an
introduction from own club.
Societies by arrangement.
Green Fees not confirmed.
Facilities ⊗ & ⅫⅠ by prior arrangement 🏌 ▆ ♀ (ex Sun)
♨ 🏠 ʆ George Low.
Location Bush Hill, Winchmore Hill
Hotel ★★59% Holtwhites Hotel, 92 Chase Side,
ENFIELD ☎ 081-363 0124 30rm(28⇄ ☜)

N22 WOOD GREEN

Muswell Hill ☎ 081-888 1764
Narrow parkland course.
18 holes, 6474yds, Par 71, SSS 71.
Club membership 500.
Visitors restricted Tue morning, weekends & bank
holidays. Must contact in advance.
Societies by arrangement.
Green Fees £33 per day; £23 per round.
Facilities ⊗ ⅫⅠ by prior arrangement 🏌 ▆ ♀ ♨ 🏠 ʈ ʆ
Ian Roberts.
Location Rhodes Av, Wood Green (off N Circular Rd at
Bounds Green)
Hotel ★★59% Holtwhites Hotel, 92 Chase Side,
ENFIELD ☎ 081-363 0124 30rm(28 ⇄ ☜)

NW7 MILL HILL

Finchley ☎ 081-346 2436
Easy walking on wooded parkland course.
18 holes, 6411yds, Par 72, SSS 71.
Club membership 500.
Visitors can play most weekdays and after mid-day at
weekends. Must contact in advance.
Societies must apply by telephone.
Green Fees £28 per round (£37 weekends and bank holidays).

Facilities	⊗ ⅷ ⮂ ▄ (no catering Mon) ♀ ⚞ 🖻 ⛳ ⚑
Location	Nether Court, Frith Ln, Mill Hill (Near Mill Hill East Tube Station)
Hotel	★★★67% Edgwarebury Hotel, Barnet Ln, ELSTREE ☎ 081-953 8227 50⇄ 🏠

Hendon ☎ 081-346 6023
Easy walking, parkland course with a good variety of trees, and providing testing golf.
18 holes, 6266yds, Par 70, SSS 70.
Club membership 560.

Visitors	must contact in advance. Restricted weekends & bank holidays.
Societies	must contact in advance.
Green Fees	£30 per day; £24 per round (£35 per round weekends & bank holidays).
Facilities	⊗ ⅷ ⮂ ▄ ♀ ⚞ 🖻 ⛳ ⚑ Stuart Murray.
Location	Sanders Ln, Mill Hill
Hotel	★★★67% Edgwarebury Hotel, Barnet Ln, ELSTREE ☎ 081-953 8227 50⇄ 🏠

Mill Hill ☎ 081-959 2339
Undulating parkland course with all holes separated by good tree and shrub cover.
18 holes, 6247yds, Par 69, SSS 70, Course record 65.
Club membership 550.

Visitors	restricted weekends & bank holidays. Must contact in advance.
Societies	must contact in advance.
Green Fees	£25 per day; £20 per round (£30 per round weekends & bank holidays).
Facilities	⊗ ⅷ (Mon, Wed & Fri) ⮂ ▄ ♀ ⚞ 🖻 ⛳ ⚑ Alex Daniel.
Leisure	snooker.
Location	100 Barnet Way, Mill Hill (On A1 S bound carriageway)
Hotel	★★★67% Edgwarebury Hotel, Barnet Ln, ELSTREE ☎ 081-953 8227 50⇄ 🏠

SE9 ELTHAM

Eltham Warren ☎ 081-850 1166
Parkland course running alongside the A210 on one side and Eltham Park on the other.
9 holes, 5840yds, Par 69, SSS 68, Course record 66.
Club membership 450.

Visitors	may not play at weekends. Must contact in advance and have a handicap certificate.
Societies	must telephone in advance.
Green Fees	£25 per day.
Facilities	⊗ ⮂ ▄ ♀ ⚞ 🖻 ⚑ Ross Taylor.
Leisure	snooker.
Location	Bexley Rd, Eltham
Hotel	★★★58% Bromley Court Hotel, Bromley Hill, BROMLEY ☎ 081-464 5011 120⇄ 🏠

Royal Blackheath ☎ 081-850 1795
A pleasant, parkland course of great character as befits the antiquity of the Club; the clubhouse dates from the 17th century. Many great trees survive and there are two ponds. The 18th requires a pitch to the green over a thick clipped hedge, which also crosses the front of the 1st tee.
18 holes, 6219yds, Par 70, SSS 70.
Club membership 750.

Visitors	must contact in advance but may play mid-week only, handicap certificate is required.
Societies	mid-week only, must apply in writing.
Green Fees	£40 per day; £30 per round.
Facilities	⊗ ⮂ ▄ ♀ ⚞ 🖻 ⛳ ⚑ Ian McGregor.
Location	Court Rd
Hotel	★★★58% Bromley Court Hotel, Bromley Hill, BROMLEY ☎ 081-464 5011 120⇄ 🏠

SE18 WOOLWICH

Shooters Hill ☎ 081-854 6368
Hilly and wooded parkland course with good view and natural hazards.
18 holes, 5736 yds, Par 69, SSS 68, Course record 62.
Club membership 960.

Visitors	must have handicap certificate.
Societies	Tue & Thu only, by arrangement.
Green Fees	£30 per day; £24 per round.
Facilities	⊗ ⅷ ⮂ ▄ ♀ ⚞ 🖻 ⚑ Michael Ridge.
Location	Eaglesfield Rd, Shooters Hill (Shooters Hill Rd from Blackheath)
Hotel	★★★71% Forte Posthouse, Black Prince Interchange, Southwold Rd, BEXLEY ☎ (0322) 526900 102⇄ 🏠

SE21 DULWICH

Dulwich & Sydenham Hill ☎ 081-693 3961
Parkland course overlooking London. Hilly with narrow fairways.
18 holes, 6192yds, Par 69, SSS 69.
Club membership 850.

Visitors	with member only weekends.
Societies	must telephone in advance & confirm in writing.
Green Fees	£30 per day; £25 per round.
Facilities	⊗ ⮂ ▄ ♀ ⚞ 🖻 ⚑ David Baillie.
Location	Grange Ln, College Rd
Hotel	★★★58% Bromley Court Hotel, Bromley Hill, BROMLEY ☎ 081-464 5011 120⇄ 🏠

SE22 EAST DULWICH

Aquarius ☎ 081-693 1626
Course laid-out on two levels around and over covered reservoir; hazards include vents and bollards.
9 holes, 5246yds, Par 66, SSS 66.
Club membership 440.

Visitors	must be accompanied by member and have a handicap certificate.
Green Fees	£10 per day.
Facilities	⮂ ♀ ⚞ 🖻 ⚑ Frederick Private.
Location	Marmora Rd, Honor Oak, Off Forest Hill Rd
Hotel	★★★58% Bromley Court Hotel, Bromley Hill, BROMLEY ☎ 081-464 5011 120⇄ 🏠

SW15 PUTNEY

Richmond Park ☎ 081-876 1795
Two public parkland courses.
Richmond Park: 36 holes, 5909yds, Par 68, SSS 68, Course record 62.
Dukes: 18 holes, 5486yds, Par 72.
▶

Visitors	welcome but not spectators or caddies.
Societies	must contact in advance.
Green Fees	not confirmed.
Facilities	⊗ ⅷ ♥ ♀ ♈ 🏠 ⚐ ✆
Location	Roehampton Gate
Hotel	★★★64% Richmond Hill, 146-150 Richmond Hill, RICHMOND ☎ 081-940 2247 & 081-940 5466 124⇥ ♠

SW19 WIMBLEDON

Royal Wimbledon ☎ 081-946 2125

A club steeped in the history of the game, it is also of great age, dating back to 1865. Of sand and heather like so many of the Surrey courses its 12th hole (par 4) is rated as the best on the course.
18 holes, 6300yds, Par 70, SSS 70, Course record 64.
Club membership 1050.

Visitors	must be guests of current club member.
Societies	welcome Wed-Thu. Must apply in writing.
Green Fees	not confirmed.
Facilities	♈ 🏠 ⚐ ✆ Hugh Boyle.
Location	29 Camp Rd
Hotel	★★★64% Richmond Hill, 146-150 Richmond Hill, RICHMOND ☎ 081-940 2247 & 081-940 5466 124⇥ ♠

Wimbledon Common ☎ 081-946 0294

Quick-drying course on Wimbledon Common. Well wooded, with long challenging short holes but no bunkers. All players must wear plain red upper garments.
18 holes, 5438yds, Par 68, SSS 66.
Club membership 250.

Visitors	with member only at weekends.
Societies	must telephone in advance.
Green Fees	not confirmed.
Facilities	⊗ ♥ ♀ ♈ 🏠 ✆ J S Jukes.
Leisure	snooker.
Location	Camp Rd
Hotel	★★★★65% Cannizaro House Hotel, West Side, Wimbledon Common, LONDON ☎ 081-879 1464 46⇥ ♠

Wimbledon Park ☎ 081-946 1250

Easy walking on parkland course. Sheltered lake provides hazard on 3 holes.
18 holes, 5465yds, Par 66, SSS 66.
Club membership 700.

Visitors	restricted weekends & bank holidays. Must contact in advance and have handicap certificate or letter of introduction.
Societies	must apply in writing.
Green Fees	£25 per day (£25 per round weekends & bank holidays).
Facilities	⊗ ♥ ♀ ♈ 🏠 ✆ D Wingrove.
Location	Home Park Rd, Wimbledon (400 yds from Wimbledon Park Station)
Hotel	★★★64% Richmond Hill, 146-150 Richmond Hill, RICHMOND ☎ 081-940 2247 & 081-940 5466 124⇥ ♠

For an explanation of symbols and abbreviations, see page 11

W7 HANWELL

Brent Valley ☎ 081-567 1287

Municipal parkland course with easy walking. The River Brent winds through the course.
18 holes, 5426yds, Par 67, SSS 66.
Club membership 350.

Visitors	no restrictions.
Societies	one month's notice required.
Green Fees	not confirmed.
Facilities	⊗ (vary with season) ⅷ by prior arrangement ♥ ♀ ♈ 🏠 ⚐ ✆ Peter Byrne.
Location	138 Church Rd, Hanwell
Hotel	★★★62% Master Robert Hotel, Great West Rd, HOUNSLOW ☎ 081-570 6261 100⇥ ♠

MERSEYSIDE

BEBINGTON Map 07 SJ38

Brackenwood ☎ 051-608 3093

Municipal parkland course with easy walking.
18 holes, 6285yds, Par 70, SSS 70.
Club membership 320.

Societies	must apply in advance.
Green Fees	not confirmed.
Facilities	♥ ♀ 🏠 ⚐ ✆
Location	Brackenwood Park (0.75m N of M53 junc 4 on B5151)
Hotel	★★★66% Bowler Hat Hotel, 2 Talbot Rd, Oxton, BIRKENHEAD ☎ 051-652 4931 29⇥ ♠

BIRKENHEAD Map 07 SJ38

Arrowe Park ☎ 051-677 1527

Pleasant municipal parkland course.
18 holes, 6435yds, Par 72, SSS 71.
Club membership 210.

Visitors	no restrictions.
Societies	must telephone in advance.
Green Fees	not confirmed.
Facilities	♥ ♈ 🏠 ⚐ ✆ Clive Scanlon.
Location	Woodchurch (1m from M53 junc 3 on A551)
Hotel	★★★66% Bowler Hat Hotel, 2 Talbot Rd, Oxton, BIRKENHEAD ☎ 051-652 4931 29⇥ ♠

Prenton ☎ 051-608 1461 & 051-608 1083

Parkland course with easy walking and views of the Welsh Hills.
18 holes, 5966yds, Par 70, SSS 69, Course record 68.
Club membership 760.

Visitors	restricted to yellow course.
Societies	welcome Wed & Fri, contact in advance.
Green Fees	£23 per day (£25 weekends & bank holidays).
Facilities	⊗ ⅷ by prior arrangement ♥ ♀ ♈ 🏠 ✆ Robin Thompson.
Leisure	snooker.
Location	Golf Links Rd, Prenton (S side of town centre off B5151)
Hotel	★★62% Riverhill Hotel, Talbot Rd, Oxton, BIRKENHEAD ☎ 051-653 3773 16⇥ ♠

Wirral Ladies ☎ 051-652 1255
Heathland course with heather and birch.
18 holes, 4966yds, SSS 70.
Club membership 450.

Visitors	must contact in advance and have an introduction from own club.
Societies	must telephone in advance.
Green Fees	not confirmed.
Facilities	⊗ ⊪ by prior arrangement ⅃ ⬤ ♀ ♔ 🏠 (Philip Chandler.
Location	93 Bidston Rd, Oxton (W side of town centre on B5151)
Hotel	★★★66% Bowler Hat Hotel, 2 Talbot Rd, Oxton, BIRKENHEAD ☎ 051-652 4931 29 ⇥ 📞

BLUNDELLSANDS
Map 07 SJ39

West Lancashire ☎ 051-924 1076
Challenging, traditional links with sandy subsoil overlooking the Mersey Estuary. There are many fine holes, particularly the four short ones.
18 holes, 6763yds, Par 72, SSS 73.
Club membership 650.

Visitors	may not play on competition days; must have a handicap certificate. Must contact in advance.
Societies	must contact in advance.
Green Fees	not confirmed.
Facilities	⊗ ⊪ by prior arrangement ⅃ ⬤ ♀ ♔ 🏠 (
Location	Hall Rd West (N side of village)
Hotel	★★★64% Blundellsands Hotel, The Serpentine, BLUNDELLSANDS ☎ 051-924 6515 41 ⇥ 📞

BOOTLE
Map 07 SJ39

Bootle ☎ 051-928 1371
Municipal seaside course, with NW wind. Testing holes: 5th (200 yds) Par 3; 7th (415 yds) Par 4.
18 holes, 6362yds, Par 70, SSS 70.

Visitors	no restrictions.
Societies	must contact in advance.
Green Fees	not confirmed.
Facilities	♀ ♔ 🏠 ↑ (
Location	Dunnings Bridge Rd (2m NE on A5036)
Hotel	★★★64% Blundellsands Hotel, The Serpentine, BLUNDELLSANDS ☎ 051-924 6515 41 ⇥ 📞

BROMBOROUGH
Map 07 SJ38

Bromborough ☎ 051-334 2155
Parkland course.
18 holes, 6650yds, Par 72, SSS 73, Course record 67.
~~*Club membership 700.*~~

Visitors	may not play on Sun, Tue mornings & Sat before 2.30pm.
Societies	normal society day Wed ; must telephone in advance.
Green Fees	£25 per day.
Facilities	⊗ ⅃ ⬤ ♀ ♔ 🏠 (Geoff Berry.
Location	Raby Hall Rd (0.5m W of Station)
Hotel	★★★66% Bowler Hat Hotel, 2 Talbot Rd, Oxton, BIRKENHEAD ☎ 051-652 4931 29 ⇥ 📞

CALDY
Map 07 SJ28

Caldy ☎ 051-625 5660
A parkland course situated on the estuary of the River Dee with many of the fairways running parallel to the river. Of Championship length, the course is subject to variable winds that noticeably alter the day to day playing of each hole. There are excellent views of North Wales and Snowdonia.
18 holes, 6675yds, Par 72, SSS 73, Course record 68.
Club membership 800.

Visitors	may play on weekdays only. Must contact in advance and have an introduction from own club.
Societies	must telephone in advance.
Green Fees	not confirmed.
Facilities	⊗ ⊪ ⅃ ⬤ ♀ ♔ 🏠 (K Jones.
Leisure	snooker.
Location	Links Hey Rd (SE side of village)
Hotel	★★61% Parkgate Hotel, Boathouse Ln, PARKGATE ☎ 051-336 5001 27 ⇥ 📞

EASTHAM
Map 07 SJ38

Eastham Lodge ☎ 051-327 3003
A 15-hole parkland course with many trees. Three holes played twice to make 18, but restricted to 15 holes in winter.
15 holes, 5484yds, Par 69, SSS 67.
Club membership 735.

Visitors	with member only at weekends.
Societies	welcome Mon, Tue & Fri. Must apply in advance.
Green Fees	£22 weekdays.
Facilities	⊗ ⊪ by prior arrangement ⅃ ⬤ ♀ ♔ 🏠 (R Boobyer.
Leisure	snooker.
Location	117 Ferry Rd (1.5m N)
Hotel	★★★66% Cromwell Hotel, High St, BROMBOROUGH ☎ 051-334 2917 31 ⇥ 📞

FORMBY
Map 07 SD30

Formby ☎ (07048) 72164
Championship seaside links through sandhills and partly through pine trees.
18 holes, 6490yds, Par 72, SSS 72, Course record 66.
Club membership 600.

Visitors	must contact in advance & have handicap certificate but may not play Wed, weekends or bank holidays.
Societies	Tues & Thu only. Must contact in advance.
Green Fees	£40 per day.
Facilities	⊗ ⅃ ⬤ ♀ ♔ 🏠 (
Location	Golf Rd (N side of town)
Hotel	★★★64% Blundellsands Hotel, The Serpentine, BLUNDELLSANDS ☎ 051-924 6515 41 ⇥ 📞

Formby Ladies ☎ (07048) 73493
Seaside links - one of the few independent ladies clubs in the country. The course has contrasting hard-hitting holes in flat country and tricky holes in sandhills and woods.
18 holes, 5374yds, Par 71, SSS 71.
Club membership 423.

▶

Visitors must contact in advance and may not play Thu or before noon Sat & Sun.
Societies must apply in advance.
Green Fees £25 per day (£31 weekends & bank holidays).
Facilities � by prior arrangement ᗷ ▆ ♀ ♨ ⌂ ⌀ Clive Harrison.
Location Golf Rd (N side of town)
Hotel ★★★64% Blundellsands Hotel, The Serpentine, BLUNDELLSANDS ☎ 051-924 6515 41⇆ ⚑

HESWALL

Map 07 SJ28

Heswall ☎ (051342) 1237
A pleasant parkland course in soft undulating country over-looking the estuary of the River Dee. There are excellent views of the Welsh hills and coastline, and a good test of golf. The clubhouse is modern and well-appointed with good facilities.
18 holes, 6472yds, Par 72, SSS 72, Course record 63.
Club membership 900.
Visitors must contact in advance & handicap certificate required.
Societies welcome Wed & Fri only, must apply in advance.
Green Fees £30 per day (£35 weekends & bank holidays).
Facilities ⊗ & ⫙ by prior arrangement ᗷ ▆ ♀ ♨ ⌂ ⌀ ⌀ Alan Thompson.
Leisure snooker, large practice area.
Location Cottage Ln (1m S off A540)
Hotel ★★61% Parkgate Hotel, Boathouse Ln, PARKGATE ☎ 051-336 5001 27⇆ ⚑

HOYLAKE

Map 07 SJ28

Hoylake Municipal ☎ 051-632 2956
Flat, generally windy semi-links course. Tricky fairways.
18 holes, 3613yds, Par 70, SSS 70, Course record 67.
Club membership 286.
Visitors must contact in advance.
Societies must telephone 051-632 4883 (M E Down)
Green Fees not confirmed.
Facilities ⊗ ⫙ ᗷ ▆ ♀ (ex Fri) ♨ ⌂ ⌀ ⌀ R Boobyer.
Location Carr Ln (SW side of town off A540)
Hotel ★★★66% Bowler Hat Hotel, 2 Talbot Rd, Oxton, BIRKENHEAD ☎ 051-652 4931 29⇆ ⚑

Royal Liverpool ☎ 051-632 3101
A world famous, windswept seaside links course.
18 holes, 6840yds, Par 72, SSS 74.
Club membership 650.
Visitors must contact in advance & have a handicap certificate. Must play with member at weekends.
Societies must contact in writing.
Green Fees not confirmed.
Facilities ⊗ ᗷ ▆ ♀ ♨ ⌂ ⌀ ⌀
Leisure snooker.
Location Meols Dr (SW side of town on A540)
Hotel ★★★66% Bowler Hat Hotel, 2 Talbot Rd, Oxton, BIRKENHEAD ☎ 051-652 4931 29⇆ ⚑

HUYTON

Map 07 SJ49

Bowring ☎ 051-489 1901
Flat parkland course.
9 holes, 2009yds, Par 34.
Club membership 80.
Visitors no restrictions.
Green Fees not confirmed.
Facilities ♨ ⌂ ⌀
Location Bowring Park, Roby Rd (On A5080 adjacent M62 junc 5)
Hotel ★56% Rockland Hotel, View Rd, RAINHILL ☎ 051-426 4603 10rm(9⇆)

Huyton & Prescot ☎ 051-489 3948
An easy walking, parkland course providing excellent golf.
18 holes, 5738yds, Par 68, SSS 68.
Club membership 700.
Visitors restricted at weekends. Must contact in advance and have an introduction from own club.
Societies must telephone in advance.
Green Fees not confirmed.
Facilities ⊗ ⫙ by prior arrangement ᗷ ▆ ♀ ♨ ⌂ ⌀ ⌀ Ronald Pottage.
Leisure snooker.
Location Hurst Park, Huyton Ln (1.5m NE off B5199)
Hotel ★56% Rockland Hotel, View Rd, RAINHILL ☎ 051-426 4603 10rm(9⇆)

LIVERPOOL

Map 07 SJ39

Allerton Park ☎ 051-428 1046
Parkland course.
18 holes, 5459yds, Par 67, SSS 67, Course record 62.
Club membership 300.
Visitors no restrictions.
Green Fees not confirmed.
Facilities ᗷ ▆ ♀ ⌂ ⌀ ⌀
Location Allerton Manor Golf Estate, Allerton Rd (5.5m SE of city centre off A562 and B5180)
Hotel ★★63% Grange Hotel, Holmfield Rd, Aigburth, LIVERPOOL ☎ 051-427 2950 25⇆ ⚑

The Childwall ☎ 051-487 0654
Parkland golf is played here over a testing course, where accuracy from the tee is well-rewarded. The course is very popular with visiting societies for the clubhouse has many amenities. Course designed by James Braid.
18 holes, 6425yds, Par 69, SSS 69, Course record 65.
Club membership 600.
Visitors must use yellow tees only and have a handicap certificate.
Societies must telephone in advance.
Green Fees not confirmed.
Facilities ⊗ ⫙ ᗷ ▆ ♀ ♨ ⌂ ⌀ ⌀ Nigel M Parr.
Leisure snooker.
Location Naylors Rd, Gateacre (7m E of city centre off B5178)
Hotel ★56% Rockland Hotel, View Rd, RAINHILL ☎ 051-426 4603 10rm(9⇆)

Lee Park ☎ 051-487 9861
Flat course with ponds in places.
18 holes, 5508mtrs, Par 71, SSS 69.
Club membership 500.

Visitors	must contact in advance and have an introduction from own club.
Societies	must contact in advance.
Green Fees	not confirmed.
Facilities	⊗ ⅢⅢ by prior arrangement ⅛ ▉ ♀ ♨
Leisure	snooker.
Location	Childwall Valley Rd (7m E of city centre off B5178)
Hotel	★★★★59% Liverpool Moat House Hotel, Paradise St, LIVERPOOL ☎ 051-709 0181 251⇌ 🐾

Liverpool Municipal ☎ 051-546 5435
Flat, easy course.
18 holes, 6588yds, Par 72, SSS 71, Course record 70.
Club membership 150.

Visitors	must contact in advance.
Societies	must contact 1 week in advance.
Green Fees	not confirmed.
Facilities	⊗ by prior arrangement ⅢⅢ by prior arrangement ⅛ ▉ ♀ ♨ 🏠 ⏰ ⎰ Dave Weston.
Location	Ingoe Ln, Kirkby (7.5m NE of city centre on A506)
Hotel	★★★★59% Liverpool Moat House Hotel, Paradise St, LIVERPOOL ☎ 051-709 0181 251⇌ 🐾

West Derby ☎ 051-228 1540 & 051-254 1034
A parkland course always in first-class condition, and so giving easy walking. The fairways are well-wooded. Care must be taken on the first nine holes to avoid the brook which guards many of the greens. A modern well-designed clubhouse with many amenities, overlooks the course.
18 holes, 6333yds, Par 72, SSS 70.
Club membership 550.

Visitors	may not play before 9.30am.
Societies	may not play on Sat, Sun & bank holidays; must contact in advance.
Green Fees	£22.50 per day; £20 per round.
Facilities	⊗ ⅢⅢ ⅛ ▉ ♀ ♨ 🏠 ⎰ Nick Brace.
Leisure	snooker.
Location	Yew Tree Ln, West Derby (4.5m E of city centre off A57)
Hotel	★★63% Grange Hotel, Holmfield Rd, Aigburth, LIVERPOOL ☎ 051-427 2950 25⇌ 🐾

Woolton ☎ 051-486 1298
Parkland course providing a good round of golf for all standards.
18 holes, 5706yds, Par 69, SSS 68.
Club membership 650.

Visitors	must contact in advance.
Societies	must apply in writing.
Green Fees	£20 per day (£28 weekends & bank holidays).
Facilities	♨ 🏠 ⎰
Leisure	snooker.
Location	Speke Rd (7m SE of city centre off A562)
Hotel	★★63% Grange Hotel, Holmfield Rd, Aigburth, LIVERPOOL ☎ 051-427 2950 25⇌ 🐾

This guide is up-dated annually – make sure you use the up-to-date edition

---

Haydock Park ☎ (0925) 228525
A well-wooded parkland course, close to the well-known racecourse, and always in excellent condition. The pleasant undulating fairways offer some very interesting golf and the 6th, 9th, 11th and 13th holes are particularly testing. The clubhouse is very comfortable.
18 holes, 6043yds, Par 70, SSS 69.
Club membership 550.

Visitors	must be member of a recognised club. With member only weekends & bank holidays. Must contact in advance.
Societies	must apply in writing.
Green Fees	£24 per day.
Facilities	⊗ ⅢⅢ ⅛ ▉ ♀ ♨ 🏠 ⎰ Peter Kenwright.
Leisure	snooker.
Location	Golborne Park, Rob Ln (0.75m NE off A49)
Hotel	★★★67% Forte Posthouse, Lodge Ln, Newton-le-Willows, HAYDOCK ☎ (0942) 717878 136⇌

Grange Park ☎ (0744) 26318
A course of Championship length set in pleasant country surroundings - playing the course it is hard to believe that industrial St Helens lies so close at hand. The course is a fine test of golf and there are many attractive holes liable to challenge all grades.
18 holes, 6429yds, Par 72, SSS 71, Course record 65.
Club membership 700.

Visitors	must contact in advance & have handicap certificate. Play allowed weekdays only.
Societies	must apply in writing.
Green Fees	£21 per round (27 holes).
Facilities	⊗ ⅢⅢ ⅛ ▉ ♀ ♨ 🏠 ⏰ ⎰ Paul G Evans.
Leisure	snooker.
Location	Prescot Rd (1.5m W on A58)
Hotel	★★★67% Forte Posthouse, Lodge Ln, Newton-le-Willows, HAYDOCK ☎ (0942) 717878 136⇌

Sherdley Park ☎ (0744) 813149
Fairly hilly course with ponds in places.
18 holes, 5941yds, Par 70, SSS 69.
Club membership 160.

Visitors	no restrictions.
Green Fees	not confirmed.
Facilities	♨ 🏠 ⏰ ⎰
Location	Sherdley Rd (2m S off A570)
Hotel	★★★67% Forte Posthouse, Lodge Ln, Newton-Le-Willows, HAYDOCK ☎ (0942) 717878 136⇌

The Hesketh ☎ (0704) 536897
Hesketh is the senior club in Southport, founded in 1885. The Championship course comprises much of the original territory plus a large area of reclaimed land on the seaward side - essentially 'Links' in character.
18 holes, 6407yds, Par 71, SSS 72.
Club membership 600. ▶

Visitors	must have a handicap certificate. May not play Tue mornings (Ladies Day) or 12.30-2pm daily.
Societies	welcome.
Green Fees	£35 per day; £25 per round (£40 weekends & bank holidays).
Facilities	⊗ ⅢⅡ ⅬⅡ 🍺 ♀ ⤳ 🏠 ⅌ ⅃ John Donoghue.
Leisure	snooker.
Location	Cockle Dick's Ln, off Cambridge Rd (1m NE of town centre off A565)
Hotel	★★65% Bold Hotel, Lord St, SOUTHPORT ☎ (0704) 532578 23rm(15⇥7 🐾)

Hillside ☎ (0704) 67169
Championship links course with natural hazards open to strong wind.
18 holes, 6850yds, Par 72, SSS 74, Course record 66.
Club membership 750.

Visitors	must contact in advance. Restricted Tue (am), weekends & bank holidays. Members only between 12-2pm.
Societies	must apply in advance.
Green Fees	£45 per day; £35 per round (£45 per round Sun).
Facilities	⊗ ⅢⅡ ⅬⅡ 🍺 ♀ ⤳ ⅃ Brian Seddon.
Leisure	snooker, putting green & practice ground.
Location	Hastings Rd, Hillside (2m SW of town centre on A565)
Hotel	★★★64% Royal Clifton Hotel, Promenade, SOUTHPORT ☎ (0704) 533771 107⇥ 🐾

Park ☎ (0704) 530133
Very flat municipal parkland course.
18 holes, 6200yds, Par 70, SSS 70.
Club membership 400.

Visitors	restricted weekends, telephone for details.
Green Fees	not confirmed.
Facilities	♀ (members only) 🏠 ⅌
Location	Park Rd (N side of town centre off A565)
Hotel	★★★64% Royal Clifton Hotel, Promenade, SOUTHPORT ☎ (0704) 533771 107⇥ 🐾

ROYAL BIRKDALE See page 141

Southport & Ainsdale ☎ (0704) 578000
'S and A', as it is known in the north is another of the fine championship courses for which this part of the country is famed. This club has staged many important events and offers golf of the highest order.
18 holes, 6603yds, Par 72, SSS 73, course record 62.
Club membership 815.

Visitors	welcome except Wed, Thu, weekends & bank holidays. Must contact club in advance & have handicap certificate.
Societies	must apply in advance.
Green fees	£40 per day; £30 per round.
Facilities	⊗ ⅢⅡ ⅬⅡ 🍺 (catering by arrangement) ♀ ⤳ 🏠 ⅌ ⅃ Michael Houghton.

For an explanation of symbols and abbreviations, see page 11

Leisure	snooker.
Location	Bradshaws Ln, Ainsdale (3m S off A565)
Hotel	★★★64% Royal Clifton Hotel, Promenade, SOUTHPORT ☎ (0704) 533771 107⇥ 🐾

Southport Municipal ☎ (0704) 535286
Municipal seaside links course. Played over by Alt Golf Club.
18 holes, 6400yds, Par 70, SSS 69.
Club membership 750.

Visitors	must contact in advance.
Societies	must telephone 6 days in advance.
Green fees	not confirmed.
Facilities	⊗ ⅬⅡ 🍺 ♀ ⤳ 🏠 ⅌ ⅃ Bill Fletcher.
Leisure	snooker.
Location	Park Rd West (N side of town centre off A565)
Hotel	★★★64% Royal Clifton Hotel, Promenade, SOUTHPORT ☎ (0704) 533771 107⇥ 🐾

Southport Old Links ☎ (0704) 28207
Seaside course with tree-lined fairways and easy walking. One of the oldest courses in Southport, Henry Vardon won the 'Leeds Cup' here in 1922.
9 holes, 6378yds, Par 72, SSS 71.
Club membership 400.

Visitors	except Wed, Sun & bank holidays. Must contact in advance & have handicap certificate.
Societies	welcome except Wed & Sun & bank holidays, must apply in advance.
Green fees	£25 per day; £18 per round (£25 per round weekends).
Facilities	⊗ ⅢⅡ by prior arrangement ⅬⅡ 🍺 ♀ ⤳ 🏠 ⅃ P Atkiss.
Location	Moss Ln, Churchtown (NW side of town centre off A5267)
Hotel	★★65% Bold Hotel, Lord St, SOUTHPORT ☎ (0704) 532578 23rm(15⇥7 🐾)

WALLASEY

Map 07 SJ29

Bidston ☎ 051-638 3412
Parkland course, with westerly winds.
18 holes, 5827yds, Par 70, SSS 71.
Club membership 550.

Visitors	must contact in advance, restricted weekends.
Societies	must apply in writing.
Green Fees	£18 per 9/18 holes.
Facilities	⊗ ⅢⅡ ⅬⅡ 🍺 ♀ ⤳ 🏠 ⅃ R J Law.
Leisure	snooker.
Location	Scoresby Rd, Leasowe, Moreton (0.5m W of M53 junc 1 entrance off A551)
Hotel	★★★66% Bowler Hat Hotel, 2 Talbot Rd, Oxton, BIRKENHEAD ☎ 051-652 4931 29⇥ 🐾

Leasowe ☎ 051-677 5852
Rather flat, semi-links, seaside course.
18 holes, 6204yds, Par 71, SSS 71.
Club membership 500.

Visitors	may not play 12.30-2pm
Societies	must contact 14 days in advance.
Green Fees	£20 per round.
Facilities	⊗ ⅢⅡ ⅬⅡ 🍺 ♀ ⤳ 🏠 ⅌ ⅃ Neil Sweeney.
Location	Moreton (2m W on A551)
Hotel	★★★66% Bowler Hat Hotel, 2 Talbot Rd, Oxton, BIRKENHEAD ☎ 051-652 4931 29⇥ 🐾

Royal Birkdale

Southport ☎(0704) 67920   **Map 07 SD31**

John Ingham writes: There are a few seaside links in the world that can be described as 'great', but Royal Birkdale, with its expanse of sandhills and willow scrub, is one of them. There have been some changes since the club was founded in 1889 and they have hosted everything that matters here, including the Open and the Ryder Cup. Some changes have been made even since Arnold Palmer hit that wondrous recovery shot that helped him win an Open in the early sixties, and led to a plaque being erected at the spot from which the divot was taken.

Well bunkered, the sandhills run along the edges of the fairways and make ideal platforms from which to view the Open Championship - played frequently here because the examination is supreme in the United Kingdom.

The links, in a wind, may be too difficult for the weekender. Certainly it found out Dai Rees in 1961 when he was chasing Palmer for the title. In the last round the course struck at the very first hole. Rees had hit his teeshot a mite to the left, and then had to wait for the players to hole out on the green ahead, before attempting a powerful shot with a lofted wood from the fairway. The ball smacked into the back of a bunker, and fell back into sand. Rees took an awful seven and Palmer beat him for the trophy - by one shot. The Welshman had stormed back in 31 but his chance to win an Open had gone forever. But Rees still touched his hat to the links, and held it in great respect as, indeed, does Arnold Palmer.

But for the amateur, another problem is simply hitting the ball far enough. If you play this terrific course from the Open Championship back tees, it measures 7080 yards and par 73 takes some getting, even with your handicap allowance!

Membership 800
Visitors must contact in advance, and have a letter of introduction from their own club with a handicap cetificate
Societies must apply in writing or by telephone in advance
Green fees on application to the club
Facilities ▥ (only for societies over 20) ⤓ ♨ ♀ ♨ ⌂ ⛳ ⛳ (Richard Bradbeer)
Location Waterloo Road, Birkdale (1.75m S of town)

18 holes, 6305yds, Par 71, SSS 71, Course record 63 (C.Pavin)

WHERE TO STAY AND EAT NEARBY

HOTELS:
SOUTHPORT
★★★ 62% Royal Clifton, Promenade. ☎(0704) 533771. 107 ⇥ ⌂
English & French cuisine

★★★ 61% Scarisbrick, Lord St. ☎(0704) 543000. 66 ⇥ ⌂
English & French cuisine

★★68% Balmoral Lodge, 41 Queens Rd. ☎(0704) 544298. 15 ⇥ ⌂

★★ 68% Stutelea Hotel & Leisure Club, Alexandra Rd. ☎(0704) 544220 20 ⇥ ⌂

RESTAURANT:
WRIGHTINGTON
✗ ✗ ✗❀ High Moor, Highmoor Ln (jct 27 off M6, take B5239). ☎ Appley Bridge (0257) 252364
English & French cuisine

Wallasey ☎ 051-691 1024
A well-established sporting links, adjacent to the Irish
Sea, with huge sandhills and many classic holes where
the player's skills are often combined with good fortune.
Large, firm greens and fine views.
18 holes, 6605yds, Par 72, SSS 73.
Club membership 700.
Visitors must be member of a recognised club &
have handicap certificate. Must contact in
advance.
Societies must apply in writing.
Green Fees not confirmed.
Facilities ⊗ by prior arrangement 🍴 🍺 ♀ ♿ 🏠 🎱
Mike Adams.
Location Bayswater Rd (N side of town centre off
A554)
Hotel ★★★66% Bowler Hat Hotel, 2 Talbot Rd,
Oxton, BIRKENHEAD
☎ 051-652 4931 29🛏 🐾

Warren ☎ 051-639 8323
Short, undulating links course with first-class greens and
prevailing winds off the sea.
9 holes, 5854yds, Par 72, SSS 68.
Club membership 150.
Visitors except Sun until 10.30.am.
Green Fees not confirmed.
Facilities 🏠 🎱 🎣 Ken Lamb.
Location Grove Rd (N side of town centre off A554)
Hotel ★★★66% Bowler Hat Hotel, 2 Talbot Rd,
Oxton, BIRKENHEAD
☎ 051-652 4931 29🛏 🐾

● NORFOLK ●

BARNHAM BROOM
Map 05 TG00

Barnham Broom Golf and Country Club
☎ (060545) 393
Attractive river valley courses with modern hotel and
leisure complex.
Hill Course: 18 holes, 6628yds, Par 72, SSS 72.
Valley Course: 18 holes, 6470yds, Par 71, SSS 71.
Visitors must contact in advance and have handicap
certificate. With member only at weekends.
Societies must apply in writing.
Green Fees £30 per day; £25 per round.
Facilities
Stephen Beckham.
Leisure hard tennis courts, heated indoor swimming
pool, squash, snooker, sauna, solarium,
gymnasium, hairdressing salon, beautician,
jacuzzi.
Location Honingham Rd (1m N, S of A47)
Hotel ★★★65% Barnham Broom Hotel
Conference & Leisure, Centre, BARNHAM
BROOM ☎ (060545) 393 52🛏 🐾
(See advertisement on page 144)

BAWBURGH
Map 05 TG10

Bawburgh ☎ (0603) 746390
An open-links. Driving range available.
18 holes, 6066yds, Par 70, SSS 69.
Club membership 750.
Visitors must contact in advance.
Societies must contact in advance.
Green Fees not confirmed.
Facilities ⊗ 🍴 🍺 ♀ ♿ 🏠 🎱 Chris Potter.
Leisure covered floodlit driving range.
Location Norwich Golf Centre, Long Ln
Hotel ★★★71% Park Farm Hotel, HETHERSETT
☎ (0603) 810264 6🛏 🐾Annexe32🛏 🐾

BRANCASTER
Map 09 TF74

Royal West Norfolk ☎ (0485) 210087
If you want to see what golf courses were like years ago,
then go to the Royal West Norfolk where tradition
exudes from both clubhouse and course. Close by the sea,
the links are laid out in the grand manner and are
characterised by sleepered greens, superb cross-
bunkering and salt marshes.
18 holes, 6428yds, Par 71, SSS 71, Course record 69.
Club membership 767.
Visitors must contact in advance and may only play
after 10am at weekends with permission.
Societies must contact in advance.
Green Fees not confirmed.
Facilities ⊗ 🍽 by prior arrangement
🍴 🍺 ♀ ♿ 🏠 🎱 🎣 R E Kimber.
Leisure practice ground.
Hotel ★★72% Titchwell Manor Hotel,
TITCHWELL ☎ (0485) 210221
11rm(7🛏 🐾) Annexe4🛏 🐾

CROMER
Map 09 TG24

Royal Cromer ☎ (0263) 512884
Seaside course set out on cliff edge, hilly and subject to wind.
18 holes, 6508yds, Par 72, SSS 71, Course record 68.
Club membership 700.
Visitors must contact in advance & have handicap
certificate.
Societies by arrangement.
Green Fees £25 per day (£30 weekends).
Facilities ⊗ 🍽 by prior arrangement 🍴 🍺 ♀ ♿ 🏠 🎱
Robin Page.
Leisure practice ground..
Location 145 Overstrand Rd (1m E on B1159)
Hotel ★★68% Red Lion, Brooke St, CROMER
☎ (0263) 514964 12🛏 🐾

DENVER
Map 05 TF60

Ryston Park ☎ Downham Market (0366) 383834
Parkland course.
9 holes, 3146yds, Par 35, SSS 70, Course record 66.
Club membership 320.
Visitors may not play weekends or bank holidays.
Societies Mon-Fri only, must telephone in advance.
Green Fees not confirmed.
Facilities ⊗ 🍽 🍴 🍺 ♀ ♿ 🏠

Location 0.5m S on A10
Hotel ★61% Crown Hotel, Bridge St,
DOWNHAM MARKET
☎ (0366) 382322 10rm(5⇄2 ⋔)

DISS
Map 05 TM18

Diss ☎ (0379) 642847
Commonland course with natural hazards.
18 holes, 6238yds, Par 73, SSS 70.
Club membership 650.
Visitors must contact in advance but may not play
weekends & bank holidays.
Societies by arrangement.
Green Fees £20 per day.
Facilities ⊗ ⋔ ⅃ ⚑ ♀ ⚒ ⌂ ⟨ Nigel Taylor.
Location Stuston (1.5m SE on B1118)
Hotel ★★60% Scole Inn, SCOLE
☎ (0379) 740481 12⇄ ⋔ Annexe11⇄ ⋔

EAST DEREHAM
Map 09 TF91

Dereham ☎ Dereham (0362) 695900
Parkland course.
9 holes, 6225yds, Par 71, SSS 70, Course record 66.
Club membership 520.
Visitors must contact in advance and have a handicap
certificate; must play with member at weekends.
Societies must contact in advance.
Green Fees £16 per day.
Facilities ⚒ ⌂ ⟨
Location Quebec Rd (N side of town centre off B1110)
Hotel ★★63% King's Head Hotel, Norwich St,
DEREHAM
☎ (0362) 693842 & 693283
10rm(4⇄2 ⋔) Annexe5⇄ ⋔

GORLESTON-ON-SEA
Map 05 TG50

Gorleston ☎ Great Yarmouth (0493) 661911
Seaside course.
18 holes, 6400yds, Par 71, SSS 71, Course record 66.
Club membership 900.
Visitors must have handicap certificate.
Societies must contact in advance.
Green Fees £20 per day/round (£25 weekends).
Facilities ⊗ ⋔ ⅃ ⚑ ♀ ⚒ ⌂ ⟨ Nick Brown.
Leisure snooker.
Location Warren Rd (S side of town centre)
Hotel ★★★70% Cliff Hotel, Gorleston, GREAT
YARMOUTH ☎ (0493) 662179 39⇄ ⋔

HUNSTANTON
Map 09 TF64

Hunstanton ☎ (0485) 532811
Links course.
18 holes, 6670yds, Par 72, SSS 72, Course record 65.
Club membership 670.
Visitors must contact in advance and be a club
member with current handicap certificate.
Restricted at weekends & may not play bank
holiday weekends.
Societies must apply in writing.

Green Fees £30 per day (£36 weekends). Reduced fees
Nov-Feb.
Facilities ⊗ (ex Mon) ⋔ by prior arrangement
⅃ ⚑ ♀ ⚒ ⌂ ⟨ John Carter.
Location 1.5m N off A149
Hotel ★★68% Caley Hall Motel, Old Hunstanton
Rd, HUNSTANTON ☎ (0485) 533486
Annexe29rm(27⇄)

KING'S LYNN
Map 09 TF62

Eagles ☎ (0553) 827147
Parkland course with plenty of water hazards and bunkers.
Also Par-3 course and floodlit, covered driving range.
9 holes, 4284yds, Par 64, SSS 61.
Club membership 350.
Visitors no restrictions.
Societies telephone in advance.
Green Fees £5.50 per 9 holes (£6.50 weekends and bank
holidays).
Facilities ⊗ ⋔ ⅃ ⚑ ♀ ⚒ ⌂ ⟨ Karl Worby.
Leisure par 3 course, floodlit driving range.
Location 39 School Rd, Tilney All Saints
Hotel ★★★65% The Duke's Head, Tuesday Market
Pl, KING'S LYNN ☎ (0553) 774996 71⇄ ⋔

King's Lynn ☎ (0553) 631654
Challenging, wooded parkland course.
18 holes, 6646yds, Par 72, SSS 72, Course record 64.
Club membership 945.
Visitors must contact in advance and have handicap
certificate.
Societies by arrangement.
Green Fees £30 (£38 weekends).
Facilities ⊗ ⋔ by prior arrangement ⅃ ⚑ ♀ ⚒ ⌂ ⟨
Chris Hanlon.
Leisure snooker.
Location Castle Rising (4m NE off A148)
Hotel ★★★65% The Duke's Head, Tuesday Market
Pl, KING'S LYNN
☎ (0553) 774996 71⇄ ⋔

MIDDLETON
Map 09 TF61

Middleton Hall ☎ King's Lynn (0553) 841800
The 9-hole King's course (played off 18 tees) is a pleasant
parkland course constructed with conservation in mind
around numerous mature trees, pond and reservoir.
Additional par 3 pitch and putt course.
9 holes, 5570yds, Par 68, SSS 67.
Club membership 300.
Visitors no restrictions.
Societies must contact in advance.
Green Fees £12 per day (£14 weekends & bank holidays).
Facilities ⊗ ⋔ ⅃ ⚑ (dinner/bar snacks summer only) ♀
⚒ ⌂ ⟨ Nigel Pickerall.
Location 4m from King's Lynn off A47
Hotel ★★★65% Butterfly Hotel, Beveridge Way,
Hardwick Narrows, KING'S LYNN
☎ (0553) 771707 50⇄ ⋔

For an explanation of symbols and
abbreviations, see page 11

MUNDESLEY

Map 09 TG33

Mundesley ☎ (0263) 720279
Seaside course, good views, windy.
9 holes, 5410yds, Par 68, SSS 66.
Club membership 400.

Visitors	restricted Wed & weekends. Must contact in advance.
Societies	must contact one month in advance.
Green Fees	not confirmed.
Facilities	⊗ ℳ & ⓑ (ex Thu) ⚌ ♀ ⚄ 🏠 (T G Symmons.
Location	Links Rd (W side of village off B1159)
Hotel	★★68% Red Lion, Brooke St, CROMER ☎ (0263) 514964 12⇄ 🐾

NORWICH

Map 05 TG20

Eaton ☎ (0603) 51686
An undulating, tree-lined parkland course with excellent trees.
18 holes, 6135yds, Par 70, SSS 69, Course record 64.
Club membership 1000.

Visitors	restricted before 11.30am weekends, must contact in advance & have handicap certificate.
Societies	by arrangement.
Green Fees	not confirmed.
Facilities	⊗ ℳ ⓑ ⚌ ♀ ⚄ 🏠 (Nigel Bundy.
Location	Newmarket Rd (2.5m SW of city centre off A11)
Hotel	★★62% Arlington Hotel, 10 Arlington Ln, Newmarket Rd, NORWICH ☎ (0603) 617841 44⇄

AA
★ ★ ★

BARNHAM BROOM HOTEL

GOLF, CONFERENCE AND LEISURE
Barnham Broom, Norwich NR9 4DD
Tel: (060545) 393/6 Fax: (060545) 8224
Due to change:
Tel: (0603) 759393 Fax: (0603) 758224

In a beautiful valley, this modern hotel and leisure complex has
52 bedrooms all with private bathrooms; a spacious lounge with
open log fire; two bars; and a host of leisure facilities including
two 18 hole championship golf courses (one par 71, one par 72),
practice holes and putting green areas.

Inside the leisure centre are a heated indoor swimming pool;
sauna; solarium; steem room; a beauty and hairdressing salon
and a fully equipped gymnasium. Other sports facilities include
four squash courts, 3 all-weather tennis courts and a full size
snooker table.

The complex also contains a spacious and comprehensively
equipped conference centre.

Prices include full English breakfast.
Children charged for meals as taken.
Host: Richard Bond.

Access: From London and the South via A11; from Midlands and the
North via A47. 10 miles west of Norwich. Norwich Airport 10 miles.

Royal Norwich ☎ (0603) 429928
Undulating heathland course.
18 holes, 6603yds, Par 72, SSS 72, Course record 67.
Club membership 650.

Visitors	must contact in advance & have handicap certificate but may not play at weekends & bank holidays.
Societies	must contact in advance.
Green Fees	£26 per day.
Facilities	⊗ ℳ (summer only) ⓑ ⚌ ♀ ⚄ 🏠 ♟ (Alan Hemsley.
Location	Drayton High Rd, Hellesdon (2.5m NW of city centre on A1067)
Hotel	★★★66% Hotel Norwich, 121-131 Boundary Rd, NORWICH ☎ (0603) 787260 108⇄ 🐾

SHERINGHAM

Map 09 TG14

Sheringham ☎ (0263) 823488
Splendid cliff-top links with gorse, good 'seaside turf'
and plenty of space. Straight driving is essential for a low
score. The course is close to the shore and can be very
windswept, but offers magnificent views.
18 holes, 6464yds, Par 70, SSS 71, Course record 66.
Club membership 700.

Visitors	must contact in advance & have handicap certificate.
Societies	must apply in writing.
Green Fees	£27 per day (£32 weekends & bank holidays).
Facilities	⊗ ℳ ⓑ ⚌ ♀ ⚄ 🏠 ⚮ (R H Emery.
Location	Weybourne Rd (W side of town centre on A149)
Hotel	★★65% Beaumaris Hotel, South St, SHERINGHAM ☎ (0263) 822370 24rm(17⇄5 🐾)

SWAFFHAM

Map 05 TF80

Swaffham ☎ (0760) 721611
Heathland course.
9 holes, 6252yds, Par 72, SSS 70.
Club membership 510.

Visitors	must contact in advance. With member only at weekends.
Societies	must contact one month in advance.
Green Fees	£18 per day/round.
Facilities	⊗ ℳ ⓑ ⚌ ♀ ⚄ 🏠 ♟ (Peter Field.
Location	Cley Rd (1.5m SW)
Hotel	★★★60% George Hotel, Station Rd, SWAFFHAM ☎ (0760) 721238 27rm(24⇄1 🐾)

THETFORD

Map 05 TL88

Thetford ☎ (0842) 752169
This is a course with a good pedigree. It was laid-out by a
fine golfer, C.H. Mayo, later altered by James Braid and
then again altered by another famous course designer,
Mackenzie Ross. It is a testing heathland course with a
particularly stiff finish.
18 holes, 6879yds, Par 72, SSS 73.
Club membership 700.

Visitors	must contact in advance & have handicap certificate. With member only at weekends.
Societies	must contact in advance.
Green Fees	£26 per day/round.
Facilities	⊗ ⅲ ⅼ ♚ ♀ ♨ 🏠 ℓ Norman Arthur.
Location	Brandon Rd (0.75m W on B1107)
Hotel	★★★62% Bell Hotel, King St, THETFORD ☎ (0842) 754455 47⇆ ☞

WATTON
Map 05 TF90

Richmond Park ☎ (0953) 881803
Meadowland course dotted with newly planted trees and set on either side of the Little Wissey River.
18 holes, 6300yds, Par 71, SSS 70.
Club membership 500.

Visitors	handicap certificates are required for Sat & Sun mornings.
Societies	apply in writing.
Green Fees	£15 (£20 weekends & bank holidays).
Facilities	⊗ ⅲ (Wed-Sat) ⅼ ♚ ♀ ♨ 🏠 ℓ Peggy Conley.
Leisure	gymnasium.
Location	Saham Rd
Hotel	★★★60% George Hotel, Station Rd, SWAFFHAM ☎ (0760) 721238 27rm(24⇆1 ☞)

WEST RUNTON
Map 09 TG14

Links Country Park Hotel & Golf Club ☎ (0263) 837691
Parkland course 500 yds from the sea, with superb views overlooking West Runton. The hotel offers extensive leisure facilities.
9 holes, 4814yds, Par 66, SSS 64.
Club membership 250.

Visitors	must have a handicap certificate.
Societies	must telephone in advance.
Green Fees	not confirmed.
Facilities	⊗ ⅲ ⅼ ♚ ♀ ♨ 🏠 ⅌ ♨ Mike Jubb.
Leisure	hard tennis courts, heated indoor swimming pool, riding, sauna, solarium.
Location	S side of village off A149
Hotel	★★70% Dormy House Hotel, Cromer Rd, WEST RUNTON ☎ (0263) 837537 16⇆ ☞

YARMOUTH, GREAT
Map 05 TG50

Great Yarmouth & Caister ☎ (0493) 728699
This great old club, which celebrated its centenary in 1982, has played its part in the development of the game. It is a fine old-fashioned links where not many golfers have bettered the SSS in competitions. The 468-yard 8th (par 4), is a testing hole.
18 holes, 6284yds, Par 70, SSS 70, Course record 63.
Club membership 775.

Visitors	restricted Sun until 11.30am. Must have an introduction from own club.
Societies	must apply in writing.
Green Fees	not confirmed.
Facilities	⊗ ⅲ by prior arrangement ♚ ♀ ♨ 🏠 ⅌ ♨ Nick Catchpole.
Location	Beach House, Caister on Sea (0.5m N off A149)
Hotel	★★★62% Imperial Hotel, North Dr, GREAT YARMOUTH ☎ (0493) 851113 39⇆ ☞

NORTH YORKSHIRE

ALDWARK
Map 08 SE46

Aldwark Manor Golf Hotel ☎ Tollerton (03473) 353
An easy walking, scenic 18-hole parkland course with holes both sides of the River Ure. The course surrounds the Victorian Aldwark Manor Golf Hotel.
18 holes, 6171yds, Par 71, SSS 69, Course record 69.
Club membership 500.

Visitors	must contact in advance, restricted weekends.
Societies	must telephone in advance.
Green Fees	£20 per day; £16 per round (£24/£20 weekends & bank holidays).
Facilities	⊗ ⅲ ⅼ ♚ ♀ ♨ 🏠 ⅌ ♨ ℓ Gary M Platt.
Hotel	★★★♨74% Aldwark Manor Hotel, ALDWARK ☎ (03473) 8146 17⇆ ☞ Annexe3⇆ ☞

BEDALE
Map 08 SE28

Bedale ☎ (0677) 422451
Secluded parkland course with many trees.
18 holes, 6565yds, Par 69, SSS 68.
Club membership 800.

Visitors	must contact in advance.
Societies	must apply in advance.
Green Fees	£18 per day/round (£28 weekends & bank holidays).

Facilities ⊗ ⑂ 🏌 💺 ♀ ⚘ 🏠 ⌀ Troy Johnson.
Location Leyburn Rd (N side of town on A684)
Hotel ★★62% Motel Leeming, Great North Rd, BEDALE ☎ (0677) 422122 40⇄ 🐾

BENTHAM   Map 07 SD66

Bentham ☎ (05242) 62455
Moorland course with glorious views.
9 holes, 5760yds, Par 70, SSS 69, Course record 69.
Club membership 480.
Visitors no restrictions.
Societies must apply in advance.
Green Fees £14 per day (£20 weekends & bank holidays).
Facilities 💺 ♀ ⚘
Location Robin Ln (N side of High Bentham)
Hotel ★★★69% Bowden Hall Resort Hotel, Bondend Ln, Upton St Leonards, GLOUCESTER ☎ (0452) 614121 72⇄ 🐾

CATTERICK GARRISON   Map 08 SE19

Catterick Garrison ☎ Richmond (0748) 833268
Scenic parkland/moorland course of Championship standard, with good views of the Pennines and Cleveland hills. Testing 1st and 3rd holes.
18 holes, 6331yds, Par 71, SSS 70, Course record 68.
Club membership 750.
Visitors must contact in advance and have a handicap certificate.
Societies must contact in writing.
Green Fees £16 per day (£24 weekends & bank holidays).
Facilities ⊗ ⑂ by prior arrangement 🏌 💺 ♀ ⚘ 🏠 ⌀ Andy Marshall.
Location Leyburn Rd (1m W)
Hotel ★★58% Bridge House Hotel, CATTERICK BRIDGE ☎ (0748) 818331 16rm(4⇄9 🐾)

COPMANTHORPE   Map 08 SE54

Pike Hills ☎ York (0904) 706566
Parkland course surrounding nature reserve. Level terrain.
18 holes, 6121yds, Par 71, SSS 69, Course record 68.
Club membership 800.
Visitors with member only weekends & bank holidays. Must contact in advance.
Societies must apply in advance.
Green Fees £20 per day/round summer.
Facilities ⊗ (ex Mon) ⑂ by prior arrangement 🏌 💺 ♀ ⚘ 🏠 ⌀ Ian Gradwell.
Location Tadcaster Rd (3m N of York on A64)
Hotel ★★★★64% Swallow Hotel, Tadcaster Rd, YORK ☎ (0904) 701000 113⇄ 🐾

EASINGWOLD   Map 08 SE56

Easingwold ☎ (0347) 21964
Parkland course with easy walking. Trees are a major feature and on six holes water hazards come into play.
18 holes, 6045yds, Par 72, SSS 70.
Club membership 575.
Visitors with member only weekends & bank holidays (winter). Must contact in advance.
Societies must apply in advance.

Green Fees not confirmed.
Facilities ⊗ ⑂ 🏌 💺 ♀ (summer weekdays) ⚘ 🏠 ⌀ John Hughes.
Leisure pool table.
Location Stillington Rd (1m S)
Hotel ★★69% Beechwood Close Hotel, 19 Shipton Rd, Clifton, YORK ☎ (0904) 658378 14⇄ 🐾

FILEY   Map 08 TA18

Filey ☎ Scarborough (0723) 513293
Parkland course with good views, windy. Stream runs through course. Testing 9th and 13th holes.
18 holes, 6104yds, Par 70, SSS 69.
Club membership 950.
Visitors except bank holidays & special competition days. Must contact in advance.
Societies must apply in advance.
Green Fees £18 per day (£23 weekends); winter £14/£18.
Facilities ⊗ ⑂ 🏌 💺 ♀ ⚘ 🏠 ⌀ D England.
Leisure snooker.
Location West Av (0.5m S)
Hotel ★65% Sea Brink Hotel, The Beach, FILEY ☎ (0723) 513257 11rm(9⇄ 🐾)

GANTON   Map 08 SE97

Ganton ☎ Sherburn (0944) 70329
Championship course, heathland, gorse-lined fairways and heavily bunkered; variable winds.
18 holes, 6720yds, Par 72, SSS 73, Course record 65.
Club membership 580.
Visitors must contact in advance and may not play at weekends.
Societies must apply in advance.
Green Fees £35 (£40 weekends).
Facilities ⊗ & ⑂ by prior arrangement 🏌 💺 ♀ ⚘ 🏠 ⌀ Gary Brown.
Location 0.25m NW off A64
Hotel ★★65% Downe Arms Hotel, WYKEHAM ☎ (0723) 862471 10⇄ 🐾

HARROGATE   Map 08 SE35

Harrogate ☎ (0423) 862999
One of Yorkshire's oldest and best courses was designed in 1897 by 'Sandy' Herd. A perfect example of golf architecture, its greens and fairways offer an interesting but fair challenge. The undulating parkland course once formed part of the ancient Forest of Knaresborough. Excellent clubhouse.
18 holes, 6241yds, Par 69, SSS 70, Course record 67.
Club membership 750.
Visitors must contact in advance & have a handicap certificate.
Societies must contact in writing.
Green Fees £30 per day; £26 per round (£40 weekends & bank holidays).
Facilities ⊗ ⑂ 🏌 💺 ♀ ⚘ 🏠 ⌀ P Johnson.
Leisure snooker.
Location Forest Ln Head, Starbeck (2.25m on A59)
Hotel ★★★69% Balmoral Hotel & Restaurant, Franklin Mount, HARROGATE ☎ (0423) 508208 20⇄ 🐾

Oakdale ☎ (0423) 567162
A pleasant, undulating parkland course which provides a good test of golf for the low handicap player without intimidating the less proficient. A special feature is an attractive stream which comes in to play on four holes. Excellent views from the clubhouse which has good facilities.
18 holes, 6456yds, Par 71, SSS 71.
Club membership 850.
Visitors except 8-9.30am & 12.30-1.30pm. Contact in advance.
Societies must apply at least one month in advance.
Green Fees £29.50 per day; £22 per round (£27.50 weekends and bank holidays).
Facilities ⊗ ⅢⅢ ⅃ ♥ ♀ ⅍ 🏠 ⍾ ℓ Richard Jessop.
Leisure snooker.
Location Oakdale (N side of town centre off A61)
Hotel ★★★65% Grants Hotel, 3-13 Swan Rd, HARROGATE ☎ (0423) 560666 41⇄ ⋔

KIRKBYMOORSIDE Map 08 SE68

Kirkbymoorside ☎ (0751) 31525
Hilly parkland course with narrow fairways, gorse and hawthorn bushes. Beautiful views.
18 holes, 6000yds, Par 69, SSS 69, Course record 67.
Club membership 600.
Visitors must contact in advance.
Societies must apply in advance.
Green Fees £15 per day (£20 weekends & bank holidays).
Facilities ⊗ ⅢⅢ ⅃ ♥ ♀ ⅍
Location Manor Vale (N side of village)
Hotel ★★♨73% Dweldapilton Hall Hotel, APPLETON-LE-MOORS ☎ (07515) 227 & 452 12⇄ ⋔

KNARESBOROUGH Map 08 SE35

Knaresborough ☎ Harrogate (0423) 862690
Undulating parkland course with mature trees.
18 holes, 6232yds, Par 70, SSS 70.
Club membership 750.
Visitors must contact in advance, restricted Tue & weekends. No visitors on bank holiday weekends.
Societies must contact at least 2 weeks in advance.
Green Fees £22 per day; £17 per round (£28/£23 weekends).
Facilities ⊗ ⅢⅢ ⅃ ♥ ♀ ⅍ 🏠 ℓ Keith I Johnstone.
Leisure practice ground.
Location Boroughbridge Rd (1.25 N on A6055)
Hotel ★★★69% Dower House Hotel, Bond End, KNARESBOROUGH ☎ (0423) 863302 28⇄ ⋔ Annexe4⇄ ⋔

MALTON Map 08 SE77

Malton & Norton ☎ (0653) 693882
Parkland course with panoramic views of the moors. Very testing 1st hole (564 yds dog-leg, left).
18 holes, 6426yds, Par 72, SSS 71.
Club membership 750.
Visitors must contact in advance.
Societies must apply in writing.
Green Fees £20-£25 per day/round.

Facilities ⊗ ⅢⅢ ⅃ ♥ ♀ ⅍ 🏠 ⍾ ℓ S I Robinson.
Location Welham Park, Norton (1m S)
Hotel ★★59% Talbot Hotel, Yorkersgate, MALTON ☎ (0653) 694031 29⇄ ⋔

MASHAM Map 08 SE28

Masham ☎ Ripon (0765) 689379
Flat parkland course crossed by River Burn, which comes into play on two holes.
9 holes, 5244yds, Par 66, SSS 66, Course record 69.
Club membership 302.
Visitors must play with member at weekends & bank holidays.
Societies must contact the secretary in advance.
Green Fees £15 per day.
Facilities ⊗ ⅢⅢ by prior arrangement ⅃ ♥ ♀ ⅍
Location Burnholme, Swinton Rd (1m SW off A6108)
Hotel ★★♨74% Jervaulx Hall Hotel, MASHAM ☎ (0677) 60235 10⇄ ⋔

PANNAL Map 08 SE35

Pannal ☎ Harrogate (0423) 872628
Fine championship course. Moorland turf but well-wooded with trees closely involved with play.
18 holes, 6659yds, Par 72, SSS 72.
Club membership 790.
Visitors must contact in advance. Restricted 8-9.30am & 12-1.30pm weekdays, after 2.30pm weekends.
Societies must apply several months in advance.
Green Fees £29 per round (£35 weekends).
Facilities ⊗ ⅢⅢ ⅃ ♥ ♀ ⅍ 🏠 ⍾ ℓ Murray Burgess.
Location Follifoot Rd (E side of village off A61)
Hotel ★★★★63% The Majestic, Ripon Rd, HARROGATE ☎ (0423) 568972 156⇄ ⋔

RICHMOND Map 07 NZ10

Richmond ☎ (0748) 825319
Parkland course.
18 holes, 5704yds, Par 70, SSS 68, Course record 64.
Club membership 600.
Visitors may not play before 11.30am on Sun.
Societies must contact in writing.
Green Fees not confirmed.
Facilities ⊗ ⅢⅢ ⅃ ♥ (no catering Mon) ♀ ⅍ 🏠 ⍾ ℓ Paul Jackson.
Location Bend Hagg (0.75m N)
Hotel ★★67% King's Head Hotel, Market Place, RICHMOND ☎ (0748) 850220 24⇄ ⋔ Annexe4⇄ ⋔

RIPON Map 08 SE37

Ripon City ☎ (0765) 603640
Hard-walking on undulating parkland course; two testing par 3's at 5th and 7th.
18 holes, 6067yds, Par 71, SSS 69.
Club membership 600.
Visitors must contact in advance & have handicap certificate.
Green Fees £18 per day (£25 weekends & bank holidays). ▶

Facilities ⊗ (ex Mon) 🍴 by prior arrangement 🏌
(ex Mon) 💺 ♀ (times vary) ⚐ 🏧 ✆ S T Davis.
Location Palace Rd (1m N on A6108)
Hotel ★★★66% Ripon Spa Hotel, Park St, RIPON
☎ (0765) 602172 40⇄ 🐾

SCARBOROUGH

Map 08 TA08

Scarborough North Cliff ☎ (0723) 360786
Seaside parkland course begining on cliff top overlooking
bay and castle. Good views.
18 holes, 6425yds, Par 71, SSS 71.
Club membership 860.
Visitors must be member of a club with handicap
certificate.
Societies must apply in writing.
Green Fees £21 per day (£26 weekends & bank holidays).
Facilities ⊗ 🍴 🏌 💺 ♀ ⚐ 🏧 ✆ ℓ S N Deller.
Location North Cliff Av (2m N of town centre off A165)
Hotel ★★★63% Esplanade Hotel, Belmont Rd,
SCARBOROUGH ☎ (0723) 360382 73⇄ 🐾

Scarborough South Cliff ☎ (0723) 374737
Parkland/seaside course designed by Dr Mackenzie.
18 holes, 6039yds, Par 70, SSS 69.
Club membership 700.
Visitors contact in advance may not play before 9.30am
Mon-Fri, 10am Sat and 10.30am Sun.
Societies must contact Secretary in advance.
Green Fees £25 per day; £20 per round (£30/£25 weekends
& bank holidays).
Facilities ⊗ 🍴 🏌 💺 ♀ ⚐ 🏧
Location Deepdale Av (1m S on A165)
Hotel ★★66% Bradley Court, 7-9 Filey Rd, South
Cliff, SCARBOROUGH
☎ (0723) 360476 40rm(22⇄17 🐾)

SELBY

Map 08 SE63

Selby ☎ (0757) 228622
Mainly flat, links-type course; prevailing SW wind. Testing
holes including the 3rd, 7th and 16th.
18 holes, 6246yds, Par 70, SSS 70, Course record 65.
Club membership 780.
Visitors restricted 11am-1pm (Nov-Mar). With member
only weekends. Must contact in advance and
have a handicap certificate.
Societies welcome Wed-Fri, must apply in advance.
Green Fees not confirmed.
Facilities ⊗ 🍴 🏌 💺 ♀ ⚐ 🏧 ✆ ℓ C A C Smith.
Leisure snooker.
Location Brayton Barff
Hotel ★★★♨68% Monk Fryston Hall, MONK
FRYSTON ☎ (0977) 682369 28⇄ 🐾

SETTLE

Map 07 SD86

Settle ☎ (0729) 825288
Picturesque parkland course.
9 holes, 4596yds, Par 64, SSS 62.
Club membership 170.
Visitors restricted on Sun.
Societies apply in writing.
Green Fees not confirmed.
Facilities ♀

Location Buckhaw Brow, Giggleswick (1m N on A65)
Hotel ★★★62% Falcon Manor Hotel, Skipton Rd,
SETTLE ☎ (0729) 823814
15⇄ 🐾 Annexe5⇄ 🐾

SKIPTON

Map 07 SD95

Skipton ☎ (0756) 795657 & 793922
Undulating parkland course with some water hazards and
panoramic views.
18 holes, 5771yds, Par 70, SSS 69.
Club membership 650.
Visitors except competition days. Must contact in advance.
Societies must apply in writing.
Green Fees £22 per day (£26 Sun & bank holidays).
Facilities ⊗ 🍴 🏌 💺 ♀ ⚐ 🏧 ✆ ℓ Peter Robinson.
Leisure snooker.
Location Off North West By-Pass (1m N on A65)
Hotel ★★★79% Devonshire Arms Country House
Hotel, BOLTON ABBEY
☎ (0756) 710441 40⇄ 🐾

STOCKTON-ON-THE-FOREST

Map 08 SE65

Forest Park ☎ York (0904) 400425
A parkland/meadowland course, opened in spring 1991, with
natural features including a stream and mature and new trees.
18 holes, 6211yds, Par 70, SSS 70.
Club membership 650.
Visitors welcome, subject to tee availability. Advisable
to contact club in advance.
Societies by prior arrangement.
Green Fees £14 per round (£20 weekends & bank holidays).
Facilities ⊗ 🍴 🏌 💺 ♀ ⚐ 🏧
Leisure driving range.
Hotel ★★★68% York Pavilion Hotel, 45 Main St,
Fulford, YORK ☎ (0904) 622099
11⇄ 🐾 Annexe10⇄ 🐾

TADCASTER

Map 08 SE44

Cocksford ☎ (0937) 834253
An attractive Par 70 parkland course that is testing but non-
strenuous.
18 holes, 5518yds, Par 70, SSS 68.
Club membership 500.
Visitors must contact club in advance.
Societies must contact in advance.
Green Fees £20 per day; £15 per round (£25/£20 weekends).
Facilities ⊗ 🍴 🏌 💺 ♀ ⚐ 🏧 ✆ 🍽 ℓ
Graham Thompson.
Leisure outdoor swimming pool.
Location Crocksford, Stutton (between York & Leeds,
A162 from Tadcaster)
Hotel ★★★(red)♨ Bilbrough Manor Country House
Hotel, BILBROUGH ☎ (0937) 834002 12⇄ 🐾

THIRSK

Map 08 SE48

Thirsk & Northallerton ☎ (0845) 522170
The course has good views of the nearby Hambleton Hills.
Testing course, mainly flat land.
9 holes, 6257yds, Par 72, SSS 70, Course record 69.
Club membership 389.

Visitors	must be a member of recognised golf club & cannot play before 9.30am. With member only Sun. Must contact in advance and have an introduction from own club.
Societies	must apply in writing.
Green Fees	not confirmed.
Facilities	⊗ by prior arrangement ⵊ by prior arrangement 🏴 💷 ♀ ♨ 🏠 ⵢ ⱡ Andrew Wright.
Location	Thornton-le-Street (2m N on A168)
Hotel	★★62% Three Tuns Hotel, Market Place, THIRSK ☎ (0845) 523124 11⇄ ⋔

WHITBY   Map 08 NZ81

Whitby ☎ (0947) 602768
Seaside course on cliff top. Good views and fresh sea breeze.
18 holes, 5706yds, Par 69, SSS 67, Course record 66.
Club membership 950.

Visitors	may not play on competition days.
Societies	must contact in writing.
Green Fees	£17.50 per day/round (£25 weekends and bank holidays).
Facilities	⊗ ⵊ 🏴 💷 ♀ ♨ 🏠 ⵢ ⱡ Andrew Brook.
Location	Low Straggleton, Sandsend Rd (1.5m NW on A174)
Hotel	★★65% White House Hotel, Upgang Lane, West Cliff, WHITBY ☎ (0947) 600469 12rm(7⇄4 ⋔)

YORK   Map 08 SE65

Fulford ☎ (0904) 413579
A flat, parkland/moorland course well-known for the superb quality of its turf, particularly the greens, and now famous as the venue for some of the best golf tournaments in the British Isles.
18 holes, 6775yds, Par 72, SSS 72.
Club membership 600.

Visitors	must contact in advance and have a handicap certificate.
Societies	must contact in writing.
Green Fees	£30 per day; £20 per round (Mon-Fri).
Facilities	⊗ ⵊ 🏴 💷 ♀ ♨ 🏠 ⱡ Bryan Hessay.
Leisure	snooker.
Location	Heslington Ln (2m SE)
Hotel	★★★★55% Viking Hotel, North St, YORK ☎ (0904) 659822 188⇄ ⋔

Heworth ☎ (0904) 424618 & 422389
11-hole parkland course, easy walking. Holes 3 to 9 played twice from different tees.
11 holes, 6141yds, Par 70, SSS 69.
Club membership 460.

Visitors	must contact in advance but may not play on Sun mornings in winter.
Societies	must contact the secretary in writing.
Green Fees	£14 per day (£19 weekends & bank holidays).
Facilities	⊗ (ex Mon) ⵊ by prior arrangement 🏴 💷 ♀ ♨ 🏠 ⵢ ⱡ Gregg Roberts.
Location	Muncaster House, Muncaster Gate (1.5m NE of city centre on A1036)
Hotel	★★★70% Dean Court Hotel, Duncombe Place, YORK ☎ (0904) 625082 40⇄ ⋔

Swallow Hall ☎ (0904) 448219
A small 18-hole, Par 3 course with 2 par 4s. Attached to a caravan park.
18 holes, 3092yds.
Club membership 100.

Visitors	no restrictions.
Societies	must telephone in advance.
Green Fees	£7 per 18 holes; £3.50 per 9 holes.
Facilities	💷 ♨ ⵢ 🏀
Location	Crockey Hill
Hotel	★★★68% York Pavilion Hotel, 45 Main St, Fulford, YORK ☎ (0904) 622099 11⇄ ⋔ Annexe10⇄ ⋔

York ☎ (0904) 491840
A pleasant, well-designed, heathland course with easy walking. The course is of good length but being flat the going does not tire. There are two testing pond holes.
18 holes, 6285yds, Par 70, SSS 70, Course record 65.
Club membership 700.

Visitors	before 9am & not between 12-1.30pm. With member only weekends. Must contact in advance.
Societies	must apply in advance.
Green Fees	£25 per day/£20 per round (£27/30 weekends & bank holidays).
Facilities	⊗ ⵊ 🏴 💷 (catering limited Fri) ♀ ♨ 🏠 ⱡ A B Mason.
Location	Lords Moor Ln, Strensall (6m NE, E of Strensall village)
Hotel	★★★70% Dean Court Hotel, Duncombe Place, YORK ☎ (0904) 625082 40⇄ ⋔

NORTHAMPTONSHIRE

CHACOMBE   Map 04 SP44

Cherwell Edge ☎ (0295) 711591
Parkland course open since 1980.
18 holes, 5800yds, Par 70, SSS 68, Course record 67.
Club membership 500.

Visitors	no restrictions.
Societies	must apply in writing.
Green Fees	not confirmed.
Facilities	⊗ ⵊ 🏴 💷 ♀ ♨ 🏠 ⵢ ⱡ
Location	0.5m S off B4525
Hotel	★★★63% Whately Hall Hotel, Banbury Cross, BANBURY ☎ (0295) 263451 74⇄ ⋔

COLD ASHBY   Map 04 SP67

Cold Ashby ☎ Northampton (0604) 740099
Undulating parkland course, nicely matured, with superb views.
18 holes, 6020yds, Par 70, SSS 69, Course record 64.
Club membership 600.

Visitors	restricted weekends before noon.
Societies	by arrangement.
Green Fees	£19 per day; £12.50 per round.
Facilities	⊗ ⵊ 🏴 💷 ♀ ♨ 🏠 ⵢ ⱡ
Location	Stanford Rd (1m W)
Hotel	★★★63% Forte Posthouse, Northampton/Rugby, CRICK ☎ (0788) 822101 88⇄ ⋔

COLLINGTREE

Map 04 SP75

Collingtree Park ☎ (0604) 700000
Superb 18-hole resort course designed by former U.S.
and British Open champion Johnny Miller. Stunning
island green at the 18th hole. Green fee includes buggy
cart and range balls. The Golf Academy includes a
driving range, practice holes, indoor video teaching
room, golf custom-fit centre.
18 holes, 6692yds, Par 72, SSS 72.
Visitors	must contact in advance & have handicap certificate.
Societies	contact in advance.
Green Fees	£30 per round (£40 weekends).
Facilities	⊗ ⊪ ⓑ ■ ♀ ♨ 🏠 ⛳ 🏌 ℓ John Cook.
Location	Windingbrook Ln (M1-junc 15 on A508 to Northampton)
Hotel	★★★★60% Swallow Hotel, Eagle Dr, NORTHAMPTON ☎ (0604) 768700 122↩ ⋔

CORBY

Map 04 SP88

Priors Hall ☎ (0536) 60756
Municipal course laid out on made-up quarry ground and
open to prevailing wind. Wet in winter.
18 holes, 6677yds, Par 72, SSS 72.
Club membership 650.
Visitors	no restrictions.
Societies	must apply in writing.
Green Fees	£6.50 (£8.30 weekends).
Facilities	⊗ ⓑ 🏠 ⛳ 🏌 ℓ Malcolm Summers.
Location	Stamford Rd, Weldon (4m NE on A43)
Hotel	★★★62% The Talbot, New St, OUNDLE ☎ (0832) 273621 40↩ ⋔

DAVENTRY

Map 04 SP56

Daventry & District ☎ (0327) 702829
A hilly course with hard walking.
18 holes, 5555yds, Par 69, SSS 67, Course record 68.
Club membership 300.
Visitors	restricted Sun mornings & weekends (Oct-Mar).
Societies	contact the club professional.
Green Fees	£16 per day; £9 per round (£12 per round weekends and bank holidays).
Facilities	⊗ (weekends only) ⓑ & ■ by prior arrangement ♀ ♨ 🏠 ⛳ 🏌 ℓ Michael Higgins.
Location	Norton Rd (1m NE)
Hotel	★★★66% Northampton Moat House, Silver Street, Town Centre, NORTHAMPTON ☎ (0604) 22441 142↩ ⋔

FARTHINGSTONE

Map 04 SP65

Farthingstone Hotel, Golf & Leisure Centre
☎ (032736) 291
Pleasant rambling course with open aspect and widespread
views.
18 holes, 6248yds, Par 71, SSS 71.
Club membership 600.
Visitors	must contact in advance.
Societies	must contact in advance.
Green Fees	£25 per day; £15 per round (£30/£20 weekends).

Facilities	⊗ ⊪ ⓑ ■ ♀ ♨ 🏠 ⛳ 🏌 ℓ
Leisure	squash, snooker, table tennis.
Location	1m W
Hotel	★★★65% Daventry Resort Hotel, Ashby Rd (A361), DAVENTRY ☎ (0327) 301777 138↩ ⋔

HELLIDON

Map 04 SP55

Hellidon Lakes Hotel & Country Club
☎ Byfield (0327) 62550
Spectacular parkland course designed by David Snell.
18 holes, 6691yds, Par 72, SSS 72.
Club membership 500.
Visitors	must contact in advance & have handicap certificate at weekends.
Societies	must telephone in advance.
Green Fees	£25 per day; £15 per round (£35/£20 weekends & bank holidays).
Facilities	⊗ ⊪ ⓑ ■ ♀ ♨ 🏠 ⛳ 🏌 ℓ John Kennedy.
Leisure	hard tennis courts, heated indoor swimming pool, fishing, riding, sauna, solarium, gymnasium.
Hotel	★★★★65% Hellidon Lakes Hotel & Country Club, HELLIDON ☎ (0327) 62550 25↩ ⋔

KETTERING

Map 04 SP87

Kettering ☎ (0536) 512074 & 511104
A very pleasant, mainly flat meadowland course with easy
walking.
18 holes, 6035yds, Par 69, SSS 69, Course record 64.
Club membership 500.
Visitors	with member only weekends & bank holidays.
Societies	by arrangement.
Green Fees	£20 per day/round.
Facilities	⊗ ⊪ ⓑ ■ (no catering Mon) ♀ ♨ 🏠 ⛳ 🏌 ℓ Kevin Theobald.
Location	Headlands (S side of town centre)
Hotel	★★61% High View Hotel, 156 Midland Rd, WELLINGBOROUGH ☎ (0933) 278733 14↩ ⋔ Annexe3rm

NORTHAMPTON

Map 04 SP76

Delapre Golf Complex ☎ (0604) 764036
Rolling parkland course, part of municipal golf complex,
which includes two 9-hole, par 3 courses, pitch-and-putt and
33 bay driving-range.
*Main Course: 18 holes, 6356yds, Par 70, SSS 70, Course
record 66.*
Hardingstone: 9 holes, 2146yds, Par 32, SSS 32.
Club membership 1000.
Visitors	must pre-book and pay in advance.
Societies	must book and pay full green fees 2 weeks in advance.
Green Fees	£6.80 per 18 holes (£8.50 weekends); £3 per 9 holes (£3.30 weekends).
Facilities	⊗ ⓑ ■ ♀ ♨ 🏠 ⛳ 🏌 ℓ John Corby.
Leisure	pitch & putt, floodlit driving range.
Location	Eagle Dr, Nene Valley Way (2m SE)
Hotel	★★★59% Westone Moat House, Ashley Way, Weston Favell, NORTHAMPTON ☎ (0604) 406262 31↩ ⋔ Annexe35↩ ⋔

Kingsthorpe ☎ (0604) 710610
Undulating parkland, town course.
18 holes, 6006yds, Par 69, SSS 69.
Club membership 650.
Visitors must contact in advance and have handicap certificate. With member only weekends & bank holidays.
Societies by arrangement.
Green Fees £20 per day/round.
Facilities ⊗ 洲 ᴸ ⬛ ♀ ᐃ 🏠 (
Location Kingsley Rd (N side of town centre on A5095)
Hotel ★★★59% Westone Moat House, Ashley Way, Weston Favell, NORTHAMPTON
☎ (0604) 406262 31🛏 ⋔ Annexe35🛏 ⋔

Northampton ☎ (0604) 845155
New parkland course with water in play on three holes.
18 holes, 6534yds, Par 72, SSS 71.
Club membership 965.
Visitors must have handicap certificate. Members only club.
Societies by arrangement.
Green Fees not confirmed.
Facilities ⊗ 洲 ᴸ ⬛ ♀ ᐃ 🏠 (Mark Chamberlain.
Location Harlestone (NW of town centre on A428)
Hotel ★★★66% Northampton Moat House, Silver Street, Town Centre, NORTHAMPTON
☎ (0604) 22441 142🛏 ⋔

Northamptonshire County ☎ (0604) 843025
Undulating heathland/woodland course with gorse, heather and fine pine woods.
18 holes, 6503yds, Par 70, SSS 71.
Club membership 900.
Visitors restricted weekends. Must contact in advance and have a handicap certificate.
Societies Wed & Thu only, must contact in advance.
Green Fees £35 day/round.
Facilities ⊗ 洲 ᴸ ⬛ ♀ ᐃ 🏠 (Tim Rouse.
Leisure practice ground.
Location Church Brampton (4m NW of town centre off A50)
Hotel ★★★59% Westone Moat House, Ashley Way, Weston Favell, NORTHAMPTON
☎ (0604) 406262 31🛏 ⋔ Annexe35🛏 ⋔

OUNDLE Map 04 TL08

Oundle ☎ (0832) 273267
Undulating parkland course, shortish but difficult. A small brook affects some of the approaches to the greens.
18 holes, 5549yds, Par 70, SSS 67.
Club membership 630.
Visitors may not play before 10.30am weekends unless with member.
Societies must apply in writing.
Green Fees £18 per day (£25 weekends).
Facilities ⊗ 洲 ᴸ ⬛ ♀ ᐃ 🏠 (R Keys.
Location Benefield Rd (1m W on A427)
Hotel ★★★62% The Talbot, New St, OUNDLE
☎ (0832) 273621 40🛏 ⋔

This guide is up-dated annually – make sure you use the up-to-date edition

STAVERTON Map 04 SP56

Staverton Park ☎ Daventry (0327) 311428
Open course, fairly testing with good views.
18 holes, 6204yds, Par 71, SSS 71.
Club membership 478.
Visitors restricted weekends. Must contact in advance.
Societies by arrangement.
Green Fees £19.50 per round (£22.50 weekends and bank holidays).
Facilities ⊗ 洲 ᴸ ⬛ ♀ ᐃ 🏠 ⌁ (Brian & Richard Mudge.
Location 0.75m NE of Staverton on A425
Hotel ★★★65% Daventry Resort Hotel, Ashby Rd (A361), DAVENTRY
☎ (0327) 301777 138🛏 ⋔

WELLINGBOROUGH Map 04 SP86

Rushden ☎ Rushden (0933) 312581
Parkland course with brook running through the middle.
10 holes, 6335yds, Par 71, SSS 70, Course record 69.
Club membership 400.
Visitors may not play Wed afternoon. With member only weekends.
Societies must apply in writing.
Green Fees £15 per day/round.
Facilities ⊗ & 洲 ᴸ ⬛ ♀ (ex Mon) ᐃ
Location Kimbolton Rd, Chelveston (2m E of Higham Ferrers on A45)
Hotel ★★★63% Hind Hotel, Sheep St, WELLINGBOROUGH
☎ (0933) 222827 34🛏 ⋔

Wellingborough ☎ (0933) 677234
An undulating parkland course with many trees. The 514-yd, 14th is a testing hole. The clubhouse is a stately home.
18 holes, 6620yds, Par 72, SSS 72, Course record 69.
Club membership 850.
Visitors must contact in advance & have handicap certificate, but may not play at weekends & bank holidays.
Societies must apply in writing.
Green Fees £27 per day; £22 per round.
Facilities ⊗ 洲 ᴸ ⬛ ♀ ᐃ 🏠 (David Clifford.
Leisure outdoor swimming pool, fishing, snooker.
Location Gt Harrowden Hall (2m N on A509)
Hotel ★★★63% Hind Hotel, Sheep St, WELLINGBOROUGH
☎ (0933) 222827 34🛏 ⋔

NORTHUMBERLAND

ALLENDALE Map 12 NY85

Allendale ☎ 091-267 5875
A newly built parkland course set 1000 feet above sea level with superb views. The course is two 9-hole loops on fairly hilly terrain. The club has recently moved to this new course having been at their previous ground for 69 years.
9 holes, 4488yds, Par 66, SSS 63.
Club membership 180.
▶

Visitors restricted Sun mornings & Aug bank holiday till 4pm.
Societies contact 2-3 weeks in advance.
Green Fees not confirmed.
Facilities 🍴 🛏 🏠
Leisure riding.
Location High Studdon Allenheads Rd (1.5m S on B6295)
Hotel ★★64% County Hotel, Priestpopple, HEXHAM
☎ (0434) 602030 9⇌ ♞

ALNMOUTH
Map 12 NU21

Alnmouth ☎ (0665) 830231
Coastal course with pleasant views.
18 holes, 6500yds, Par 71, SSS 71, Course record 65.
Club membership 850.
Visitors may not play Wed, Fri, weekends & bank holidays. Must contact in advance.
Societies by arrangement.
Green Fees not confirmed.
Facilities ⊗ 🍴 🛏 🍴 ♀ ☖ 🏠 🛏
Location Foxton Hall (1m NE)
Hotel ★★★57% White Swan Hotel, Bondgate Within, ALNWICK ☎ (0665) 602109 43⇌ ♞

Alnmouth Village ☎ (0665) 830370
Seaside course with part coastal view.
9 holes, 6078yds, Par 70, SSS 70.
Club membership 480.
Visitors no restrictions.
Societies must contact in advance.
Facilities ♀ ☖
Location Marine Rd (E side of village)
Hotel ★★★57% White Swan Hotel, Bondgate Within, ALNWICK ☎ (0665) 602109 43⇌ ♞

ALNWICK
Map 12 NU11

Alnwick ☎ (0665) 602632
Parkland course offering a fair test of golfing skills.
9 holes, 5387yds, Par 66, SSS 66.
Club membership 402.
Visitors may not play on competition days.
Societies must contact in advance.
Green Fees £15 per day; £10 per round (£20 per day; £15 per round weekends & bank holidays).
Facilities 🛏 🍴 ♀ ☖
Location Swansfield Park (S side of town)
Hotel ★★★57% White Swan Hotel, Bondgate Within, ALNWICK ☎ (0665) 602109 43⇌ ♞

BAMBURGH
Map 12 NU13

Bamburgh Castle ☎ (06684) 378
This is not a long, links course, but there are those who have played golf all over the world who say that for sheer breathtaking beauty this northern seaside gem cannot be bettered. And the course itself is the greatest fun to play. Magnificent views of Farne Island, Lindisfarne and Holy Island.
18 holes, 5465yds, Par 68, SSS 67, Course record 63.
Club membership 650.

Visitors with member only bank holidays & competition days. Must contact in advance & have handicap certificate.
Societies apply in writing.
Green Fees on application.
Facilities ⊗ 🍴 🛏 🍴 (no catering Tue) ♀ ☖ 🏠
Location 6m E of A1 via B1341 or B1342
Hotel ★★69% Lord Crewe Arms, Front St, BAMBURGH
☎ (06684) 243 25rm(20⇌ ♞)

BEDLINGTON
Map 12 NZ28

Bedlingtonshire ☎ (0670) 822087
Meadowland/parkland course with easy walking. Under certain conditions the wind can be a distinct hazard.
18 holes, 6813yds, Par 73, SSS 73, Course record 65.
Club membership 950.
Visitors must contact in advance.
Societies apply in advance to the Professional.
Green Fees not confirmed.
Facilities ⊗ 🍴 🛏 🍴 ♀ ☖ 🏠 🍴 ♩ Marcus Webb.
Location Acorn Bank (1m SW on A1068)
Hotel ★★★★54% Holiday Inn Newcastle, Great North Rd, SEATON BURN
☎ 091-236 5432 150⇌ ♞

BELLINGHAM
Map 12 NY88

Bellingham ☎ (0434) 220530
9-hole downland course with natural hazards and 18 tees.
9 holes, 5245yds, Par 67, SSS 66, Course record 63.
Club membership 340.
Visitors must adhere to start sheet weekdays & Sat, no play on Sun until after 5pm.
Societies must contact in advance.
Green Fees £10 per day (£15 per round weekends).
Facilities ⊗ 🛏 🍴 (catering by prior arrangement) ♀ ☖
Leisure practice ground.
Location Boggle Hole (N side of village on B6320)
Hotel ★★66% Riverdale Hall Hotel, BELLINGHAM
☎ (0434) 220254 20⇌ ♞

BERWICK-UPON-TWEED
Map 12 NT95

Berwick-upon-Tweed (Goswick) ☎ (0289) 87256
Natural seaside links course, with undulating fairways, elevated tees and good greens.
18 holes, 6425yds, Par 72, SSS 71, Course record 64.
Club membership 500.
Visitors may only play between 10am-noon & after 2pm weekends. Must contact in advance.
Societies party of 8 or more by arrangement.
Green Fees £24 per day; £18 per round (£32/£24 weekends).
Facilities 🍴 by prior arrangement 🛏 🍴 ♀ ☖ 🏠 ♩ Paul Terras.
Location Goswick (6m S off A1)
Hotel ★★★61% Turret House Hotel, Etal Rd, Tweedmouth, BERWICK-UPON-TWEED
☎ (0289) 330808 13⇌ ♞

Magdalene Fields ☎ (0289) 306384

Seaside course with natural hazards formed by sea bays. Last 9 holes open to winds. Testing 18th hole over bay (par 3).

18 holes, 6526yds, Par 72, SSS 71, Course record 70.

Club membership 450.

Visitors	must contact in advance. Must possess individual sets of clubs.
Societies	must contact in advance.
Green Fees	£15 per day (£17 weekends).
Facilities	⊗ ⅫⅢ ⅃ 🍺 (catering by arrangement) ♀ ♨ ⚑
Location	Magdalene Fields (E side of town centre)
Hotel	★★★61% Turret House Hotel, Etal Rd, Tweedmouth, BERWICK-UPON-TWEED ☎ (0289) 330808 13⇄ ⋒

BLYTH

Map 12 NZ38

Blyth ☎ (0670) 367728

Course built over old colliery. Parkland with water hazards.

18 holes, 6300yds, Par 72, SSS 71.

Club membership 815.

Visitors	with member only after 3pm & at weekends.
Societies	apply in writing.
Green Fees	not confirmed.
Facilities	⊗ ⅫⅢ ⅃ 🍺 ♀ ♨ 🏠 ⚑ B Rumney.
Leisure	pool table.
Location	New Delaval (6m N of Whitley Bay)
Hotel	★★67% Windsor Hotel, South Pde, WHITLEY BAY ☎ 091-251 8888 64⇄ ⋒

CRAMLINGTON

Map 12 NZ27

Arcot Hall ☎ 091-236 2794

A wooded parkland course, reasonably flat.

18 holes, 6389yds, Par 70, SSS 70.

Club membership 700.

Visitors	with member only weekends & bank holidays. Must be member of a Golf Club.
Societies	welcome midweek only, contact in advance.
Green Fees	£22 per day (£25 weekends & bank holidays).
Facilities	⊗ ⅫⅢ ⅃ 🍺 ♀ ♨ 🏠 ⚑ Graham Cant.
Leisure	snooker.
Location	2m SW off A1
Hotel	★★★★54% Holiday Inn Newcastle, Great North Rd, SEATON BURN ☎ 091-236 5432 150⇄ ⋒

EMBLETON

Map 12 NU22

Dunstanburgh Castle ☎ (0665) 576562

Rolling links designed by James Braid, with castle and bird sanctuary either side. Superb views.

18 holes, 6039yds, Par 70, SSS 69.

Club membership 410.

Visitors	no restrictions.
Societies	contact in advance.
Green Fees	£12.50 per day; £15 per round (£17.50 per day weekends & bank holidays).
Facilities	⊗ ⅫⅢ by prior arrangement ⅃ 🍺 ♀ ♨ 🏠 ⚑
Location	0.5m E
Hotel	★★72% Beach House Hotel, Sea Front, SEAHOUSES ☎ (0665) 720337 14⇄ ⋒

HEXHAM

Map 12 NY96

Hexham ☎ (0434) 603072

A very pretty undulating parkland course with interesting natural contours. From parts of the course, particularly the elevated 6th tee, there are the most exquisite views of the valley below. As good a parkland course as any in the North of England.

18 holes, 6000yds, Par 70, SSS 68.

Club membership 700.

Visitors	advance booking advisable.
Societies	welcome weekdays, contact in advance.
Green Fees	£26 per day; £20 per round (£32/£26 weekends & bank holidays).
Facilities	⊗ ⅫⅢ by prior arrangement ⅃ 🍺 ♀ ♨ 🏠 ⚑ ⚑ Martin W Forster.
Leisure	squash, snooker.
Location	Spital Park (1m NW on B6531)
Hotel	★★★65% Beaumont Hotel, Beaumont St, HEXHAM ☎ (0434) 602331 23⇄ ⋒

Tynedale ☎ (0434) 608154

Flat, easy moorland course. Bounded by river and railway.

9 holes, 5643yds, Par 69, SSS 67.

Club membership 346.

Visitors	may not play Sun mornings.
Societies	must contact in advance.
Green Fees	£10 (£12 weekends).
Facilities	⊗ ⅫⅢ ⅃ 🍺 ♀ ♨ 🏠 ⚑ ⚑ Claire Brown.
Leisure	pool table.
Location	Tyne Green (N side of town)
Hotel	★★★65% Beaumont Hotel, Beaumont St, HEXHAM ☎ (0434) 602331 23⇄ ⋒

MORPETH

Map 12 NZ28

Morpeth ☎ (0670) 519980 & 504942

Parkland course with views of the Cheviots.

18 holes, 6206yds, Par 72, SSS 70, Course record 67.

Club membership 700.

Visitors	restricted weekends & bank holidays. Must contact in advance and have a handicap certificate.
Societies	apply in writing.
Green Fees	£25 per day; £20 per round (£33/£25 weekends & bank holidays).
Facilities	⊗ ⅫⅢ ⅃ 🍺 ♀ ♨ 🏠 ⚑ Martin Jackson.
Leisure	snooker.
Location	The Common (S side of town centre on A197)
Hotel	★★★★75% Linden Hall Hotel, LONGHORSLEY ☎ (0670) 516611 45⇄ ⋒

NEWBIGGIN-BY-THE-SEA

Map 12 NZ38

Newbiggin-by-the-Sea ☎ (0670) 817344

Seaside-links course.

18 holes, 6452yds, Par 72, SSS 71, Course record 68.

Club membership 500.

Visitors	must contact in advance and may not play before 10am or on competition days.
Societies	must apply in writing.
Green Fees	£12 (£17 weekends & bank holidays).
Facilities	⊗ ⅫⅢ by prior arrangement ⅃ 🍺 ♀ ♨ 🏠 ⚑ ⚑ David J Fletcher. ▶

Leisure   snooker.
Location   Prospect Place (N side of town)
Hotel   ★★★★▲▲75% Linden Hall Hotel,
               LONGHORSLEY ☎ (0670) 516611 45⇌ ♠

PONTELAND   Map 12 NZ17

Ponteland ☎ (0661) 822689
Open parkland course offering testing golf and good views.
18 holes, 6524yds, Par 72, SSS 71, Course record 66.
Club membership 720.
Visitors   with member only Fri, weekends & bank
               holidays.
Societies welcome Tue & Thu only.
Green Fees £22.50 per day/round.
Facilities ⊗ ⅷ ᒪ ♨ ♀ ⚲ 🏠 ⌂ Alan Crosby.
Location   53 Bell Villas (0.5m E on A696)
Hotel   ★★★64% Airport Moat House Hotel,
               Woolsington, NEWCASTLE UPON TYNE
               AIRPORT ☎ (0661) 24911 100⇌ ♠

PRUDHOE   Map 12 NZ06

Prudhoe ☎ (0661) 832466
Parkland course with natural hazards and easy walking.
18 holes, 5812yds, Par 69, SSS 68, Course record 63.
Club membership 700.
Visitors   must contact in writing.
Societies must contact in writing.
Green Fees £18 per day (£25 weekends).
Facilities ⊗ ⅷ ᒪ ♨ ♀ ⚲ 🏠 ⌂ John Crawford.
Location   Eastwood Park (E side of town centre off A695)
Hotel   ★★64% County Hotel, Priestpopple, HEXHAM
               ☎ (0434) 602030 9⇌ ♠

ROTHBURY   Map 12 NU00

Rothbury ☎ (0669) 20718
Very flat parkland course alongside the River Coquet.
9 holes, 2788yds, Par 68, SSS 67, Course record 64.
Club membership 400.
Visitors   may not play at weekends.
Societies may not play at weekends.
Green Fees not confirmed.
Facilities ♀ (evenings/weekends) ⚲
Location   Old Race Course (S side of town off B6342)
Hotel   ★★★57% White Swan Hotel, Bondgate Within,
               ALNWICK ☎ (0665) 602109 43⇌ ♠

SEAHOUSES   Map 12 NU23

Seahouses ☎ Alnwick (0665) 720794
Typical links course with many hazards, including the famous
10th, 'Logans Loch', water hole.
18 holes, 5462yds, Par 67, SSS 67, Course record 67.
Club membership 450.
Visitors   must contact in advance for weekends.
Societies apply in writing.
Green Fees £15 per day (£20 weekends & bank holidays).
Facilities ⊗ ⅷ ᒪ ♨ (no catering Tue unless by prior
               arrangement) ♀ (ex Tue) ⚲ 🏠
Location   Beadnell Rd (S side of village on B1340)
Hotel   ★★70% Olde Ship Hotel, SEAHOUSES
               ☎ (0665) 720200 12⇌ ♠ Annexe3⇌ ♠

STOCKSFIELD   Map 12 NZ06

Stocksfield ☎ (0661) 843041
Challenging course: parkland (9 holes), woodland (9 holes).
18 holes, 5594yds, Par 68, SSS 68.
Club membership 700.
Visitors   welcome except weekends until 4pm. Must
               contact in advance.
Societies must contact in advance.
Green Fees £20 per day; £15 per round (£20 per round
               weekends & bank holidays).
Facilities ⊗ ⅷ by prior arrangement ᒪ ♨ ♀ ⚲ 🏠 ⌂ ⌂
               Stephen Mckenna.
Location   New Ridley Rd (2.5m SE off A695)
Hotel   ★★★65% Beaumont Hotel, Beaumont St,
               HEXHAM ☎ (0434) 602331
               23⇌ ♠

WARKWORTH   Map 12 NU20

Warkworth ☎ (0665) 711596
Seaside links course, with good views and alternative tees for
the back nine.
9 holes, 5817yds, Par 70, SSS 68 or 58 holes.
Club membership 440.
Visitors   welcome except Tue & Sat.
Societies apply in writing.
Green Fees £10 per day (£15 weekends & bank holidays).
Facilities ⊗ ⅷ ᒪ ♨ (catering by arrangement) ♀ ⚲
Location   The Links (0.5m E of village off A1068)
Hotel   ★★★57% White Swan Hotel, Bondgate Within,
               ALNWICK ☎ (0665) 602109 43⇌ ♠

NOTTINGHAMSHIRE

EAST LEAKE   Map 08 SK52

Rushcliffe ☎ (0509) 852959
Hilly, tree-lined and picturesque parkland course.
18 holes, 6020yds, Par 70, SSS 68, Course record 65.
Club membership 800.
Visitors   restricted weekends & bank holidays 9.30-11am
               & 3-4.30pm.
Societies must apply in advance.
Green Fees £22 per day (£25 weekends).
Facilities ⊗ ⅷ ᒪ ♨ (restricted Mon & Fri in winter) ♀
               ⚲ 🏠 ⌂ Tim Smart.
Leisure   snooker.
Location   Stocking Ln (1m N)
Hotel   ★★★62% Novotel Nottingham Derby, Bostock
               Ln, LONG EATON ☎ (0602) 720106 110⇌ ♠

KEYWORTH   Map 08 SK63

Stanton on the Wolds ☎ Nottingham (0602) 372006
Parkland course, fairly flat with stream running through four
holes.
18 holes, 6437yds, Par 73, SSS 71.
Club membership 900.
Visitors   restricted Tue & competition days. Must contact
               in advance & have handicap certificate.

Societies must apply in Oct
Green Fees £24 per day/round.
Facilities ⊗ ⍮ ⓑ ♥ ♀ ⌂ 🍴 (
Location E side of village
Hotel ★★65% Rufford Hotel, 53 Melton Road,West Bridgford, NOTTINGHAM
☎ (0602) 814202 35🛏

KIRKBY IN ASHFIELD   Map 08 SK55

Notts ☎ Mansfield (0623) 753225
Undulating heathland Championship course.
18 holes, 7020yds, Par 73, SSS 74.
Club membership 500.
Visitors must contact in advance & have handicap certificate. With member only weekends & bank holidays.
Societies must apply in advance.
Green Fees not confirmed.
Facilities ⊗ ⍮ ⓑ ♥ ♀ ⌂ 🏠 🍴 (Brian Waites.
Leisure driving range.
Location Hollinwell (1.5m SE off A611)
Hotel ★★★★62% Swallow Hotel, Carter Ln East, SOUTH NORMANTON
☎ (0773) 812000 161🛏🛏

MANSFIELD   Map 08 SK56

Sherwood Forest ☎ (0623) 26689
As the name suggests, the Forest is the main feature of this natural heathland course with its heather, silver birch and pine trees. The homeward nine holes are particularly testing. The 11th and 14th are notable par 4 holes on this well-bunkered course designed by the great James Braid.
18 holes, 6714yds, Par 71, SSS 73.
Club membership 749.
Visitors allowed Mon, Thu & Fri only. Must contact in advance and have a handicap certificate.
Societies welcome Mon, Thu & Fri, must apply in advance.
Green Fees on application.
Facilities ⊗ ⍮ ⓑ ♥ ♀ ⌂ 🏠 (Kenneth Hall.
Location Eakring Rd (2.5m E)
Hotel ★★★61% Forte Posthouse Nottingham/Derby, Bostocks Ln, SANDIACRE ☎ (0602) 397800 91🛏🛏

MANSFIELD WOODHOUSE   Map 08 SK56

Mansfield Woodhouse ☎ Mansfield (0623) 23521
Easy walking on heathland.
9 holes, 2446yds, Par 68, SSS 64 or 2446yds, Par 68, SSS 64.
Club membership 130.
Visitors no restrictions.
Societies must contact by telephone.
Green Fees £2.95 (9 holes), £4.30 (18 holes).
Facilities ⊗ ⓑ ♥ ♀ 🏠 🍴 (Leslie Highfield.
Location Leeming Ln North (N side of town centre off A60)
Hotel ★★64% Pine Lodge Hotel, 281-283 Nottingham Rd, MANSFIELD ☎ (0623) 22308 21rm(19🛏🛏)

NEWARK-ON-TRENT   Map 08 SK75

Newark ☎ (0636) 626282
Wooded, parkland course in secluded situation with easy walking.
18 holes, 6421yds, Par 71, SSS 71.
Club membership 650.
Visitors must contact in advance and have handicap certificate.
Societies must apply in writing.
Green Fees £23 per day; £18 per round.
Facilities ⊗ ⍮ ⓑ ♥ ♀ ⌂ 🏠 (Tony Bennett.
Leisure snooker.
Location Coddington (4m E on A17)
Hotel ★★69% Grange Hotel, 73 London Rd, NEWARK ☎ (0636) 703399 10🛏🛏 Annexe5🛏🛏

NOTTINGHAM   Map 08 SK53

Beeston Fields ☎ (0602) 257062
Parkland course with sandy subsoil and wide, tree-lined fairways. The par 3, 14th has elevated tee and small bunker-guarded green.
18 holes, 6414yds, Par 71, SSS 71, Course record 68.
Club membership 750.
Visitors must contact in advance and have a handicap certificate.
Societies must apply in advance.
Green Fees £20.
Facilities ⊗ ⍮ ⓑ ♥ ♀ ⌂ 🏠 🍴 (Alun Wardle.
Leisure snooker.
Location Beeston (4m SW off A52)
Hotel ★★★61% Forte Posthouse Nottingham/Derby, Bostocks Ln, SANDIACRE ☎ (0602) 397800 91🛏🛏

Bramcote Hills ☎ (0602) 281880
A Pay and Play, 18-hole Par 3 course with challenging greens.
18 holes, 1500yds, Par 54.
Visitors no restrictions
Societies telephone in advance.
Green Fees £4.30 per 18 holes (£4.90 weekends).
Facilities ♥ 🏠 (
Location Thoresby Rd, Derby Rd, Bramcote (off A52 Derby rd)
Hotel ★★66% Priory Hotel, Derby Rd, Wollaton Vale, NOTTINGHAM ☎ (0602) 221691 31🛏

Bulwell Forest ☎ (0602) 770576
Municipal heathland course with many natural hazards. Very tight fairways and subject to wind.
18 holes, 5606yds, Par 68, SSS 67, Course record 62.
Club membership 450.
Visitors restricted weekends. Must contact in advance.
Societies must apply in writing.
Green Fees not confirmed.
Facilities ⊗ ⓑ ♥ ♀ ⌂ 🏠 🍴 (C D Hall.
Location Hucknall Rd, Bulwell (4m NW of city centre on A611)
Hotel ★★★70% Nottingham Moat House, Mansfield Rd, NOTTINGHAM ☎ (0602) 602621 172🛏🛏

Chilwell Manor ☎ (0602) 258958
Flat parkland course.
18 holes, 6379yds, Par 70, SSS 70.
Club membership 750.

Visitors	with member only weekends. Must contact in advance and have a handicap certificate.
Societies	welcome Mon, must apply in advance.
Green Fees	not confirmed.
Facilities	catering by prior arrangement ♀ ♨ 🍴 (E McCausland.
Location	Meadow Ln, Chilwell (4m SW on A6005)
Hotel	★★60% Europa Hotel, 20 Derby Rd, LONG EATON ☎ (0602) 728481 19rm(14 ⇄ ↿)

Edwalton Municipal ☎ (0602) 234775 & 231576
Gently sloping, 9-hole parkland course. Also 9-hole Par 3 and large practice ground.
9 holes, 3372yds, Par 72, SSS 72, Course record 72.
Club membership 870.

Visitors	booking system in operation.
Societies	prior booking necessary.
Green Fees	£4.20 per 9 holes; £2.30 par 3.
Facilities	⊗ ⅲ by prior arrangement ♭ ♨ ♨ 🍴 (John Staples.
Leisure	par 3 course.
Location	Wellin Ln, Edwalton (S of Nottingham, off A606)
Hotel	★★★69% Swans Hotel & Restaurant, 84-90 Radcliffe Rd, West Bridgford, NOTTINGHAM ☎ (0602) 814042 31⇄ ↿

Mapperley ☎ (0602) 265611
Hilly meadowland course but with easy walking.
18 holes, 6283yds, Par 71, SSS 70.
Club membership 650.

Visitors	must be member of recognised club and have a handicap certificate.
Societies	must apply in writing and pay a deposit.
Green Fees	£18.50 per day; £15.50 per round (£20.50/£17.50 weekends and bank holidays).
Facilities	⊗ ⅲ by prior arrangement ♭ ♨ ♀ ♨ 🍴 (Paul Richmond.
Leisure	pool table.
Location	Central Av, Mapperley Plains (3m NE of city centre off B684)
Hotel	★★★★60% Forte Crest, Saint James's St, NOTTINGHAM ☎ (0602) 470131 139⇄

Nottingham City ☎ (0602) 278021 & 276916
A pleasant municipal parkland course on the city outskirts.
18 holes, 6218yds, Par 69, SSS 70, Course record 64.
Club membership 425.

Visitors	restricted Sat 7am-3pm.
Societies	welcome except weekends.
Green Fees	£6.80 (£8 weekends).
Facilities	⊗ ⅲ by prior arrangement ♭ ♨ ♀ ♨ 🍴 (Cyril Jepson.
Location	Bulwell Hall Park (4m NW of city centre off A6002)
Hotel	★★★70% Nottingham Moat House, Mansfield Rd, NOTTINGHAM ☎ (0602) 602621 172⇄ ↿

Wollaton Park ☎ (0602) 787574
A pleasant, fairly level course set in a park close to the centre of Nottingham, with red and fallow deer herds. The fairways are tree-lined. The 502-yd dog-leg 15th is a notable hole. The stately home - Wollaton Hall - is situated in the park.
18 holes, 6494yds, Par 71, SSS 71, Course record 64.
Club membership 770.

Visitors	by arrangement with the professional.
Societies	welcome Tue & Fri, must apply in advance.
Green Fees	not confirmed.
Facilities	⊗ ⅲ ♭ ♨ (all catering by arrangement) ♀ by arrangement ♨ 🍴 (John Lower.
Leisure	snooker.
Location	Wollaton Park (2.5m W of city centre off A52)
Hotel	★★★69% Swans Hotel & Restaurant, 84-90 Radcliffe Rd, West Bridgford, NOTTINGHAM ☎ (0602) 814042 31⇄ ↿

OXTON
Map 08 SK65

Oakmere Park ☎ Nottingham (0602) 653545
Set in rolling parkland in the heart of picturesque Robin Hood country. The par 4 (16th) and par 5 (1st) are notable. Thirty-bay floodlit driving range.
North Course: 18 holes, 6617mtrs, Par 72, SSS 72.
South Course: 9 holes, 3216mtrs, Par 37, SSS 37.
Club membership 450.

Visitors	must contact in advance.
Societies	must apply in writing or telephone.
Green Fees	North £16 per round (£20 weekends); South £6 per round (£8 weekends).
Facilities	⊗ ⅲ ♭ ♨ ♀ ♨ 🍴 (Geoff Norton.
Leisure	30 bay floodlit driving range.
Location	Oaks Ln (1m NW off A6097)
Hotel	★★★64% Saracen's Head Hotel, Market Place, SOUTHWELL ☎ (0636) 812701 27⇄ ↿

RADCLIFFE-ON-TRENT
Map 08 SK63

Radcliffe-on-Trent ☎ (0602) 333000
Fairly flat, parkland course with three good finishing holes: 16th (427 yds) par 4; 17th (180 yds) through spinney, par 3; 18th (331 yds) dog-leg par 4. Excellent views.
18 holes, 6381yds, Par 70, SSS 71.
Club membership 650.

Visitors	restricted Tue.
Societies	welcome Wed.
Green Fees	£21 per day (£26 weekends & bank holidays).
Facilities	⊗ ⅲ ♭ ♨ ♀ ♨ 🍴 (Robert Ellis.
Location	Drewberry Ln, Cropwell Rd (1m SE off A52)
Hotel	★★★69% Swans Hotel & Restaurant, 84-90 Radcliffe Rd, West Bridgford, NOTTINGHAM ☎ (0602) 814042 31⇄ ↿

RETFORD
Map 08 SK78

Retford ☎ (0777) 703733
A wooded, parkland course.
18 holes, 6301yds, Par 71, SSS 70, Course record 71.
Club membership 722.

Visitors advisable to contact in advance, welcome except before 11am on Tue, and with member only at weekends and holidays.
Societies apply in writing or telephone.
Green Fees £20 per day; £15 per round.
Facilities ⊗ 〗 ⅃ 🖤 ♀ ᗝ ᒪ (Stuart Betteridge.
Location Brecks Rd, Ordsall (1.5m S A620, between Worksop & Gainsborough)
Hotel ★★★69% Clumber Park Hotel, Clumber Park, WORKSOP ☎ (0623) 835333 48⇆ ⋔

RUDDINGTON   Map 08 SK53

Ruddington Grange ☎ Nottingham (0602) 846141
Undulating parkland course with water hazards on 12 holes.
18 holes, 6490yds, Par 72, SSS 72, Course record 71.
Club membership 650.
Visitors a handicap certificate is required, contact in advance if possible. Play may be restricted Sat & Wed mornings.
Societies must contact in advance.
Green Fees £20 per day.
Facilities ⊗ 〗 ⅃ 🖤 ♀ ᗝ ᒪ (R Daibell.
Location Wilford Rd (5m S of Nottingham, A60 to Ruddington)
Hotel ★★★69% Swans Hotel & Restaurant, 84-90 Radcliffe Rd, West Bridgford, NOTTINGHAM ☎ (0602) 814042 31⇆ ⋔

SERLBY   Map 08 SK68

Serlby Park ☎ (0777) 818268
Parkland course.
9 holes, 5325yds, Par 66, SSS 66.
Club membership 300.
Visitors must be accompanied by member.
Green Fees not confirmed.
Facilities ♀ (weekends) ᗝ ᒪ
Location E side of village off A638
Hotel ★★★64% Charnwood Hotel, Sheffield Rd, BLYTH ☎ (0909) 591610 20⇆ ⋔

SUTTON IN ASHFIELD   Map 08 SK45

Coxmoor ☎ Mansfield (0623) 557359
Undulating moorland/heathland course with easy walking and excellent views. The clubhouse is modern with a well-equipped games room. The course lies adjacent to Forestry Commission land over which there are several footpaths and extensive views.
18 holes, 6251yds, Par 73, SSS 70.
Club membership 600.
Visitors restricted weekends & bank holidays. Must contact in advance.
Societies must apply in advance.
Green Fees £27 per day.
Facilities ⊗ 〗 ⅃ 🖤 ♀ ᗝ ᒪ (David Ridley.
Leisure snooker.
Location Coxmoor Rd (2m SE off A611)
Hotel ★★★★62% Swallow Hotel, Carter Ln East, SOUTH NORMANTON ☎ (0773) 812000 161⇆ ⋔

WORKSOP   Map 08 SK57

Kilton Forest ☎ (0909) 472488 & 486563
Slightly undulating, parkland course on the north edge of Sherwood Forest. Includes three ponds.
18 holes, 6569yds, Par 72, SSS 72.
Club membership 450.
Visitors must contact in advance, restricted Sun.
Societies must contact in writing.
Green Fees £6.28 per round (£7.50 weekends & bank holidays).
Facilities ⊗ 〗 ⅃ 🖤 ♀ ᗝ ᒪ ⋔ (Peter W Foster.
Leisure bowling green.
Location Blyth Rd (1m NE of town centre on B6045)
Hotel ★★★60% Ye Olde Bell Hotel, BARNBY MOOR ☎ (0777) 705121 55⇆ ⋔

Lindrick ☎ (0909) 475282
Heathland course with some trees and masses of gorse.
18 holes, 6377yds, Par 69, SSS 70.
Club membership 500.
Visitors must contact in advance. Restricted Tue & weekends.
Societies welcome except Tue (am) & weekends.
Green Fees £40 per day/round (£45 weekends).
Facilities ⊗ 〗 ⅃ 🖤 ♀ ᗝ ᒪ (Peter Cowen.
Leisure snooker.
Location Lindrick Common (3m NW on A57)
Hotel ★★★60% Ye Olde Bell Hotel, BARNBY MOOR ☎ (0777) 705121 55⇆ ⋔

Worksop ☎ (0909) 472696
Adjacent to Clumber Park this course has a heathland-type terrain, with gorse, broom, oak and birch trees. Fast, true greens, dry all year round.
18 holes, 6651yds, Par 72, SSS 73.
Club membership 500.
Visitors by arrangement with professional (0909) 477732
Societies must apply in advance.
Green Fees £25 weekday; £18 round (£25 weekends & bank holidays).
Facilities ⊗ 〗 ⅃ 🖤 ♀ ᗝ ᒪ (J R King.
Leisure snooker.
Location Windmill Ln (1.75m S off A620)
Hotel ★★★60% Ye Olde Bell Hotel, BARNBY MOOR ☎ (0777) 705121 55⇆ ⋔

OXFORDSHIRE

ABINGDON   Map 04 SU49

Drayton Park ☎ (0235) 550607
Set in the heart of the Oxfordshire countryside, an 18-hole parkland course designed by Hawtree. Five lakes and sand based greens.
18 holes, 6500yds, Par 67, SSS 68.
Club membership 450.
Visitors may phone to book, must have golf shoes, no jeans or tracksuits.
Societies contact in advance.
Green Fees £11 per 18 Holes (£14 weekends).
Facilities ⊗ 〗 ⅃ 🖤 ♀ ᗝ ᒪ (Dinah Masey, Tony Williams.

▶

Leisure	21 bay driving range,9 hole par 3 course.
Location	Steventon Rd, Drayton Village (between Oxford & Newbury,off A34 at Didcot)
Hotel	★★★59% The Upper Reaches, Thames St, ABINGDON ☎ (0235) 522311 25⇌ ⋔

BURFORD

Map 04 SP21

Burford ☎ (099382) 2583
Created out of open-farmland, this parkland course has high quality fairways and greens.
18 holes, 6405yds, Par 71, SSS 71.
Club membership 800.

Visitors	must contact in advance. No visitors Tue (Ladies Day), & weekends.
Societies	by contact in advance.
Green Fees	£25 per day.
Facilities	⊗ ∭ ⅙ ⬛ ♀ ♨ 🛍 ⊓ᶠ ʦ Norman Allen.
Location	Swindon Rd (0.5m S off A361)
Hotel	★★67% Golden Pheasant Hotel, High St, BURFORD ☎ (099382) 3223 & 3417 12⇌ ⋔

CHESTERTON

Map 04 SP52

Chesterton Country ☎ Bicester (0869) 242023
Laid out over one-time farmland. Well-bunkered, and water hazards increase the difficulty of the course.
18 holes, 6230yds, Par 71, SSS 70, Course record 68.
Club membership 750.

Visitors	must pre-book for weekends & bank holidays.
Societies	must contact in advance.
Green Fees	£15 per day; £12 per round (£24/£18 weekends & bank holidays).
Facilities	⊗ ∭ by prior arrangement ⅙ ⬛ ♀ ♨ 🛍 ʦ J W Wilkshire.
Leisure	snooker.
Location	0.5m W on A4095
Hotel	★★67% Jersey Arms Hotel, MIDDLETON STONEY ☎ (086989) 234 & 505 6⇌ Annexe10⇌

CHIPPING NORTON

Map 04 SP32

Chipping Norton ☎ (0608) 642383
Pleasant downland course open to winds.
18 holes, 6280yds, Par 71, SSS 70, Course record 66.
Club membership 850.

Visitors	with member only at weekends. Must contact in advance.
Societies	must apply in writing.
Green Fees	£22 per day/round.
Facilities	⊗ ∭ ⅙ ⬛ ♀ ♨ 🛍 ⊓ᶠ ʦ Bob Gould.
Location	Southcombe (1.5m E on A44)
Hotel	★★66% Chadlington House Hotel, CHADLINGTON ☎ (060876) 437 11rm(5⇌5 ⋔)

A golf course name printed in ***bold italics*** means we have been unable to verify information with the club's management for the current year

FRILFORD

Map 04 SU49

Frilford Heath ☎ (0865) 390864
Two 18-hole heathland courses. Both the Red and the Green courses are of outstanding interest and beauty. Heather, pine, birch and, in particular, a mass of flowering gorse enhance the terrain. The greens are extensive.
18 holes, 6768yds, Par 73, SSS 73, Course record 65.
Club membership 900.

Visitors	restricted weekends & bank holidays. Must contact in advance and have an introduction from own club.
Societies	Mon, Wed & Fri only.
Green Fees	not confirmed.
Facilities	⊗ ∭ ⬛ ♀ ♨ 🛍 ⊓ᶠ ʦ Derek Craik.
Location	Abingdon (1m N off A338)
Hotel	★★★62% Abingdon Lodge Hotel, Marcham Rd, ABINGDON ☎ (0235) 553456 63⇌ ⋔

HENLEY-ON-THAMES

Map 04 SU78

Aspect Park ☎ (0491) 577562 & 578306
Parkland course. 18-hole course due to open Summer 1994.
9 holes, 5626yds, Par 68, SSS 66, Course record 69.
Club membership 500.

Visitors	must contact in advance, handicap certificate required weekend am.
Societies	must contact in advance.
Green Fees	£16 per 18 holes; £8 per 9 holes.
Facilities	⊗ ∭ ⅙ ⬛ ♀ ♨ 🛍 ⊓ᶠ ʦ Roger Frost.
Location	Remenham Hill
Hotel	★★★62% Red Lion Hotel, Hart St, HENLEY-ON-THAMES ☎ (0491) 572161 26rm(23⇌ ⋔)

Badgemore Park ☎ (0491) 572206
Parkland course with many trees and easy walking. The 13th is a very difficult par 3 hole played over a valley to a narrow green.
18 holes, 6112yds, Par 69, SSS 69.
Club membership 880.

Visitors	must contact in advance & have handicap certificate.
Societies	must apply in writing.
Green Fees	£27 per day (£30 weekends).
Facilities	⊗ ∭ by prior arrangement ⅙ ⬛ ♀ ♨ 🛍 ʦ Jonathon Dunn.
Leisure	squash.
Location	1m W
Hotel	★★★62% Red Lion Hotel, Hart St, HENLEY-ON-THAMES ☎ (0491) 572161 26rm(23⇌ ⋔)

Henley ☎ (0491) 575742
Undulating parkland course. 6th hole, blind (par 4), with steep hill.
18 holes, 6130yds, Par 69, SSS 69, Course record 65.
Club membership 830.

Visitors	must contact in advance & have handicap certificate & can play Mon-Fri, except bank holidays.
Societies	must contact in advance.
Green Fees	£30 per round (£25 per round Nov-Feb).
Facilities	⊗ ∭ ⅙ ⬛ ♀ ♨ 🛍 ⊓ᶠ ʦ Mark Howell.
Location	Harpsden (1.25m S off A4155)
Hotel	★★★62% Red Lion Hotel, Hart St, HENLEY-ON-THAMES ☎ (0491) 572161 26rm(23⇌ ⋔)

NUFFIELD
Map 04 SU68

Huntercombe ☎ (0491) 641207
This heathland/woodland course overlooks the
Oxfordshire plain and has many attractive and interesting
fairways and greens. Walking is easy after the 3rd which
is a notable hole. The course is subject to wind and grass
pot bunkers are interesting hazards.
18 holes, 6301yds, Par 70, SSS 70, Course record 63.
Club membership 600.
Visitors   must contact in advance and have a
                 handicap certificate.
Societies   must contact in advance.
Green Fees   £31.50 per day (per round weekends).
Facilities   ⊗ ⅃ ⌶ ♥ ♀ ⚘ 🏠 ƒ John B Draycott.
Location   N off A423
Hotel   ★★★65% Shillingford Bridge Hotel,
                 Shillingford, WALLINGFORD
                 ☎ (086732) 8567 23🛏 ⓡAnnexe10🛏 ⓡ

OXFORD
Map 04 SP50

North Oxford ☎ (0865) 54415
Gently undulating parkland course.
18 holes, 5736yds, Par 67, SSS 67.
Club membership 650.
Visitors   must contact in advance & play with member
                 only at weekends.
Societies   must contact in advance.
Green Fees   £25 per round.
Facilities   ⊗ ⅃ by prior arrangement ⌶ ♥ ♀ ⚘ 🏠 ƒ
                 R J Harris.
Location   Banbury Rd (3m N of city centre on A423)
Hotel   ★★★63% Oxford Moat House, Godstow Rd,
                 Wolvercote Rbt, OXFORD
                 ☎ (0865) 59933 155🛏

Southfield ☎ (0865) 242158
Home of the City, University and Ladies Clubs, and well-
known to graduates throughout the world. A challenging
course, in varied parkland setting, providing a real test
for players.
18 holes, 5973yds, Par 69, SSS 69.
Club membership 850.
Visitors   with member only at weekends.
Societies   must apply in writing.
Green Fees   £24 per day.
Facilities   ⊗ ⅃ by prior arrangement ⌶ ♥ ♀ ⚘ 🏠 ƒ
                 Tony Rees.
Location   Hill Top Rd (1.5m SE of city centre off B480)
Hotel   ★★★65% Eastgate Hotel, The High, Merton
                 St, OXFORD ☎ (0865) 248244 43🛏

SHRIVENHAM
Map 04 SU28

Shrivenham Park ☎ (0793) 783853
Parkland course with easy walking. The par 4, 17th is a
difficult dog-leg.
18 holes, 5527yds, Par 68.
Club membership 300.
Visitors   no restrictions.
Societies   must apply in advance.
Green Fees   £16.50 per day; £10 per round (£20/£13
                 weekends).

Facilities   ⊗ ⅃ ⌶ ♥ ♀ ⚘ 🏠 ♈ ƒ Simmon Jerreries.
Location   Pennyhooks (0.5m NE of town centre)
Hotel   ★★★62% Forte Crest Hotel, Oxford Rd,
                 Stratton St Margaret, SWINDON
                 ☎ (0793) 831333 94🛏 ⓡ

TADMARTON
Map 04 SP33

Tadmarton Heath ☎ Hook Norton (0608) 737278
A mixture of heath and sandy land, the course, which is
open to strong winds, incorporates the site of an old
Roman encampment. The clubhouse is an old farm
building with a 'holy well' from which the greens are
watered. The 7th is a testing hole over water.
18 holes, 5682yds, Par 69, SSS 68, Course record 63.
Club membership 600.
Visitors   with member only at weekends. Must
                 contact in advance and have an introduction
                 from own club.
Societies   by arrangement.
Green Fees   not confirmed.
Facilities   ⊗ ⅃ ⌶ ♥ ♀ ⚘ 🏠 ♈ ƒ Les Bond.
Leisure   fishing.
Location   1m SW of Lower Tadmarton off B4035
Hotel   ★★61% Olde School Hotel, Church St,
                 BLOXHAM ☎ (0295) 720369
                 11🛏 ⓡ Annexe27🛏 ⓡ

SHROPSHIRE

BRIDGNORTH
Map 07 SO79

Bridgnorth ☎ (0746) 763315
A pleasant course laid-out on parkland on the bank of the
River Severn.
18 holes, 6673yds, Par 73, SSS 72.
Club membership 725.
Visitors   must contact in advance but may not play on Wed.
Societies   must contact in writing.
Green Fees   £18 per round (£24 weekends).
Facilities   ⊗ ⅃ ⌶ ♥ (no catering Mon) ♀ (ex Mon)
                 ⚘ 🏠 ƒ Paul Hinton.
Leisure   fishing.
Location   Stanley Ln (1m N off B4373)
Hotel   ★★60% Falcon Hotel, Saint John St, Lowtown,
                 BRIDGNORTH ☎ (0746) 763134
                 15rm(5🛏7 ⓡ)

CHURCH STRETTON
Map 07 SO49

Church Stretton ☎ (0694) 722281
Hillside course constructed by James Braid on the lower
slopes of the Long Mynd.
18 holes, 5008yds, Par 66, SSS 65, Course record 63.
Club membership 500.
Visitors   may not play before 10.30am at weekends &
                 bank holidays. Must contact in advance & have
                 handicap certificate.
Societies   must contact in advance.
Green Fees   not confirmed.
Facilities   ⊗ ⅃ ⌶ ♥ ♀ ⚘ 🏠 ⋈ ƒ P Seal (weekends
                 only).

▶

Location Trevor Hill (NW side of village off B4370)
Hotel ★★71% Mynd House Hotel, Little Stretton,
CHURCH STRETTON ☎ (0694) 722212 8➪ ฿

LILLESHALL   Map 07 SJ71

Lilleshall Hall ☎ Telford (0952) 603840
Heavily-wooded parkland course. Easy walking.
18 holes, 5906yds, Par 68, SSS 68, Course record 65.
Club membership 650.
Visitors must contact in advance and play with member
at weekends.
Societies must apply in writing by Dec for the following
year.
Green Fees not confirmed.
Facilities ⊗ ℳ 🍺 ♀ ♣ 🏌 ฿ N Bramall.
Location Newport (3m SE)
Hotel ★★64% Royal Victoria Hotel, St Mary's St,
NEWPORT ☎ (0952) 820331 24rm(16➪7 ฿)

LUDLOW   Map 07 SO57

Ludlow ☎ Bromfield (058477) 285
A long-established parkland course in the middle of the
racecourse. Very flat, quick drying, with broom and gorse-
lined fairways.
18 holes, 6193yds, Par 70, SSS 70.
Club membership 650.
Visitors must play with member at weekends in winter.
Must contact in advance and have a letter of
introduction.
Societies must contact in writing.
Green Fees £18 per day (£24 weekends).
Facilities ⊗ ℳ 🍺 & ▼ (ex Mon) ♀ ♣ 🏌 ฿ Russell
Price.
Location Bromfield (2m N off A49)
Hotel ★★★68% The Feathers at Ludlow, Bull Ring,
LUDLOW ☎ (0584) 875261 40➪ ฿

MARKET DRAYTON   Map 07 SJ63

Market Drayton ☎ (0630) 652266
Parkland course in quiet, picturesque surroundings providing
a good test of golf. Bungalow on course is made available for
golfing holidays.
18 holes, 6400yds, Par 71, SSS 70.
Club membership 550.
Visitors may not play on Sun; must play with member on
Sat. Must contact in advance.
Societies must contact in advance.
Green Fees £20 per day.
Facilities ⊗ ℳ 🍺 ▼ ♀ ♣ 🏌 ฿ Russel Clewes.
Location Sutton (1m SW)
Hotel ★★61% Corbet Arms Hotel, High St, MARKET
DRAYTON
☎ (0630) 652037 11➪ ฿

MEOLE BRACE   Map 07 SJ41

Meole Brace ☎ (0743) 364050
Pleasant municipal course.
12 holes, 3066yds, Par 43, SSS 42.
Visitors no restrictions.
Green Fees not confirmed.

Facilities ♣ 🏌 ฿
Location NE side of village off A49
Hotel ★★★62% Lion Hotel, Wyle Cop,
SHREWSBURY
☎ (0743) 353107 59➪ ฿

OSWESTRY   Map 07 SJ22

Mile End ☎ (0691) 670580 & 671246
Opened in June 1992, a gently undulating 9-hole parkland-
type course. Well-spaced holes in 70 acres.
9 holes, 6130yds, Par 70, SSS 69.
Club membership 270.
Visitors must have handicap certificate or proof of
membership to bona fide Club.
Green Fees £14 per day (£18 weekends).
Facilities ⊗ 🍺 ▼ ♀ ♣ 🏌 ฿ Scott Carpenter.
Leisure driving range.
Location Mile End
Hotel ★★★67% Wynnstay Hotel, Church St,
OSWESTRY
☎ (0691) 655261 27➪ ฿

Oswestry ☎ Queens Head (069188) 535
Parkland course laid-out on undulating ground.
18 holes, 6024yds, Par 70, SSS 69.
Club membership 700.
Visitors must be a member of a recognised Golf Club.
Must contact in advance.
Societies Wed & Fri only. Must contact in advance.
Green Fees £18 per day (£25 weekends).
Facilities ⊗ ℳ 🍺 ▼ ♀ ♣ 🏌 ฿ David Skelton.
Leisure snooker.
Location Aston Park (2m SE on A5)
Hotel ★★★67% Wynnstay Hotel, Church St,
OSWESTRY ☎ (0691) 655261 27➪ ฿

PANT   Map 07 SJ22

Llanymynech ☎ Llanymynech (0691) 830983
Upland course on the site of an early Iron Age/Roman hillfort
with far-reaching views. The 4th fairway crosses the Welsh
border.
18 holes, 6114yds, Par 70, SSS 69, Course record 65.
Club membership 805.
Visitors must contact in advance & must play with
member after 4.30pm.
Societies must contact in writing.
Green Fees £18 per day; £12 per round (£25/£19 weekends
& bank holidays).
Facilities ⊗ ℳ 🍺 ▼ ♀ ♣ 🏌 🏌 ฿ Andrew P Griffiths.
Location 0.5m SW off A483
Hotel ★★★67% Wynnstay Hotel, Church St,
OSWESTRY ☎ (0691) 655261 27➪ ฿

SHIFNAL   Map 07 SJ70

Shifnal ☎ Telford (0952) 460330
Well-wooded parkland course. Walking is easy and an
attractive country mansion serves as the clubhouse.
18 holes, 6468yds, Par 71, SSS 71, Course record 64.
Club membership 560.
Visitors must play with member on weekends & bank
holidays. Must contact in advance and have an
introduction from own club.

Societies must contact in advance.
Green Fees not confirmed.
Facilities ⊗ ⅢⅢ ᵇ ⬛ (no catering Mon) ♀ ♨ 🛋 ⎰ Justin Flanagan.
Leisure snooker.
Location Decker Hill (1m N off B4379)
Hotel ★★★★62% Park House Hotel, Silvermere Park, Park St, SHIFNAL
☎ (0952) 460128 54 ⇆ 🐾

SHREWSBURY   Map 07 SJ41

Shrewsbury ☎ (0743) 872976
Parkland course. First nine flat, second undulating with good views.
18 holes, 6300yds, Par 70, SSS 70.
Club membership 872.
Visitors may only play between 10am-noon and after 2.15pm at weekends. Must contact in advance and have a handicap certificate.
Societies must contact in writing.
Green Fees £20 per day; £15 per round (£25 per round/day weekends and bank holidays).
Facilities ⊗ ⅢⅢ ᵇ ⬛ ♀ ♨ 🛋 ⎰ Peter Seal.
Leisure snooker.
Location Condover (4m S off A49)
Hotel ★★★56% Radbrook Hall Hotel, Radbrook Rd, SHREWSBURY
☎ (0743) 236676 28 ⇆ 🐾

TELFORD   Map 07 SJ61

The Shropshire ☎ (0952) 677866
Pay and Play, 3 loops of 9-holes. Also tuition hole, practice green, 12 hole pitch and putt and 18-hole contoured putting green.
Blue: 9 holes, 3286yds, Par 35, SSS 35.
Silver: 9 holes, 3303yds, Par 36, SSS 36.
Gold: 9 holes, 3334yds, Par 36, SSS 36.
Club membership 250.
Visitors must book 7 days in advance.
Societies must book in advance.
Green Fees £10 per 18 holes (£15 weekends & bank holidays).
Facilities ⊗ ⅢⅢ ᵇ ⬛ ♀ ♨ 🛋 ⎰⎰ ⎰ Mike Booker, Kevin Short.
Leisure fishing, riding, snooker, boules, archery, pitch & putt.
Location Muxton Grange, Muxton
Hotel ★★★69% Holiday Inn, St Quentin Gate, TELFORD ☎ (0952) 292500 100 ⇆ 🐾

Telford Hotel Golf & Country Club ☎ (0952) 585642
Rolling parkland course with easy walking. Three lakes and large sand traps are hazards to the fine greens.
18 holes, 6766yds, Par 72, SSS 72.
Club membership 625.
Visitors must have a handicap certificate or be member of recognised Golf Club. Must contact in advance.
Societies must contact by telephone or post
Green Fees £25 per day (£30 weekends & bank holidays).
Facilities ⊗ ⅢⅢ ᵇ ⬛ ♀ ♨ 🛋 ⎰⎰ ⎰ Graham Farr.
Leisure heated indoor swimming pool, squash, snooker, sauna, solarium, gymnasium, 9 hole par 3 course, driving range.

Location Sutton Hill (4m S of town centre off A442)
Hotel ★★★68% Telford Hotel Golf & Country Club, Great Hay Dr, Sutton Hill, TELFORD
☎ (0952) 585642 86 ⇆ 🐾

WELLINGTON   Map 07 SJ61

Wrekin ☎ Telford (0952) 244032
Downland course with some hard walking but rewarding views.
18 holes, 5699yds, Par 66, SSS 67.
Club membership 700.
Visitors must contact in advance.
Societies must telephone in advance.
Green Fees not confirmed.
Facilities ⊗ ⅢⅢ ᵇ ⬛ ♀ ♨ 🛋 ⎰
Location Ercall Woods (1.25m S off B5061)
Hotel ★★★64% Buckatree Hall Hotel, The Wrekin, Wellington, TELFORD
☎ (0952) 641821 64 ⇆ 🐾

WESTON-UNDER-REDCASTLE   Map 07 SJ52

Hawkstone Park Hotel ☎ (0939) 200611
Two courses in a beautiful setting, both with natural hazards and good views. Hawkstone Course has been established for over 50 years and enjoys a superb setting whilst the newer Weston course has developed well.
18 holes, 6203yds, Par 72, SSS 70.
Club membership 450.
Visitors must contact in advance.
Green Fees not confirmed.
Facilities ♨ 🛋 ⎰⎰ ⎰
Location N side of village .75m E of A49
Hotel ★★64% Bear Hotel, HODNET
☎ (063084) 214 & 788 6 ⇆ 🐾

WHITCHURCH   Map 07 SJ54

Hill Valley ☎ (0948) 3584 due to change to 663584
This parkland course opened in 1975, and its Main Course was designed to championship standard by Peter Alliss and Dave Thomas. The hilly terrain is enhanced by many glorious views. There are natural water hazards on seven holes. Also 9-hole Northern Course and par 3 course.
Championship: 18 holes, 6517yds, Par 72, SSS 71.
Northern: 18 holes, 6050yds, Par 72, SSS 69.
Par 3: 9 holes, 793yds, Par 27.
Club membership 600.
Visitors must contact in advance. Restricted Sun.
Societies must contact in advance; a deposit will be required.
Green Fees Championship: £18 (£24 weekends); Northern £9 (£12 weekends).
Facilities ⊗ ⅢⅢ ᵇ ⬛ ♀ ♨ 🛋 ⎰⎰ ⎰ A R Minshall.
Leisure hard tennis courts, squash, snooker.
Location Terrick Rd (1m N)
Hotel ★★★63% Terrick Hall Country Hotel, Hill Valley, WHITCHURCH ☎ (0948) 3031
10 ⇆ 🐾 Annexe7 ⇆ 🐾

WORFIELD　　　　　　　　Map 07 SO79

Worfield ☎ (0746) 64372 & 64541
Opened in 1991, this undulating course with good-sized
greens, well placed bunkers and 2 lakes, rated highly in a golf
magazine survey.
18 holes, 6798yds, Par 73, SSS 73.
Club membership 500.
Visitors　　must contact in advance, weekends only
　　　　　　　after 10am.
Societies　contact in advance.
Green Fees　£20 per day; £15 per round (£25/£20 weekends).
Facilities　⊗ ⅲ ⅃ ⬛ ♀ ⚲ 🏠 ℂ Steve Russell.
Location　3m W of Bridgenorth, off A454
Hotel　　★★★♨74% Old Vicarage Hotel, WORFIELD
　　　　　☎ (07464) 497　10⇥ ℂ Annexe4⇥ ℂ

SOMERSET

BURNHAM-ON-SEA　　　　　　Map 03 ST34

Brean ☎ Brean Down (0278) 751570
Level and open moorland course with water hazards.
Facilities of 'Brean Leisure Park' adjoining.
18 holes, 5714yds, Par 69, SSS 68.
Club membership 550.
Visitors　　may not play on Sat & Sun before 1pm. Must
　　　　　　　have a handicap certificate.
Societies　weekdays only. Must contact in advance.
Green Fees　£12/18 (£15/18 weekends).
Facilities　⊗ & ⅲ by prior arrangement
　　　　　　　⅃ ⬛ ♀ ⚲ 🏠 ⚲ 🏠 ℂ Sue Spencer.
Leisure　outdoor and indoor heated swimming pools,
　　　　　　fishing, riding, sauna.
Location　Coast Rd, Brean (6m N on coast rd)
Hotel　　★★65% Battleborough Grange Country Hotel,
　　　　　Bristol Rd, BRENT KNOLL
　　　　　☎ (0278) 760208　18rm(8⇥6 ℂ)

Burnham & Berrow ☎ Burham-on-Sea (0278) 783137
Links championship course with large sandhills.
Championship: 18 holes, 6327yds, Par 71, SSS 72,
Course record 66.
9 Hole: 9 holes, 6332yds, Par 72, SSS 70.
Club membership 940.
Visitors　　must contact in advance & have handicap
　　　　　　　certificate.
Societies　must apply in advance.
Green Fees　£28 per day (£40 weekends & bank
　　　　　　　holidays); 9 hole £8 per day.
Facilities　⊗ ⅲ by prior arrangement ⅃ ⬛ ♀ ⚲
　　　　　　　🏠 ⚲ 🏠 ℂ Mark Crowther-Smith.
Location　St Christopher's Way (N side of town off
　　　　　　B3140)
Hotel　　★★65% Battleborough Grange Country
　　　　　Hotel, Bristol Rd, BRENT KNOLL
　　　　　☎ (0278) 760208　18rm(8⇥6 ℂ)

CHARD　　　　　　　　Map 03 ST30

Windwhistle Golf, Squash & Country Club
☎ (0460) 30231
Parkland course at 735 ft above sea level with outstanding
views over the Somerset Levels to the Bristol Channel and
South Wales.
East/West Course: 18 holes, 6500yds, Par 73, SSS 71.
Club membership 600.
Visitors　　must contact in advance.
Societies　by prior arrangement.
Green Fees　on application.
Facilities　⊗ ⅲ ⅃ (catering by arrangement) ⬛ ♀ ⚲ 🏠
Leisure　squash.
Location　Cricket St Thomas (3m E on A30)
Hotel　　★★65% Shrubbery Hotel, ILMINSTER
　　　　　☎ (0460) 52108　13⇥ ℂ

ENMORE　　　　　　　　Map 03 ST23

Enmore Park ☎ Bridgwater (0278) 671481
Hilly, parkland course with water features on foothills of
Quantocks. Wooded countryside and views of Quantocks and
Mendips. 1st and 10th are testing holes.
18 holes, 6241yds, Par 71, SSS 71, Course record 66.
Club membership 800.
Visitors　　restricted competition days & weekends.
Societies　must apply in writing.
Green Fees　not confirmed.
Facilities　⊗ ⅲ (in summer) ⅃ ⬛ ♀ ⚲ 🏠 ℂ
　　　　　　　Nigel Wixon.
Leisure　large practice area.
Location　1m E
Hotel　　★★★70% Walnut Tree Inn, North Petherton,
　　　　　BRIDGWATER
　　　　　☎ (0278) 662255　28⇥

GURNEY SLADE　　　　　　Map 03 ST64

Mendip ☎ Oakhill (0749) 840570
Undulating downland course offering an interesting test of
golf on superb fairways.
18 holes, 6330yds, Par 71, SSS 70, Course record 65.
Club membership 780.
Visitors　　must contact in advance and have handicap
　　　　　　　certificate weekends.
Societies　must apply in advance.
Green Fees　not confirmed.
Facilities　⊗ ⅲ ⅃ ⬛ ♀ ⚲ 🏠 ⚲ ℂ
Location　1.5m S off A37
Hotel　　★★★68% Centurion Hotel, Charlton Ln,
　　　　　MIDSOMER NORTON
　　　　　☎ (0761) 417711　44⇥ ℂ

LANGPORT　　　　　　　Map 02 ST42

Long Sutton ☎ Long Sutton (0458) 241017
Gentle, undulating, Pay and Play course.
18 holes, 6148yds, Par 70, SSS 69, Course record 72.
Club membership 450.
Visitors　　advisable to book at weekends.
Societies　contact in advance.
Green Fees　£18 per day; £17 per round (£24/£16 weekends).
Facilities　⊗ ⅃ ⬛ ♀ ⚲ 🏠 ⚲ ℂ Stewart Adwick.

Leisure	driving range.
Location	Long Load (5m NW of Yeovil off A372)
Hotel	★★★68% The Hollies, Bower Hinton, MARTOCK ☎ (0935) 822232 Annexe15⇔ ♠

MINEHEAD   Map 03 SS94

Minehead & West Somerset ☎ (0643) 702057
Flat seaside links, very exposed to wind, with good turf set on a shingle bank. The last five holes adjacent to the beach are testing. The 215-yard 18th is wedged between the beach and the club buildings and provides a good finish.
18 holes, 6228yds, Par 71, SSS 71, Course record 68.
Club membership 543.

Visitors	no restrictions.
Societies	must contact in writing.
Green Fees	£19.50 (£23 weekends & bank holidays).
Facilities	⊗ �🎜 🖫 🍸 ♀ ♨ 🏠 ⫟ ⌁ ⌇ I Read.
Location	The Warren (E side of town centre)
Hotel	★★★67% Northfield Hotel, Northfield Rd, MINEHEAD ☎ (0643) 705155 24⇔ ♠

TAUNTON   Map 03 ST22

Taunton & Pickeridge ☎ (082342) 537
Downland course with extensive views.
18 holes, 5927yds, Par 69, SSS 68, Course record 66.
Club membership 600.

Visitors	must contact in advance and have an introduction from own club.
Societies	must telephone in advance.
Green Fees	not confirmed.
Facilities	⊗ ⃥🎜 🖫 🍸 ♀ ♨ 🏠 ⌇ Graham Glew.
Leisure	snooker.
Location	Corfe (4m S off B3170)
Hotel	★★★59% County Hotel, East St, TAUNTON ☎ (0823) 337651 66⇔ ♠

Taunton Vale ☎ West Monkton (0823) 412220 & 412880
An 18 hole and a 9 hole golf course in a parkland complex occupying 156 acres in the Vale of Taunton. Complex includes a floodlit driving range.
Charlton: 18 holes, 6072yds, Par 70, SSS 69.
Durston: 9 holes, 2004yds, Par 32, SSS 60.
Club membership 700.

Visitors	dress code is applied.
Societies	must telephone in advance.
Green Fees	18 holes: £20 per day; £14 per round (£25/£17.50 weekends). 9 holes: £10 per day; £7 per round (£13/£8.75 weekends).
Facilities	⊗ ⃥🎜 by prior arrangement 🖫 🍸 ♀ ♨ 🏠 ⫟ ⌇ Martin Keitch.
Leisure	floodlit driving range.
Location	Creech Heathfield
Hotel	★★★59% County Hotel, East St, TAUNTON ☎ (0823) 337651 66⇔ ♠

Vivary Park Municipal ☎ (0823) 333875
A parkland course, tight and narrow with ponds.
18 holes, 4620yds, Par 63, SSS 63.

Visitors	must contact in advance.
Societies	apply in writing.
Green Fees	not confirmed.
Facilities	♨ 🏠 ⫟ ⌇
Leisure	snooker.
Location	Fons George (S side of town centre off A38)

Hotel	★★65% Falcon Hotel, Henlade, TAUNTON ☎ (0823) 442502 11⇔ ♠

WEDMORE   Map 03 ST44

Isle of Wedmore ☎ (0934) 712452
Gentle undulating course designed to maintain natural environment. Existing woodland and hedgerow enhanced by new planting. Magnificent panoramic views of Cheddar Valley and Glastonbury Tor.
18 holes, 5732yds, Par 70, SSS 69.
Club membership 500.

Visitors	no restrictions.
Societies	contact in advance.
Green Fees	£10 (£15 weekends).
Facilities	⊗ ⃥🎜 🖫 🍸 ♀ ♨ 🏠 ⫟ ⌇ Graham Coombe.
Leisure	snooker.
Location	Lineage (off B3139 between Wells & Burnham-on-Sea)
Hotel	★★★65% Swan Hotel, Sadler St, WELLS ☎ (0749) 678877 38⇔ ♠

WELLS   Map 03 ST54

Wells (Somerset) ☎ (0749) 675005
Beautiful wooded course with wonderful views. The prevailing SW wind complicates the 448-yd, 3rd.
18 holes, 6014yds, Par 70, SSS 69, Course record 62.
Club membership 800.

Visitors	must contact in advance & have handicap certificate weekends. Tee times restricted.
Societies	must apply in writing. ▶

Green Fees £19 per day; £16 per round (£22/£20 weekends & public holidays).
Facilities ⊗ ⅲ ⅃ ☕ ♀ △ 🏠 ⅰ ⅰ Andrew England.
Location East Horrington Rd (1.5m E off B3139)
Hotel ★★★65% Swan Hotel, Sadler St, WELLS
☎ (0749) 678877 38⇄ 🐾

YEOVIL   Map 03 ST51

> **Yeovil** ☎ (0935) 75949 & 22965
> The opener lies by the River Yeo before the gentle climb to high downs with good views. The outstanding 14th and 15th holes present a challenge, being below the player with a deep railway cutting on the left of the green.
> *Old: 18 holes, 6144yds, Par 72, SSS 70,*
> *Course record 64.*
> *New: 9 holes, 5016yds, Par 68, SSS 66.*
> *Club membership 720.*
> **Visitors** must contact in advance. Handicap certificate required on 18 hole at all times & on 9 hole at weekends.
> **Societies** Mon, Wed & Fri only, must contact in advance.
> **Green Fees** 18 hole: £30 per day; £20 per round. 9 hole: £20 per day; £12 per round.
> **Facilities** ⊗ ⅲ ⅃ ☕ ♀ △ 🏠 ⅰ ⅰ Geoff Kite.
> **Leisure** snooker.
> **Location** Sherborne Rd (1m E on A30)
> **Hotel** ★★★64% The Manor Hotel, Hendford, YEOVIL ☎ (0935) 23116
> 20⇄ 🐾 Annexe21⇄ 🐾

● SOUTH YORKSHIRE ●

BARNSLEY   Map 08 SE30

Barnsley ☎ (0226) 382856
Undulating municipal parkland course with easy walking apart from last 4 holes. Testing 8th and 18th holes.
18 holes, 6042yds, Par 69, SSS 69, Course record 64.
Club membership 450.
Visitors no restrictions.
Societies by arrangement.
Green Fees not confirmed.
Facilities ⊗ by prior arrangement ⅃ ☕ ♀ △ 🏠 ⅰ ⅰ Mike Melling.
Location Wakefield Rd, Staincross (3m N on A61)
Hotel ★★★67% Ardsley Moat House, Doncaster Rd, Ardsley, BARNSLEY
☎(0226) 289401 73⇄ 🐾

BAWTRY   Map 08 SK69

Austerfield Park ☎ Doncaster (0302) 710841 & 710850
Long moorland course with postage stamp 8th and testing 618-yd 7th. Driving range attached.
18 holes, 6854yds, Par 73, SSS 73, Course record 72.
Club membership 600.
Visitors no restrictions.
Societies must apply in writing.
Green Fees £15 per day; £11 per round (£19/£15 weekends).
Facilities ⊗ ⅲ ⅃ ☕ ♀ △ 🏠 ⅰ

Leisure bowling green (flat), driving range.
Location Cross Ln (2m NE on A640)
Hotel ★★65% Falcon Hotel, Henlade, TAUNTON
☎ (0823) 442502 11⇄ 🐾

CONISBROUGH   Map 08 SK59

Crookhill Park Municipal ☎ Rotherham (0709) 862979
A rolling parkland course.
18 holes, 5839yds, Par 70, SSS 68.
Club membership 500.
Visitors restricted weekends before 9am. Must contact in advance.
Societies by arrangement.
Green Fees £7.50 per round.
Facilities ⅃ ☕ ♀ △ 🏠 ⅰ ⅰ Richard Swaine.
Leisure pool table.
Location Carr Ln (1.5m SE on B6094)
Hotel ★★★62% Danum Swallow Hotel, High St, DONCASTER ☎ (0302) 342261 66⇄ 🐾

DONCASTER   Map 08 SE50

Doncaster ☎ (0302) 868316
Pleasant undulating heathland course with wooded surroundings. Quick drying, ideal autumn, winter and spring.
18 holes, 6230yds, Par 69, SSS 70.
Club membership 600.
Visitors may not play before 11am weekends & bank holidays.
Societies must contact in advance.
Green Fees £20 per day; £18 per round.
Facilities △ 🏠 ⅰ ⅰ Graham Bailey.
Location 278 Bawtry Rd, Bessacarr (5m SE on A638)
Hotel ★★★64% Mount Pleasant Hotel, Great North Rd, ROSSINGTON
☎ (0302) 868696 & 868219 32⇄ 🐾

Doncaster Town Moor ☎ (0302) 535286
Easy walking, but testing, heathland course with good true greens. Friendly club. Notable hole is 11th (par 4), 464 yds. Situated in centre of racecourse.
18 holes, 6094yds, Par 69, SSS 69, Course record 67.
Club membership 520.
Visitors may not play on Sun morning.
Societies must contact in advance.
Green Fees £15 per day (£17 weekends & bank holidays); £13 per round (£15 weekends & bank holidays).
Facilities ☕ ♀ △ 🏠 ⅰ Steve Poole.
Location The Bell Vue Club, Belle Vue (1.5m E,at racecourse,on A638)
Hotel ★★★62% Danum Swallow Hotel, High St, DONCASTER ☎ (0302) 342261 66⇄ 🐾

Owston Park ☎ (0302) 330821
A flat course surrounded by woodland. A lot of mature trees and a few ditches in play. A practice putting green and chipping area.
9 holes, 3042yds, Par 36, SSS 71.
Visitors no restrictions.
Societies contact in advance.
Green Fees £3 per 9 holes (£2 back nine midweek,£3 weekends).
Facilities △ 🏠 ⅰ ⅰ Mike Parker.

Location Owston Hall, nr Carcroft (6m N of Doncaster on A19)
Hotel ★★★62% Danum Swallow Hotel, High St, DONCASTER ☎ (0302) 342261 66⇆ ᴙ

Wheatley ☎ (0302) 831655
Fairly flat well-bunkered, lake-holed, parkland course.
18 holes, 6169yds, Par 70, SSS 69.
Club membership 600.
Visitors must contact in advance and have an introduction from own club.
Societies must contact in advance.
Green Fees not confirmed.
Facilities ⊗ ᵧⅢ ᑦ ᴠ ♀ ⚐ ᒲ (T C Parkinson.
Location Armthorpe Rd (NE side of town centre off A18)
Hotel ★★★64% Mount Pleasant Hotel, Great North Rd, ROSSINGTON
☎ (0302) 868696 & 868219 32⇆ ᴙ

HICKLETON   Map 08 SE40

Hickleton ☎ Rotherham (0709) 896081
Undulating parkland course with stream running through; designed by Neil Coles and Brian Huggett.
18 holes, 6403yds, Par 71, SSS 71.
Club membership 600.
Visitors restricted weekends after 2.30pm. Must contact in advance.
Societies must contact in advance on (0709) 888436.
Green Fees £17 per day (£20 weekends; £25 bank holidays).
Facilities ⊗ ᵧⅢ ᑦ & ᴠ by prior arrangement ♀ by arrangement ⚐ ᒲ (Paul Shepherd.
Location 0.5m W on B6411
Hotel ★★★62% Danum Swallow Hotel, High St, DONCASTER ☎ (0302) 342261 66⇆ ᴙ

HIGH GREEN   Map 08 SK39

Tankersley Park ☎ Sheffield (0742) 468247
Akin to an inland links, this parkland course is hilly, windy and has good views.
18 holes, 6212yds, Par 69, SSS 71.
Club membership 500.
Visitors may not play Tue. With member only at weekends. Must contact in advance.
Societies must apply in writing.
Green Fees not confirmed.
Facilities ⊗ ᵧⅢ by prior arrangement ᑦ ᴠ ♀ ⚐ ᒲ (Ian Kirk.
Location 1m NE
Hotel ★★69% Rutland Hotel, 452 Glossop Rd, Broomhill, SHEFFIELD ☎ (0742) 664411 73rm(68 ⇆1 ᴙ) Annexe17⇆ ᴙ

RAWMARSH   Map 08 SK49

Wath ☎ (0709) 872149
Parkland course, not easy in spite of its length; 17th hole (par 3) is a difficult 244yds with narrow driving area.
18 holes, 5857yds, Par 68, SSS 68.
Club membership 550.
Visitors must play with member at weekends. Must contact in advance and have a handicap certificate.
Societies must contact in writing.
Green Fees £16 per day/round.

Facilities ⊗ & ᵧⅢ (Apr-Sept) ᑦ (ex Sun) ᴠ (dinner weekdays only) ♀ ⚐ ᒲ (Chris Bassett.
Location Abdy Ln (2.5m N off A633)
Hotel ★★66% Brentwood Hotel, Moorgate Rd, ROTHERHAM ☎ (0709) 382772 33⇆ ᴙ Annexe10⇆ ᴙ

ROTHERHAM   Map 08 SK49

Grange Park ☎ (0709) 559497
Parkland/meadowland course, with panoramic views especially from the back nine. The golf is testing, particularly at the 1st, 4th and 18th holes (par 4), and 8th, 12th and 15th (par 5).
18 holes, 6461yds, Par 71, SSS 70.
Club membership 325.
Visitors no restrictions.
Societies apply in writing.
Green Fees £5.50 per round (£6.50 weekends & bank holidays).
Facilities ⊗ ᵧⅢ ᑦ ᴠ ♀ ⚐ ᒲ (Eric Clark.
Location Upper Wortley Rd (3m NW off A629)
Hotel ★★66% Brentwood Hotel, Moorgate Rd, ROTHERHAM ☎ (0709) 382772 33⇆ ᴙ Annexe10⇆ ᴙ

Phoenix ☎ (0709) 363864
Undulating meadowland course with variable wind.
18 holes, 6145yds, Par 71, SSS 69, Course record 66.
Club membership 750.
Visitors no restrictions.
Societies must apply in writing.
Green Fees £18 per day (£24 weekends & bank holidays).
Facilities ⊗ ᵧⅢ by prior arrangement ᑦ ᴠ ♀ ⚐ ᒲ (Andrew Limb.
Leisure hard tennis courts, squash, fishing, snooker, gymnasium.
Location Pavilion Ln, Brinsworth (SW side of town centre off A630)
Hotel ★★66% Brentwood Hotel, Moorgate Rd, ROTHERHAM ☎ (0709) 382772 33⇆ ᴙ Annexe10⇆ ᴙ

Rotherham Golf Club Ltd ☎ (0709) 850812 & 850466
Parkland course with easy walking along tree-lined fairways.
18 holes, 6324yds, Par 70, SSS 70.
Club membership 440.
Visitors must contact in advance. Restricted weekends & bank holidays.
Societies must contact in advance.
Green Fees £25 per day (£30 weekends & bank holidays).
Facilities ⊗ ᵧⅢ ᑦ ᴠ ♀ ⚐ ᒲ (Simon Thornhill.
Leisure snooker.
Location Thrybergh Park, Thrybergh (3.5m E on A630)
Hotel ★★66% Brentwood Hotel, Moorgate Rd, ROTHERHAM ☎ (0709) 382772 33⇆ ᴙ Annexe10⇆ ᴙ

Sitwell Park ☎ (0709) 541046
Parkland course with easy walking.
18 holes, 5914yds, Par 69, SSS 68.
Club membership 500.
Visitors must contact in advance, restricted weekends.
Societies must contact in advance.
Green Fees £24 per day; £20 per round (£28/£24 weekends & bank holidays).

▶

165

Facilities ⊗ 〗⊞ ₤ ■ ♀ ♨ 🏠 ♪ Nic Taylor.
Leisure snooker.
Location Shrogs Wood Rd
Hotel ★★66% Brentwood Hotel, Moorgate Rd,
ROTHERHAM ☎ (0709) 382772
33⇄ ☞ Annexe10⇄ ☞

SHEFFIELD   Map 08 SK38

Abbeydale ☎ (0742) 360743
Parkland course, well-kept and wooded. Testing hole: 12th,
par 3.
18 holes, 6419yds, Par 72, SSS 71.
Club membership 750.
Visitors restricted Wed 10am-1.30pm. Must contact in
advance.
Societies must apply in writing.
Green Fees not confirmed.
Facilities ⊗ 〗⊞ ₤ ■ ♀ ♨ 🏠 ♪ Nigel Perry.
Leisure snooker.
Location Twentywell Ln, Dore (4m SW of city centre
off A621)
Hotel ★★★64% Forte Crest, Manchester Rd,
Broomhill, SHEFFIELD
☎ (0742) 670067 135⇄ ☞

Beauchief Municipal ☎ (0742) 367274
Municipal course with natural water hazards. The rolling land
looks west to the Pennines and a 12th-century abbey adorns
the course.
18 holes, 5452yds, Par 67, SSS 66, Course record 65.
Club membership 450.
Visitors no restrictions.
Societies weekdays only, must apply in writing.
Green Fees £7.50 per round.
Facilities ⊗ 〗 by prior arrangement ₤ ■ ♀ ♨ 🏠 ⫟ ♪
Brian English.
Location Abbey Ln (4m SW of city centre off A621)
Hotel ★★★68% Beauchief Hotel, 161 Abbeydale Rd,
SHEFFIELD
☎ (0742) 620500 41⇄ ☞

Birley Wood ☎ (0742) 647262
Undulating meadowland course with well-varied features,
easy walking and good views. Practice range and green.
18 holes, 5452yds, Par 68, SSS 67, Course record 61.
Club membership 100.
Visitors no restrictions.
Societies apply in writing.
Green Fees not confirmed.
Facilities ♨ 🏠 ⫟ ♪ Peter Ball.
Location Birley Ln (4.5m SE of city centre off A621)
Hotel ★★★65% Mosborough Hall Hotel, High St,
Mosborough, SHEFFIELD
☎ (0742) 484353 23⇄ ☞

Concord Park ☎ (0742) 456806
Hilly municipal parkland course with some fairways wood-
flanked, good views, often windy. Eight par 3 holes.
18 holes, 4321yds, Par 65, SSS 62, Course record 56.
Club membership 170.
Visitors no restrictions.
Green Fees not confirmed.
Facilities ♨

Location Shiregreen Ln (3.5m N of city centre on B6086
off A6135)
Hotel ★★★64% Forte Crest, Manchester Rd,
Broomhill, SHEFFIELD
☎ (0742) 670067 135⇄ ☞

Dore & Totley ☎ (0742) 360492
Flat parkland course.
18 holes, 6265yds, Par 70, SSS 70.
Club membership 580.
Visitors must contact in advance & have handicap
certificate but may not play 9.30am-noon & after
2.30pm.
Societies must apply in writing.
Green Fees £25 per day.
Facilities ⊗ by prior arrangement 〗⊞ ₤ ■ ♀ ♨ 🏠 ♪
Neil Cheetham.
Leisure snooker.
Location Bradway Rd, Bradway (7m S of city centre on
B6054 off A61)
Hotel ★★★64% Forte Crest, Manchester Rd,
Broomhill, SHEFFIELD
☎ (0742) 670067 135 ⇄ ☞

Hallamshire Golf Club Ltd ☎ (0742) 302153
Situated on a shelf of land at a height of 850 ft.
Magnificent views to the west. Moorland turf, long
carries over ravine. Good natural drainage.
18 holes, 6396yds, Par 71, SSS 71.
Club membership 550.
Visitors no restrictions.
Societies by arrangement.
Green Fees not confirmed.
Facilities 〗 (ex Sun) ₤ ■ ♀ ♨ 🏠 ♪ G R Tickell.
Location Redmires Rd, Sandygate
Hotel ★★★64% Forte Crest, Manchester Rd,
Broomhill, SHEFFIELD
☎ (0742) 670067 135⇄ ☞

Hillsborough ☎ (0742) 343608 & 349151
Beautiful moorland/woodland course 500 ft above sea-level,
reasonable walking.
18 holes, 6216yards, Par 71, SSS 70.
Club membership 700.
Visitors restricted weekends. Advance booking
advisable.
Societies must apply in writing.
Green Fees £28 (£20 Sun after 2.30pm).
Facilities ⊗ 〗 by prior arrangement ₤ ■ ♀ ♨ 🏠 ♪
Graham Walker.
Leisure snooker.
Location Worrall Rd (3m NW of city centre off A616)
Hotel ★★69% Rutland Hotel, 452 Glossop Rd,
Broomhill, SHEFFIELD ☎ (0742) 664411
73rm(68⇄1 ☞) Annexe17⇄ ☞

Lees Hall ☎ (0742) 554402
Parkland/meadowland course with panoramic view of city.
18 holes, 6137yds, Par 71, SSS 69, Course record 63.
Club membership 725.
Visitors restricted Wed.
Societies must apply in writing.
Green Fees not confirmed.
Facilities ⊗ & 〗 (ex Tue) ₤ by prior arrangement
(ex Tue) ■ ♀ ♨ 🏠 ♪ J R Wilkinson.

Leisure	snooker.
Location	Hemsworth Rd, Norton (3.5m S of city centre off A6102)
Hotel	★★★64% Forte Crest, Manchester Rd, Broomhill, SHEFFIELD ☎ (0742) 670067 135⇄ ♙

Tinsley Park Municipal Golf ☎ (0742) 42237
Undulating meadowland course with plenty of trees and rough.
18 holes, 6064yds, Par 71, SSS 69.
Club membership 420.

Visitors	no restrictions.
Societies	apply in writing to Sheffield City Council, Recreation Dept., Meersbrook Park, Sheffield.
Green Fees	not confirmed.
Facilities	⊗ ⫫ ⅃ & ♥ by prior arrangement ♀ (ex Mon) ⚘ 🏠 ⚑ (A P Highfield.
Location	High Hazels Park (4m E of city centre off A630)
Hotel	★★★65% Mosborough Hall Hotel, High St, Mosborough, SHEFFIELD ☎ (0742) 484353 23⇄ ♙

SILKSTONE   Map 08 SE20

Silkstone ☎ Barnsley (0226) 790328
Parkland/downland course, fine views over the Pennines. Testing golf.
18 holes, 6078yds, Par 70, SSS 70.
Club membership 600.

Visitors	with member only at weekends.
Societies	apply in writing.
Green Fees	£22 per day.
Facilities	⊗ ⫫ ⅃ ♥ ♀ ⚘ (Kevin Guy.
Leisure	snooker.
Location	Field Head, Elmhurst Ln (1m E off A628)
Hotel	★★★67% Ardsley Moat House, Doncaster Rd, Ardsley, BARNSLEY ☎ (0226) 289401 73⇄ ♙

STOCKSBRIDGE   Map 08 SK29

Stocksbridge & District ☎ Sheffield (0742) 882003
Hilly moorland course.
18 holes, 5200yds, Par 65, SSS 65, Course record 65.
Club membership 450.

Visitors	no restrictions.
Societies	apply to secretary.
Green Fees	£15 per day (£24 weekends).
Facilities	⊗ ⫫ ⅃ ♥ ♀ ⚘
Location	30 Royd Ln, Townend (S side of town centre)
Hotel	★★★64% Forte Crest, Manchester Rd, Broomhill, SHEFFIELD ☎ (0742) 670067 135⇄ ♙

THORNE   Map 08 SE61

Thorne ☎ (0405) 812084 & 815173
Picturesque parkland course with 6000 newly planted trees.
18 holes, 5366yds, Par 68, SSS 65, Course record 66.
Club membership 300.

Visitors	no restrictions.
Societies	apply in writing or phone.
Green Fees	£7 (£8 weekends).

Facilities	⊗ ⫫ by prior arrangement ⅃ ♥ ♀ ⚘ 🏠 ⚑ (Richard Highfield.
Location	Kirton Ln (14m SE of Pontefract of of M18)
Hotel	★★67% Belmont Hotel, Horsefair Green, THORNE ☎ (0405) 812320 23⇄ ♙

WORTLEY   Map 08 SK39

Wortley ☎ Sheffield (0742) 885294
Well-wooded, undulating parkland course sheltered from prevailing wind.
18 holes, 5983yds, Par 68, SSS 69.
Club membership 300.

Visitors	may not play before 9am (10am on Tue and weekends). Must contact in advance and have a handicap certificate.
Societies	Wed & Fri only, by arrangement. Apply in writing.
Green Fees	£21 per round (£25 weekends & bank holidays).
Facilities	⊗ ⫫ by prior arrangement ⅃ ♥ ♀ ⚘ 🏠 ⚑ (J Tilson.
Location	Hermit Hill Ln (0.5m NE of village off A629)
Hotel	★★★64% Forte Crest, Manchester Rd, Broomhill, SHEFFIELD ☎ (0742) 670067 135⇄ ♙

STAFFORDSHIRE

BARLASTON   Map 07 SJ83

Barlaston ☎ (0782) 372795
Picturesque meadowland course designed by Peter Alliss.
18 holes, 5800yds, Par 69, SSS 68, Course record 68.
Club membership 600.

Visitors	may not play before 10am weekends and bank holidays.
Societies	apply in writing.
Green Fees	not confirmed.
Facilities	⊗ ⫫ ⅃ ♥ ♀ ⚘ 🏠 (Ian Rogers.
Leisure	fishing.
Location	Meaford Rd
Hotel	★★★67% Stone House Hotel, STONE ☎ (0785) 815531 48⇄ ♙

BROCTON   Map 07 SJ91

Brocton Hall ☎ (0785) 661901
Parkland course with gentle slopes in places, easy walking.
18 holes, 6095yds, Par 69, SSS 69.
Club membership 750.

Visitors	not competition days. Must contact in advance.
Societies	must apply in advance.
Green Fees	£25 per day (£30 weekends & bank holidays).
Facilities	⊗ ⫫ ⅃ (dinner/bar snacks by arrangement) ♀ ⚘ 🏠 (R G Johnson.
Leisure	snooker.
Location	NW side of village off A34
Hotel	★★65% Garth Hotel, Wolverhampton Rd, Moss Pit, STAFFORD ☎ (0785) 56124 60⇄ ♙

THE RIVERSIDE HOTEL & GOLF CLUB

AA ★★★ (Egon Ronay Recommended)

Facilities include:
22 bedrooms, a superb restaurant,
a bar that stays open till you go to bed.
Affiliated 18 hole golf course a short walk away.

Send for our brochure
and special weekend golf package.

TELEPHONE: 0283 511234

Riverside Drive, Branston, Burton-on-Trent,
Staffordshire DE14 3EP

Host: Bruce Elliott-Bateman

BURTON-UPON-TRENT   Map 08 SK22

Branston ☎ (0283) 43207
Parkland course, adjacent to River Trent, on undulating
ground with natural water hazards.
18 holes, 6541yds, Par 72, SSS 71.
Club membership 700.
Visitors   must contact in advance. With member only
                  weekends.
Societies   must apply in writing.
Green Fees   not confirmed.
Facilities   ⊗ ∭ ⅃ ♥ ♀ ⚘ ☖ ⵟ ୧
                  Steve Warner.
Location   Burton Rd, Branston (1.5m SW on A5121)
Hotel   ★★★62% Riverside Hotel, Riverside Dr,
                  Branston, BURTON UPON TRENT
                  ☎ (0283) 511234 22⇨

Burton-upon-Trent ☎ (0283) 44551
Undulating parkland course with a major feature. There
are testing par 3s at 10th and 12th. The 18th has a lake around
its green.
18 holes, 6555yds, Par 71, SSS 71, Course record 67.
Club membership 600.
Visitors   must contact in advance and have a handicap
                  certificate or play with member.
Societies   must contact in writing for parties of 16 & over.
Green Fees   £25 per day; £20 per round (£30 per day; £25
                  per round weekends & bank holidays).
Facilities   ⊗ & ∭ by prior arrangement & ⅃ (ex Mon)
                  ♥ ♀ ⚘ ☖ ⵟ ୧ Gary Stafford.
Leisure   snooker.

Location   43 Ashby Rd East (2m E on A50)
Hotel   ★★★62% Riverside Hotel, Riverside Dr,
                  Branston, BURTON UPON TRENT
                  ☎ (0283) 511234 22⇨

CANNOCK   Map 07 SJ91

Cannock Park ☎ (0543) 578850
Part of a large leisure centre, this parkland-type course plays
alongside Cannock Chase. Good drainage, open most of year.
18 holes, 4559yds, Par 66, SSS 65.
Visitors   no restrictions.
Societies   weekdays only, apply in writing.
Green Fees   £4.40 (£6.60 weekends) prices not confirmed.
Facilities   ⊗ ∭ ⅃ ♥ ♀ ⚘ ☖ ⵟ ୧ David Dunk.
Leisure   heated indoor swimming pool, sauna, solarium,
                  gymnasium.
Location   Stafford Rd (4m S of Brocton)
Hotel   ★★★68% Roman Way Hotel, Watling St,
                  Hatherton, CANNOCK
                  ☎ (0543) 572121 56⇨ ୧

ENVILLE   Map 07 SO88

Enville ☎ Kinver (0384) 872074
Easy walking on two fairly flat parkland/moorland courses -
the 'Highgate' and the 'Lodge'.
Highgate: 18 holes, 6556yds, Par 72, SSS 72.
Lodge: 18 holes, 6217yds, Par 70, SSS 70.
Club membership 900.
Visitors   must play with member at weekends. Must
                  contact in advance and have a handicap
                  certificate.
Societies   must contact in writing.
Green Fees   weekdays £22 per round; £26.50 per 27 holes;
                  £32 per 36 holes.
Facilities   ⊗ ∭ ⅃ ♥ ♀ ⚘ ☖ ୧ Sean Power.
Location   Highgate Common (2m NE)
Hotel   ★★64% Talbot Hotel, High St, STOURBRIDGE
                  ☎ (0384) 394350 25rm(13⇨7 ୧)

GOLDENHILL   Map 07 SJ85

Goldenhill ☎ Stoke-on-Trent (0782) 784715
Rolling parkland course with water features on six of the
back nine holes.
Goldenhill Golf Course: 18 holes, 5957yds, Par 71, SSS 68.
Club membership 400.
Visitors   contact in advance for weekend play.
Societies   must apply in writing.
Green Fees   not confirmed.
Facilities   ⊗ ∭ by prior arrangement & ♥ ♀ ⚘ ☖ ⵟ ୧
                  Tony Clingan.
Location   Mobberley Rd (on A50, 4m N of Stoke)
Hotel   ★★★66% Manor House Hotel, Audley Rd,
                  ALSAGER
                  ☎ (0270) 884000 57⇨ ୧

HAZELSLADE   Map 07 SK01

Beau Desert Golf Club ☎ Hednesford (0543) 422626
Woodland course.
18 holes, 6300yds, Par 70, SSS 71, Course record 64.
Club membership 500.

Visitors	restricted weekends.
Societies	apply in writing.
Green Fees	£30 per rday (£45 weekends & bank holidays).
Facilities	⊗ & ⅲ by prior arrangement ㋡ 🍴 ♀ ⚲ 🏁 (Barry Stevens.
Location	0.5m NE of village
Hotel	★★★68% Roman Way Hotel, Watling St, Hatherton, CANNOCK ☎ (0543) 572121 56⇌ ↟

HIMLEY   Map 07 SO89

Himley Hall Golf Centre ☎ Wolverhampton (0902) 895207
Parkland course set in grounds of Himley Hall Park, with
lovely views. Large practice area including a pitch-and-putt.
9 holes, 3125yds, Par 36, SSS 36.
Club membership 200.

Visitors	restricted weekends. Must contact in advance.
Green Fees	not confirmed.
Facilities	⊗ ㋡ 🍴 ⚲
Leisure	putting green, 9 hole pitch & putt.
Location	Log Cabin, Himley Hall Park (0.5m E on B4176)
Hotel	★★★66% Himley Country Club & Hotel, School Rd, HIMLEY ☎ (0902) 896716 76⇌ ↟

LEEK   Map 07 SJ95

Leek ☎ (0538) 384779
Undulating, challenging moorland course.
18 holes, 6240yds, Par 70, SSS 70, Course record 63.
Club membership 750.

Visitors	must contact in advance & have handicap certificate, restricted before 3pm.
Societies	must apply in advance.
Green Fees	£22.50 per day (£30 weekends & bank holidays).
Facilities	⊗ ⅲ ㋡ 🍴 ♀ ⚲ 🏁 (Peter A Stubbs.
Leisure	snooker.
Location	Birchall (0.75m S on A520)
Hotel	★★★70% Stakis Grand Hotel, 66 Trinity St, Hanley, STOKE-ON-TRENT ☎ (0782) 202361 128⇌ ↟

LICHFIELD   Map 07 SK10

Seedy Mill ☎ (0543) 417333
New, gently-rolling parkland course in picturesque rural
setting. Lakes and streams are abundant, and there are four
challenging Par 3s. Well contoured green, good bunkering.
Also a superb 9-hole Par 3 course.
18 holes, 6247yds, Par 72, SSS 70.
Club membership 1100.

Visitors	must contact in advance & play to max. offical handicap standard (28 men, 36 ladies).
Societies	must contact in advance.
Green Fees	£12-£18 per round.
Facilities	⊗ ⅲ ㋡ 🍴 ♀ ⚲ 🏁 (Andrew Bolton.
Leisure	9 hole par 3 course.
Location	Elmhurst (at Elmhurst, 1.5m N of Lichfield, off A515)
Hotel	★★★63% Little Barrow Hotel, Beacon St, LICHFIELD ☎ (0543) 414500 24⇌ ↟

Whittington Barracks ☎ (0543) 432317
18 magnificent holes winding their way through
heathland and trees, presenting a good test for the serious
golfer. Leaving the fairway can be severely punished.
The dog-legs are most tempting, inviting the golfer to
chance his arm. Local knowledge is a definite advantage.
Clear views of the famous three spires of Lichfield
Cathedral.
18 holes, 6547yds, Par 70, SSS 71, Course record 65.
Club membership 600.

Visitors	must have handicap certificate, restricted weekends. Must contact in advance.
Societies	welcome Wed & Thu, must apply in writing.
Green Fees	£32 per day.
Facilities	⊗ (ex Mon) ⅲ by prior arrangement ㋡ 🍴 ♀ ⚲ 🏁 ↟ (Adrian Sadler.
Leisure	snooker.
Location	Tamworth Rd (2.5m SE on A51)
Hotel	★★★63% Little Barrow Hotel, Beacon St, LICHFIELD ☎ (0543) 414500 24⇌ ↟

NEWCASTLE-UNDER-LYME   Map 07 SJ84

Newcastle Municipal ☎ (0782) 627596
Open course on the side of a hill without mature trees.
18 holes, 6367yds, Par 72, SSS 70, Course record 68.
Club membership 273.

Visitors	must contact in advance.
Green Fees	£6.50 per round (£8 weekends).
Facilities	⊗ ㋡ 🍴 ♀ ⚲ 🏁 ↟ (Mark Shryane.
Location	Keele Rd (2m W on A525)
Hotel	★★★63% Forte Posthouse, Clayton Rd, NEWCASTLE-UNDER-LYME ☎ (0782) 717171 122⇌ ↟

Newcastle-Under-Lyme ☎ (0782) 618526 & 617006
Parkland course.
18 holes, 6229yds, Par 72, SSS 71.
Club membership 600.

Visitors	must contact in advance & have handicap certificate. With member only weekends.
Societies	welcome Wed & Thu (pm). Phone (0782) 617006 in advance.
Green Fees	£25 per day/round..
Facilities	⊗ ⅲ ㋡ 🍴 ♀ ⚲ 🏁 (Paul Symonds.
Leisure	snooker.
Location	Whitmore Rd (1m SW on A53)
Hotel	★★60% The Borough Arms Hotel, King St, NEWCASTLE-UNDER-LYME ☎ (0782) 629421 30⇌ ↟Annexe15⇌

Wolstanton ☎ (0782) 622413
Meadowland/parkland course in an urban area.
18 holes, 5807yds, Par 68, SSS 68.
Club membership 720.

Visitors	with member only at weekends & bank holidays.
Societies	must apply in advance.
Green Fees	£18 per day/round.
Facilities	⊗ ⅲ ㋡ 🍴 ♀ ⚲ ⚲
Leisure	snooker.
Location	Dimsdale Old Hall, Hassam Pde, Wolstanton (1.5m NW of Newcastle, off A34)
Hotel	★★★63% Forte Posthouse, Clayton Rd, NEWCASTLE-UNDER-LYME ☎ (0782) 717171 122⇌ ↟

ONNELEY   Map 07 SJ74

Onneley ☎ Stoke-on-Trent (0782) 750577
A tight, picturesque, hillside parkland course.
9 holes, 5584yds, Par 70, SSS 67, Course record 68.
Club membership 400.
Visitors   restricted weekends & bank holidays.
Societies   must apply in writing.
Green Fees   £15 per round.
Facilities   ⓑ ☕ (Tue-Thu & Fri evening) ♀ (Tue-Fri) ⏛
Location   2m from Woore on A525
Hotel   ★★69% Wheatsheaf Inn at Onneley, Barhill Rd,
                   ONNELEY ☎ (0782) 751581 5🐾

PATTINGHAM   Map 07 SO89

Patshull Park Hotel Golf & Country Club ☎
Wolverhampton (0902) 700100
Picturesque course set in 280 acres of glorious Capability
Brown landscaped parkland. Designed by John Jacobs, the
course meanders alongside trout fishing lakes. Many leisure
facilities.
Patshull Park Golf & Country Club: 18 holes, 6412yds, Par
72, SSS 71.
Club membership 500.
Visitors   must contact in advance & have handicap
                   certificate.
Societies   must apply in advance.
Green Fees   £20 per round (£25 weekends).
Facilities   ⊗ 🏛 ⓑ ☕ ♀ ⏛ 🏠 ⛳ 🍴 Ⅼ Duncan
                   McDowall.
Leisure   hard tennis courts, heated indoor swimming
                   pool, fishing, snooker, sauna, solarium,
                   gymnasium.
Location   Off A464
Hotel   ★★★♨74% Old Vicarage Hotel, WORFIELD
                   ☎ (07464) 497 10⇥ 🐾 Annexe4⇥ 🐾

PERTON   Map 07 SO89

Perton Park ☎ Wolverhampton (0902) 380103 & 380073
Flat meadowland course set in open countryside.
18 holes, 7007yds, Par 73, SSS 72.
Club membership 400.
Visitors   only wide wheel trolleys, no jeans & shirt must
                   have collars.
Societies   welcome anytime, phone for further information.
Green Fees   £5 per round, £6 Fri (£10 weekends & bank
                   holidays).
Facilities   ⊗ 🏛 ⓑ ☕ ♀ ⏛ 🏠 ⛳ Ⅼ Robert Franklin.
Leisure   snooker, putting green & bowling green.
Location   Wrottesley Park Rd (3m W of Wolverhampton,
                   off A454 or A41)
Hotel   ★★68% Ely House Hotel, 53 Tettenhall Rd,
                   WOLVERHAMPTON
                   ☎ (0902) 311311 18⇥ 🐾

STAFFORD   Map 07 SJ92

Stafford Castle ☎ (0785) 223821
Parkland type course.
9 holes, 6073yds, Par 71, SSS 69.
Club membership 400.
Visitors   restricted weekends (am).

Societies   welcome Mon-Fri, must apply in advance.
Green Fees   not confirmed.
Facilities   ⊗ 🏛 ⓑ ☕ ♀ ⏛ 🏠 ⛳
Location   Newport Rd (SW side of town centre off A518)
Hotel   ★★61% Swan Hotel, Greengate St, STAFFORD
                   ☎ (0785) 58142 32⇥ 🐾

STOKE-ON-TRENT   Map 07 SJ84

Burslem ☎ (0782) 837006
On the outskirts of Tunstall, a moorland course with hard
walking.
9 holes, 5354yds, Par 66, SSS 66, Course record 64.
Club membership 250.
Visitors   except Sun & with member only Sat & bank
                   holidays.
Societies   must telephone in advance.
Green Fees   not confirmed.
Facilities   🏛 by prior arrangement ⓑ by prior arrangement
                   ☕ ♀ ⏛
Location   Wood Farm, High Ln, Tunstall (4m N of city
                   centre on B5049)
Hotel   ★★★70% Stakis Grand Hotel, 66 Trinity St,
                   Hanley, STOKE-ON-TRENT
                   ☎ (0782) 202361 128⇥ 🐾

Greenway Hall ☎ (0782) 503158
Moorland course with fine views of the Pennines.
18 holes, 5678yds, Par 67, SSS 67, Course record 64.
Club membership 400.
Visitors   may not play Sat & Sun mornings.
Societies   must telephone in advance.
Green Fees   not confirmed.
Facilities   ♀ ⏛
Location   Stanley Rd, Stockton Brook (5m NE off A53)
Hotel   ★★★70% Stakis Grand Hotel, 66 Trinity St,
                   Hanley, STOKE-ON-TRENT
                   ☎ (0782) 202361 128⇥ 🐾

Trentham ☎ (0782) 658109
Parkland course. The par 3, 4th is a testing hole reached over
a copse of trees.
18 holes, 6644yds, Par 72, SSS 72.
Club membership 680.
Visitors   must have handicap certificate. May not play Sat
                   & Sun mornings.
Societies   must apply in writing.
Green Fees   £25 per day (£30 Sun afternoons).
Facilities   ⊗ 🏛 by prior arrangement ⓑ ☕ ♀ ⏛ 🏠 ⛳ 🍴 Ⅼ
                   Mark Budz.
Leisure   squash, snooker.
Location   14 Barlaston Old Rd, Trentham (3m S off
                   A5035)
Hotel   ★★★70% Stakis Grand Hotel, 66 Trinity St,
                   Hanley, STOKE-ON-TRENT
                   ☎ (0782) 202361 128⇥ 🐾

Trentham Park ☎ (0782) 658800
Fine woodland course.
18 holes, 6403yds, Par 71, SSS 71, Course record 67.
Club membership 640.
Visitors   restricted competition days.
Societies   welcome Wed & Fri, must apply in advance.
Green Fees   £20 per day (£25 weekends).
Facilities   ⊗ 🏛 ⓑ ☕ ♀ ⏛ 🏠 Ⅼ Jim McLeod.
Leisure   snooker.

Location   Trentham Park (3m SW off A34)
Hotel   ★★★63% Forte Posthouse, Clayton Rd,
              NEWCASTLE-UNDER-LYME
              ☎ (0782) 717171 122⇄ ⁍

STONE   Map 07 SJ93

Meadow Vale ☎ (0785) 760900
Opened in 1992, a gently undulating meadowland course with
streams and ponds as features.
18 holes, 6500yds, Par 72, SSS 72.
Club membership 300.
Visitors   must contact in advance, with member only
              weekends am.
Societies   contact in advance.
Green Fees £15 per round/day (£20 weekends).
Facilities   ⊗ ᛗ ⅃ ⅃ ♀ ⅄ ⌂ ℓ Stephen R Bassil.
Location   Cold Norton
Hotel   ★★★67% Stone House Hotel, STONE
              ☎ (0785) 815531 48⇄ ⁍

Stone ☎ (0785) 813103
9-hole parkland course with easy walking and 18 different
tees.
9 holes, 6299yds, Par 71, SSS 70, Course record 65.
Club membership 350.
Visitors   with member only weekends & bank holidays.
Societies   must apply in writing.
Green Fees £20 per day; £15 per round.
Facilities   ⊗ ᛗ ⅃ ⅃ (no catering Mon) ♀ ⅄
Leisure   snooker.
Location   Filleybrooks (0.5m W on A34)
Hotel   ★★★67% Stone House Hotel, STONE
              ☎ (0785) 815531 48⇄ ⁍

TAMWORTH   Map 04 SK20

Drayton Park ☎ (0827) 251139
Parkland course designed by James Braid. Club established
since 1897.
18 holes, 6214yds, Par 71, SSS 71, Course record 65.
Club membership 450.
Visitors   restricted weekends. Must contact in advance.
Societies   must apply in writing.
Green Fees weekday £27 per day/round.
Facilities   ⊗ ᛗ ⅃ ⅃ ♀ ⅄ ⌂ ℓ M W Passmore.
Leisure   snooker.
Location   Drayton Park (2m S on A4091)
Hotel   ★★★★68% The Belfry, Lichfield Rd, WISHAW
              ☎ (0675) 470301 219⇄

Tamworth Municipal ☎ (0827) 53850
First-class municipal, parkland course and a good test of golf.
18 holes, 6083mtrs, Par 73, SSS 72, Course record 65.
Club membership 700.
Visitors   must contact in advance.
Societies   must contact in writing.
Green Fees not confirmed.
Facilities   ⅃ ⅃ ♀ ⅄ ⌂ ⅂℩ ℓ Barry Jones.
Leisure   snooker.
Location   Eagle Dr (2.5m E off B5000)
Hotel   ★★61% Angel Croft Hotel, Beacon St,
              LICHFIELD ☎ (0543) 258737
              11rm(3⇄6 ⁍) Annexe8⇄ ⁍

UTTOXETER   Map 07 SK03

Uttoxeter ☎ (0889) 564884
Downland course with open aspect.
18 holes, 5468yds, Par 68, SSS 68.
Club membership 750.
Visitors   restricted weekends.
Societies   must apply in advance.
Green Fees £20 per day; £13 per round (£17 per round
              weekends & bank holidays).
Facilities   ⊗ & ᛗ by prior arrangement ⅃ (Tue-Sun only)
             ⅃ ♀ ⅄ ⌂ ℓ John Pearsall.
Location   Wood Ln (1m SE off B5017)
Hotel   ★★★58% Ye Olde Dog & Partridge Hotel,
              High St, TUTBURY
              ☎ (0283) 813030 3⇄ Annexe14⇄ ⁍

WESTON   Map 07 SJ92

Ingestre Park ☎ (0889) 270304
Parkland course set in the grounds of Ingestre Hall, former
home of the Earl of Shrewsbury, with mature trees and
pleasant views.
18 holes, 6334yds, Par 70, SSS 70, Course record 67.
Club membership 750.
Visitors   with member only weekends & bank holidays.
Societies   must apply in advance.
Green Fees £17 per round.
Facilities   ⊗ ᛗ ⅃ ⅃ ♀ ⅄ ⌂ ℓ Danny Scullion.
Leisure   snooker.
Location   2m SE off A51
Hotel   ★★★64% Tillington Hall, Eccleshall Rd,
              STAFFORD ☎ (0785) 53531 90⇄ ⁍

WHISTON   Map 07 SK04

Whiston Hall ☎ (0538) 266260
A challenging 18-hole course in scenic countryside and
incorporating many natural obstacles.
18 holes, 5434yds, Par 71, SSS 68, Course record 68.
Club membership 235.
Visitors   reasonable dress on the course.
Societies   contact in advance.
Green Fees £8 per round (£10 weekends & bank holidays).
Facilities   ⅃ (wknds & Tue evening in summer) ⅃ ♀ ⅄
Leisure   snooker, pool table, darts.
Location   Whiston Hall (off A52, 3m NE of Cheadle)
Hotel   ★★★70% Stakis Grand Hotel, 66 Trinity St,
              Hanley, STOKE-ON-TRENT
              ☎ (0782) 202361 128⇄ ⁍

Remember – prior to playing a stroke or
making a practise swing, the players should
ensure that no one is standing close by and
that no one should move, talk or stand close
to or directly behind the ball or the hole
when a player is addressing the ball or
making a stroke

SUFFOLK

ALDEBURGH   Map 05 TM45

Aldeburgh ☎ (0728) 452890
A most enjoyable and not unduly difficult seaside course; ideal for golfing holidaymakers. A bracing and fairly open terrain with some trees and heathland.
18 holes, 6330yds, Par 68, SSS 71, Course record 65.
River Course: 9 holes, 2114yds, Par 32, SSS 32.
Club membership 750.
Visitors   must contact in advance & have handicap certificate for 18 hole course.
Societies   must contact in advance.
Green Fees not confirmed.
Facilities   ⊗ by prior arrangement ⓛ ▼ ♀ ⚐ ⛳ ⛴ K R Preston.
Location   Saxmundham Rd (1m W on A1094)
Hotel   ★★★67% Wentworth Hotel, Wentworth Rd, ALDEBURGH
       ☎ (0728) 452312   31rm(24⇌4 ♜)

BECCLES   Map 05 TM49

Wood Valley ☎ (0502) 712244
Heathland course with natural hazards and particularly exposed to wind.
9 holes, 2779yds, Par 68, SSS 67.
Club membership 200.
Visitors   must play with member on Sun.
Societies   must contact in advance.
Green Fees £10 (£11 weekends and bank holidays).
Facilities   ⊗ & ⅷ by prior arrangement ⓛ ▼ ♀ ⚐ ⛳
Location   The Common (NE side of town)
Hotel   ★★61% Waveney House Hotel, Puddingmoor, BECCLES ☎ (0502) 712270 & 712817
       13rm(7 ⇌4 ♜)

BUNGAY   Map 05 TM38

Bungay & Waveney Valley ☎ (0986) 892337
Heathland course partly comprising Neolithic stone workings, easy walking.
18 holes, 5950yds, Par 69, SSS 68, Course record 64.
Club membership 756.
Visitors   must contact in advance. With member only weekends & bank holidays.
Societies   must contact in advance.
Green Fees £18 per day/round.
Facilities   ⊗ & ⅷ (ex Mon) ⓛ ▼ ♀ ⚐ ⛳ ⛴ Nigel Whyte.
Leisure   large practice area.
Location   Outney Common (0.5m NW on A143)
Hotel   ★★60% Scole Inn, SCOLE
       ☎ (0379) 740481   12⇌ ♜ Annexe11⇌ ♜

A golf course name printed in ***bold italics***
means we have been unable to verify
information with the club's management for
the current year

BURY ST EDMUNDS   Map 05 TL86

Bury St Edmunds ☎ (0284) 755979
Undulating parkland course with easy walking and attractive short holes.
18 holes, 6615yds, Par 72, SSS 72, Course record 69 or 9 holes, 2332yds, Par 31, SSS 31.
Club membership 830.
Visitors   with member only at weekends.
Societies   must apply in writing.
Green Fees £23 per round 18 holes; £11 per 2 rounds 9 holes.
Facilities   ⊗ ⅷ (summer) ⓛ ▼ ♀ ⚐ ⛳ ⛴ Mark Jillings.
Leisure   snooker.
Location   Tuthill (2m NW on B1106 off A45)
Hotel   ★★★76% Angel Hotel, Angel Hill, BURY ST EDMUNDS ☎ (0284) 753926 41⇌ ♜

Fornham Park ☎ (0284) 706777
Flat parkland course with many water hazards. Also country club facilities.
18 holes, 6209yds, Par 71, SSS 70, Course record 67.
Club membership 650.
Visitors   must contact in advance but may not play Tue afternoon or weekends before 1pm.
Societies   by arrangement.
Green Fees £20 per day; £15 per round (£25 per round weekends).
Facilities   ⊗ ⅷ ⓛ ▼ ♀ ⚐ ⛳ ⛴ Sean Clark.
Location   St John's Hill Plantation, The Street, Fornham All Saints (2m N off A134)
Hotel   ★★★♨72% Ravenwood Hall Hotel, Rougham, BURY ST EDMUNDS ☎ (0359) 70345 7⇌ Annexe7⇌

CRETINGHAM   Map 05 TM26

Cretingham ☎ Earl Soham (0728) 685275
Parkland course.
9 holes, 1995yds, Par 62, SSS 59.
Club membership 360.
Visitors   no restrictions.
Societies   must telephone in advance.
Green Fees £7 per day (£10 weekends & bank holidays).
Facilities   ⊗ ⓛ ▼ ♀ ⚐ ⛳ ⛴ Colin Jenkins.
Leisure   hard tennis courts, outdoor swimming pool, snooker, table tennis & pool table.
Location   2m from A1120 at Earl Soham
Hotel   ★★68% Crown Hotel, Market Hill, FRAMLINGHAM ☎ (0728) 723521 14⇌

FELIXSTOWE   Map 05 TM33

Felixstowe Ferry ☎ (0394) 286834
Seaside links course, pleasant views, easy walking. Testing 491-yd, 7th hole.
18 holes, 6324yds, Par 72, SSS 70, Course record 68.
Club membership 800.
Visitors   may not play before 9am. A handicap certificate required
Societies   must contact in advance.
Green Fees £20 (£24 weekends).
Facilities   ⊗ ⓛ ▼ ♀ ⚐ ⛵ ⛴ Ian MacPherson.

Location   Ferry Rd (NE side of town centre)
Hotel   ★★★67% Orwell Moat House Hotel, Hamilton
               Rd, FELIXSTOWE
               ☎ (0394) 285511 58⊂⇥ ✆

FLEMPTON   Map 05 TL86

Flempton ☎ Bury St Edmunds (0284) 728291
Breckland course.
9 holes, 6080yds, Par 70, SSS 70.
Club membership 300.
Visitors   must have handicap certificate. With member
               only weekends & bank holidays.
Societies must apply in writing.
Green Fees £24 per day; £19 per round.
Facilities ⊗ ⅏ ⅃ 🍽 ⅄ 🏠 ℓ Jamie Perks.
Location   0.5m W on A1101
Hotel   ★★66% Suffolk Hotel, 38 The Buttermarket,
               BURY ST EDMUNDS
               ☎ (0284) 753995 33⊂⇥ ✆

HALESWORTH   Map 05 TM37

St Helena ☎ (0986) 875567
A 27-hole professionally designed parkland complex of three
9-hole courses, giving 6 playing options of 3 x 18-hole Par 72
and 3 x Par 36 9-hole.
Saint: 9 holes, 3277yds, Par 36, SSS 36.
Helena: 9 holes, 3303yds, Par 36, SSS 36.
Halesworth: 9 holes, 3059yds, Par 36, SSS 36.
Club membership 460.
Visitors   a certified handicap certificate is required for
               Saint and Helena course, proprietory golf wear
               and shoes must be worn.
Societies apply in advance.
Green Fees Saint & Helena, 18 holes £10-£16; Halesworth 9
               holes £5-£7.10, 18 holes £10-£14.20.
Facilities ⊗ ⅏ ⅃ 🍽 ⅄ 🏠 ℓ Johnny Johnson.
Leisure   riding, floodlit covered driving range.
Location   Bramfield Rd (9m W of Southwold)
Hotel   ★★★69% Swan Hotel, Market Place,
               SOUTHWOLD ☎ (0502) 722186
               27⊂⇥ ✆ Annexe18⊂⇥

HAVERHILL   Map 05 TL64

Haverhill ☎ (0440) 61951
Parkland course with small river running through three
fairways.
9 holes, 5707yds, Par 68, SSS 67, Course record 67.
Club membership 445.
Visitors   may not play on bank holidays before 1pm.
Societies must contact in advance.
Green Fees £15 per day (£21 weekends & bank holidays).
Facilities ⅃ 🍽 ⅄ 🏠 ℓ Simon Mayfield.
Location   Coupals Rd (1m SE off A604)
Hotel   ★★65% Bell Hotel, Market Hill, CLARE
               ☎ (0787) 277741 9rm(3⊂⇥4 ✆) Annexe11⊂⇥

We make every effort to ensure that our
information is accurate but details may
change after we go to print

HINTLESHAM   Map 05 TM04

Hintlesham Hall ☎ (047387) 761
Magnificent new championship length course blending
harmoniously with the ancient parkland surrounding this
exclusive hotel. The 6630yd parkland course was
designed by Hawtree and Son, one of the oldest
established firms of golf course architects in the world.
The course is fair but challenging for low and high
handicappers alike. Hotel offers beautiful
accommodation, excellent cuisine and many
facilities.
18 holes, 6630yds, Par 72, SSS 72.
Club membership 300.
Visitors   must contact in advance.
Societies must telephone in advance.
Green Fees £45 per day; £26 per round (£75/£45
               weekends).
Facilities ⊗ ⅏ ⅃ 🍽 ⅄ 🏠 🤵 ℓ Alastair Spink.
Leisure   hard tennis courts, heated outdoor swim-
               ming pool, fishing, snooker, sauna, croquet.
Location   In village on A1071
Hotel   ★★★(red)♨♨ Hintlesham Hall Hotel,
               HINTLESHAM
               ☎ (047387) 334 & 268 33⊂⇥ ✆

IPSWICH   Map 05 TM14

Ipswich ☎ (0473) 728941
Many golfers are surprised when they hear that Ipswich
has, at Purdis Heath, a first-class golf course. In some
ways it resembles some of Surrey's better courses; a
beautiful heathland/parkland course with two lakes and
easy walking.
*18 holes, 6405yds, Par 71, SSS 71 or 9 holes, 1930yds,
Par 31, SSS 59.*
Club membership 850.
Visitors   must contact in advance & have a handicap
               certificate for 18 hole courses.
Societies must contact in advance.
Green Fees 18 hole: £30 per day (£36 weekends). 9
               hole: £7.50 per day (£10 weekends).
Facilities ⊗ ⅏ by prior arrangement ⅃ 🍽 ⅄ 🏠 ℓ
               Stephen Whymark.
Location   Purdis Heath (E side of town centre
               off A1156)
Hotel   ★★★70% Marlborough Hotel,
               Henley Rd, IPSWICH
               ☎ (0473) 257677 22⊂⇥ ✆

Rushmere ☎ (0473) 725648
Heathland course with gorse and prevailing winds. Testing
5th hole - dog leg, 419 yards (par 4).
18 holes, 6287yds, Par 70, SSS 70, Course record 66.
Club membership 800.
Visitors   restricted weekends & bank holidays.
Societies by arrangement.
Green Fees £18 per day.
Facilities ⊗ ⅃ 🍽 ⅄ 🏠 🤵 ℓ N T J McNeill.
Location   Rushmere Heath (2m E off A12)
Hotel   ★★★70% Marlborough Hotel,
               Henley Rd, IPSWICH
               ☎ (0473) 257677 22⊂⇥ ✆

LOWESTOFT
Map 05 TM59

Rookery Park ☎ (0502) 560380
Parkland course with a 9-hole, Par 3 adjacent.
18 holes, 6385yds, Par 72, SSS 72.
Club membership 1000.
Visitors must have handicap certificate.
Societies by arrangement.
Green Fees £20 per round (£25 weekends & bank holidays);
Par 3 course £5 per 18 holes.
Facilities ⊗ 川 ᒥ ☱ ♀ ♈ ☎ ᛏ Ⅼ Martin Ellsworthy.
Leisure snooker.
Location Carlton Colville (3.5m SW on A146)
Hotel ★★63% Broadlands Hotel, Bridge Rd, Oulton
Broad, LOWESTOFT ☎ (0502) 516031 52⇌

NEWMARKET
Map 05 TL66

Links ☎ (0638) 663000
Gently undulating parkland.
18 holes, 6424yds, Par 72, SSS 71, Course record 66.
Club membership 700.
Visitors must have handicap certificate, restricted Sun
after 11.30am.
Societies must contact in advance.
Green Fees £24 per day/round (£28 weekends & bank
holidays).
Facilities ⊗ 川 ᒥ ☱ ♀ ♈ ☎ Ⅼ John Sharkey.
Location Cambridge Rd (1m SW on A1034)
Hotel ★★★65% Newmarket Moat House, Moulton
Rd, NEWMARKET ☎ (0638) 667171 47⇌ ☞

NEWTON
Map 05 TL94

Newton Green ☎ Newton Green (0787) 77217
Flat, commonland course.
9 holes, 5488yds, Par 68, SSS 67.
Club membership 450.
Visitors must contact in advance but may not play on
Tue, weekends & bank holidays.
Green Fees not confirmed.
Facilities ⊗ 川 ᒥ ☱ ♀ ♈ ☎ Ⅼ Tim Cooper.
Location Sudbury Rd (W side of village on A134)
Hotel ★★★64% Bull Hotel, Hall St, LONG MELFORD
☎ (0787) 78494 25⇌ ☞

SOUTHWOLD
Map 05 TM57

Southwold ☎ (0502) 723234
Commonland course with 4-acre practice ground and
panoramic views of the sea.
9 holes, 3004yds, Par 70, SSS 69.
Club membership 450.
Visitors restricted Sun, bank holidays & competition
days. Must contact in advance.
Societies must apply in writing.
Green Fees not confirmed.
Facilities ⊗ 川 by prior arrangement ᒥ ☱ ♀ ♈ ☎ Ⅼ
Brian Allen.
Location The Common (0.5m W off A1095)
Hotel ★★★69% Swan Hotel, Market Place,
SOUTHWOLD
☎ (0502) 722186 27⇌ ☞ Annexe18⇌

STOWMARKET
Map 05 TM05

Stowmarket ☎ Rattlesden (0449) 736473 & 736392
Parkland course.
18 holes, 6101yds, Par 69, SSS 69.
Club membership 600.
Visitors must contact in advance & have handicap
certificate, but cannot play Wed mornings.
Societies Thu & Fri only, by arrangement.
Green Fees £24 per day; £19 per round (£33/£25 weekends).
Facilities ⊗ 川 ᒥ ☱ (no catering Mon) ♀ ♈ ☎ Ⅼ
C Aldred.
Location Lower Rd, Onehouse (2.5m SW off B115)
Hotel ★★59% Cedars Hotel, Needham Rd,
STOWMARKET ☎ (0449) 612668 24⇌ ☞

THORPENESS
Map 05 TM45

Thorpeness ☎ Aldeburgh (0728) 452176
The holes of this moorland course are pleasantly varied
with several quite difficult par 4's. Natural hazards
abound. The 15th, with its sharp left dog-leg, is one of
the best holes. Designed by James Braid.
18 holes, 6241yds, Par 69, SSS 71, Course record 66.
Club membership 390.
Visitors must book in advance.
Societies by arrangement.
Green Fees £30 per day; £20 per round (£40/£25
weekends).
Facilities ⊗ 川 ᒥ ☱ ♀ ♈ ☎ ⨝ Ⅼ Tony Pennock.
Leisure snooker, practice range.
Location W side of village off B1353
Hotel ★64% White Horse Hotel, Station Rd,
LEISTON ☎ (0728) 830694
10rm(1⇌7 ☞) Annexe3 ☞

UFFORD
Map 05 TM25

Ufford Park Hotel Golf & Leisure
☎ Woodbridge (0394) 382836
A challenging new course opened in autumn 1991. The 18-
hole Par 70 course is set in ancient parkland has many natural
features including 11 water hazards retaind from the original
parkland. There is also an extensive hotel and leisure
complex beside the course.
18 holes, 6058yds, Par 70, SSS 70.
Visitors no restrictions.
Societies must telephone in advance.
Green Fees £15 per round (£18 weekends & bank holidays).
Facilities ⊗ 川 ᒥ ☱ ♀ ♈ ☎ ᛏ ⨝ Ⅼ Stuart Robertson.
Leisure heated indoor swimming pool, sauna, solarium,
gymnasium, spa bath, table tennis.
Location Yarmouth Rd
Hotel ★★★⩗73% Seckford Hall Hotel,
WOODBRIDGE ☎ (0394) 385678
24⇌ ☞ Annexe10⇌ ☞

WALDRINGFIELD
Map 05 TM24

Waldringfield Heath ☎ (047336) 768
Easy walking heathland course with long drives on 1st, 5th
(586yds) and 10th tees.
18 holes, 6153yds, Par 71, SSS 69.
Club membership 660.

Visitors   welcome Mon-Fri, weekends & bank holidays
                    after noon.
Societies   advance booking required.
Green Fees   £15 per day; £10 per 18 holes (£16/£12
                    weekends & bank holidays).
Facilities   ⊗ (Mon-Fri) 🏌 ⚑ ♀ 🍴 🏠 ♦ Tony Dobson.
Location   Newbourne Rd (3m NE of Ipswich off old A12)
Hotel   ★★★♨73% Seckford Hall Hotel,
                    WOODBRIDGE ☎ (0394) 385678
                    24⇆ ♦ Annexe10⇆ ♦

WITNESHAM   Map 05 TM15

Fynn Valley ☎ (0473) 785267 & 785463
Undulating parkland course plus Par-3 nine-hole and driving
range.
18 holes, 5580yds, Par 69, SSS 67, Course record 62.
Club membership 550.
Visitors   ladies priority on Thu am, members only Sun
                    until noon.
Societies   must apply in advance.
Green Fees   £20 per day; £10 per 9 holes; £15 per 18 holes.
Facilities   ⊗ ▥ by prior arrangement 🏌 ⚑ ♀ 🍴 🏠 ♦
                    Robin Mann.
Location   4m N of Ipswich
Hotel   ★★★70% Marlborough Hotel, Henley Rd,
                    IPSWICH ☎ (0473) 257677 22⇆ ♦

WOODBRIDGE   Map 05 TM24

Woodbridge ☎ (0394) 382038
A beautiful course, one of the best in East Anglia. It is
situated on high ground and in different seasons present
golfers with a great variety of colour. Some say that of
the many good holes the 14th is the best.
18 holes, 6314yds, Par 70, SSS 70, Course record 64.
Course number 2: 9 holes, 2243yds, Par 62, SSS 62.
Club membership 900.
Visitors   must play with member at weekends & bank
                    holidays. Must contact in advance and
                    handicap certificate required for 18 hole
                    course.
Societies   must contact in writing up to 1 year in
                    advance.
Green Fees   £25 per day/round (18 hole); £12 (9 hole).
Facilities   ⊗ & ▥ by prior arrangement
                    🏌 ⚑ ♀ 🍴 🏠 ♦ Leslie Jones.
Location   Bromeswell Heath (2.5m NE off A1152)
Hotel   ★★★♨73% Seckford Hall Hotel,
                    WOODBRIDGE ☎ (0394) 385678
                    24⇆ ♦ Annexe10 ⇆ ♦

WORLINGTON   Map 05 TL67

Royal Worlington & Newmarket ☎ (0638) 712216
Inland 'links' course. Favourite 9-hole course of many
golf writers.
9 holes, 3105yds, Par 35, SSS 70.
Club membership 325.
Visitors   with member only at weekends. Must
                    contact in advance and have a handicap
                    certificate.
Societies   must apply in writing.
Green Fees   £30 per day; £20 after noon winter & 2pm
                    summer.

Facilities   ⊗ by prior arrangement 🏌 ⚑ ♀ 🍴 🏠 ♦
                    Malcolm Hawkins.
Location   0.5m SE
Hotel   ★★★62% Riverside Hotel, Mill St,
                    MILDENHALL
                    ☎ (0638) 717274 21⇆ ♦

SURREY

ADDLESTONE   Map 04 TQ06

New Zealand ☎ (0932) 345049
Heathland course set in trees and heather.
18 holes, 6012yds, Par 68, SSS 69.
Club membership 320.
Visitors   must contact in advance.
Societies   contact in advance.
Green Fees   £45 per day; £35 per round (£55 weekends).
Facilities   ⊗ 🏌 ⚑ ♀ 🍴 🏠 ♦ Vic Elvidge.
Location   Woodham Ln (1.5m W of Weybridge)
Hotel   ★★★63% Ship Thistle Hotel, Monument Green,
                    WEYBRIDGE ☎ (0932) 848364 39⇆ ♦

ASHFORD   Map 04 TQ07

Ashford Manor ☎ (0784) 252049
Parkland course, looks easy but is difficult.
18 holes, 6343yds, Par 70, SSS 70.
Club membership 600.
Visitors   must contact in advance and have an
                    introduction from own club.
Societies   must contact in advance.
Green Fees   not confirmed.
Facilities   🍴 🏠 ♦
Location   Fordbridge Rd (2m E of Staines via A308
                    Staines by-pass)
Hotel   ★★★58% Thames Lodge Hotel,
                    Thames St, STAINES
                    ☎ (0784) 464433 44⇆ ♦

BANSTEAD   Map 04 TQ25

Banstead Downs ☎ 081-642 2284
Downland course with narrow fairways and hawthorns.
18 holes, 6169yds, Par 69, SSS 69.
Club membership 542.
Visitors   must have handicap certificate. With member
                    only weekends.
Societies   welcome.
Green Fees   £30 before noon; £20 afternoons.
Facilities   ⊗ 🏌 ⚑ ♀ 🏠 ♦
Location   Burdon Ln, Belmont, Sutton (1.5m N on A217)
Hotel   ★★62% Heathside Hotel, Brighton Rd,
                    BURGH HEATH
                    ☎ (0737) 353355 73⇆ ♦

Cuddington ☎ 081-393 0952
Parkland course with easy walking and good views.
18 holes, 6394yds, Par 70, SSS 70, Course record 61.
Club membership 790.   ▶

Visitors	must contact in advance and have a handicap certificate or letter of introduction.
Societies	welcome Thu, must apply in advance.
Green Fees	£30 per day/round.
Facilities	⊗ ⓑ 🖤 ♀ 🛆 🏠 ⓕ James Morgan.
Location	Banstead Rd (N of Banstead station on A2022)
Hotel	★★62% Heathside Hotel, Brighton Rd, BURGH HEATH ☎ (0737) 353355 73⇆ ⚑

BRAMLEY Map 04 TQ04

Bramley ☎ Guildford (0483) 892696
Downland course, fine views from top.
18 holes, 5966yds, Par 69, SSS 69, Course record 67.
Club membership 780.

Visitors	must play with member at weekends & bank holidays. Must contact in advance.
Societies	must telephone in advance.
Green Fees	£30 per day; £25 per round.
Facilities	⊗ �🍴 ⓑ 🖤 (summer only) ♀ (summer only) 🛆 🏠 ⓕ G Peddie.
Leisure	driving range.
Location	0.5m N on A281
Hotel	★★★★62% Forte Crest, Egerton Rd, GUILDFORD ☎ (0483) 574444 111⇆ ⚑

BROOKWOOD Map 04 SU95

West Hill ☎ (0483) 474365
Worplesdon's next-door neighbour and a comparably great heath-and-heather course. Slightly tighter than Worplesdon with more opportunities for getting into trouble - but a most interesting and challenging course with wonderful greens. Water also provides natural hazards. The 15th is a testing par 3.
18 holes, 6368yds, Par 69, SSS 70, Course record 65.
Club membership 568.

Visitors	must contact in advance & have handicap certificate, restricted weekends & bank holidays.
Societies	must apply in writing.
Green Fees	£42 per day; £32 per round.
Facilities	⊗ ⍾ ⓑ 🖤 (catering by arrangement) ♀ 🛆 🏠 ⓕ John C Clements.
Leisure	practice golf range & putting green.
Location	Bagshot Rd (E side of village on A332)
Hotel	★★★★⚑80% Pennyhill Park Hotel, London Rd, BAGSHOT ☎ (0276) 71774 22⇆ ⚑ Annexe54⇆ ⚑

CAMBERLEY Map 04 SU86

Camberley Heath ☎ (0276) 23258
One of the great 'heath and heather' courses so frequently associated with Surrey. Several very good short holes - especially the 8th. The 10th is a difficult and interesting par 4, as also is the 17th, where the drive must be held well to the left as perdition lurks on the right. Course architect Harry Colt.
18 holes, 6337yds, Par 72, SSS 70.
Club membership 600.

Visitors	must play with member weekends. Must contact in advance and have a handicap certificate.

Societies	must apply in advance.
Green Fees	£50 per day; £30 per round.
Facilities	⊗ ⓑ 🖤 ♀ 🛆 🏠 ⓕ Gary Smith.
Location	Golf Dr (1.25m SE of town centre off A325)
Hotel	★★★★⚑80% Pennyhill Park Hotel, London Rd, BAGSHOT ☎ (0276) 71774 22⇆ ⚑ Annexe54⇆ ⚑

CHERTSEY Map 04 TQ06

Barrow Hills ☎ (0256) 72037
Parkland course with natural hazards.
18 holes, 3090yds, Par 56, SSS 53, Course record 58.
Club membership 235.

Visitors	restricted at weekends & bank holidays in the afternoons. Must be accompanied by member.
Green Fees	not confirmed.
Facilities	🖤
Location	Longcross (3m W on B386)
Hotel	★★★58% Thames Lodge Hotel, Thames St, STAINES ☎ (0784) 464433 44⇆ ⚑

Laleham ☎ (0932) 564211
Well-bunkered parkland/meadowland course.
18 holes, 6210yds, Par 70, SSS 70, Course record 65.
Club membership 600.

Visitors	must contact in advance. No visitors at weekends or before 9.30am weekdays.
Societies	must contact in writing.
Green Fees	£25 per day, £16.50 after 3pm.
Facilities	⊗ ⍾ by prior arrangement ⓑ 🖤 ♀ 🛆 🏠 ⓕ
Leisure	snooker.
Location	Laleham Reach (1.5m N)
Hotel	★★★58% Thames Lodge Hotel, Thames St, STAINES ☎ (0784) 464433 44⇆ ⚑

CHIPSTEAD Map 04 TQ25

Chipstead ☎ Downland (0737) 555781
Hilly parkland course, hard walking, good views. Testing 18th hole.
18 holes, 5454yds, Par 67, SSS 67.
Club membership 650.

Visitors	restricted weekends.
Societies	must apply in advance.
Green Fees	£25 per day (£20 after 2pm).
Facilities	⊗ ⓑ 🖤 ♀ 🛆 🏠 ⓕ Gary Torbett.
Location	How Ln (0.5m N of village)
Hotel	★★★★62% Selsdon Park Hotel, Sanderstead, CROYDON ☎ 081-657 8811 170⇆ ⚑

COBHAM Map 04 TQ16

Silvermere ☎ (0932) 866007
Parkland course with many very tight holes through woodland, 17th has 170-yd carry over the lake. Driving range.
18 holes, 6333yds, Par 71, SSS 71.
Club membership 850.

Visitors	may not play at weekends until 1pm. Must contact in advance.
Societies	must contact by telephone.
Green Fees	£16.50 per round (£21 weekends & bank holidays).

SURREY

Facilities ⊗ 🎿 🝙 ♨ ♀ ♨ 🏠 ⛳ ℂ Doug McClelland.
Leisure fishing, 34 bay driving range.
Location Redhill Rd (2.25m NW off A245)
Hotel ★★★61% Thatchers Resort Hotel, Epsom Rd,
EAST HORSLEY ☎ (04865) 4291
36⇄ 🐾 Annexe23⇄ 🐾

CRANLEIGH
Map 04 TQ03

Fernfell Golf & Country Club ☎ (0483) 268855
Scenic woodland/parkland course at the base of the Surrey
hills, easy walking. Clubhouse in 400-year-old barn.
18 holes, 5071yds, Par 68, SSS 67, Course record 68.
Club membership 1000.
Visitors may not play at weekends. Must contact in
advance.
Societies must contact in advance.
Green Fees not confirmed.
Facilities ⊗ 🎿 🝙 ♨ ♀ ♨ 🏠 ⛳ ℂ Trevor Longmuir.
Leisure hard tennis courts, heated outdoor swimming
pool, snooker, sauna.
Location Barhatch Ln (1m N)
Hotel ★★★★62% Forte Crest, Egerton Rd,
GUILDFORD ☎ (0483) 574444 111⇄ 🐾

DORKING
Map 04 TQ14

Betchworth Park ☎ (0306) 882052
Parkland course, with hard walking on southern ridge of
Boxhill.
18 holes, 6266yds, Par 69, SSS 70.
Club membership 715.
Visitors restricted Tue & Wed (am), Fri & weekends.
Must contact in advance.
Societies welcome Mon and Thu, must apply in advance.
Green Fees weekday £31 per day; £25 per round (Sun pm
£43).
Facilities ⊗ 🝙 ♨ ♀ ♨ 🏠 ℂ R Blackie.
Location Reigate Rd (1m E on A25)
Hotel ★★★56% The White Horse, High St, DORKING
☎ (0306) 881138 36⇄ 🐾 Annexe32⇄ 🐾

Dorking ☎ (0306) 889786
Undulating parkland course, easy slopes, wind-sheltered.
Testing holes: 5th 'Tom's Puddle' (par 4); 7th 'Rest and Be
Thankful' (par 4); 9th 'Double Decker' (par 4).
9 holes, 5163yds, Par 66, SSS 65, Course record 64.
Club membership 425.
Visitors with member only weekends & bank holidays.
Must contact in advance.
Societies must apply in writing.
Green Fees not confirmed.
Facilities ⊗ & 🎿 (ex Mon) 🝙 ♨ ♀ ♨ 🏠 ⛳ ℂ Paul
Napier.
Location Chart Park (1m S on A24)
Hotel ★★★★62% The Burford Bridge, Burford
Bridge, Box Hill, DORKING
☎ (0306) 884561 48⇄ 🐾

EAST HORSLEY
Map 04 TQ05

Drift ☎ (0483) 284641
Woodland course with sheltered fairways and many ponds.
18 holes, 5957yds, Par 71, SSS 68.
Club membership 800.

Visitors must contact in advance. With member only
weekends & bank holidays.
Societies must apply in writing.
Green Fees £30 per day (£20 after 1pm).
Facilities ⊗ 🝙 ♨ ♀ ♨ 🏠 ℂ Joe Hagen.
Location 1.5m N off B2039
Hotel ★★★61% Thatchers Resort Hotel, Epsom Rd,
EAST HORSLEY ☎ (04865) 4291 36 ⇄ 🐾
Annexe23 ⇄ 🐾

EFFINGHAM
Map 04 TQ15

Effingham ☎ Bookham (0372) 452203
Easy-walking downland course laid out on 27-acres with
tree-lined fairways. It is one of the longest of the Surrey
courses with wide subtle greens that provide a
provocative but by no means exhausting challenge. Fine
views.
18 holes, 6488yds, Par 71, SSS 71, Course record 64.
Club membership 960.
Visitors must contact in advance. With member only
weekends & bank holidays.
Societies must apply in advance.
Green Fees £35 per day, £27.50 after 2pm.
Facilities ⊗ (ex Mon & Tue) 🝙 by prior arrangement
🝙 ♨ ♀ ♨ 🏠 ⛳ ℂ Steve Hoatson.
Leisure hard and grass tennis courts, squash,
snooker.
Location Guildford Rd (W side of village on A246)
Hotel ★★★61% Thatchers Resort Hotel, Epsom
Rd, EAST HORSLEY ☎ (04865) 4291
36⇄ 🐾 Annexe23⇄ 🐾

ENTON GREEN
Map 04 SU94

West Surrey ☎ Godalming (0483) 421275
A good parkland-type course in rolling, well-wooded
setting. Some fairways are tight with straight driving at a
premium. The 17th is a testing hole with a long hill walk.
18 holes, 6300yds, Par 71, SSS 70, Course record 65.
Club membership 700.
Visitors must be member of recognised club with
handicap certificate & contact in advance.
Societies must apply in writing.
Green Fees £33.50 per day; £23.50 per round (£41 per
day/round weekends & bank holidays).
Facilities ⊗ 🝙 ♨ ♀ ♨ 🏠 ℂ John Hoskison.
Leisure snooker.
Location S side of village
Hotel ★★★62% Bush Hotel, The Borough,
FARNHAM ☎ (0252) 715237 66⇄ 🐾

EPSOM
Map 04 TQ26

Epsom ☎ (03727) 21666
Downland course.
18 holes, 5701yds, Par 69, SSS 68, Course record 66.
Club membership 900.
Visitors restricted to after midday weekends & bank
holidays.
Societies must contact in advance.
Green Fees £12 per round (£18 weekends & bank holidays).
Facilities ⊗ 🎿 by prior arrangement 🝙 ♨ ♀ ♨ 🏠 ℂ
Bob Wynn. ▶

Location Longdown Ln South, Epsom Downs (SE side of
town centre on B288)
Hotel ★★62% Heathside Hotel, Brighton Rd, BURGH
HEATH ☎ (0737) 353355 73⇥ ♞

Horton Park Country Club ☎ 081-394 2626
Parkland course.
18 holes, 5208yds, Par 69, SSS 65.
Club membership 625.
Visitors must book for weekends.
Societies must telephone in advance.
Green Fees not confirmed.
Facilities ⊗ ⅷ (Thu-Sat evenings) ╚ ➡ ♀ ⚞ ⚑ ℓ
Gary Clements.
Location Hook Rd
Hotel ★★62% Heathside Hotel, Brighton Rd, BURGH
HEATH ☎ (0737) 353355 73⇥ ♞

ESHER   Map 04 TQ16

Moore Place ☎ (0372) 463533
Public course on attractive, undulating parkland laid out some
60 years ago by Harry Vardon. Examples of most of the trees
that will survive in the UK are to be found on the course.
Testing short holes at 4th, 5th and 7th.
9 holes, 2062yds, Par 32, SSS 30, Course record 25.
Club membership 150.
Societies
Green Fees not confirmed.
Facilities ⊗ ⅷ ╚ ➡ ♀ ⚞ ⚑ ℓ David Allen.
Location Portsmouth Rd (SW side of town centre on
A244)
Hotel ★★★63% Ship Thistle Hotel, Monument Green,
WEYBRIDGE ☎ (0932) 848364 39 ⇥ ♞

Sandown Golf Centre ☎ (0372) 463340
Flat parkland course in middle of racecourse. Additional
facilities include a driving range, and a pitch-and-putt course.
New Course: 9 holes, 2828yds, Par 35, SSS 34.
Par 3: 9 holes, 1193yds, Par 27.
Club membership 650.
Visitors restricted weekends & bank holidays.
Societies must apply in writing.
Green Fees New course £5 (£6.50 weekends); Par 3 course
£3.40 (£4.25 weekends).
Facilities ⊗ ╚ ➡ ♀ ⚞ ⚑ ℓ Neal Bedward.
Location Sandown Park, More Ln (1m NW off A307)
Hotel ★★63% Haven Hotel, Portsmouth Rd, ESHER
☎ 081-398 0023 16⇥ ♞ Annexe4⇥ ♞

Thames Ditton & Esher ☎ 081-398 1551
Commonland course, public right of way.
18 holes, 5190yds, Par 66, SSS 65.
Club membership 400.
Visitors may not play on Sun mornings.
Societies must contact in advance.
Green Fees £10 per round (£12 weekends).
Facilities ⊗ & ⅷ by prior arrangement ╚ ➡ ♀ ⚞ ⚑ ℓ
Rodney Hutton.
Location Marquis of Granby, Portsmouth Rd (1m NE on
A307)
Hotel ★★63% Haven Hotel, Portsmouth Rd, ESHER
☎ 081-398 0023 16⇥ ♞ Annexe4⇥ ♞

FARNHAM   Map 04 SU84

Farnham ☎ (0252) 782109
A mixture of meadowland and heath with quick drying
sandy subsoil. Several of the earlier holes have
interesting features, the finishing holes rather less.
18 holes, 6325yds, Par 72, SSS 70.
Club membership 705.
Visitors must be member of recognised club & have
handicap certificate. With member only
weekends.
Societies must apply in writing one year in advance.
Green Fees £30 per day; £25 per round.
Facilities ⊗ ⅷ ╚ ➡ ♀ ⚞ ⚑ ℓ Grahame Cowlishaw.
Location The Sands (3m E off A31)
Hotel ★★★62% Bush Hotel, The Borough,
FARNHAM ☎ (0252) 715237 66⇥ ♞

Farnham Park ☎ (0252) 715216
Municipal parkland course in Farnham Park.
9 holes, 1163yds, Par 27.
Visitors must contact in advance for weekends and bank
holidays.
Societies must apply in advance.
Green Fees £3.25 (£4.10 weekends).
Facilities ⊗ ╚ ➡ ⚞ ⚑ ℓ Peter Chapman.
Location Folly Hill, Farnham Park (N side of town centre
on A287)
Hotel ★★★62% Bush Hotel, The Borough,
FARNHAM ☎ (0252) 715237 66⇥ ♞

GODALMING   Map 04 SU94

Broadwater Park ☎ (0483) 429955
A Par-3 public course with floodlit driving range.
9 holes, 1323yds, Par 54.
Club membership 200.
Visitors welcome except Sat am when competitions in
progress.
Societies apply in writing.
Green Fees £3.75 per 9 holes (£4.25 weekends).
Facilities ⊗ ╚ ➡ ♀ ⚞ ⚑ ℓ Kevin D Milton.
Leisure 16 bay covered driving range.
Location Guildford Rd, Farncombe (4m SW of Guildford)
Hotel ★★64% Inn on the Lake, Ockford Rd,
GODALMING ☎ (0483) 415575
20rm(17⇥ ♞)

GUILDFORD   Map 04 SU94

Guildford ☎ (0483) 63941
A downland course but with some trees and much scrub.
The holes provide an interesting variety of play, an
invigorating experience.
18 holes, 6080yds, Par 69, SSS 70.
Club membership 700.
Visitors must contact in advance. With member only
weekends & bank holidays.
Societies must apply in advance.
Green Fees £35 per day; £25 per round.
Facilities ⊗ & ⅷ by prior arrangement
╚ ➡ ♀ ⚞ ⚑ ℓ P G Hollington.
Leisure snooker.

Location	High Path Rd, Merrow (E side of town centre off A246)
Hotel	★★★★62% Forte Crest, Egerton Rd, GUILDFORD ☎ (0483) 574444 111⇄ 🏮

Milford ☎ (0483) 419200
A Peter Alliss/Clive Clark designed course due to open August 1993. The design has cleverly incorporated a demanding course within an existing woodland and meadow area.
18 holes, 6224yds, Par 71.
Club membership 750.
Visitors   must contact in advance and have handicap certificate, restricted at weekends.
Societies   contact in advance.
Green Fees £20 (£25 weekends and bank holidays).
Facilities ⊗ ⅏ ⅃ 🍺 ♀ ♨ 📷 ⛳ ⌦
Location   Milford (6m SW, leave A3 Milford then A3100 to Enton)
Hotel   ★★64% Inn on the Lake, Ockford Rd, GODALMING ☎ (0483) 415575 20rm(17⇄ 🏮)

HINDHEAD   Map 04 SU83

Hindhead ☎ (0428) 604614
A good example of a Surrey heath-and-heather course, and most picturesque. Players must be prepared for some hard walking. The first nine fairways follow narrow valleys requiring straight hitting; the second nine are much less restricted.
18 holes, 6373yds, Par 70, SSS 70, Course record 65.
Club membership 820.
Visitors   must contact in advance and have a handicap certificate.
Societies   Wed & Thu only
Green Fees £35 per day, £27 after 2pm (£32/42 weekends).
Facilities ⊗ ⅏ ⅃ 🍺 ♀ ♨ 📷 ⛳ ⌦ N Ogilvy.
Leisure   snooker.
Location   Churt Rd (1.5m NW on A287)
Hotel   ★★★67% Frensham Pond Hotel, CHURT ☎ (025125) 5161 41⇄ 🏮 Annexe12⇄ 🏮

KINGSWOOD   Map 04 TQ25

Kingswood ☎ Mogador (0737) 832188
Flat parkland course, easy walking.
18 holes, 6855yds, Par 72, SSS 73.
Club membership 630.
Visitors   restricted before noon weekends.
Societies   must apply in advance.
Green Fees £40 per day; £30 per round (£65/£42 weekends).
Facilities ⊗ & ⅏ by prior arrangement ⅃ 🍺 ♀ ♨ 📷 ⛳ ⌦ Martin Platts.
Leisure   squash, snooker.
Location   Sandy Ln (5m S of village off A217)
Hotel   ★★62% Heathside Hotel, Brighton Rd, BURGH HEATH ☎ (0737) 353355 73⇄ 🏮

LEATHERHEAD   Map 04 TQ15

Leatherhead ☎ Oxshott (037284) 3966
Parkland course with numerous ditches and only two hills, so walking is easy.
18 holes, 6157yds, Par 71, SSS 69.
Club membership 650.
Visitors   restricted Sat & Sun (am). Must contact in advance.
Societies   must apply in advance.
Green Fees £30 per round (£42.50 weekends & bank holidays).
Facilities ⊗ ⅏ ⅃ 🍺 ♀ ♨ 📷 ⛳ ⌦ Richard Hurst.
Leisure   sauna, practice ground, putting green.
Location   Kingston Rd (0.25m from junct 9 of M25, on A243)
Hotel   ★★★★61% Thatchers Resort Hotel, Epsom Rd, EAST HORSLEY ☎ (04865) 4291 36⇄ 🏮 Annexe23⇄ 🏮

Tyrrells Wood ☎ (0372) 376025
Parkland course with easy walking. Snooker.
18 holes, 6234yds, Par 71, SSS 70.
Club membership 800.
Visitors   must contact in advance & play Yellow tee markers only. Handicap certificate required. Restricted weekends.
Societies   must apply in writing.
Green Fees not confirmed.
Facilities ⊗ ⅏ ⅃ 🍺 ♀ ♨ 📷 ⛳ ⌦
Leisure   snooker.
Location   1.25m N on A244
Hotel   ★★★★62% The Burford Bridge, Burford Bridge, Box Hill, DORKING ☎ (0306) 884561 48⇄ 🏮

LIMPSFIELD   Map 05 TQ45

Limpsfield Chart ☎ (0883) 722106
Tight heathland course set in National Trust land.
9 holes, 5718yds, Par 70, SSS 68, Course record 64.
Club membership 350.
Visitors   with member only weekends & not before 3.30pm Thu.
Societies   must apply in advance.
Green Fees £18 per day/round (£20 weekends).
Facilities ⊗ ⅏ by prior arrangement ⅃ 🍺 ♀ ♨ 📷
Location   Westerham Rd (1m E on A25)
Hotel   ★★★65% Reigate Manor Hotel, Reigate Hill, REIGATE ☎ (0737) 240125 51⇄ 🏮

LINGFIELD   Map 05 TQ34

Lingfield Park ☎ (0342) 834602
Difficult and challenging, tree-lined parkland course set in 210 acres of beautiful Surrey countryside. Driving range.
18 holes, 6473yds, Par 71, SSS 72.
Club membership 700.
Visitors   must be accompanied by member on Sat & Sun.
Societies   must telephone in advance; Mon-Fri only.
Green Fees £30 per day; £20 per round.
Facilities ⊗ ⅃ 🍺 ♀ ♨ 📷 ⛳ ⌦ C K Morley.
Leisure   driving range, golf practice ground.

▶

Location	Racecourse Rd (entrance next to Lingfield race course)
Hotel	★★★63% Woodbury House Hotel, Lewes Rd, EAST GRINSTEAD ☎ (0342) 313657 13⇥ ↟ Annexe1 ↟

OCKLEY
Map 04 TQ14

Gatton Manor Hotel Golf & Country Club ☎ (0306) 627555
Undulating course through woods and over many challenging water holes.
18 holes, 6145yds, Par 72, SSS 69.
Club membership 300.

Visitors	must give 2 weeks prior notice. Restricted Sun (am).
Societies	must apply in advance.
Green Fees	£15 per round (£20 weekends).
Facilities	⊗ ∭ ╚ ▬ ♀ ♨ 🏠 ⛳ 🚩 ⛾ 𝄞 Rae Sargent.
Leisure	grass tennis courts, fishing, bowls.
Location	1.5m SW off A29
Hotel	★★★56% The White Horse, High St, DORKING ☎ (0306) 881138 36⇥ ↟ Annexe32⇥ ↟

OTTERSHAW
Map 04 TQ06

Foxhills ☎ (0932) 872050
A pair of parkland courses designed in the grand manner and with American course-design in mind. One course is tree-lined, the other, as well as trees, has massive bunkers and artificial lakes which contribute to the interest. Both courses offer testing golf and they finish on the same long 'double green'. Par 3 'Manor' course also available.
Chertsey: 18 holes, 6658yds, Par 73, SSS 72, Course record 65.
Longcross: 18 holes, 6406yds, Par 72, SSS 71.
Manor: 9 holes, 1300yds, Par 27.
Club membership 1100.

Visitors	restricted before noon weekends.
Societies	welcome Mon-Fri, must apply in advance.
Green Fees	£40 per round/£60 per day (£50 per round weekends & bank holidays).
Facilities	⊗ ∭ ╚ ▬ ♀ ♨ 🏠 🚩 ⛾ 𝄞 Bernard Hunt MBE.
Leisure	hard tennis courts, outdoor and indoor heated swimming pools, squash, snooker, sauna, solarium, gymnasium, clay shoot, croquet lawn, archery, boule.
Location	Stonehill Rd (1m NW)
Hotel	★★★58% Thames Lodge Hotel, Thames St, STAINES ☎ (0784) 464433 44⇥ ↟

PIRBRIGHT
Map 04 SU95

Goal Farm ☎ (0483) 473183 & 473205
Beautiful lanscaped parkland 'Pay and Play' course with excellent greens.
9 holes, 1273yds, Par 54, SSS 48.
Club membership 400.

Visitors	may not play on Sat & Thu mornings.
Green Fees	not confirmed.
Facilities	🏠 🚩
Location	Gole Rd (1.5m NW on B3012)
Hotel	★★★67% Forte Crest, Lynchford Rd, FARNBOROUGH ☎ (0252) 545051 110⇥ ↟

PUTTENHAM
Map 04 SU94

Puttenham ☎ Guildford (0483) 810498
Picturesque tree-lined heathland course offering testing golf, easy walking.
18 holes, 6214yds, Par 71, SSS 70.
Club membership 650.

Visitors	with member only weekends. Must contact in advance.
Societies	must apply in advance.
Green Fees	not confirmed.
Facilities	⊗ (weekdays) ∭ (Wed/Thu) ╚ ♀ ♨ 🏠 ⛾ Gary Simmons.
Location	1m SE on B3000
Hotel	★★★62% Bush Hotel, The Borough, FARNHAM ☎ (0252) 715237 66⇥ ↟

REDHILL
Map 04 TQ25

Redhill & Reigate ☎ Reigate (0737) 240777
Parkland course.
18 holes, 5238yds, Par 67, SSS 66.
Club membership 600.

Visitors	may not play before 11am weekends or after 2pm Sun (Jun-Sep). Must contact in advance.
Societies	must apply in writing.
Green Fees	£12 per round (£18 weekends).
Facilities	⊗ ∭ by prior arrangement ╚ ▬ ♀ ♨ 🏠 🚩 ⛾ Barry Davies.
Location	Clarence Rd, Pendelton Rd (1m S on A23)
Hotel	★★★65% Reigate Manor Hotel, Reigate Hill, REIGATE ☎ (0737) 240125 51⇥ ↟

REIGATE
Map 04 TQ25

Reigate Heath ☎ (0737) 242610 & 243077
Heathland course.
9 holes, 5554yds, Par 67, SSS 67.
Club membership 500.

Visitors	with member only weekends & bank holidays. Must contact in advance.
Societies	must apply in writing.
Green Fees	not confirmed.
Facilities	⊗ ∭ by prior arrangement ╚ ▬ ♀ ♨ 🏠 ⛾ George Gow.
Location	1.5m W off A25
Hotel	★★★65% Reigate Manor Hotel, Reigate Hill, REIGATE ☎ (0737) 240125 51⇥ ↟

RIPLEY
Map 04 TQ05

Wisley ☎ (0483) 211022
A 27-hole course designed by Robert Trent Jones Jnr, and the first that this well-known American golf architect has designed in the UK. Penncross Bent grasses have been used to provide a superb playing surface.
The Church: 9 holes, 3355yds, Par 36, SSS 73.
The Mill: 9 holes, 3473yds, Par 36, SSS 73.
The Garden: 9 holes, 3385yds, Par 36, SSS 73.
Club membership 475.

Visitors	may only play with member.
Green Fees	£35.

Facilities	⊗ 🎿 🏐 🍴 ♀ ♨ 🏠 ♩ Bill Reid.
Leisure	fishing, snooker, sauna.
Hotel	★★★61% Thatchers Resort Hotel, Epsom Rd, EAST HORSLEY ☎ (04865) 4291 36⇥ ♩ Annexe23⇥ ♩

TANDRIDGE — Map 05 TQ35

Tandridge ☎ Oxted (0883) 712274
Rolling parkland, Colt designed course; good views.
18 holes, 6250yds, Par 70, SSS 70.
Club membership 750.

Visitors	must contact in advance & have handicap certificate. Visitors welcome Mon,Wed,Thu also evening green fees after 5pm Mon-Thu.
Societies	must apply in advance.
Green Fees	£40 per day, £31 after 12.30pm, £15 after 5pm.
Facilities	⊗ 🏐 by prior arrangement 🍴 ♀ ♨ 🏠 ♩ ♩
Location	2m SE junc 6 M25, 1.5m E of Godstone on A25
Hotel	★★★74% Nutfield Priory, NUTFIELD ☎ (0737) 822066 52⇥ ♩

TILFORD — Map 04 SU84

Hankley Common ☎ Frensham (025125) 2493
A natural heathland course subject to wind. Greens are first rate. The 18th, a long par 4, is most challenging, the green being beyond a deep chasm which traps any but the perfect second shot. The 7th is a spectacular one-shotter.
18 holes, 6418yds, Par 71, SSS 71, Course record 62.
Club membership 700.

Visitors	handicap certificate required, restricted Wed & alternate weekends. Must contact in advance and have an introduction from own club.
Societies	apply in writing.
Green Fees	not confirmed.
Facilities	⊗ 🏐 🍴 ♀ ♨ 🏠 ♩ Peter Stow.
Location	0.75m SE
Hotel	★★★67% Frensham Pond Hotel, CHURT ☎ (025125) 5161 41⇥ ♩ Annexe12⇥ ♩

VIRGINIA WATER — Map 04 TQ06

WENTWORTH See page 183

WALTON-ON-THAMES — Map 04 TQ16

Burhill ☎ (0932) 227345
A relatively short and easy parkland course with some truly magnificent trees. The 18th is a splendid par 4 requiring a well-placed drive and a long firm second. This course is always in immaculate condition.
18 holes, 6224yds, Par 69, SSS 70.
Club membership 1100.

Visitors	may not play Fri-Sun unless introduced by member. Must contact in advance & have handicap certificate.
Societies	Wed & Thu only, apply in writing.
Green Fees	not confirmed.
Facilities	⊗ 🏐 🍴 (catering Tue-Thu only) ♀ (Tue-Thu) ♨ 🏠 ♩ Lee Johnson.

Leisure	squash, badminton.
Location	Burwood Rd (2m S)
Hotel	★★★63% Ship Thistle Hotel, Monument Green, WEYBRIDGE ☎ (0932) 848364 39⇥ ♩

WALTON-ON-THE-HILL — Map 04 TQ25

WALTON HEATH See page 185

WEST BYFLEET — Map 04 TQ06

West Byfleet ☎ Byfleet (0932) 343433
An attractive course set against a background of woodland and gorse. The 13th is the famous 'pond' shot with a water hazard and two bunkers fronting the green. No less than six holes of 420 yards or more.
18 holes, 6211yds, Par 70, SSS 70, Course record 64.
Club membership 650.

Visitors	with member only weekends. Restricted Thu (Ladies Day). Must contact in advance.
Societies	must apply in writing.
Green Fees	not confirmed.
Facilities	⊗ 🎿 🏐 🍴 ♀ ♨ 🏠 ♩ David Regan.
Leisure	snooker.
Location	Sheerwater Rd (W side of village on A245)
Hotel	★★★61% Thatchers Resort Hotel, Epsom Rd, EAST HORSLEY ☎ (04865) 4291 36⇥ ♩ Annexe23⇥ ♩

WEST END — Map 04 SU96

Windlemere ☎ (0276) 858727
A parkland course, undulating in parts with natural water hazards. There is also a floodlit driving range.
9 holes, 2673yds, Par 34.

Visitors	no restrictions.
Societies	must contact in advance.
Green Fees	not confirmed.
Facilities	🏐 🍴 ♀ ♨ 🏠 ♩ ♩ David Thomas & Alistair Kelso.
Leisure	12 bay driving range.
Location	Windlesham Rd (N side of village off A319)
Hotel	★★★★♨80% Pennyhill Park Hotel, London Rd, BAGSHOT ☎ (0276) 71774 22⇥ ♩ Annexe54⇥ ♩

A golf course name printed in ***bold italics*** means we have been unable to verify information with the club's management for the current year

Remember – unless stated otherwise, two-ball matches should have precedence over and be entitled to pass any three- or four-ball match and any match playing a whole round may pass a match playing a shorter round

WEYBRIDGE   Map 04 TQ06

St George's Hill ☎ (0932) 842406
Comparable and similar to Wentworth, a feature of this
course is the number of long and difficult par 4s. To
score well it is necessary to place the drive - and long
driving pays handsomely. Walking is hard on this
undulating, heavily wooded course with plentiful heather
and rhododendrons.
A+B Course: 18 holes, 6569yds, Par 70, SSS 71.
A+C Course: 18 holes, 6097yds, Par 70, SSS 69.
B+C Course: 18 holes, 6210yds, Par 70, SSS 70.
Club membership 600.
Visitors   must contact in advance and have a
                   handicap certificate.
Societies   must contact in advance.
Green Fees   £40 per day; £30 per round.
Facilities   ⊗ ⅏ by prior arrangement ♨ ♀ ♨ 🏠 ⚡
                   A C Rattue.
Location   2m S off B374
Hotel   ★★★63% Ship Thistle Hotel, Monument
                   Green, WEYBRIDGE
                   ☎ (0932) 848364 39⇆ 🐾

WOKING   Map 04 TQ05

Hoebridge Golf Centre ☎ (0483) 722611
Public courses set in parkland. Also 25-bay floodlit driving
range.
Main Course: 18 holes, 6536yds, Par 72, SSS 71.
Shey Course: 9 holes, 2294yds, Par 33.
Maybury: 18 holes, 2230yds, Par 54.
Club membership 400.
Visitors   must contact in advance.
Societies   Mon-Fri only; must contact in advance.
Green Fees   not confirmed.
Facilities   ⊗ ⅏ 🍴 ♨ ♀ ♨ 🏠 ⚡ ⚡ Tim Powell.
Leisure   snooker.
Location   Old Woking Rd, Old Woking (1m SE of Woking
                   Rd)
Hotel   ★★★★♨80% Pennyhill Park Hotel, London
                   Rd, BAGSHOT ☎ (0276) 71774
                   22⇆ 🐾 Annexe54⇆ 🐾

Pyrford ☎ Guildford (0483) 723555
Due to open September 1993. Designed by Peter Alliss and
Clive Clark and set between Surrey woodlands, the fairways
weave between water courses while the greens and tees are
connected by rustic bridges.
18 holes, 6201yds, Par 72.
Club membership 650.
Visitors   must contact in advance and have handicap
                   certificate, limited weekends.
Societies   must contact in advance.
Green Fees   £25 (£30 bank holidays and weekends).
Facilities   ⊗ ⅏ 🍴 ♨ ♀ ♨ 🏠 ⚡ ⚡ Jeremy Bennett.
Leisure   sauna.
Location   Pyrford (in Warren Lane, 2m from Woking)
Hotel   ★★★★♨80% Pennyhill Park Hotel, London
                   Rd, BAGSHOT ☎ (0276) 71774
                   22⇆ 🐾 Annexe54⇆ 🐾

Worplesdon ☎ (0483) 472277
The scene of the celebrated mixed-foursomes
competition. Accurate driving is essential on this
heathland course. The short 10th across a lake from tee to
green is a notable hole, and the 18th provides a
wonderfully challenging par-4 finish.
18 holes, 6440yds, Par 71, SSS 71, Course record 64.
Club membership 590.
Visitors   must play with member at weekends & bank
                   holidays. Must contact in advance and have
                   a handicap certificate.
Societies   must contact in writing.
Green Fees   £50 per day; £40 per round.
Facilities   ♨ ♨ ⚡ ⚡ J Christine.
Location   Heath House Rd (3.5m SW off B380)
Hotel   ★★★★♨80% Pennyhill Park Hotel,
                   London Rd, BAGSHOT ☎ (0276) 71774
                   22⇆ 🐾 Annexe54⇆ 🐾

WOLDINGHAM   Map 05 TQ35

North Downs ☎ (0883) 652057
Downland course, 850 ft above sea-level, with several testing
holes.
18 holes, 5843yds, Par 69, SSS 68, Course record 66.
Club membership 700.
Visitors   must play with member at weekends and bank
                   holidays. Must contact in advance and have a
                   handicap certificate.
Societies   must contact in writing.
Green Fees   £28 per day/round.
Facilities   ⊗ ⅏ 🍴 ♨ ♀ ♨ 🏠 ⚡ Peter Ellis.
Location   Northdown Rd (0.75m S)
Hotel   ★★59% Sevenoaks Park Hotel, Seal Hollow Rd,
                   SEVENOAKS ☎ (0732) 454245
                   16rm(3⇆3 🐾) Annexe10⇆ 🐾

TYNE & WEAR

BACKWORTH   Map 12 NZ37

Backworth ☎ 091-268 1048
Parkland course with easy walking, natural hazards and good
scenery.
9 holes, 5930yds, Par 71, SSS 69, Course record 66.
Club membership 500.
Visitors   may not play on Tue & Thu after 5pm & Sun
                   mornings. Must have an introduction from own
                   club.
Societies   must contact in writing.
Green Fees   not confirmed.
Facilities   ⊗ ⅏ 🍴 & 🍴 ♨ by prior arrangement ♀ ♨
Leisure   archery, bowls, cricket, football.
Location   The Hall (W side of town on B1322)
Hotel   ★★★63% Ship Thistle Hotel, Monument Green,
                   WEYBRIDGE
                   ☎ (0932) 848364 39⇆ 🐾

Wentworth Club

Virginia Water
☎ Wentworth (0344) 842201

Map O4 TQO6

*J*ohn Ingham writes: Among the really famous inland courses in England you have to name Wentworth. The challenge, in terms of sheer yards, is enormous. But the qualities go beyond this, and include the atmosphere, the heathland, the silver birch and fairway-side homes.

The West Course is the one every visitor wishes to play. You can't possibly name the best hole. Bernard Gallacher, the course professional, has his view, but you may select the 7th where the drive rolls downhill and the second shot has to be played high up to a stepped green. The closing holes really sort out the best of them too.

The clubhouse offers Country Club facilities not typical of many British golf courses. The pro shop resembles a plush city store; evening hospitality events are frequent and society meetings here are catered for as at few other centres for sport, and it's all done in five-star style. Probably it is during the World Match-Play championship when Wentworth can be seen at its best. The tents are up, the superstars pile in and out of huge cars and the air is one of luxury and opulence.

One of the attractions of Wentworth is that the great players, including Ben Hogan and Sam Snead, have played here. Gary Player has won marvellously at Wentworth, beating Tony Lema after being seven down in the 36-hole match! Great competitors from the past have stamped their mark here. Arnold Palmer, back in the 1960s, beat Neil Coles in the Match-Play final but then, a generation later, faced young Seve Ballesteros. The Spaniard saved his bacon by pitching in for an eagle three at the last against Palmer, to take the clash into extra holes, where he won.

Visitors	weekdays only. Must contact in advance, and have a letter of introduction from their own club or a current handicap certificate
Societies	apply in advance (handicap restrictions)
Green fees	(per round) West Course £80; East Course £60; Edinburgh Course £65
Facilities	⊗ ⊞ ⊾ ⚌ ♀ (all day) breakfast from 7am, (private rooms) ⌂ ☎ ☂ ⌀ (Bernard Gallacher)
Leisure	driving range, tennis (hardcourt & grass), outdoor-heated swimming pool, gymnasium
Location	Wentworth Drive (W side of Virginia Water, at junction of A30 and A329)

54 holes. West Course: 18 holes, 6945yds, Par 73, SSS 74, Course record 63 (Wayne Riley) East Course: 18 holes, 6176yds, Par 68, SSS 70, Course record 62 Edinburgh: 18 holes, 6979yds, Par 72, SSS 73, Course record 68

WHERE TO STAY AND EAT NEARBY

HOTELS:

ASCOT

★★★★ 59% Berystede, Bagshot Rd, Sunninghill. ☎ (0344) 23311. 91 ⇥ 𝕽 European cuisine

★★66% Highclere, 19 Kings Road, Sunninghill. ☎ (0344) 25220. 12 ⇥ 𝕽 European cuisine

BAGSHOT

★★★★❀❀⚓ 76% Pennyhill Park, London Rd. ☎ (0276) 71774. 22 ⇥ 𝕽 Annexe 54 ⇥ 𝕽. English & French cuisine

RESTAURANTS:

BRAY

✕✕✕✕❀❀❀❀ The Waterside, River Cottage, Ferry Rd. ☎ Maidenhead (0628) 20691. French cuisine

EGHAM

✕✕❀❀ La Bonne Franquette, 5 High St. ☎ (0784) 439494. French cuisine

BIRTLEY — Map 12 NZ25

Birtley ☎ 091-410 2207
Parkland course.
9 holes, 5660yds, Par 66, SSS 67, Course record 63.
Club membership 270.

Visitors must play with member at weekends.
Societies apply in writing, must contact 1 month in advance in summer.
Green Fees £10 per round.
Facilities)|||(by prior arrangement ⛾ ☕ 🍷 ⛭
Location Portobello Rd
Hotel ★★★61% Forte Posthouse, Emerson District 5, WASHINGTON ☎ 091-416 2264 138⇌ ⛳

BOLDON — Map 12 NZ36

Boldon ☎ 091-536 5360 & 091-536 4182
Parkland links course, easy walking, distant sea views, windy.
18 holes, 6362yds, Par 72, SSS 70, Course record 67.
Club membership 700.

Visitors may not play after 3.30pm at weekends & bank holidays. Must contact in advance.
Societies must contact in advance.
Green Fees not confirmed.
Facilities ⊗)|||(⛾ ☕ 🍷 ⛭ 🏪 🚩 ⛳
Leisure snooker.
Location Dipe Ln, East Boldon (S side of village off A184)
Hotel ★★★71% Swallow Hotel, Queen's Pde, Seaburn, SUNDERLAND ☎ 091-529 2041 66⇌ ⛳

CHOPWELL — Map 12 NZ15

Garesfield ☎ (0207) 561278
Undulating parkland course with good views and picturesque woodland surroundings.
18 holes, 6603yds, Par 72, SSS 72.
Club membership 720.

Visitors weekends after 4pm only, unless with member. Must contact in advance.
Societies must contact in advance.
Green Fees £15 per day; £13 per day (£15 weekends & bank holidays).
Facilities ⊗ &)|||(by prior arrangement ⛾ ☕ 🍷 ⛭ 🏪
Location 0.5m N
Hotel ★★★62% Swallow Hotel, Newgate Arcade, NEWCASTLE UPON TYNE ☎ 091-232 5025 93⇌ ⛳

FELLING — Map 12 NZ26

Heworth ☎ (0632) 692137
Fairly flat, parkland course.
18 holes, 6437yds, Par 71, SSS 71, Course record 69.
Club membership 500.

Visitors may not play Sat & before 10am Sun.
Societies must apply in writing.
Green Fees not confirmed.
Facilities ⊗ &)|||(by prior arrangement ⛾ ☕ 🍷 ⛭
Location Gingling Gate, Heworth (On A195, 5m NW of junc with A1(M))
Hotel ★★★61% Forte Posthouse, Emerson District 5, WASHINGTON ☎ 091-416 2264 138⇌ ⛳

GATESHEAD — Map 12 NZ26

Ravensworth ☎ 091-487 6014
Moorland/parkland course 600 ft above sea-level with fine views. Testing 13th hole (par 3).
18 holes, 5872yds, Par 68, SSS 68.
Club membership 600.

Visitors no restrictions.
Societies must contact in advance.
Green Fees £15 per round (£23 weekends & bank holidays).
Facilities ⊗)|||(⛾ ☕ (lunch/dinner by prior arrangement ex Mon) 🍷 ⛭ 🏪 ⛳ David Race.
Location Moss Heaps, Wrekenton (3m SE off A6127)
Hotel ★★★66% Swallow Hotel-Gateshead, High West St, GATESHEAD ☎ 091-477 1105 103⇌ ⛳

GOSFORTH — Map 12 NZ26

Gosforth ☎ 091-285 3495
Parkland course with natural water hazards, easy walking.
18 holes, 6043yds, Par 69, SSS 69.
Club membership 480.

Visitors may not play on Tue & competition days.
Societies must contact in advance.
Green Fees not confirmed.
Facilities ⊗ (ex Mon))|||((ex Mon,Tue and Fri) ⛾ ☕ 🍷 ⛭ 🏪 🚩 ⛳ David Race.
Location Broadway East (N side of town centre off A6125)
Hotel ★★★★67% Swallow Gosforth Park Hotel, High Gosforth Park, Gosforth, NEWCASTLE UPON TYNE ☎ 091-236 4111 178⇌ ⛳

Gosforth Park ☎ 091-236 4480
A flat, tree-lined parkland course with a burn running through many holes. There is also a 30-bay covered floodlit driving range and a 9-hole pitch-putt.
18 holes, 6100yds, Par 71, SSS 70, Course record 66.
Club membership 650.

Visitors must contact in advance.
Societies must apply in writing.
Green Fees £10 (£12 weekends).
Facilities ⊗)|||(⛾ ☕ 🍷 ⛭ 🏪 🚩 ⛳ G Garland & M Leighton.
Leisure floodlit driving range, pitch & putt.
Location Parklands Golf Club, High Gosforth Park (2m N on B1318 off A6125)
Hotel ★★★★67% Swallow Gosforth Park Hotel, High Gosforth Park, Gosforth, NEWCASTLE UPON TYNE ☎ 091-236 4111 178⇌ ⛳

HOUGHTON-LE-SPRING — Map 12 NZ35

Houghton-le-Spring ☎ 091-584 1198
Hilly, downland course with natural slope hazards.
18 holes, 6416yds, Par 72, SSS 71.
Club membership 600.

▶

ᥕalton ℋeath

Walton-on-the-Hill   Map O4 TQ25
☎ Tadworth (0747) 812380

John Ingham writes: Several historic names are etched on the Honours Board at Walton Heath, almost 700 feet above sea level. The rare atmosphere here is justified because these Surrey courses can claim to be the toughest inland examination in Britain. Walton Heath is famous for staging the Ryder Cup and the European Open Championship but older players will remember it best for the Match-Play Championship battles that involved Sir Henry Cotton and Dai Rees as well as huge money matches that brought names such as Bobby Locke and Fred Daly to public prominence.

Once owned by the News of the World newspaper, MP's, Lords and significant members of the press would be invited down to Walton Heath by Sir Emsley Carr, who was one of the first to employ a lady as Secretary and manager of a well-known championship venue.

The courses were designed in 1903 by Herbert Fowler, who used natural hollows and channels for drainage, so the fairways equal the best on any seaside links and quickly dry out, even after a severe storm.

Erratic shots, wide of the prepared surface, are wickedly punished and weekend players are tormented in awful fashion. Nobody escapes undamaged from the gorse and bracken but it is the heather, with those tough stems, that really snarl up any attempt at an over-ambitious recovery shot. So be advised - if you're caught off the fairway, don't attempt anything fancy. Play back on the shortest route to comparative security.

While the Old Course is most frequently played by visitors, the New Course is very challenging and requires all the subtle shots required if you are to get the ball near the hole. And, in the clubhouse, they serve a spectacular lunch.

Membership 900
Visitors weekdays only. Must contact in advance, and have a letter of introduction fromtheir own club or a handicap certificate
Societies apply in writing
Green fees per day: £57 before 11.30, £47 after 11.30
Facilities ⊗ 🍽 (3.30-7pm) ♀ 🛏 🏌 ⛳ ((Ken Macpherson)
Location Deans Lane (SE side of village, off B2032)

36 holes. Old Course: 18 holes, 6801yds, Par 72, SSS 73, Course record 65 (Peter Townsend) New Course: 18 holes, 6609 yds, Par 72, SSS 72, Course record 64 (Clive Clark)

WHERE TO STAY AND EAT NEARBY

HOTELS:
BURGH HEATH
★★ 62% Heathside, Brighton Rd.
☎ (0737) 353355. 73 ⇤ ↑.
English & French cuisine

DORKING
★★★★ 62% The Burford Bridge, Burford Bridge, Box Hill (2m NE A24)
☎ (0306) 884561. 48 ⇤ ↑

REIGATE
★★★ 65% Reigate Manor, Reigate Hill. ☎ (0737) 240125. 51 ⇤ ↑
English & French cuisine

STOKE D'ABERNON
★★★❀68% Woodlands Park, Woodlands Ln.
☎ Oxshott (037284) 3933. 59(58 ⇤ ↑).
English & French cuisine

RESTAURANTS:
DORKING
✕✕❀❀Partners West Street, 2-4 West St. ☎ (0306) 882826.
French cuisine

SUTTON
✕❀❀Partners Brasserie, 23 Stonecot Hill. ☎ 081-644 7743.
English & French cuisine

Visitors may not play on Sun/competition days.
Societies must contact secretary in advance.
Green Fees £18 per day; £15 per round (£23/£20 weekends).
Facilities ⊗ (ex Thu) ▥ (ex Wed & Thu)
⮯ ▬ ⵗ ⚥ 🕮 ⛳ 𝄐 Stephen Bradbury.
Location Copt Hill (0.5m E on B1404)
Hotel ★★★70% Ramside Hall Hotel,
Carrville, DURHAM
☎ 091-386 5282 82⇄ 🐾

NEWCASTLE UPON TYNE　　Map 12 NZ26

City of Newcastle ☎ 091-285 1775
A well-manicured parkland course in the Newcastle suburbs,
subject to wind.
18 holes, 6508yds, Par 72, SSS 71, Course record 67.
Club membership 570.
Visitors may not play mens competition days.
Societies by arrangement.
Green Fees £19 per day (£21 weekends & bank holidays).
Facilities ⊗ ▥ ⮯ ▬ ⵗ ⚥ 𝄐 Anthony J Matthew.
Leisure snooker.
Location Three Mile Bridge (3m N on A1)
Hotel ★★★64% Airport Moat House Hotel,
Woolsington, NEWCASTLE UPON
TYNE AIRPORT ☎ (0661) 24911
100⇄ 🐾

Newcastle United ☎ 091-286 4693
Moorland course with natural hazards.
18 holes, 6484yds, Par 72, SSS 71, Course record 68.
Club membership 500.
Visitors must play with member at weekends.
Societies must contact in writing.
Green Fees £12.50 weekdays.
Facilities ⊗ ▥ ⮯ ▬ ⵗ ⚥ 🕮
Location Ponteland Rd, Cowgate (1.25m NW of city
centre off A6127)
Hotel ★★★59% Imperial Hotel, Jesmond Rd,
NEWCASTLE UPON TYNE
☎ 091-281 5511 129⇄ 🐾

Northumberland ☎ 091-236 2498
Many golf courses have been sited inside racecourses,
although not so many survive today. One which does is
the Northumberland Club's course at High Gosforth
Park. Naturally the course is flat but there are plenty of
mounds and other hazards to make it a fine test of golf. It
should be said that not all the holes are within the
confines of the racecourse, but both inside and out there
are some good holes. This is a Championship course.
18 holes, 6629yds, Par 72, SSS 72.
Club membership 550.
Visitors may not play at weekends or competition
days. Must contact in advance and have
handicap certificate.
Societies must apply in writing.
Green Fees £30 per round; £35 per day.
Facilities ⊗ ▥ ⮯ & ▬ by prior arrangement ⵗ ⚥
Location High Gosforth Park (4m N of city centre
off A1)
Hotel ★★★★67% Swallow Gosforth Park Hotel,
High Gosforth Park, Gosforth,
NEWCASTLE UPON TYNE
☎ 091-236 4111 178⇄ 🐾

Westerhope ☎ 091-286 9125
Attractive parkland course with tree-lined fairways, and easy
walking. Good open views towards the airport.
18 holes, 6468yds, Par 72, SSS 71, Course record 64.
Club membership 778.
Visitors with member only at weekends.
Societies must apply in writing.
Green Fees £22 per day; £16 per round.
Facilities ⊗ ▥ ⮯ ▬ ⵗ ⚥ 🕮 𝄐 Nigel Brown.
Location Bowerbank, Whorlton Grange, Westerhope
(4.5m NW of city centre off B6324)
Hotel ★★★★67% Swallow Gosforth Park Hotel, High
Gosforth Park, Gosforth,
NEWCASTLE UPON TYNE
☎ 091-236 4111 178⇄ 🐾

RYTON　　Map 12 NZ16

Ryton ☎ 091-413 3737
Parkland course.
18 holes, 5968yds, Par 70, SSS 68.
Club membership 400.
Visitors with member only at weekends.
Societies apply in writing to secretary.
Green Fees £16 per day (£16 per round weekends).
Facilities ⊗ & ▥ by prior arrangement ⮯ ▬ ⵗ ⚥
Location Clara Vale (NW side of town off A695)
Hotel ★★64% County Hotel, Priestpopple, HEXHAM
☎ (0434) 602030 9⇄ 🐾

Tyneside ☎ 091-413 2177
Open parkland course, not heavily bunkered. Water hazard,
hilly, practice area.
18 holes, 6042yds, Par 70, SSS 69, Course record 65.
Club membership 660.
Visitors must have a handicap certificate. Must contact in
advance to play at weekends.
Societies must apply in writing.
Green Fees £20 per day; £16 per round (£25 per round
weekends).
Facilities ⊗ ▥ ⮯ ▬ ⵗ ⚥ 🕮 𝄐 Malcolm Gunn.
Location Westfield Ln (NW side of town off A695)
Hotel ★★64% County Hotel, Priestpopple, HEXHAM
☎ (0434) 602030 9⇄ 🐾

SOUTH SHIELDS　　Map 12 NZ36

South Shields ☎ 091-456 0475
A slightly undulating downland course on a limestone base
ensuring good conditions underfoot. Open to strong winds,
the course is testing but fair. There are fine views of the
coastline.
18 holes, 6264yds, Par 71, SSS 70.
Club membership 800.
Visitors must contact in advance and have a letter of
introduction.
Societies by arrangement.
Green Fees £20 per day (£25 weekends & bank holidays).
Facilities ⊗ ▥ ⮯ ▬ ⵗ ⚥ 🕮 ⛳ 𝄐 Gary Parsons.
Location Cleadon Hills (SE side of town centre off
A1300)
Hotel ★★★60% Sea Hotel, Sea Rd, SOUTH SHIELDS
☎ 091-427 0999 33⇄ 🐾

Whitburn ☎ 091-529 2144
Parkland course.
18 holes, 5773yds, Par 69, SSS 68.
Club membership 600.
Visitors   restricted weekends, Tue & competition days.
Societies   must apply in writing.
Green Fees £15 per day (£20 weekends & bank holidays).
Facilities   ⊗ 🕸 🖪 💺 ♀ 🛆 ⚐ (David Stephenson.
Leisure   snooker.
Location   Lizard Ln (2.5m SE off A183)
Hotel   ★★★71% Swallow Hotel, Queen's Pde, Sea-
                 burn, SUNDERLAND ☎ 091-529 2041 66⇆ 🐾

SUNDERLAND   Map 12 NZ35

Wearside ☎ 091-534 2518
Open, undulating parkland course rolling down to the
River Wear and beneath the shadow of the famous
Penshaw Monument built on the lines of an Athenian
temple it is a well-known landmark. Two ravines cross
the course presenting a variety of challenging holes.
18 holes, 6373yds, Par 71, SSS 74, Course record 64.
Club membership 729.
Visitors   may not play before 9.30am & after 4pm.
                 Must have an introduction from own club.
Societies   must apply in writing.
Green Fees not confirmed.
Facilities   ⊗ 🕸 by prior arrangement 🖪 💺 ♀ 🛆 🏠 (
                 Steven Wynn.
Location   Coxgreen (3.5m W off A183)
Hotel   ★★★71% Swallow Hotel, Queen's Pde,
                 Seaburn, SUNDERLAND
                 ☎ 091-529 2041 66⇆ 🐾

TYNEMOUTH   Map 12 NZ36

Tynemouth ☎ 091-257 4578
Well-drained parkland/downland course, easy walking.
18 holes, 6082yds, Par 70, SSS 69, Course record 65.
Club membership 824.
Visitors   must play with member weekends & bank holidays.
Societies   must contact in writing.
Green Fees not confirmed.
Facilities   ⊗ 🕸 🖪 💺 ♀ 🛆 🏠 (J P McKenna.
Location   Spital Dene (0.5m W)
Hotel   ★★★56% Park Hotel, Grand Pde,
                 TYNEMOUTH ☎ 091-257 1406 49rm(43⇆ 🐾)

WALLSEND   Map 12 NZ26

Wallsend ☎ 091-262 1973
Parkland course.
18 holes, 6608yds, Par 72, SSS 72, Course record 68.
Club membership 750.
Visitors   may not play before 12.30pm weekends. Must
                 contact in advance.
Societies   must apply in writing.
Green Fees not confirmed.
Facilities   ⊗ 🕸 & 🖪 (summer only) 💺 ♀ 🛆 🏠 (Ken
                 Phillips.
Location   Rheydt Av, Bigges Main (NW side of town
                 centre off A193)
Hotel   ★★★60% Newcastle Moat House, Coast Rd,
                 WALLSEND
                 ☎ 091-262 8989 & 091-262 7044 150⇆ 🐾

WASHINGTON   Map 12 NZ25

Washington Moat House ☎ (091) 4172626
Championship-standard course. Also a 9-hole (par 3) course,
putting green and 21-bay floodlit driving range. 'Bunkers
Bar' at the 10th tee is one of the few 'spike' bars in the
country.
18 holes, 6267yds, Par 73, SSS 71.
Club membership 650.
Visitors   must contact in advance. May not play before
                 10am or between noon & 2pm at weekends.
Societies   must apply in writing.
Green Fees not confirmed.
Facilities   ⊗ 🕸 🖪 💺 ♀ 🛆 🏠 ⚐ 🍴 (
Leisure   heated indoor swimming pool, squash, sauna,
                 solarium, gymnasium, 21 bay floodlit driving
                 range.
Location   Stone Cellar Rd, High Usworth
Hotel   ★★★65% Washington Moat House, Stone
                 Cellar Rd, District 12, High Usworth,
                 WASHINGTON ☎ 091-417 2626 106⇆ 🐾

WHICKHAM   Map 12 NZ26

Whickham ☎ 091-488 7309
Parkland course, some uphill walking, fine views.
18 holes, 6129yds, Par 68, SSS 69, Course record 61.
Club membership 600.
Visitors   must have an introduction from own club.
Societies   by arrangement.
Green Fees not confirmed.   ▶

Facilities ⊗ & ⟩⫴ by prior arrangement ⬚ ⬛ ⍾ ⏃ 🏠
Leisure snooker.
Location Hollinside Park (1.5m S)
Hotel ★★★66% Swallow Hotel-Gateshead, High West St, GATESHEAD
☎ 091-477 1105 103↩ 🐾

WHITLEY BAY   Map 12 NZ37

Whitley Bay ☎ 091-252 0180
Downland course close to the sea. A stream runs through the undulating terrain.
18 holes, 6617yds, Par 71, SSS 72, Course record 66.
Club membership 700.
Visitors with member only at weekends & bank holidays.
Societies Mon-Fri, by arrangement.
Green Fees £25 per day; £18 per round.
Facilities ⊗ ⟩⫴ ⬚ ⬛ (no catering Mon) ⍾ (ex Mon) ⏃ 🏠 (W J Light.
Location Claremont Rd (NW side of town centre off A1148)
Hotel ★★59% Holmedale Hotel, 106 Park Av, WHITLEY BAY
☎ 091-251 3903 & 091-253 1162 18↩ 🐾

W A R W I C K S H I R E

ATHERSTONE   Map 04 SP39

Atherstone ☎ (0827) 713110
Parkland course, established in 1894 and laid out on hilly ground.
18 holes, 6235yds, Par 73, SSS 70.
Club membership 350.
Visitors handicap certificate required. With member only weekends (ex Sun) & bank holidays.
Societies weekdays only, by prior arrangement with secretary. Handicap certificates are required.
Green Fees £17 per day/round (£21 bank holidays).
Facilities ⊗ ⟩⫴ ⬚ ⬛ ⍾ ⏃ 🏠
Location The Outwoods, Coleshill Rd (0.5m S on B4116)
Hotel ★★66% Old Red Lion Hotel, Long St, ATHERSTONE
☎ (0827) 713156 22↩ 🐾

BRANDON   Map 04 SP47

City of Coventry-Brandon Wood ☎ Coventry (0203) 543141
Municipal parkland course surrounded by fields and bounded by River Avon on east side. Floodlit driving range.
18 holes, 6610yds, Par 72, SSS 72, Course record 68.
Club membership 350.
Visitors telephone for details.
Societies telephone in advance.
Green Fees £7.50 (£10 weekends).
Facilities catering by arrangement ⏃ 🏠 ⍥ (Chris Gledhill.
Leisure driving range, floodlit bays.
Location Brandon Ln (1m W)
Hotel ★★★60% The Brandon Hall, Main St, BRANDON ☎ (0203) 542571 60↩ 🐾

COLESHILL   Map 04 SP28

Maxstoke Park ☎ (0675) 464915
Parkland course with easy walking. Numerous trees and a lake form natural hazards.
18 holes, 6478yds, Par 71, SSS 71.
Club membership 600.
Visitors with member only at weekends & bank holidays.
Societies must telephone in advance.
Green Fees £25 per round.
Facilities ⊗ ⬚ ⬛ ⍾ ⏃ 🏠 (R A Young.
Location Castle Ln (2m E)
Hotel ★★63% Coleshill Hotel, 152 High St, COLESHILL ☎ (0675) 465527 15↩ 🐾 Annexe8↩ 🐾

KENILWORTH   Map 04 SP27

Kenilworth ☎ (0926) 58517
Parkland course in open hilly situation. Club founded in 1887.
18 holes, 6413yds, Par 72, SSS 71.
Club membership 700.
Visitors welcome except competition days. Must contact in advance.
Societies apply in writing.
Green Fees £25 per day (£37 weekends).
Facilities ⊗ ⟩⫴ ⬚ ⬛ ⍾ ⏃ 🏠 ⍥ (Steven Yates.
Leisure snooker.
Location Crew Ln (0.5m NE)
Hotel ★★64% Clarendon House Hotel, Old High St, KENILWORTH ☎ (0926) 57668 31↩ 🐾

LEA MARSTON   Map 04 SP29

Lea Marston Hotel & Leisure Complex ☎ Curdworth (0675) 470707
Par 3, 'pay-and-play' course, with water hazards, out of bounds, and large bunkers. The venue for the past two years of the Midlands Professional Par 3 Competition. Golf driving range.
9 holes, 783yds, Par 27.
Visitors no restrictions.
Societies must telephone in advance.
Green Fees not confirmed.
Facilities ⊗ ⟩⫴ ⬚ ⬛ ⍾ 🏠 ⍥ ⍥ (Andrew Jinks & Neil McEwan.
Leisure hard tennis courts, sauna, solarium, gymnasium.
Location Haunch Ln
Hotel ★★★64% Lea Marston Hotel & Leisure Complex, Haunch Ln, LEA MARSTON ☎ (0675) 470468 22↩ 🐾

LEAMINGTON SPA   Map 04 SP36

Leamington & County ☎ (0926) 425961
Undulating parkland course with extensive views.
18 holes, 6424yds, Par 71, SSS 71.
Club membership 700.
Visitors no restrictions.
Societies telephone in advance.
Green Fees £28 per day; £25 per round (£37 per round weekends).
Facilities ⊗ ⟩⫴ ⬚ ⬛ ⍾ ⏃ 🏠 (I A Grant.

Leisure   snooker.
Location   Golf Ln, Whitnash (S side of town centre)
Hotel   ★★★59% Manor House Hotel, Avenue Rd,
LEAMINGTON SPA
☎ (0926) 423251 53⇥ ʳ⌐

Newbold Comyn ☎ (0926) 421157
Municipal parkland course with hilly front nine. The par 4,
9th is a 467-yd testing hole.
18 holes, 6315yds, Par 70, SSS 70.
Club membership 420.
Visitors   no restrictions.
Societies   apply to professional.
Green Fees not confirmed.
Facilities   ♀⅋⌂ᵀʳ⌐ Don Knight.
Location   Newbold Ter East (0.75m E of town centre off
B4099)
Hotel   ★★★59% Manor House Hotel, Avenue Rd,
LEAMINGTON SPA
☎ (0926) 423251 53⇥ ʳ⌐

NUNEATON   Map 04 SP39

Nuneaton ☎ (0203) 347810
Undulating moorland and woodland course.
18 holes, 6429yds, Par 71, SSS 71, Course record 67.
Club membership 675.
Visitors   with member only at weekends.
Societies   apply in writing.
Green Fees £22 per day/round.
Facilities   ⊗ ⅋ (ex Wed) ᏝᏛ (no catering Mon,
restricted Oct-Mar.) ♀⅋⌂ᵀ Graham Davison.
Leisure   snooker.
Location   Golf Dr, Whitestone (2m SE off B4114)
Hotel   ★★66% Old Red Lion Hotel, Long St,
ATHERSTONE ☎ (0827) 713156 22⇥ ʳ⌐

Purley Chase ☎ Chapel End (0203) 393118
Meadowland course with tricky water hazards on eight holes
and undulating greens. 13-bay driving range.
18 holes, 6772yds, Par 72, SSS 72.
Club membership 700.
Visitors   welcome except mornings at weekend &
competition days.
Societies   by prior arrangement at least 3 weeks in
advance.
Green Fees £15 per round (£18 weekends & bank holidays).
Facilities   ⊗ ⅋ (Fri & Sat) ᏝᏛ♀⅋⌂ᵀ David
Llewelyn.
Leisure   fishing, 13 bay driving range.
Location   Ridge Ln (2m NW off B4114)
Hotel   Longshoot Toby Hotel, Watling St, NUNEATON
☎ (0203) 329711 Annexe47⇥ ʳ⌐

RUGBY   Map 04 SP57

Rugby ☎ (0788) 542306
Parkland course with brook running through the middle and
crossed by a viaduct.
18 holes, 5457yds, Par 68, SSS 67.
Club membership 550.
Visitors   weekends & bank holidays with member only.
Must contact in advance and have an
introduction from own club.
Societies   apply in writing.

Green Fees not confirmed.
Facilities   ⊗ & ⅋ by prior arrangement (ex Tue) ᏝᏛ♀
⅋⌂ᵀ D Sutherland.
Leisure   snooker.
Location   Clifton Rd (1m NE on B5414)
Hotel   ★★★60% Grosvenor Hotel, Clifton Rd, RUGBY
☎ (0788) 535686 21⇥ ʳ⌐

STONELEIGH   Map 04 SP37

Stoneleigh Deer Park ☎ Coventry (0203) 639991
Parkland course in old deer park with many mature trees. The
River Avon meanders through the course and comes into play
on 4 holes. Also 9-hole course.
Tantara: 18 holes, 6083yds, Par 71, SSS 69.
Avon: 9 holes, 1251yds, Par 27.
Club membership 900.
Visitors   must contact in advance, no visitors at weekends
except by prior arrangement.
Societies   by prior arrangement.
Green Fees Tantara £14 per round (£19 weekend). Avon £5
(£8 weekends).
Facilities   ⊗ ⅋ᏝᏛ♀⅋⌂ᵀ Sid Mouland.
Location   The Old Deer Park, Coventry Rd (3m NE of
Kenilworth)
Hotel   ★★66% Old Mill Hotel, Mill Hill, BAGINTON
☎ (0203) 303588 20⇥

STRATFORD-UPON-AVON   Map 04 SP25

Stratford Oaks ☎ (0789) 731571
American styled, parkland course designed by Howard Swan.
18 holes, 6100yds, Par 71, SSS 69, Course record 66.
Club membership 600.
Visitors   no restrictions.
Societies   telephone in advance.
Green Fees £12 per round (£15 weekends).
Facilities   ⊗ ⅋ᏝᏛ♀⅋⌂ᵀ Fraser Leek.
Location   Bearley Rd, Snitterfield (4m N of Stratford-
upon-Avon)
Hotel   ★★★74% Windmill Park Hotel & Country
Club, Warwick Rd, STRATFORD-UPON-AVON
☎ (0789) 731173 100⇥

Stratford-upon-Avon ☎ (0789) 205749
Beautiful parkland course. The par 3, 16th is tricky and the
par 5, 17th and 18th, provide a tough end.
18 holes, 6309yds, Par 72, SSS 70, Course record 64.
Club membership 750.
Visitors   restricted on Wed. Must contact in advance.
Societies   must telephone in advance.
Green Fees not confirmed.
Facilities   ⊗ ⅋ᏝᏛ♀⅋⌂ᵀ N D Powell.
Location   Tiddington Rd (0.75m E on B4086)
Hotel   ★★★63% Alveston Manor Hotel, Clopton
Bridge, STRATFORD-UPON-AVON
☎ (0789) 204581 108⇥ ʳ⌐

Welcombe Hotel ☎ (0789) 295252
Wooded parkland course of great character and boasting
superb views of the River Avon, Stratford and the Cotswolds.
Set within the hotel's 157-acre estate, it has two lakes and
water features.
18 holes, 6217yds, Par 70, SSS 70, Course record 67.
Club membership 400.

►

WELCOMBE
HOTEL & GOLF COURSE
STRATFORD-UPON-AVON
Warwickshire
Fax:(0789) 414666
Telephone: (0789) 295252   Telex: 31347

The Welcombe, a Jacobean-style luxury hotel, is situated within a 157 acre parkland estate with its own 18-hole Par 70 Golf Course, just 1½ miles from the centre of Stratford-upon-Avon. The club house facilities include a bar with pub style menu, professional shop and changing facilities and is a short walk away from the luxury of this superb hotel.

**Special golfing packages throughout the year –
Rates and brochure on request.**

ORIENT-EXPRESS HOTELS

Visitors   welcome except before 11am weekends. Must contact in advance.
Societies   booking via Hotel.
Green Fees   £32 per day (£40 weekends).
Facilities   ⊗ ⍭ ⬗ ➤ ♀ ⚘ ⌂ ⚐ ⌕
Leisure   hard tennis courts, fishing, snooker, putting green.
Location   Warwick Rd (1.5m NE off A46)
Hotel   ★★★★64% Welcombe Hotel and Golf Course, Warwick Rd, STRATFORD-UPON-AVON ☎ (0789) 295252 76⇄ ꜰ

TANWORTH-IN-ARDEN   Map 07 SP17

Ladbrook Park ☎ (05644) 2264
Parkland course lined with trees.
18 holes, 6427yds, Par 71, SSS 71, Course record 65.
Club membership 750.
Visitors   with member only weekends. Must contact in advance & have handicap certificate.
Societies   telephone in advance.
Green Fees   £30 per day/round.
Facilities   ⊗ ⍭ ⬗ ➤ ♀ ⚘ ⌂ ⚐ Steve Harrison.
Leisure   snooker.
Location   Poolhead Ln (1m NW on A4023)
Hotel   ★★★63% St John's Swallow Hotel, 651 Warwick Rd, SOLIHULL ☎ 021-711 3000 177⇄ ꜰ

WARWICK   Map 04 SP26

Warwick ☎ (0926) 494316
Parkland course with easy walking. Driving range with floodlit bays.
9 holes, 2682yds, Par 34, SSS 66, Course record 67.
Club membership 150.
Visitors   welcome except Sun mornings and racedays.
Green Fees   £3.80 per round (£5.50 weekends).
Facilities   ➤ ♀ ⚘ ⌂ ⚐ ⌕ Steve Hutchinson.
Leisure   snooker, floodlit driving range.
Location   The Racecourse (W side of town centre)
Hotel   ★★58% Lord Leycester Hotel, Jury St, WARWICK ☎ (0926) 491481 52⇄ ꜰ

WEST MIDLANDS

ALDRIDGE   Map 07 SK00

Druids Heath ☎ (0922) 55595
Testing, undulating heathland course.
18 holes, 6914yds, Par 72, SSS 73.
Club membership 635.
Visitors   must contact in advance & have handicap certificate. Weekend play permitted after 2pm.
Societies   must contact in advance.
Green Fees   £25 per day/round (£29.50 weekends).

Facilities 🏌 🍴 ♀ ⛳ 🏠 (Mark P Daubney.
Location   Stonnall Rd (NE side of town centre off A454)
Hotel   ★★★66% Fairlawns Hotel, 178 Little Aston
               Road,Aldridge, WALSALL
               ☎ (0922) 55122 35🛏 📶

BIRMINGHAM   Map 07 SP08

Brandhall ☎ 021-552 2195
Private golf club on municipal parkland course, easy walking,
good hazards. Testing holes: 1st-502 yds (par 5); 10th-455
yds dog-leg (par 5).
18 holes, 5734yds, Par 70.
Club membership 300.
Visitors   restricted weekends. Must contact in advance.
Societies   by arrangement.
Green Fees not confirmed.
Facilities ⊗ (ex Tue) 🍴 by prior arrangement 🍺 (ex Tue)
                ♀ (playing guests only) 🏠 ⛳ (G Mercer.
Location   Heron Rd, Oldbury, Warley (5.5m W of city
                centre off A4123)
Hotel   ★★★62% Forte Posthouse Birmingham, Chapel
                Ln, GREAT BARR ☎ 021-357 7444 192🛏 📶

Cocks Moors Woods Municipal ☎ 021-444 3584
Tree-lined, parkland course.
18 holes, 5888yds, Par 69, SSS 68.
Club membership 250.
Visitors   no restrictions.
Societies   must contact in advance.
Green Fees not confirmed.
Facilities ⛳ 🏠 ⛳
Location   Alcester Rd South, Kings Heath (5m S of city
                centre on A435)
Hotel   ★★★★58% Forte Crest, Smallbrook
                Queensway, BIRMINGHAM
                ☎ 021-643 8171 253🛏 📶

Edgbaston ☎ 021-454 1736
Parkland course in lovely country.
18 holes, 6118yds, Par 69, SSS 69.
Club membership 880.
Visitors   must contact in advance and have handicap
                certificate.
Societies   must apply in writing.
Green Fees £32 per day (£42 weekends & bank
                holidays); winter £25/£35.
Facilities ⊗ 🍴 by prior arrangement 🏌 🍺 ♀ ⛳ 🏠 (
                Andrew H Bownes.
Leisure   snooker.
Location   Church Rd, Edgbaston (1m S of city centre
                on B4217 off A38)
Hotel   ★★★★59% Plough & Harrow, Hagley Rd,
                Edgbaston, BIRMINGHAM
                ☎ 021-454 4111 44🛏 📶

Great Barr ☎ 021-358 4376
Parkland course with easy walking. Pleasant views of Barr
Beacon National Park.
18 holes, 6545yds, Par 73, SSS 72.
Club membership 600.
Visitors   restricted at weekends. Must have an
                introduction from own club.
Societies   must contact in writing.
Green Fees not confirmed.

Facilities ⊗ by prior arrangement 🍴 by prior arrangement
                🏌 🍺 ♀ ⛳ 🏠 ⛳ (S Doe.
Leisure   snooker.
Location   Chapel Ln, Great Barr (6m N of city centre off A
                34)
Hotel   ★★★62% Forte Posthouse Birmingham, Chapel
                Ln, GREAT BARR ☎ 021-357 7444 192🛏 📶

Handsworth ☎ 021-554 0599 & 021-554 3387
Undulating parkland course with some tight fairways but
subject to wind.
18 holes, 6272yds, Par 70, SSS 70.
Club membership 820.
Visitors   restricted weekends, bank holidays & Xmas.
                Must contact in advance and have a handicap
                certificate.
Societies   Mon-Fri only, must apply in writing.
Green Fees £25 per day.
Facilities ⊗ 🍴 🏌 🍺 ♀ ⛳ 🏠 (L Bashford.
Leisure   squash, snooker.
Location   Sunningdale Close, Handsworth Wood (3.5m
                NW of city centre off A4040)
Hotel   ★★★61% West Bromwich Moat House,
                Birmingham Rd, WEST BROMWICH
                ☎ 021-553 6111 180🛏 📶

Harborne ☎ 021-427 3058
Parkland course in hilly situation, with brook running
through.
18 holes, 6235yds, Par 70, SSS 70, Course record 65.
Club membership 616.
Visitors   must contact in advance & have a handicap
                certificate; may not play weekends, bank
                holidays or 27 Dec-1 Jan.
Societies   must telephone in advance.
Green Fees £29 per day/round.
Facilities ⊗ 🍴 🏌 🍺 (no catering weekends)
                ♀ ⛳ 🏠 ⛳ (Alan Quarterman.
Leisure   snooker.
Location   40 Tennal Rd, Harborne (3.5 m SW of city
                centre off A4040)
Hotel   ★★★★59% Plough & Harrow, Hagley Rd,
                Edgbaston, BIRMINGHAM
                ☎ 021-454 4111 44🛏 📶

Harborne Church Farm ☎ 021-427 1204
Parkland course with water hazards and easy walking. Some
holes might prove difficult.
9 holes, 2366yds, Par 66, SSS 63, Course record 63.
Club membership 250.
Visitors   no restrictions.
Green Fees £6 per round (18 holes); £3.30 (9 holes).
Facilities ⊗ 🍴 🏌 🍺 ⛳ 🏠 ⛳ (Mark J Hampton.
Location   Vicarage Rd, Harborne (3.5m SW of city centre
                off A4040)
Hotel   ★★★62% Apollo Hotel, 243-247 Hagley Rd,
                Edgbaston, BIRMINGHAM
                ☎ 021-455 0271 126🛏 📶

Hatchford Brook ☎ 021-743 9821
Fairly flat, municipal parkland course.
18 holes, 6200yds, Par 69, SSS 69.
Club membership 400.
Visitors   no restrictions.
Green Fees not confirmed.
Facilities ⛳ 🏠 ⛳ (P Smith.   ▶

Location Coventry Rd, Sheldon (6m E of city centre on A45)
Hotel ★★★61% Forte Posthouse, Coventry Rd, Elmdon, BIRMINGHAM AIRPORT
☎ 021-782 8141 136⇌ ℞

Hilltop ☎ 021-554 4463
Testing and hilly municipal parkland course.
18 holes, 6114yds, Par 71, SSS 69.
Club membership 400.
Visitors no restrictions.
Societies telephone in advance
Green Fees £6.60 per round.
Facilities ⊗ ⅢⅢ ┗ ■ ♀ ⌂ ⚐ ℓ Kevin Highfield.
Location Park Ln, Handsworth (3.5m N of city centre off A4040)
Hotel ★★★61% West Bromwich Moat House, Birmingham Rd, WEST BROMWICH
☎ 021-553 6111 180⇌ ℞

Moseley ☎ 021-444 2115
Parkland course with a lake, pond and stream to provide natural hazards. The par-3, 5th goes through a cutting in woodland to a tree and garden-lined amphitheatre, and the par-4, 6th entails a drive over a lake to a dog-leg fairway.
18 holes, 6285yds, Par 70, SSS 70, Course record 64.
Club membership 560.
Visitors may not play at weekends. Must contact in advance and have an introduction from own club.
Societies welcome.
Green Fees not confirmed.
Facilities ⊗ (ex Mon) ⅢⅢ by prior arrangement
┗ ■ ♀ ⌂ ⌂ ℓ G Edge.
Location Springfield Rd, Kings Heath (4m S of city centre on B4146 off A435)
Hotel ★★65% Norwood Hotel, 87-89 Bunbury Rd, Northfield, BIRMINGHAM
☎ 021-411 2202 15⇌ ℞

Rose Hill ☎ 021-453 3159
Hilly municipal course overlooking the city.
18 holes, 6010yds, Par 69, SSS 69, Course record 64.
Club membership 300.
Visitors may not play between 9 & 10.30am weekends.
Societies must contact in advance.
Green Fees £6.60 per round.
Facilities ⊗ ■ ♀ ⌂ ⌂ ⚐ ℓ Mike March.
Location Rosehill, Rednal (10m SW of city centre on B4096)
Hotel ★★65% Norwood Hotel, 87-89 Bunbury Rd, Northfield, BIRMINGHAM
☎ 021-411 2202 15⇌ ℞

Warley ☎ 021-429 2440
Municipal parkland course in Warley Woods.
9 holes, 2606yds, Par 33, SSS 64, Course record 62.
Club membership 150.
Visitors no restrictions.
Green Fees not confirmed.
Facilities ⊗ ┗ ■ ⌂ ⌂ ⚐ ℓ David Owen.
Location Lightswood Hill, Bearwood (4m W of city centre off A456)
Hotel ★★★62% Apollo Hotel, 243-247 Hagley Rd, Edgbaston, BIRMINGHAM
☎ 021-455 0271 126⇌ ℞

COVENTRY

Map 04 SP37

Ansty Golf Centre ☎ (0203) 621341
18-hole Pay and Play course of two 9-hole loops. Membership competitions for handicaps. Driving range and putting green.
18 holes, 5793yds, Par 71, SSS 69.
Visitors no restrictions.
Societies welcome.
Green Fees £9 per 18 holes; £4.50 per 9 holes (£11/£6 weekends).
Facilities ⊗ ⅢⅢ ┗ ■ ♀ ⌂ ⌂ ⚐ ℓ Andy Gorman, Rob Challis.
Leisure range & putting green.
Location Brinklow Rd, Ansty (3m from city centre via A4600)
Hotel ★★★70% Ansty Hall, ANSTY
☎ (0203) 612222 25⇌ ℞ Annexe6⇌ ℞

Coventry ☎ (0203) 414152
The scene of several major professional events, this undulating parkland course has a great deal of quality. More than that, it usually plays its length, and thus scoring is never easy, as many professionals have found to their cost.
18 holes, 6613yds, Par 73, SSS 72.
Club membership 760.
Visitors must contact in advance & have handicap certificate, but may not play at weekends.
Societies by arrangement.
Green Fees £30 per day.
Facilities ⊗ ⅢⅢ ┗ ■ ♀ ⌂ ⌂ ℓ Philip Weaver.
Leisure snooker.
Location Finham Park (3m S of city centre on A444)
Hotel ★★★62% Hylands Hotel, Warwick Rd, COVENTRY ☎ (0203) 501600 55⇌ ℞

Coventry Hearsall ☎ (0203) 713470
Parkland course with fairly easy walking. A brook provides an interesting hazard.
18 holes, 5603yds, Par 70, SSS 67, Course record 63.
Club membership 600.
Visitors with member only at weekends.
Societies by arrangement.
Green Fees not confirmed.
Facilities ⌂ ⌂ ℓ Jason Sawyer.
Location Beechwood Av (1.5m SW of city centre off A429)
Hotel ★★★62% Hylands Hotel, Warwick Rd, COVENTRY ☎ (0203) 501600 55⇌ ℞

The Grange ☎ (0203) 451465
Flat parkland course with very tight out of bounds on a number of holes, and a river which affects play on five of them. Well-bunkered, with plenty of trees.
9 holes, 6002yds, Par 72, SSS 69.
Club membership 300.
Visitors may not play after 2pm weekdays or before noon on Sun.
Societies must contact in advance.
Green Fees £10 per round (weekdays);£15 per day.
Facilities ♀ ⌂
Location Copsewood, Binley Rd (2m E of city centre on A428)
Hotel ★★★61% The Chace Hotel, London Rd, Willenhall, COVENTRY
☎ (0203) 303398 67⇌ ℞

Windmill Village ☎ (0203) 402065 & 407241
An 18-hole course over rolling parkland with lakes and ponds. Other leisure facilities available.
18 holes, 5101yds, Par 69, SSS 67, Course record 66.
Club membership 500.

Visitors	welcome except before noon at weekends. Must contact in advance.
Societies	telephone and confirm in writing.
Green Fees	£9.40 per 18 holes (£12.50 weekends).
Facilities	⊗ 川 ᒪ ▼ ♀ ᐃ ⚲ ⌂ 《 Robert Hunter.
Leisure	heated indoor swimming pool, fishing, snooker, sauna, solarium, gymnasium.
Location	Birmingham Rd, Allesley (off A45 W of Coventry)
Hotel	★★★69% Brooklands Grange Hotel & Restaurant, Holyhead Rd, COVENTRY ☎ (0203) 601601 30⇌ ✯

DUDLEY   Map 07 SO99

Dudley ☎ (0384) 233877
Exposed and very hilly parkland course.
18 holes, 5704yds, Par 69, SSS 68.
Club membership 350.

Visitors	may not play at weekends.
Societies	must contact in advance.
Green Fees	£18 per day; £15 per round.
Facilities	⊗ ᒪ ▼ ♀ ᐃ ⌂ 《 Paul Taylor.
Leisure	snooker.
Location	Turner's Hill, Rowley Regis, Warley (2m S of town centre off B4171)
Hotel	★★60% Station Hotel, Birmingham Rd, DUDLEY ☎ (0384) 253418 38⇌ ✯

Swindon ☎ Wombourne (0902) 897031
Attractive undulating woodland/parkland course, with spectacular views.
Old Course: 18 holes, 6042yds, Par 71, SSS 69.
New Course: 9 holes, 1135yds, Par 27.
Club membership 700.

Visitors	cannot bring narrow wheel trolleys.
Societies	Mon-Fri only, telephone in advance.
Green Fees	£15 per 18 holes (£25 weekends & bank holidays).
Facilities	⊗ 川 ᒪ ▼ ♀ ᐃ ⌂
Leisure	fishing, snooker.
Location	Bridgnorth Rd, Swindon
Hotel	★★60% Station Hotel, Birmingham Rd, DUDLEY ☎ (0384) 253418 38⇌ ✯

HALESOWEN   Map 07 SO98

Halesowen ☎ 021-501 3606
Parkland course in convenient position.
18 holes, 5754yds, Par 69, SSS 68, Course record 65.
Club membership 600.

Visitors	may not play weekends.
Societies	must apply in writing.
Green Fees	£16 per round.
Facilities	⊗ 川 ᒪ ▼ ♀ ᐃ ⌂ ⚲ 《 David Down.
Leisure	snooker.
Location	The Leasowes (1m E)
Hotel	★★★62% Apollo Hotel, 243-247 Hagley Rd, Edgbaston, BIRMINGHAM ☎ 021-455 0271 126⇌ ✯

KNOWLE   Map 07 SP17

Copt Heath ☎ (0564) 772650
Parkland course designed by H. Vardon.
18 holes, 6500yds, Par 71, SSS 71.
Club membership 700.

Visitors	must contact in advance & use yellow tees only. With member only weekends & bank holidays.
Societies	by arrangement.
Green Fees	£35 per day/round.
Facilities	⊗ 川 ᒪ ▼ ♀ ᐃ ⌂ 《 B J Barton.
Location	1220 Warwick Rd (On A41 0.25m S of junc 5 of M42)
Hotel	★★★63% St John's Swallow Hotel, 651 Warwick Rd, SOLIHULL ☎ 021-711 3000 177⇌ ✯

MERIDEN   Map 04 SP28

Forest of Arden Hotel Golf and Country Club
☎ Meridan (0676) 22335
Two parkland courses, set within the grounds of Packington Park, with extensive water hazards and offering a fine test of golf. On-site hotel with many leisure facilities.
Arden Course: 18 holes, 6472yds, Par 72, SSS 71.
Aylesford Course: 18 holes, 6258yds, Par 72, SSS 69.
Club membership 800.

Visitors	must have handicap certificate, but may not play weekends (unless hotel resident). Must contact in advance.
Societies	by arrangement.
Green Fees	not confirmed.
Facilities	⊗ 川 ᒪ ▼ ♀ ᐃ ⌂ ⛳ ⚲ 《 Mike Tarn.
Leisure	hard tennis courts, heated indoor swimming pool, squash, fishing, snooker, sauna, solarium, gymnasium, steam room, beauty salon.
Location	Maxstoke Ln (1m SW on B4102)
Hotel	★★★71% Forest of Arden Hotel, Golf & Country Club, Maxstoke Ln, MERIDEN ☎ (0676) 22335 152⇌ ✯ (See advertisement on p194)

North Warwickshire ☎ (0676) 22259
Parkland course with easy walking.
9 holes, 3186yds, Par 72, SSS 70, Course record 67.
Club membership 425.

Visitors	restricted Thu, weekends & bank holidays. Must contact in advance.
Societies	must apply in writing.
Green Fees	£18 per round.
Facilities	ᒪ & ▼ (ex Mon) ♀ ᐃ ⌂ 《 Simon Edwin.
Location	Hampton Ln (1m SW on B4102)
Hotel	★★★68% Manor Hotel, MERIDEN ☎ (0676) 22735 74⇌ ✯

SEDGLEY   Map 07 SO99

Sedgley Golf Centre ☎ (0902) 880503
Public Pay and Play course. Undulating contours and mature trees with extensive views over surrounding countryside.
9 holes, 3147yds, Par 72, SSS 71.
Club membership 150.

Visitors	booking advisable for weekends.
Societies	telephone in advance.

▶

FOREST OF ARDEN HOTEL
GOLF & COUNTRY CLUB

★★★

Venue for the
1993 Murphy's English Open Golf Championship

A superb Hotel Golf and Leisure Complex offering first class facilities and a choice of two 18 hole golf courses in a spectacular parkland setting.

The Arden Championship Course, 7096 yards par 72
The Aylesford Course, 6258 yards par 72

Visitors and societies welcome by prior arrangement.

Special midweek and weekend inclusive golf breaks and golf tuition holidays available.

For further information and a brochure please telephone

0676 22335

The Forest of Arden Hotel Golf and Country Club, Maxstoke Lane, Meriden, North Warwickshire

---

Green Fees £5.50 per 18 holes (£6 weekends); £3.50 per 9 holes (£4 weekends).
Facilities 🏊 (weekends) 🍺 ♀ (limited) 🏨 ♬ David Fereday.
Leisure driving range.
Location Sandyfields Rd (2m N of Dudley,on A459)
Hotel ★★★66% Himley Country Club & Hotel, School Rd, HIMLEY
☎ (0902) 896716 76➡️ 🐾

SOLIHULL   Map 07 SP17

Olton ☎ 021-705 1083
Parkland course with prevailing southwest wind.
18 holes, 6232yds, Par 69, SSS 71, Course record 63.
Club membership 600.
Visitors may not play Wed & with member only at weekends.
Societies by arrangement.
Green Fees £35 per day.
Facilities ⊗ & ♨ by prior arrangement 🏊 🍺 ♀ 🏨 ♬
Leisure snooker.
Location Mirfield Rd (1m NW off A41)
Hotel ★★★63% St John's Swallow Hotel, 651 Warwick Rd, SOLIHULL
☎ 021-711 3000 177➡️ 🐾

For an explanation of symbols and abbreviations, see page 11

Robin Hood ☎ 021-706 0061
Pleasant parkland course with easy walking and open to good views. Modern clubhouse.
18 holes, 6635yds, Par 72, SSS 72.
Club membership 700.
Visitors must contact in advance. With member only at weekends.
Societies must contact in advance.
Green Fees £33 per day; £28 per round.
Facilities 🍺 ♀ 🏊 🏨 ♬ R S Thompson.
Location St Bernards Rd (2m W off B4025)
Hotel ★★★63% St John's Swallow Hotel, 651 Warwick Rd, SOLIHULL
☎ 021-711 3000 177➡️ 🐾

Shirley ☎ 021-744 6001
Fairly flat parkland course.
18 holes, 6510yds, Par 72, SSS 71, Course record 68.
Club membership 500.
Visitors may not play bank holidays & with member only at weekends. Handicap certificate is required.
Societies must contact in advance.
Green Fees not confirmed.
Facilities ⊗ ♨ 🏊 🍺 ♀ 🏨 ♬ C J Wicketts.
Leisure snooker.
Location Stratford Rd, Monkpath (3m SW off A34)
Hotel ★★★67% Regency Hotel, Stratford Rd, Shirley, SOLIHULL
☎ 021-745 6119 112➡️ 🐾

STOURBRIDGE   Map 07 SO98

Hagley Golf & Country Club ☎ (0562) 883701
Undulating parkland course set beneath the Clent Hills; there are superb views. Testing 15th, par 5, 557 yards.
18 holes, 6353yds, Par 72, SSS 72.
Club membership 640.
Visitors restricted Wed & with member only at weekends.
Societies Mon-Fri only, must apply in writing.
Green Fees £25 per day; £20 per round.
Facilities ⊗ ♨ 🏊 🍺 ♀ 🏨 ♬ Iain Clark.
Leisure squash.
Location Wassell Grove, Hagley (1m E of Hagley off A456)
Hotel ★★64% Talbot Hotel, High St, STOURBRIDGE
☎ (0384) 394350 25rm(13➡️7 🐾)

Stourbridge ☎ (0384) 395566
Parkland course.
18 holes, 6178yds, Par 69, SSS 69, Course record 63.
Club membership 720.
Visitors may not play Wed mornings & weekends. Must have a handicap certificate.
Societies must apply in writing.
Green Fees not confirmed.
Facilities ⊗ ♨ by prior arrangement 🏊 🍺 ♀ 🏨 ♬ ♬ William H Firkins.
Leisure snooker.
Location Worcester Ln, Pedmore (2m from town centre)
Hotel ★★64% Talbot Hotel, High St, STOURBRIDGE
☎ (0384) 394350 25rm(13➡️7 🐾)

SUTTON COLDFIELD
Map 07 SP19

THE BELFRY See page 197

Little Aston ☎ 021-353 2066
Parkland course.
18 holes, 6724yds, par 72, SSS 73.
Club membership 250.
Visitors   must contact in advance & have handicap
certificate, but may not play at weekends.
Societies   must apply in writing.
Green fees   on application.
Facilities   ⊗ ⅏ ▟ ▆ ♀ ♨ 🏠 ℓ John Anderson.
Location   streetly (3.5m NW off A454)
Hotel   ★★★67% Moor Hall Hotel, Moor Hall Dr, Four
Oaks, SUTTON COLDFIELD
☎ 021-308 3751 75🛏 ☞

Moor Hall ☎ 021-308 6130
Parkland course. The 14th is a notable hole.
18 holes, 6249yds, par 70, SSS 70, course record 64.
Club membership 600.
Visitors   must contact in advance. with member only
weekends & bank holidays.
Societies   must apply in writing.
Green fees   £32 per day; £25 per round.
Facilities   ⊗ ⅏ ▟ ▆ ♀ ♨ 🏠 ⚑ ℓ Alan Partridge.
Leisure   snooker.
Location   Moor Hall Dr (2.5 m N of town centre off A453)
Hotel   ★★★67% Moor Hall Hotel, Moor Hall Dr, Four
Oaks, SUTTON COLDFIELD
☎ 021-308 3751 75🛏 ☞

Pype Hayes ☎ 021-351 1014
Attractive, fairly flat course with excellent greens.
18 holes, 5811yds, par 70.
Club membership 300.
Green fees   not confirmed.
Facilities   ⊗ ▆ ♨ 🏠 ⚑ ℓ James Bayliss.
Location   Eachelhurst Rd, Walmley (2.5m S off B4148)
Hotel   ★★★67% Marston Farm, Bodymoor Heath,
SUTTON COLDFIELD
☎ (0827) 872133 37🛏 ☞

Sutton Coldfield ☎ 021-353 9633
A fine natural, heathland course, with tight fairways, gorse,
heather and trees; which is surprising as the high-rise
buildings of Birmingham are not far away.
18 holes, 6541yds, par 72, SSS 71.
Club membership 600.
Visitors   must contact in advance & have handicap certificate.
Societies   must apply in writing.
Green fees   £30 per day.
Facilities   ⊗ ⅏ ▟ ▆ ♀ ♨ 🏠 ℓ Jerry Hayes.
Leisure   snooker.
Location   Thornhill Rd, Streetly (3m NW on B4138)
Hotel   ★★★67% Moor Hall Hotel, Moor Hall Dr, Four
Oaks, SUTTON COLDFIELD
☎ 021-308 3751 75🛏 ☞

If you know of a golf course that welcomes
visitors and is not already in this guide, we
should be grateful for information

Walmley ☎ 021-373 0029
Pleasant parkland course with many trees. The hazards are
not difficult.
18 holes, 6537yds, par 72, SSS 72, course record 67.
Club membership 700.
Visitors   with member only at weekends. must contact in
advance.
Societies   must contact in advance.
Green fees   £25 per round..
Facilities   ⊗ ⅏ ▟ ▆ (no catering mon) ♀ (ex mon)
♨ 🏠 ℓ M J Skerritt.
Leisure   snooker.
Location   Brooks Rd, Wylde Green (2m S off A5127)
Hotel   ★★★67% Marston Farm, Bodymoor Heath,
SUTTON COLDFIELD
☎ (0827) 872133 37🛏 ☞

WALSALL
Map 07 SP09

Bloxwich ☎ Bloxwich (0922) 405724
Undulating parkland course with natural hazards and subject
to strong north wind.
18 holes, 6286yds, Par 71, SSS 70, Course record 65.
Club membership 532.
Visitors   may not play at weekends.
Societies   must apply in writing.
Green Fees   not confirmed.
Facilities   ⊗ ⅏ ▟ ▆ ♀ ♨ 🏠 ℓ Gary Broadbent.
Leisure   snooker.
Location   Stafford Rd, Bloxwich (3m N of town centre on A34)
Hotel   ★★★58% Baron's Court Hotel, Walsall Rd,
Walsall Wood, WALSALL
☎ (0543) 452020 100🛏

Calderfields ☎ (0922) 640540
Parkland course with lake.
18 holes, 6590yds, Par 73, SSS 72.
Club membership 700.
Visitors no restrictions.
Societies telephone in advance.
Green Fees £12 per round (£16 weekends).
Facilities ⊗ 🏧 🛗 🍺 ♀ ⚒ 🏠 ⛳ (Roger Griffin.
Leisure fishing.
Location Aldridge Rd (on A454)
Hotel ★★★66% Fairlawns Hotel, 178 Little Aston Road, Aldridge, WALSALL
  ☎ (0922) 55122 35🛏 🏌

Walsall ☎ (0922) 613512
Well-wooded parkland course with easy walking.
18 holes, 6243yds, Par 70, SSS 70, Course record 66.
Club membership 700.
Visitors may not play weekends & bank holidays.
Societies must apply in writing.
Green Fees not confirmed.
Facilities ⊗ 🏧 🛗 🍺 ♀ ⚒ 🏠 ⛳ (Richard Lambert.
Leisure snooker.
Location The Broadway (1m S of town centre off A34)
Hotel ★★★62% Forte Posthouse, Birmingham Rd, WALSALL
  ☎ (0922) 33555 98🛏 🏌

WEST BROMWICH

Map 07 SP09

Dartmouth ☎ 021-588 2131
Meadowland course with undulating but easy walking. The 617 yd (par 5) first hole is something of a challenge.
9 holes, 6060yds, Par 71, SSS 70, Course record 66.
Club membership 350.
Visitors with member only at weekends.
Societies must apply in writing.
Green Fees not confirmed.
Facilities ⊗ & 🏧 by prior arrangement 🛗 🍺 ♀ ⚒ 🏠 (Nigel Wylie.
Leisure snooker.
Location Vale St (E side of town centre off A4041)
Hotel ★★★61% West Bromwich Moat House, Birmingham Rd, WEST BROMWICH
  ☎ 021-553 6111 180🛏 🏌

Sandwell Park ☎ 021-553 4637
Undulating parkland course situated in the Sandwell Valley.
18 holes, 6470yds, Par 71, SSS 72.
Club membership 600.
Visitors must contact in advance. With member only weekends.
Societies must apply in writing.
Green Fees £32.50 per day/round..
Facilities ⊗ 🏧 🛗 🍺 ♀ ⚒ 🏠 (Nigel Wylie.
Leisure snooker.
Location Birmingham Rd (SE side of town centre off A4040)
Hotel ★★★61% West Bromwich Moat House, Birmingham Rd, WEST BROMWICH
  ☎ 021-553 6111 180🛏 🏌

This guide is up-dated annually – make sure you use the up-to-date edition

---

WOLVERHAMPTON

Map 07 SO99

Oxley Park ☎ (0902) 20506
Parkland course with easy walking on the flat.
18 holes, 6028yds, Par 71, SSS 69.
Club membership 615.
Visitors must contact in advance. Must be introduced by member during winter weekends.
Societies must contact in advance.
Green Fees £22 per day (£24 weekends); £18 per round (£20 weekends).
Facilities ⊗ by prior arrangement 🛗 🍺 (No catering Sun/Mon) ♀ ⚒ 🏠 (Les Burlison.
Leisure snooker.
Location Stafford Rd, Bushbury (N of town centre off A449)
Hotel ★★68% Ely House Hotel, 53 Tettenhall Rd, WOLVERHAMPTON
  ☎ (0902) 311311 18🛏 🏌

Penn ☎ (0902) 341142
Heathland course just outside the town.
18 holes, 6465yds, Par 70, SSS 71, Course record 67.
Club membership 620.
Visitors must be member of recognised club, can only play weekdays & must use yellow tees.
Societies must apply in writing.
Green Fees £25 per day; £20 per round.
Facilities ⊗ & 🏧 (ex Sun & Mon) 🛗 🍺 (ex Mon & Wed) ♀ ⚒ 🏠 ⛳ (Alistair Briscoe.
Leisure snooker.
Location Penn Common, Penn (SW side of town centre off A449)
Hotel ★★★60% Park Hall Hotel, Park Drive, Goldthorn Park, WOLVERHAMPTON
  ☎ (0902) 331121 57🛏 🏌

South Staffordshire ☎ (0902) 751065
A parkland course.
18 holes, 6500yds, Par 71, SSS 71.
Club membership 570.
Visitors must contact in advance but may not play weekends & before 2pm Tue.
Societies must contact in advance.
Green Fees £25 per day/round.
Facilities ⊗ 🏧 🛗 🍺 ♀ ⚒ 🏠 (Jim Rhodes.
Leisure snooker.
Location Danescourt Rd, Tettenhall (3m NW off A41)
Hotel ★★68% Ely House Hotel, 53 Tettenhall Rd, WOLVERHAMPTON
  ☎ (0902) 311311 18🛏 🏌

Wergs ☎ (0902) 742225
Open parkland course.
18 holes, 6949yds, Par 72, SSS 73.
Club membership 300.
Visitors no restrictions.
Societies apply in writing.
Green Fees £15 per day (£20 weekends).
Facilities ⊗ 🏧 🛗 🍺 ♀ ⚒ 🏠
Location Keepers Ln, Tettenhall
Hotel ★★68% Ely House Hotel, 53 Tettenhall Rd, WOLVERHAMPTON
  ☎ (0902) 311311 18🛏 🏌

The Belfry

Sutton Coldfield ☎(0675) 470301   **Map 07 SP19**

John Ingham writes: When professional people are commissioned to turn a piece of farmland into a golf course and hotel complex, they are flattered - and delighted. This happened to Peter Alliss and Dave Thomas, two celebrated tournament competitors. The challenge they were offered: turn an unsympathetic piece of land into a good golf course. The resulting Belfry Golf Club was opened in 1977.

Since that date the two architects have every reason to be proud. The course, set in 370 acres of parkland, has staged more than one of the popular Ryder Cup matches, and the two courses - the Brabazon and the Derby - named after two Lords, have received thousands of visitors. These visitors have been entertained with a kindly reception, enhanced by a really excellent hotel.

In the sixteen years since its establishment, the saplings and newly-created greens have settled down very well and presented a worthwhile face to the world. One of the big challenges of The Belfry are the lakes and many water hazards that gobble up wild shots. Many a famous player, such as Seve Ballesteros, has had balls sinking without trace at the Brabazon's famously testing 18th hole. This monster requires the player to clear the lake twice in its 455-yard drive to reach an uphill, three-tiered, 60-yard long green.

As a public course, The Belfry is open to all-comers every day. This obviously means a great deal of traffic, although there are many other worthwhile courses in the West Midlands such as Handsworth and Little Aston. However, The Belfry is excellently managed and kept in top condition by a team now fully experienced in catering for every golfer.

In its fine parkland setting the club has become well known for its accommodation and fine business facilities and, being so well placed for the NEC, Birmingham and the international airport, it attracts a variety of golfers.

Visitors	must contact in advance. A handicap certificate is required for the Brabazon course
Societies	must telephone in advance
Green fees	Brabazon £50 per round; Derby £20 per round
Facilities	⊗ 爪 ㅏ ■ ♀ ♨ 🛆 🏠 ⛳ 🏌 ☏ (P McGovern and S Wordsworth)
Leisure	hard tennis courts, heated indoor swimming pool, squash, snooker, sauna, solarium. Nightclub in grounds of Belfry
Location	Lichfield Rd, Wishaw (exit junc 9 M42 4m E)

36 holes. Brabazon: 18 holes, 6975yds, Par 73, SSS 73. Course record 63
Derby: 18 holes, 5953yds Par 69, SSS 69

WHERE TO STAY AND EAT NEARBY

HOTELS:
WISHAW
★★★★68%The Belfry, Lichfield Rd.
☎ Curdworth (0675) 470301, 219 ⊷

★★★50% Moxhull Hall, Holly Lane.
☎ 021 - 329 2056, 21 ⊷ 🍴

LEA MARSTON
★★★64% Lea Marston Hotel and Leisure Complex.
☎ Curdworth (0675) 470468, 22 ⊷ 🍴

SUTTON COLDFIELD
★★★59% Sutton Court 60-66 Lichfield Rd. ☎ 021-3 55 6071, 56 ⊷ 🍴
Annexe 8 ⊷ 🍴

★★★★❀❀ 74% New Hall, Walmley Rd. ☎ 021-378 2442

WEST SUSSEX

ANGMERING   Map 04 TQ00

Ham Manor ☎ (0903) 783288
Two miles from the sea, this parkland course has fine springy turf and provides an interesting test in two loops of nine holes each.
18 holes, 6243yds, Par 70, SSS 70, Course record 62.
Club membership 850.
Visitors   must have a handicap certificate. Must contact in advance and have an introduction from own club.
Societies   must contact in writing.
Green Fees   not confirmed.
Facilities   ⊗ ∭ by prior arrangement
                 🏌 🍺 ♀ 🛄 🏡 ⚑ ⚐ Simon Buckley.
Leisure   snooker, bowling green, table tennis.
Location   0.75m SW
Hotel   ★★★58% Chatsworth Hotel, Steyne, WORTHING ☎ (0903) 236103 107⇔ �$

BOGNOR REGIS   Map 04 SZ99

Bognor Regis ☎ (0243) 865867
This flattish, parkland course has more variety than is to be found on some of the South Coast courses. The club is also known far and wide for its enterprise in creating a social atmosphere. The course is open to the prevailing wind.
18 holes, 6238yds, Par 70, SSS 70, Course record 64.
Club membership 650.
Visitors   restricted Tue; must play with member at weekends Apr-Oct. Must contact in advance and have a handicap certificate.
Societies   must contact in writing.
Green Fees   £25 per day or round (£30 weekends).
Facilities   ⊗ by prior arrangement 🏌 🍺 ♀ 🛄 🏡 ⚐ Robin P Day.
Location   Downview Rd, Felpham (1.5m NE off A259)
Hotel   ★62% Black Mill House Hotel, Princess Av, Aldwick, BOGNOR REGIS ☎ (0243) 821945 & 865596 22rm(18⇔ �$) Annexe4rm

CHICHESTER   Map 04 SU80

Chichester Golf Centre ☎ (0243) 533833
Set amongst lush farmland, this challenging course has four lakes which bring water into play on seven holes. The 2nd, 8th and 15th are particularly challenging holes. Floodlit driving range.
18 holes, 6177yds, Par 72, SSS 69, Course record 67.
Club membership 200.
Visitors   a strict dress code is in operation. It is advisable to contact in advance.
Societies   must contact in advance.
Green Fees   £17.50 per day; £12 per round (£25/£17.50 weekends).
Facilities   ⊗ 🍺 🛄 🏡 ⚑ ⚐ Carl Rota.
Leisure   covered floodlit driving range.

Location   Hoe Farm, Hunston (3m S of Chichester, on B2145 at Hunston)
Hotel   ★★★62% The Dolphin & Anchor, West St, CHICHESTER ☎ (0243) 785121 49⇔ �$

Goodwood ☎ (0243) 774968
Downland course designed by the master architect, James Braid. Many notable holes, particularly the finishing ones: 17 down an avenue of beech trees and 18 along in front of the terrace. Superb views of the downs and the coast.
18 holes, 6401yds, Par 72, SSS 71.
Club membership 900.
Visitors   must contact in advance and have handicap certificate.
Societies   must contact in writing.
Green Fees   not confirmed.
Facilities   ⊗ ∭ 🏌 🍺 ♀ 🛄 🏡 ⚐ K MacDonald.
Leisure   snooker.
Location   4.5m NE off A27
Hotel   ★★★66% Goodwood Park Hotel, Golf & Country Club, GOODWOOD ☎ (0243) 775537 89⇔ �$

COPTHORNE   Map 04 TQ33

Copthorne ☎ (0342) 712033 & 712508
Despite it having been in existence since 1892, this club remains one of the lesser known Sussex courses. It is hard to know why because it is most attractive with plenty of trees and much variety.
18 holes, 6505yds, Par 71, SSS 71, Course record 68.
Club membership 600.
Visitors   restricted at weekends after 1pm. Must contact in advance.
Societies   Thu & Fri only; must contact well in advance.
Green Fees   not confirmed.
Facilities   ⊗ ∭ (Wed evening) 🏌 🍺 ♀ 🛄 🏡 ⚐ Joe Burrell.
Location   Borers Arms Rd (E side of village junc 10 of M23 off A264)
Hotel   ★★★★63% Copthorne Hotel, Copthorne Rd, COPTHORNE ☎ (0342) 714971 227⇔ �$

Effingham Park ☎ (0342) 716528
Parkland course.
9 holes, 1749yds, Par 30, Course record 26.
Club membership 430.
Visitors   restricted at weekends after 1pm.
Green Fees   not confirmed.
Facilities   ⊗ 🏌 🍺 ♀ 🛄 🏡 ⚑ ⚐ Ian Dryden.
Leisure   heated indoor swimming pool, sauna, solarium, gymnasium, dance studio, jacuzzi, steam room.
Location   2m E on B2028
Hotel   ★★★★63% Copthorne Hotel, Copthorne Rd, COPTHORNE ☎ (0342) 714971 227⇔ �$

> A golf course name printed in ***bold italics*** means we have been unable to verify information with the club's management for the current year

CRAWLEY
Map 04 TQ23

Cottesmore ☎ (0293) 528256
The old North Course is undulating with four holes over water. The new South Course is shorter and less testing. But both are lined with silver birch, pine and oak, with rhododendrons ablaze in June.
Old Course: 18 holes, 6113yds, Par 72, SSS 70.
New South Course: 18 holes, 5469yds, Par 69, SSS 68.
Club membership 1300.
Visitors may only play after noon on Old Course at weekends. Must contact in advance.
Societies Mon, Wed & Fri Apr-1 Nov. Must contact in advance.
Green Fees not confirmed.
Facilities ⊗ ⅏ ⅃ ⬛ ♀ ♨ ⬜ ⚑ ⅃ Steve Laycock.
Leisure hard tennis courts, heated indoor swimming pool, squash, sauna, solarium, gymnasium.
Location Buchan Hill, Pease Pottage (3m SW 1m W of M23 junc 11)
Hotel ★★★58% Goffs Park Hotel, 45 Goffs Park Road, Crawley, CRAWLEY ☎ (0293) 535447 37⇆ ⚑ Annexe28⇆ ⚑

Gatwick Manor ☎ (0293) 538587
Interesting, pay and play short course.
9 holes, 2492yds, Par 56, SSS 50, Course record 24.
Club membership 63.
Visitors no restrictions.
Societies must telephone in advance.
Green Fees not confirmed.
Facilities ⊗ ⅏ ⅃ ⬛ ♀ ⬜ ⚑ ⅃ C Jenkins.
Location Lowfield Heath (2m N on A23)
Hotel ★★62% Gatwick Manor Hotel, London Rd, Lowfield Heath, Crawley, CRAWLEY ☎ (0293) 526301 & 535251 30⇆ ⚑

Ifield Golf & Country Club ☎ (0293) 520222
Parkland course.
18 holes, 6314yds, Par 70, SSS 70, Course record 66.
Club membership 800.
Visitors may not play after 3pm Fri; must play with member at weekends. Must contact in advance and have a handicap certificate.
Societies Mon-Wed afternoons & Thu.
Green Fees £27 per day; £20 per round.
Facilities ⊗ ⬛ ♀ ♨ ⬜ ⅃ Jon Earl.
Leisure squash, snooker.
Location Rusper Rd, Ifield (1m W side of town centre off A23)
Hotel ★★★59% George Hotel, High St, CRAWLEY ☎ (0293) 524215 86⇆ ⚑

HAYWARDS HEATH
Map 05 TQ32

Haywards Heath ☎ (0444) 414866
Pleasant parkland course with several challenging par 4s and 3s.
18 holes, 6204yds, Par 71, SSS 70.
Club membership 750.
Visitors must be a member of a recognised golf club and have a handicap certificate. Must contact in advance.
Societies Wed & Thu only

Green Fees £25 per round; £30 per day (£30 per round; £35 per day weekends & bank holidays).
Facilities ⊗ & ⅏ by prior arrangement ⅃ ⬛ ♀ ♨ ⬜ ⚑ ⅃ Michael Henning.
Location High Beech Ln (1.25m N off B2028)
Hotel ★★★75% Ockenden Manor, Ockenden Ln, CUCKFIELD ☎ (0444) 416111 22⇆ ⚑

Paxhill Park ☎ (0444) 484467 & 484000
A relatively flat parkland course designed by Patrick Tallack.
18 holes, 6172yds, Par 71, SSS 69, Course record 69.
Club membership 440.
Visitors welcome but may not play weekend mornings.
Societies must contact in advance.
Green Fees £20 per day; £12.50 per round (£17.50 per round weekends).
Facilities ⊗ ⅏ ⅃ ⬛ ♀ ♨ ⬜ ⚑ ⅃ Steve Dunkley.
Location East Mascalls Ln, Lindfield
Hotel ★★★60% The Birch Hotel, Lewes Rd, HAYWARDS HEATH ☎ (0444) 451565 53⇆ ⚑

LITTLEHAMPTON
Map 04 TQ00

Littlehampton ☎ (0903) 717170
A delightful seaside links in an equally delightful setting - and the only links course in the area.
18 holes, 6202yds, Par 70, SSS 70, Course record 66.
Club membership 650.
Visitors must have handicap certificate
Societies welcome Mon, Tue & Fri.
Green Fees £24 per day (£30 weekends).
Facilities ⊗ ⅃ ⬛ ♀ ♨ ⬜ ⅃
Location Rope Walk, West Beach (1m W off A259)
Hotel ★★★64% Norfolk Arms Hotel, High St, ARUNDEL ☎ (0903) 882101 21⇆ Annexe13⇆

MANNINGS HEATH
Map 04 TQ22

Mannings Heath ☎ Horsham (0403) 210228
The course meanders up hill and down dale over heathland with streams affecting 11 of the holes. Wooded valleys protect the course from strong winds. Famous holes at 12th (the 'Waterfall', par 3), 13th (the 'Valley', par 4).
18 holes, 6402yds, Par 73, SSS 71, Course record 66.
Club membership 710.
Visitors must contact in advance & have handicap certificate.
Societies must contact in advance.
Green Fees not confirmed.
Facilities ⊗ ⅏ ⅃ ⬛ ♀ ♨ ⬜ ⚑ ⅃ Peter Harrison.
Location Goldings Ln (N side of village)
Hotel ★★★★♨♨74% South Lodge Hotel, Brighton Rd, LOWER BEEDING ☎ (0403) 891711 39⇆

MIDHURST
Map 04 SU82

Cowdray Park ☎ (0730) 813599
Parkland course, hard walking up to 4th green.
18 holes, 6212yds, Par 70, SSS 70, Course record 68.
Club membership 700.
Visitors may play after 9am on weekdays, 11am Sat & 3pm Sun. Must contact in advance and have a handicap certificate.

▶

Societies must contact in writing.
Green Fees £20 per day/round (£25 weekends & bank holidays).
Facilities ⊗ ⅷ by prior arrangement Ꮭ 🖤 ♀ ⚸ 🏠 🏌 ₹ Stephen Hall.
Location 1m E on A272
Hotel ★★★68% Spread Eagle Hotel, South St, MIDHURST ☎ (0730) 816911 37⇄ ℟ Annexe4 ℟

PULBOROUGH

Map 04 TQ01

West Sussex ☎ (0798) 872563
Heathland course.
18 holes, 6221yds, Par 68, SSS 70, Course record 61.
Club membership 800.
Visitors must contact in advance and have a handicap certificate. Must contact in advance and have an introduction from own club.
Societies Wed & Thu only. Must contact in advance.
Green Fees on application.
Facilities ⊗ Ꮭ 🖤 ♀ ⚸ 🏠 ₹ Tim Packham.
Location Golf Club Ln, Wiggon Holt (1.5m E off A283)
Hotel ★★★64% Roundabout Hotel, Monkmead Ln, WEST CHILTINGTON ☎ (0798) 813838 23⇄ ℟

PYECOMBE

Map 04 TQ21

Pyecombe ☎ (0273) 845372
Typical downland course on the inland side of the South Downs. Hilly, but magnificent views.
18 holes, 6278yds, Par 71, SSS 70, Course record 71.
Club membership 624.
Visitors may not play after 9.15 weekdays, 2pm Sat & 3pm Sun.
Societies must contact in advance.
Green Fees £18 per day; £15 per round (£25 weekends).
Facilities ⊗ ⅷ by prior arrangement Ꮭ 🖤 ♀ ⚸ 🏠 🏌 ₹ C R White.
Location Clayton Hill (E side of village on A273)
Hotel ★★67% Whitehaven Hotel, 34 Wilbury Rd, HOVE ☎ (0273) 778355 17⇄ ℟

SELSEY

Map 04 SZ89

Selsey ☎ (0243) 602203
Fairly difficult seaside course, exposed to wind and has natural ditches.
9 holes, 5932yds, Par 68, SSS 68.
Club membership 433.
Visitors must have a handicap certificate, and play with member at weekends.
Societies must contact in writing.
Green Fees not confirmed.
Facilities ⊗ & ⅷ (ex Tue) Ꮭ 🖤 ♀ ⚸ 🏠 ₹ Peter Grindley.
Leisure hard tennis courts, bowling green.
Location Golf Links Ln (1m N off B2145)
Hotel ★★★62% The Dolphin & Anchor, West St, CHICHESTER ☎ (0243) 785121 49⇄ ℟

WEST CHILTINGTON

Map 04 TQ01

West Chiltington ☎ (0798) 813574
The Main Course is situated on gently undulating, well-drained greensand and offers panoramic views of the Sussex Downs. Three large double greens provide an interesting feature to this new course. Also 9-hole short course and 13-bay driving range.
18 holes, 6000yds, Par 70, SSS 69, Course record 67 or 9 holes, 3000yds, Par 28.
Club membership 750.
Visitors it is advisable to contact the club in advance for weekends. Tee times can be booked in advance.
Societies telephone for booking form.
Green Fees not confirmed.
Facilities ⊗ ⅷ Ꮭ 🖤 ♀ (all day) ⚸ 🏠 🏌 ₹ B Barnes & R Tisdall.
Leisure driving range.
Location Broadford bridge Rd (on N side of village)
Hotel ★★★64% Roundabout Hotel, Monkmead Ln, WEST CHILTINGTON ☎ (0798) 813838 23⇄ ℟

WORTHING

Map 04 TQ10

Hill Barn Municipal ☎ (0903) 37301
Downland course with views of both Isle of Wight and Brighton.
18 holes, 6224yds, Par 70, SSS 70.
Club membership 1000.
Visitors no restrictions.
Societies must telephone in advance.
Green Fees not confirmed.
Facilities ⊗ ⅷ Ꮭ 🖤 ♀ ⚸ 🏠 🏌 ₹ A Higgins.
Leisure croquet.
Location Hill Barn Ln (N side of town at junction of A24/A27)
Hotel ★★★58% Chatsworth Hotel, Steyne, WORTHING ☎ (0903) 236103 107⇄ ℟

Worthing ☎ (0903) 60801
The High Course, short and tricky with entrancing views, will provide good entertainment. 'Lower Course' is considered to be one of the best downland courses in the country.
Lower Course: 18 holes, 6519yds, Par 71, SSS 72, Course record 66.
Upper Course: 18 holes, 5243yds, Par 66, SSS 66.
Club membership 1146.
Visitors must contact in advance and have an introduction from own club.
Societies must contact in writing 6 months in advance.
Green Fees not confirmed.
Facilities ⊗ ⅷ (Fri) Ꮭ 🖤 ♀ ⚸ 🏠 ₹ S Rolley.
Leisure snooker.
Location Links Rd (N side of town centre off A27)
Hotel ★★65% Ardington Hotel, Steyne Gardens, WORTHING ☎ (0903) 230451 55rm(52⇄ ℟)

> Entries with a shaded background identify courses that are considered to be particularly interesting

WEST YORKSHIRE

ALWOODLEY
Map 08 SE24

Alwoodley ☎ Leeds (0532) 681680
A fine heathland course with length, trees and abundant heather. Many attractive situations - together a severe test of golf.
18 holes, 6686yds, Par 72, SSS 72, Course record 67.
Club membership 250.
Visitors   must contact in advance, restricted Tue, weekends & bank holidays.
Societies   must apply in advance.
Green Fees £35 per day/round.
Facilities ⊗ Ⅶ ┗ ♥ ♀ ♨ 🏠 ☇ John Green.
Location   Wigton Ln (5m N off A61)
Hotel   ★★★66% Harewood Arms Hotel, Harrogate Rd, HAREWOOD
☎ (0532) 886566 24⇔ 🐾

BAILDON
Map 07 SE13

Baildon ☎ (0274) 595162
Moorland course with much bracken rough. The 5th is a hard climb.
18 holes, 6225yds, Par 70, SSS 70, Course record 64.
Club membership 600.
Visitors   restricted Tue & weekends.
Societies   may not play Tue & weekends; must contact in advance.
Green Fees not confirmed.
Facilities ⊗ Ⅶ by prior arrangement ┗ ♥ (no catering Mon) ♀ (ex Mon) ♨ 🏠 ☇ R Masters.
Leisure   snooker.
Location   Moorgate (N off A6038)
Hotel   ★★★69% Hollings Hall, Hollins Hall, Baildon, SHIPLEY ☎ (0274) 530053 59⇔ 🐾

BINGLEY
Map 07 SE13

Bingley St Ives ☎ Bradford (0274) 562436
Parkland/moorland course.
18 holes, 6312yds, Par 71, SSS 71.
Club membership 650.
Visitors   restricted Mon-Fri after 4.30pm & Sat.
Societies   must apply in advance.
Green Fees £25 per day; £20 per round.
Facilities ⊗ Ⅶ ┗ ♥ ♀ ♨ 🏠 ☇ Ray Firth.
Leisure   snooker.
Location   The Mansion, St Ives Estate, Harden (0.75m W off B6429)
Hotel   ★★★65% Oakwood Hall Hotel, Lady Ln, BINGLEY ☎ (0274) 564123 & 563569 16⇔ 🐾

BRADFORD
Map 07 SE13

Bradford Moor ☎ (0274) 638313
Parkland course, hard walking.
9 holes, 5880yds, Par 70, SSS 68, Course record 67.
Club membership 376.
Visitors   no restrictions.
Societies   must contact in advance.

Green Fees £8 per round (£10 weekends).
Facilities ⊗ Ⅶ ┗ ♥ ♀ ♨ 🏠 ☇ ☇ Ron Hughes.
Leisure   snooker.
Location   Scarr Hall, Pollard Ln (2m NE of city centre off A658)
Hotel   ★★66% Park Drive Hotel, 12 Park Dr, BRADFORD ☎ (0274) 480194 11⇔ 🐾

Clayton ☎ (0274) 880047
Moorland course, difficult in windy conditions.
9 holes, 5407yds, Par 68, SSS 67, Course record 63.
Club membership 350.
Visitors   may not play after 4pm on Sun.
Societies   must contact in advance.
Green Fees not confirmed.
Facilities ⊗ Ⅶ ┗ ♥ (no catering Mon) ♀ (not Mon) ♨
Leisure   snooker.
Location   Thornton View Rd, Clayton (2.5m W of city centre on A647)
Hotel   ★★★57% Novotel Bradford, Merrydale Rd, BRADFORD ☎ (0274) 683683 132⇔ 🐾

East Bierley ☎ (0274) 681023
Hilly moorland course with narrow fairways. Two par 3 holes over 200 yds.
9 holes, 4700yds, Par 64, SSS 63.
Club membership 200.
Visitors   restricted Sat (am), Sun & Mon evening. Must contact in advance.
Societies   must apply in writing.
Green Fees £10 per day (£12.50 weekends).
Facilities ⊗ Ⅶ ┗ ♥ ♀ ♨
Leisure   snooker.
Location   South View Rd, East Bierley (4m SE of city centre off A650)
Hotel   ★★★57% Novotel Bradford, Merrydale Rd, BRADFORD ☎ (0274) 683683 132⇔ 🐾

Headley ☎ (0274) 833481
Hilly moorland course, short but very testing, windy, fine views.
9 holes, 4914yds, Par 64, SSS 64.
Club membership 350.
Visitors   must play with member at weekends. Must contact in advance.
Societies   must telephone in advance.
Green Fees £10 weekdays.
Facilities ⊗ ┗ ♥ (catering summer only) ♀ (summer only) ♨
Location   Headley Ln, Thornton (4m W of city centre off B6145 at Thornton)
Hotel   ★★66% Park Drive Hotel, 12 Park Dr, BRADFORD ☎ (0274) 480194 11⇔ 🐾

Phoenix Park ☎ (0274) 667573
Very short, tight, moorland course, rather testing.
9 holes, 2491yds, Par 66, SSS 64, Course record 66.
Club membership 260.
Visitors   restricted weekends.
Societies   must apply in advance.
Green Fees not confirmed.
Facilities ♀ ♨ 🏠
Location   Phoenix Park, Thornbury (E side of city centre on A647)
Hotel   ★★66% Park Drive Hotel, 12 Park Dr, BRADFORD ☎ (0274) 480194 11⇔ 🐾

Queensbury ☎ (0274) 882155
Undulating woodland/parkland course.
9 holes, 5400yds, Par 66, SSS 65, Course record 64.
Club membership 400.
Visitors restricted weekends. Must have a handicap
certificate.
Societies must apply in advance.
Green Fees £13 per day (£20 weekends & bank holidays).
Facilities ⊗ ﹚Ⅲ by prior arrangement 🍴 ♨ ♀ ♿ 🏌 ✆ 🏌 🏌
Geoff Howard.
Leisure snooker.
Location Brighouse Rd, Queensbury (4m from Bradford
on A647)
Hotel ★★66% Park Drive Hotel, 12 Park Dr,
BRADFORD ☎ (0274) 480194 11⇔ ♙

South Bradford ☎ (0274) 679195
Hilly course with good greens, trees and ditches. Interesting
short 2nd hole (par 3) 200 yds, well-bunkered and played
from an elevated tee.
9 holes, 6028yds, Par 70, SSS 69.
Club membership 305.
Visitors restricted competition days and before 3.30pm
weekends and bank holidays unless
accompanied by member.
Societies must apply in writing.
Green Fees £12 per day (£20 weekends & bank holidays).
Facilities ⊗ 🍴 & ♨ ♀ ♿ ✆ 🏌
Leisure snooker.
Location Pearson Rd, Odsal (2m S of city centre off A638)
Hotel ★★★57% Novotel Bradford, Merrydale Rd,
BRADFORD ☎ (0274) 683683 132⇔ ♙

West Bowling ☎ (0274) 724449
Undulating, tree-lined parkland course. Testing hole: 'the
coffin' short par 3, very narrow.
18 holes, 5657yds, Par 69, SSS 67.
Club membership 400.
Visitors restricted before 9.30am, 12-1.30pm &
weekends. Must contact in advance and have a
letter of introduction.
Societies must apply in writing.
Green Fees £22 day/round (£28 weekends).
Facilities ⊗ ﹚Ⅲ by prior arrangement 🍴 ♨ ♀ ♿ ✆ 🏌 🏌
Allan Swaine.
Leisure snooker.
Location Newall Hall, Rooley Ln (S side of city centre
off A638)
Hotel ★★★57% Novotel Bradford, Merrydale Rd,
BRADFORD ☎ (0274) 683683 132⇔ ♙

West Bradford ☎ West Bradford (0274) 542767
Parkland course, windy, especially 3rd, 4th, 5th and 6th
holes. Hilly but not hard.
18 holes, 5741yds, Par 69, SSS 68.
Club membership 440.
Visitors restricted Sat.
Societies must apply in writing.
Green Fees £15 per day (£22 weekends).
Facilities ⊗ ﹚Ⅲ 🍴 ♨ ♀ (ex Mon) ♿ ✆ 🏌 Nigel M
Barber.
Leisure snooker.
Location Chellow Grange Rd (W side of city centre
off B6269)
Hotel ★★★69% Hollings Hall, Hollins Hall, Baildon,
SHIPLEY ☎ (0274) 530053 59⇔ ♙

CLECKHEATON
Map 08 SE12

Cleckheaton & District ☎ (0274) 851266
Parkland course with gentle hills.
18 holes, 5769yds, Par 71, SSS 68.
Club membership 550.
Visitors must contact in advance and have an
introduction from own club.
Societies weekdays only; must contact in advance.
Green Fees not confirmed.
Facilities ⊗ (ex Mon) ﹚Ⅲ by prior arrangement 🍴 (ex
2pm-4pm) ♨ (ex 2pm-4pm) ♀ ♿ ✆ 🏌 🏌 Mike
Ingham.
Leisure snooker.
Location Bradford Rd (1.5m NW on A638 junc 26 M62)
Hotel ★★★57% Novotel Bradford, Merrydale Rd,
BRADFORD ☎ (0274) 683683 132⇔ ♙

DEWSBURY
Map 08 SE22

Hanging Heaton ☎ (0924) 461606
Arable land course, easy walking, fine views. Testing 4th
hole (par 3).
9 holes, 5400mtrs, Par 69, SSS 67.
Club membership 550.
Visitors must play with member at weekends & bank
holidays. Must contact in advance.
Societies must telephone in advance.
Green Fees £12 per day.
Facilities ⊗ ﹚Ⅲ by prior arrangement (no catering Mon)
♀ (ex Mon) ♿ ✆ 🏌
Leisure snooker.
Location White Cross Rd (0.75m NE off A653)
Hotel ★★★60% Forte Posthouse, Queen's Dr, Ossett,
WAKEFIELD ☎ (0924) 276388 99⇔ ♙

ELLAND
Map 07 SE12

Elland ☎ (0422) 372505
Parkland course.
9 holes, 2815yds, Par 66, SSS 66, Course record 64.
Club membership 300.
Visitors must be members of recognised golf club.
Green Fees £12 (£20 weekends and bank holidays).
Facilities ⊗ ﹚Ⅲ (ex Mon) 🍴 ♨ (dinner by arrangement)
♀ ♿ ✆ 🏌 Michael Allison.
Location Hammerstones, Leach Ln (1m SW)
Hotel ★★★★64% Forte Crest, Clifton Village,
BRIGHOUSE ☎ (0484) 400400 94⇔ ♙

FENAY BRIDGE
Map 08 SE11

Woodsome Hall ☎ Huddersfield (0484) 602971
Historic clubhouse; parkland course with views.
18 holes, 6080yds, Par 70, SSS 69.
Club membership 900.
Visitors must contact in advance & have handicap
certificate. Restricted weekends & competitions.
Societies must apply in writing.
Green Fees £25 per day/round (£30 weekends & bank
holidays).
Facilities ⊗ ﹚Ⅲ 🍴 ♨ (no catering Mon) ♀ ♿ ✆ 🏌
Michael Higginbottom.
Leisure snooker.

Location	1.5m SW off A629
Hotel	★★★66% The George Hotel, St George's Square, HUDDERSFIELD ☎ (0484) 515444 59rm(47⇥)

GARFORTH

Map 08 SE43

Garforth ☎ Leeds (0532) 862021
Parkland course with fine views, easy walking.
18 holes, 6005yds, Par 69, SSS 69.
Club membership 500.

Visitors	must contact in advance and have handicap certificate. With member only weekends & bank holidays.
Societies	must apply in advance.
Green Fees	£26 per day; £21 per round.
Facilities	⊗ ⅢⅠ ⓛ ▆ ♀ ⚲ 📷 ⚐ ⚑ K Findlater.
Leisure	snooker.
Location	1m N
Hotel	★★★65% Stakis Leeds Windmill Hotel, Ring Rd, Seacroft, LEEDS ☎ (0532) 732323 100⇥ ⚑

GUISELEY

Map 08 SE14

Bradford ☎ (0943) 875570
Moorland course with eight par 4 holes of 360 yds or more.
18 holes, 6259yds, Par 71, SSS 71.
Club membership 600.

Visitors	must have a handicap certificate. May not play Sun.
Societies	welcome Mon-Fri, must apply in advance.
Green Fees	£25 per day/round (£32 weekends).
Facilities	⊗ ⅢⅠ ⓛ ▆ ♀ ⚲ 📷 ⚑
Leisure	snooker.
Location	Hawksworth Ln (SW side of town centre off A6038)
Hotel	★★★53% Cow & Calf Hotel, Moor Top, ILKLEY ☎ (0943) 607335 20⇥ ⚑

HALIFAX

Map 07 SE02

Halifax ☎ (0422) 244171
Hilly moorland course crossed by streams, natural hazards, and offering fine views. Testing 172-yd 17th (par3).
18 holes, 6037yds, Par 70, SSS 70, Course record 64.
Club membership 500.

Visitors	restricted competition days. Must contact in advance.
Societies	must apply in advance.
Green Fees	£20 per day (£30 weekends); with handicap certificate £15 per day (£25 weekends).
Facilities	⊗ ⅢⅠ ⓛ ▆ (No catering Mon) ♀ ⚲ 📷 ⚑ Steven Foster.
Leisure	snooker.
Location	Bob Hall, Union Ln, Ogden (4m NW off A629)
Hotel	★★★73% Holdsworth House Hotel, Holmfield, HALIFAX ☎ (0422) 240024 40⇥ ⚑

Lightcliffe ☎ (0422) 202459
Heathland course.
9 holes, 5388yds, Par 68, SSS 68.
Club membership 545.

Visitors	must be a member of a recognised Golf Club.
Societies	must contact 21 days in advance.
Green Fees	£12 (£16 weekends).
Facilities	⊗ ⅢⅠ by prior arrangement ⓛ ▆ ♀ ⚲ 📷 ⚑ Warren Locketty.
Location	Knowle Top Rd, Lightcliffe (3.5m E on A58)
Hotel	★★★73% Holdsworth House Hotel, Holmfield, HALIFAX ☎ (0422) 240024 40⇥ ⚑

West End ☎ (0422) 353608
Semi-moorland course.
18 holes, 6003yds, Par 68, SSS 69, Course record 65.
Club membership 530.

Visitors	may play between 10am-2pm. Must contact in advance & have handicap certificate.
Societies	must apply in writing.
Green Fees	£20 per day; £15 per round (£25/£18 weekends & bank holidays).
Facilities	⊗ ⅢⅠ ⓛ ▆ ♀ ⚲ 📷 ⚑ David Rishworth.
Leisure	snooker.
Location	Paddock Ln, Highroad Well (W side of town centre off A646)
Hotel	★★★73% Holdsworth House Hotel, Holmfield, HALIFAX ☎ (0422) 240024 40⇥ ⚑

HEBDEN BRIDGE

Map 07 SD92

Hebden Bridge ☎ (0422) 842896
Moorland course with splendid views.
9 holes, 5113yds, Par 68, SSS 65, Course record 63.
Club membership 300.

Visitors	advisable to contact in advance, restricted competition days.
Societies	by arrangment with directors.
Green Fees	£7.50 per round (£10 weekends).
Facilities	⊗ by prior arrangement ⅢⅠ by prior arrangement ⓛ ▆ (no catering Mon) ♀ ⚲
Location	Mount Skip, Wadsworth (1.5m E off A6033)
Hotel	★★68% Hebden Lodge Hotel, New Rd, HEBDEN BRIDGE ☎ (0422) 845272 12⇥ ⚑

HOLYWELL GREEN

Map 07 SE01

Halifax Bradley Hall ☎ Halifax (0422) 374108
Moorland/parkland course, tightened by recent tree planting, easy walking.
18 holes, 6213yds, Par 70, SSS 70, Course record 65.
Club membership 608.

Visitors	no restrictions.
Societies	must apply in writing.
Green Fees	£22 per day; £18 per round (£30/£25 weekends & bank holidays).
Facilities	⊗ ⅢⅠ ⓛ ▆ (no catering Mon & Tue) ♀ ⚲ 📷 ⚑ Peter Wood.
Leisure	snooker.
Location	S on A6112
Hotel	★★68% Rock Inn Hotel & Churchills Restaurant, HOLYWELL GREEN ☎ (0422) 379721 18⇥ ⚑

HUDDERSFIELD Map 07 SE11

Bradley Park ☎ (0484) 539988
Parkland course, challenging with good mix of long and short holes. Also 14-bay floodlit driving range and 9-hole par 3 course, ideal for beginners. Superb views.
18 holes, 6220yds, Par 70, SSS 70.
Par 3: 9 holes, 1019yds, Par 27.
Club membership 300.
Visitors must contact for weekend play.
Societies welcome midweek only, must apply by letter.
Green Fees not confirmed.
Facilities ⊗ ⅷ by prior arrangement ⬧ ♨ ♀ ⚐ ⚲ ⚑ ⚍ Parnel Reilly.
Leisure 14 bay floodlit driving range.
Location Off Bradley Rd (3m N on A6107)
Hotel ★★★66% The George Hotel, St George's Square, HUDDERSFIELD
☎ (0484) 515444 59rm(47⇨)

Crosland Heath ☎ (0484) 653216
Moorland course with fine views over valley.
18 holes, 5972yds, Par 70, SSS 70.
Club membership 350.
Visitors must contact in advance and have an introduction from own club.
Societies must telephone in advance.
Green Fees not confirmed.
Facilities ⊗ ⅷ ⬧ ♨ ♀ ⚐ ⚑ ⚍ Richard Jessop.
Location Felk Stile Rd, Crosland Heath (SW off A62)
Hotel ★★★66% The George Hotel, St George's Square, HUDDERSFIELD
☎ (0484) 515444 59rm(47⇨)

Huddersfield ☎ (0484) 426203
A testing heathland course of championship standard laid out in 1891.
18 holes, 6364yds, Par 71, SSS 71.
Club membership 730.
Visitors restricted Tue (Ladies Day). Must contact in advance.
Societies welcome Mon-Fri, must apply in writing.
Green Fees not confirmed.
Facilities ⊗ ⅷ ⬧ ♨ by prior arrangement ♀ (by prior arrangement) ⚐ ⚑ ⚍ Paul Carman.
Leisure snooker.
Location Fixby Hall, Lightridge Rd, Fixby (2m N off A641)
Hotel ★★★66% The George Hotel, St George's Square, HUDDERSFIELD
☎ (0484) 515444 59rm(47⇨)

Longley Park ☎ (0484) 422304
Lowland course.
9 holes, 5269yds, Par 66, SSS 66.
Club membership 440.
Visitors must contact in advance & have handicap certificate, restricted Thu & weekends.
Societies must apply in writing.
Green Fees £11.50 per round (£14 weekends).
Facilities ⊗ ⅷ ⬧ ♨ (no catering Mon) ♀ ⚐ ⚑ ⚍ Neil Suckling.
Location Maple St, Off Somerset Rd (0.5m SE of town centre off A629)
Hotel ★★★66% The George Hotel, St George's Square, HUDDERSFIELD
☎ (0484) 515444 59rm(47⇨)

ILKLEY Map 07 SE14

Ben Rhydding ☎ (0943) 608759
Moorland/parkland course with splendid views over the Wharfe valley.
9 holes, 4711yds, Par 65, SSS 64.
Club membership 300.
Visitors may only play with member at weekends. No visitors before noon on Sun.
Green Fees £10 per day/round (£15 per day/round bank holidays).
Location High Wood, Ben Rhydding (SE side of town)
Hotel ★★76% Rombalds Hotel & Restaurant, 11 West View, Wells Rd, ILKLEY
☎ (0943) 603201 15⇨ ⚑

Ilkley ☎ (0943) 600214
This beautiful parkland course is situated in Wharfedale and the Wharfe is a hazard on each of the first seven holes. In fact, the 3rd is laid out entirely on an island in the middle of the river.
18 holes, 6262yds, Par 69, SSS 70.
Club membership 500.
Visitors advisable to contact in advance.
Societies welcome except Tue, Fri & weekends.
Green Fees not confirmed.
Facilities ⊗ ⅷ ⬧ ♨ ♀ ⚐ ⚑ ⚍ John L Hammond.
Leisure fishing, snooker.
Location Middleton (W side of town centre off A65)
Hotel ★★76% Rombalds Hotel & Restaurant, 11 West View, Wells Rd, ILKLEY
☎ (0943) 603201 15⇨ ⚑

KEIGHLEY Map 07 SE04

Branshaw ☎ Haworth (0535) 643235 & 647441
Picturesque moorland course with fairly narrow fairways and good greens. Extensive views.
18 holes, 5858yds, Par 69, SSS 69.
Club membership 500.
Visitors must contact professional in advance.
Societies telephone professional (0535) 647441.
Green Fees £15 per day (£20 weekends).
Facilities ⊗ ⅷ ⬧ ♨ ♀ ⚐ ⚑ ⚍ John Nolan.
Location Branshaw Moor, Oakworth (2m SW on B6143)
Hotel ★★68% Dalesgate Hotel, 406 Skipton Rd, Utley, KEIGHLEY
☎ (0535) 664930 21⇨ ⚑

Keighley ☎ (0535) 604778
Parkland course with good views down the Aire Valley.
18 holes, 6149yds, Par 69, SSS 70, Course record 65.
Club membership 600.
Visitors restricted Sat & Sun. Must contact in advance.
Societies must apply in advance.
Green Fees £25 per day; £21 per round (£27/23 weekends).
Facilities ⊗ ⅷ ⬧ ♨ ♀ ⚐ ⚑ ⚍ Mike Bradley.
Location Howden Park, Utley (1m NW of town centre off B6143)
Hotel ★★68% Dalesgate Hotel, 406 Skipton Rd, Utley, KEIGHLEY
☎ (0535) 664930 21⇨ ⚑

LEEDS

Map 08 SE33

Brandon ☎ (0532) 737471
An 18-hole links type course enjoying varying degrees of
rough, water and sand hazards.
18 holes, 3650yds, Par 58, SSS 62, Course record 57.
Club membership 100.
Visitors must have own set of golf clubs.
Societies must telephone in advance.
Green Fees £7 (£8 weekend & bank holidays).
Facilities �b ⚑ 🏠
Location Holywell Ln, Shadwell
Hotel ★★★65% Stakis Leeds Windmill Hotel, Ring
Rd, Seacroft, LEEDS
☎ (0532) 732323 100⇌ 🐾

Gotts Park ☎ (0532) 638232
Municipal parkland course; very hilly in part.
18 holes, 4960yds, Par 65, SSS 64, Course record 63.
Club membership 250.
Visitors no restrictions.
Green Fees £5.75 per round (£6.75 weekends & bank
holidays).
Facilities Cafeteria 🏠 ⚑ ﹖ John K Simpson.
Location Armley Ridge Rd (3m W of city centre off
A647)
Hotel ★★★★66% The Queen's, City Square, LEEDS
☎ (0532) 431323 188⇌ 🐾

Headingley ☎ (0532) 679573
An undulating course with a wealth of natural features
offering fine views from higher ground. Its most striking
hazard is the famous ravine at the 18th. Leeds's oldest course,
founded in 1892.
18 holes, 6298yds, Par 69, SSS 70, Course record 64.
Club membership 630.
Visitors must contact in advance. Restricted before 9.30
& 12-1.45pm.
Societies must telephone in advance and confirm in
writing.
Green Fees £30 per day; £25 per round (£36 per day/round
weekends & bank holidays).
Facilities ⊗ ⅲ �b ▦ ♀ ⚑ 🏠 ﹖ Andrew Dyson.
Leisure snooker.
Location Back Church Ln, Adel (5.5m N of city centre
off A660)
Hotel ★★★67% Forte Crest Leeds/Bradford, Leeds
Rd, BRAMHOPE
☎ (0532) 842911 126⇌ 🐾

Horsforth ☎ (0532) 586819
Moorland course overlooking airport.
18 holes, 6243yds, Par 71, SSS 70, Course record 66.
Club membership 750.
Visitors restricted Sat & with member only Sun.
Societies must apply in writing.
Green Fees not confirmed.
Facilities ⊗ ⅲ �b ▦ ♀ ⚑ 🏠 ﹖ Laurie Turner.
Leisure snooker.
Location Layton Rise, Layton Rd, Horsforth (6.5m NW of
city centre off A65)
Hotel ★★★67% Forte Crest Leeds/Bradford, Leeds
Rd, BRAMHOPE
☎ (0532) 842911 126⇌ 🐾

Leeds ☎ (0532) 658775
Parkland course with pleasant views.
18 holes, 6097yds, Par 69, SSS 69.
Club membership 600.
Visitors with member only weekends, yellow tees only.
Must contact in advance.
Societies must apply in writing.
Green Fees £25 per day; £19 per round.
Facilities ⊗ ⅲ �b ▦ (catering limited Mon) ♀ ⚑ 🏠 ﹖ ﹖
Simon Longster.
Leisure snooker.
Location Elmete Ln (5m NE of city centre on A6120 off
A58)
Hotel ★★★65% Stakis Leeds Windmill Hotel, Ring
Rd, Seacroft, LEEDS
☎ (0532) 732323 100⇌ 🐾

Middleton Park Municipal ☎ (0532) 700449
Parkland course.
18 holes, 5263yds, Par 68, SSS 66, Course record 65.
Club membership 300.
Visitors no restrictions.
Green Fees £6.20 per round (£6.75 weekends).
Facilities ⚑ ﹖
Location Middleton Park, Middleton (3m S off A653)
Hotel ★★★65% Stakis Leeds Windmill Hotel, Ring
Rd, Seacroft, LEEDS
☎ (0532) 732323 100⇌ 🐾

Moor Allerton ☎ (0532) 661154
The Moor Allerton Club has 27 holes set in 220 acres of
undulating parkland, with magnificent views extending
across the Vale of York. The Championship Course was
designed by Robert Trent Jones, the famous American
course architect, and is the only course of his design in
the British Isles.
Lakes: 18 holes, 6314yds, Par 71, SSS 72.
Blackmoor: 18 holes, 6502yds, Par 71, SSS 72.
High Course: 18 holes, 6672yds, Par 72, SSS 73.
Club membership 1000.
Visitors restricted Sun.
Societies must apply in advance.
Green Fees £35 per day (£45 Sat).
Facilities ⊗ ⅲ by prior arrangement (ex weekends)
�b ▦ ♀ ⚑ 🏠 ﹖ Richard Lane.
Leisure snooker, sauna, 6 bay covered driving range.
Location Coal Rd, Wike (5.5m N of city centre on
A61)
Hotel ★★★66% Harewood Arms Hotel,
Harrogate Rd, HAREWOOD
☎ (0532) 886566 24⇌ 🐾

Moortown ☎ (0532) 686521
Championship course, tough but fair. Springy moorland
turf, natural hazards of heather, gorse and streams,
cunningly placed bunkers and immaculate greens.
18 holes, 6826yds, Par 71, SSS 74.
Club membership 550.
Visitors weekend by prior arrangement
Societies must apply in advance.
Green Fees £40 per day; £35 per round (£45/£40
weekends).
Facilities ⊗ ⅲ �b ▦ ♀ ⚑ 🏠 ﹖ Byron Hutchinson.
Leisure snooker. ▶

Location	Harrogate Rd, Alwoodley (6m N of city centre on A61)
Hotel	★★★66% Harewood Arms Hotel, Harrogate Rd, HAREWOOD ☎ (0532) 886566 24➪ ♠

Oulton Hall ☎ (0532) 823152
27-hole championship-length municipal course. Although municipal, a dress rule is applied. 16-bay driving range.
27 holes, 6550yds, Par 71, SSS 70.
Visitors must wear golf shoes and abide by dress rules.
Societies contact in advance.
Green Fees £6.20 (£6.75 weekends).
Facilities ⊗ ㋪ ♜ ♀ ⚐ ⛳
Leisure driving range.
Location Rothwell (junc 30 on M62)
Hotel Oulton Hall, ROTHWELL
☎ (0925) 65050 146➪ ♠

Roundhay ☎ (0532) 662695
Attractive municipal parkland course, natural hazards, easy walking.
9 holes, 5166yds, Par 65, SSS 70.
Club membership 350.
Visitors no restrictions.
Societies must apply in advance to Leeds City Council.
Green Fees £5.80 per round (£6.15 weekends & bank holidays).
Facilities ⚐ ⛳ Jim Pape.
Location Park Ln (4m NE of city centre off A58)
Hotel ★★★65% Stakis Leeds Windmill Hotel, Ring Rd, Seacroft, LEEDS
☎ (0532) 732323 100➪ ♠

Sand Moor ☎ (0532) 685180
A beautiful, undulating course overlooking Lord Harewood's estate and the Eccup Reservoir. The course is wooded with some holes adjacent to water. The 12th is perhaps the most difficult where the fairway falls away towards the reservoir.

18 holes, 6429yds, Par 71, SSS 71, Course record 62.
Club membership 553.
Visitors restricted weekends & bank holidays. Must contact in advance and have an introduction from own club.
Societies must apply in advance.
Green Fees not confirmed.
Facilities ⊗ ⅏ (Mon-Fri) ♜ ♀ ⚐ ⛳ Mr J R Foss.
Leisure snooker.
Location Alwoodley Ln (5m N of city centre off A61)
Hotel ★★★67% Forte Crest Leeds/Bradford, Leeds Rd, BRAMHOPE
☎ (0532) 842911 126➪ ♠

South Leeds ☎ (0532) 700479
Parkland couse, windy, hard walking, good views.
18 holes, 5769yds, Par 69, SSS 68.
Club membership 632.
Visitors must contact in advance & have handicap certificate. No play weekends & bank holidays.
Societies must apply in advance.
Green Fees £18 per day/round.
Facilities ⊗ ⅏ ㋪ & ♜ by prior arrangement (no catering Mon) ♀ (ex Mon) ⚐ ⛳ Mike Lewis.

Location Gipsy Ln, Beeston (3m S of city centre off A653)
Hotel ★★★★66% The Queen's, City Square, LEEDS
☎ (0532) 431323 188➪ ♠

Temple Newsam ☎ (0532) 645624
Two parkland courses. Testing long 13th (563 yds) on second course.
Lord Irwin: 18 holes, 6460yds, Par 69, SSS 71.
Lady Dorothy: 18 holes, 6276yds, Par 70, SSS 70.
Club membership 520.
Visitors no restrictions.
Societies must apply in advance.
Green Fees £6.20 per day (£6.75 weekends).
Facilities ⊗ (weekends only) ㋪ ♜ (weekends only) ♀ ⚐ ⛳ David Bulmer.
Leisure snooker.
Location Temple-Newsam Rd (3.5m E of city centre off A63)
Hotel ★★★65% Stakis Leeds Windmill Hotel, Ring Rd, Seacroft, LEEDS
☎ (0532) 732323 100➪ ♠

MARSDEN
Map 07 SE01

Marsden ☎ (0484) 844253
Moorland course with good views, natural hazards, windy.
9 holes, 5702yds, Par 68, SSS 68.
Club membership 200.
Visitors must play with member at weekends.
Societies Mon-Fri; must contact in advance.
Green Fees £10 per day.
Facilities ⊗ ⅏ ㋪ ♜ ♀ ⚐ ⛳ A J Bickerdike.
Leisure hard tennis courts.
Location Mount Rd, Hemplow (S side off A62)
Hotel ★★★61% Briar Court Hotel, Halifax Road,Birchencliffe, HUDDERSFIELD
☎ (0484) 519902 48➪ ♠

MELTHAM
Map 07 SE01

Meltham ☎ Huddersfield (0484) 850227
Parkland course with good views. Testing 548 yd, 13th hole (par 5).
18 holes, 6145yds, Par 70, SSS 70, Course record 65.
Club membership 535.
Visitors restricted Sat & Wed (Ladies Day).
Societies must apply in advance.
Green Fees £20 per day (£25 weekends & bank holidays).
Facilities ⊗ ⅏ ㋪ ♜ ♀ ⚐ ⛳ Paul Davies.
Leisure snooker.
Location Thick Hollins Hall (SE side of village off B6107)
Hotel ★★★66% The George Hotel, St George's Square, HUDDERSFIELD
☎ (0484) 515444 59rm(47➪)

MIRFIELD
Map 08 SE21

Dewsbury District ☎ (0924) 492399
Heathland/parkland course with panoramic view from top, hard walking. Ponds in middle of 3rd fairway, left of 5th green and 17th green.
18 holes, 6248yds, Par 71, SSS 71.
Club membership 650.

Visitors restricted weekends before 4pm & bank holidays. Must contact in advance.
Societies must apply in advance.
Green Fees not confirmed.
Facilities ⊗ ⍲ ⅃ ⚑ ♀ ♨ 🛎 ⛳ 🍴
Leisure snooker.
Location Sands Ln (1m S off A644)
Hotel ★★★66% The George Hotel, St George's Square, HUDDERSFIELD ☎ (0484) 515444 59rm(47⇌)

MORLEY
Map 08 SE22

Howley Hall ☎ Batley (0924) 478417
Parkland course with easy walking and good views.
18 holes, 6029yds, Par 71, SSS 69.
Club membership 500.
Visitors standard course only. Must contact in advance.
Societies must apply in writing.
Green Fees £22 per day; £18 per round (£25 day/round weekends).
Facilities ♀ 🛎 🍴
Location Scotchman Ln (1.5m S on B6123)
Hotel ★★66% Alder House Hotel, Towngate Rd, off Healey Ln, BATLEY ☎ (0924) 444777 22rm(21⇌🐾)

NORMANTON
Map 08 SE32

Normanton ☎ Wakefield (0924) 892943
A pleasant, flat course with tight fairways in places and an internal out of bounds requiring accuracy.
9 holes, 5288yds, Par 66, SSS 66.
Club membership 250.
Visitors may not play on Sun.
Societies mid-week only.
Green Fees not confirmed.
Facilities ⊗ ⍲ ⅃ ⚑ ♀ ♨ 🛎 ⛳ 🍴 Martin Evans.
Location Snydale Rd (0.5m SE on B6133)
Hotel ★★★61% Swallow Hotel, Queens St, WAKEFIELD ☎ (0924) 372111 64⇌🐾

OSSETT
Map 08 SE22

Low Laithes ☎ (0924) 273275
Testing parkland course.
18 holes, 6463yds, Par 72, SSS 71.
Club membership 575.
Visitors may not play weekends and bank holidays. Must contact in advance.
Societies welcome Mon-Fri, must apply in advance.
Green Fees £20 per day/round.
Facilities ⊗ ⍲ ⅃ ⚑ ♀ ♨ 🛎 ⛳ 🍴 P Browning.
Location Parkmill Ln, Flushdyke (1.5m SE off A128)
Hotel ★★★63% Forte Posthouse Northampton/Rugby, CRICK ☎ (0788) 822101 88⇌🐾

Use the AA *Hotels* or *Bed and Breakfast*
Guides to extend your choice of
accommodation

OTLEY
Map 08 SE24

Otley ☎ (0943) 465329
An expansive course with magnificent views across Wharfe-dale. It is well-wooded with streams crossing the fairway. The 4th is a fine hole which generally needs two woods to reach the plateau green. The 17th is a good short hole.
18 holes, 6235yds, Par 70, SSS 70.
Club membership 700.
Visitors restricted Sat.
Societies must apply in writing.
Green Fees £23 per day (£28 weekends & bank holidays).
Facilities ⊗ & ⍲ by prior arrangement ⅃ ♀ ♨ 🛎 🍴 Simon Poot.
Leisure snooker.
Location Off West Busk Ln (1.5m SW off A6038)
Hotel ★★★67% Forte Crest Leeds/Bradford, Leeds Rd, BRAMHOPE ☎ (0532) 842911 126⇌🐾

OUTLANE
Map 07 SE01

Outlane ☎ Halifax (0422) 374762
Moorland course.
18 holes, 6003yds, Par 71, SSS 69, Course record 67.
Club membership 500.
Visitors must contact in advance but may not play Sat & before 10.30am Sun.
Societies must contact 14 days in advance.
Green Fees £18 per day (£25 weekends & bank holidays).
Facilities ⊗ (ex Mon) ⍲ by prior arrangement ⅃ (ex Mon) ♀ ♨ 🛎 ⛳ 🍴 David Chapman.
Location Slack Ln (S side of village off A640)
Hotel ★★★66% Old Golf House Hotel, New Hey Rd, OUTLANE ☎ (0422) 379311 50⇌🐾

PONTEFRACT
Map 08 SE42

Mid Yorkshire ☎ (0977) 704522
An 18-hole championship-standard course opened in 1992.
18 holes, 6500yds, Par 72, SSS 72, Course record 68.
Club membership 500.
Visitors must contact in advance, with member only at weekends.
Societies apply in writing to the secretary.
Green Fees £25.
Facilities ⊗ ⍲ ⅃ ⚑ ♀ ♨ 🛎 ⛳ ⛳ 🍴 Peter Scott.
Leisure golf academy with 28 driving bays.
Location Havercroft Ln, Darrington (2m W)
Hotel ★★★🏊65% Wentbridge House Hotel, WENTBRIDGE ☎ (0977) 620444 12⇌🐾

Pontefract & District ☎ (0977) 792241
Parkland course.
18 holes, 6227yds, Par 72, SSS 70.
Club membership 800.
Visitors welcome except Wed & weekends. Must contact in advance and have a handicap certificate.
Societies welcome except Wed & weekends.
Green Fees £24 per day (£30 weekends & bank holidays).
Facilities ♨ 🛎 🍴 J Coleman.
Location Park Ln (1.5m W on B6134)
Hotel ★★★🏊65% Wentbridge House Hotel, WENTBRIDGE ☎ (0977) 620444 12⇌🐾

PUDSEY
Map 08 SE23

Fulneck ☎ (0532) 565191
Picturesque, hilly parkland course. Compact but strenuous.
9 holes, 5432yds, Par 67, SSS 65, Course record 64.
Club membership 300.
Visitors must contact in advance. With member only weekends & bank holidays.
Societies must apply in writing.
Green Fees £12 per round.
Facilities ⊗ ℍ ⓛ ☕ (catering by prior arrangement) ♀ ⛰
Leisure pool table.
Location S side of town centre
Hotel ★★★57% Novotel Bradford, Merrydale Rd, BRADFORD ☎ (0274) 683683 132⇆ ♟

Woodhall Hills ☎ (0532) 564771
Meadowland course, prevailing SW winds, fairly hard walking. Testing holes: 8th, 377 yd (par 4); 14th, 206 yd (par 3).
18 holes, 6102yds, Par 71, SSS 69, Course record 66.
Club membership 612.
Visitors restricted Mon-Fri until 9.30am.
Societies must apply in writing.
Green Fees not confirmed.
Facilities ⊗ ℍ ⓛ ☕ by prior arrangement ♀ ⛰ ⓑ ℓ Darren Tear.
Leisure snooker.
Location Calverley (2.5m NW off A647)
Hotel ★★66% Park Drive Hotel, 12 Park Dr, BRADFORD ☎ (0274) 480194 11⇆ ♟

RAWDON
Map 08 SE23

Rawdon Golf & Lawn Tennis Club ☎ (0532) 506040
Undulating parkland course.
9 holes, 5980yds, Par 72, SSS 69.
Club membership 700.
Visitors must contact in advance & have handicap certificate. With member only at weekends.
Societies must contact in advance.
Green Fees £10 per day.
Facilities ⊗ ℍ ⓛ ☕ ♀ ⛰ ⓑ ℓ Syd Wheldon.
Leisure hard and grass tennis courts, snooker.
Location Buckstone Dr (S side of town off A65)
Hotel ★★★67% Forte Crest Leeds/Bradford, Leeds Rd, BRAMHOPE ☎ (0532) 842911 126⇆ ♟

RIDDLESDEN
Map 07 SE04

Riddlesden ☎ Keighley (0535) 602148
Undulating moorland course with two quarry hazards, prevailing west winds, some hard walking and beautiful views.
18 holes, 4247yds, Par 63, SSS 61.
Club membership 250.
Visitors restricted before 2pm weekends.
Societies must apply in writing.
Green Fees £10 per day (£15 weekends).
Facilities ⊗ ℍ ⓛ ☕ ♀ ⛰
Location Howden Rough (1m NW)
Hotel ★★68% Dalesgate Hotel, 406 Skipton Rd, Utley, KEIGHLEY ☎ (0535) 664930 21⇆ ♟

SCARCROFT
Map 08 SE34

Scarcroft ☎ Leeds (0532) 892311
Undulating parkland course with prevailing west wind and easy walking.
18 holes, 6031yds, Par 71, SSS 69.
Club membership 667.
Visitors must contact in advance
Societies must contact in advance.
Green Fees £30 per day; £25 per round (£35 weekends & bank holidays).
Facilities ⊗ ℍ (ex Sun & Mon) ⓛ ☕ ♀ (ex Sun) ⛰ ⓑ ℸ ℓ Martin Ross.
Leisure snooker.
Location Syke Ln (0.5m N of village off A58)
Hotel ★★★65% Stakis Leeds Windmill Hotel, Ring Rd, Seacroft, LEEDS ☎ (0532) 732323 100⇆ ♟

SHIPLEY
Map 07 SE13

Northcliffe ☎ Bradford (0274) 584085
Parkland course with magnificent views of moors. Testing 1st hole (18th green 100 feet below tee).
18 holes, 5839yds, Par 71, SSS 68.
Club membership 657.
Visitors no restrictions.
Societies must apply in writing.
Green Fees £20 per day (£25 weekends & bank holidays).
Facilities ⊗ ℍ ⓛ ☕ ♀ ⛰ ⓑ ℸ ℓ M Hillas.
Leisure snooker.
Location High Bank Ln (1.25m SW off A650)
Hotel ★★★69% Hollings Hall, Hollins Hall, Baildon, SHIPLEY ☎ (0274) 530053 59⇆ ♟

SILSDEN
Map 07 SE04

Silsden ☎ Steeton (0535) 652998
Tight downland course which can be windy. Good views of the Aire Valley.
14 holes, 4870yds, Par 65, SSS 64, Course record 61.
Club membership 300.
Visitors may not play before 11am on Sun.
Societies must apply in advance.
Green Fees £10 per day (£16 weekends).
Facilities ⊗ ℍ ⓛ (catering by prior arrangement) ☕ ♀ ⛰
Location High Brunthwaite (1m E)
Hotel ★★68% Dalesgate Hotel, 406 Skipton Rd, Utley, KEIGHLEY ☎ (0535) 664930 21⇆ ♟

SOWERBY
Map 07 SE02

Ryburn ☎ Halifax (0422) 831355
Moorland course, easy walking.
9 holes, 4984yds, Par 66, SSS 64, Course record 64.
Club membership 200.
Visitors must contact in advance.
Societies apply in writing.
Green Fees £15 (£20 weekends & bank holidays).
Facilities ⊗ ℍ ⓛ & ☕ by prior arrangement ♀ ⛰

Location The Shaw, Norland (1m S of Sowerby Bridge off A58)
Hotel ★★70% The Hobbit Hotel, Hob Ln, Norland, SOWERBY BRIDGE
☎ (0422) 832202 17⇄ ⋔Annexe5⇄ ⋔

TODMORDEN
Map 07 SD92

Todmorden ☎ (0706) 812986
Pleasant moorland course.
9 holes, 5818yds, Par 68, SSS 68.
Club membership 180.
Visitors restricted Sat (pm) & competition days.
Societies must contact in advance.
Green Fees £15 per day (£20 weekends).
Facilities ⊗ ⫛ ⤧ & ⬤ (Thu-Sun. Other times by prior arrangement) ⵌ ⌂
Location Rive Rocks, Cross Stone Rd (NE off A646)
Hotel ★★★64% Scaitcliffe Hall, Burnley Rd, TODMORDEN
☎ (0706) 818888 13⇄ ⋔

WAKEFIELD
Map 08 SE32

City of Wakefield ☎ (0924) 367442 & 360282
Parkland course.
18 holes, 6299yds, Par 72, SSS 70.
Club membership 850.
Visitors restricted weekends.
Societies must apply in advance.
Green Fees £7.20 per day/round (£9.60 weekends & bank holidays).
Facilities ⊗ & ⫛ by prior arrangement
⤧ ⬤ ⵌ ⌂ ⋔ Roger Holland.
Location Lupset Park, Horbury Rd (1.5m W of city centre on A642)
Hotel ★★★60% Forte Posthouse, Queen's Dr, Ossett, WAKEFIELD ☎ (0924) 276388 99⇄ ⋔

Painthorpe House ☎ (0924) 255083
Undulating meadowland course, easy walking.
9 holes, 4520yds, Par 62, SSS 62, Course record 66.
Club membership 150.
Visitors restricted weekends.
Societies must apply in advance.
Green Fees not confirmed.
Facilities ⊗ ⫛ ⤧ & ⬤ by prior arrangement
⬤ by prior arrangement ⵌ ⌂
Leisure bowling green.
Location Painthorpe Ln, Painthorpe, Crigglestone (2m S off A636)
Hotel ★★★60% Forte Posthouse, Queen's Dr, Ossett, WAKEFIELD ☎ (0924) 276388 99⇄ ⋔

Wakefield ☎ (0924) 255104
A well-sheltered meadowland/heath course with easy walking and good views.
18 holes, 6611yds, Par 72, SSS 72, Course record 66.
Club membership 550.
Visitors strict dress code.
Societies must apply in writing.
Green Fees £25 per day/round (£27 weekends & bank holidays).
Facilities ⊗ ⫛ ⤧ ⬤ ⵌ ⌂ ⋔ I M Wright.
Leisure snooker.

Location Woodthorpe Ln, Sandal (3m S off A61)
Hotel ★★★60% Forte Posthouse, Queen's Dr, Ossett, WAKEFIELD ☎ (0924) 276388 99⇄ ⋔

WETHERBY
Map 08 SE44

Wetherby ☎ (0937) 582527
Parkland course with fine views.
18 holes, 5888yds, Par 69, SSS 68.
Club membership 750.
Societies welcome Mon & Wed-Fri, must apply in writing.
Green Fees not confirmed.
Facilities ⊗ ⫛ ⤧ ⬤ ⵌ ⌂ ⋔
Location Linton Ln (1m W off A661)
Hotel ★★★60% Wetherby Resort Hotel, Leeds Rd, WETHERBY ☎ (0937) 583881 72⇄ ⋔

WIGHT, ISLE OF

COWES
Map 04 SZ49

Cowes ☎ (0983) 292303
Fairly level, tight parkland course with difficult par 3s and Solent views.
9 holes, 5934yds, Par 70, SSS 68, Course record 66.
Club membership 300.
Visitors restricted Thu, Fri & Sun mornings.
Societies must contact in writing.
Green Fees not confirmed.
Facilities ⊗ ⤧ ⬤ ⵌ ⋔
Location Crossfield Av (NW side of town)
Hotel ★★62% Fountain Hotel, High St, COWES ☎ (0983) 292397 20⇄

EAST COWES
Map 04 SZ59

Osborne ☎ (0983) 295421
Undulating parkland course in the grounds of Osborne House. Quiet and peaceful situation.
9 holes, 6276yds, Par 70, SSS 70, Course record 66.
Club membership 350.
Visitors restricted Tue 9am-1pm & weekends before noon. Handicap certificate required.
Societies must contact in advance.
Green Fees £16 per day (£19 weekends & bank holidays).
Facilities ⊗ ⫛ by prior arrangement ⤧ ⬤ ⵌ ⌂ ⋔ Andrew Scullion.
Location Osborne House Estate (E side of town centre off A3021)
Hotel ★★59% Cowes Hotel, 260 Artic Rd, COWES ☎ (0983) 291541 15⇄ ⋔

FRESHWATER
Map 04 SZ38

Freshwater Bay ☎ (0983) 752955
A downland/seaside links with wide fairways and spectacular coastal views of the Solent and Channel.
18 holes, 5662yds, Par 68, SSS 68, Course record 64.
Club membership 600.
▶

Visitors may not play before 9.30am weekdays & 10am Sun.
Societies must telephone in advance.
Green Fees £18 per day (£22 weekends & bank holidays).
Facilities ⊗ ⅶ 🍴 🛍 🍺 ♀ ♨ ⛳
Location Afton Down (0.5m E of village off A3055)
Hotel ★★★59% Albion Hotel, FRESHWATER
☎ (0983) 753631 42⇄ ℟

NEWPORT   Map 04 SZ48

Newport ☎ (0983) 525076
Downland course, fine views.
9 holes, 5704yds, Par 68, SSS 67, Course record 64.
Club membership 300.
Visitors may not play after 3pm Sat & noon Sun.
Societies must telephone in advance.
Green Fees not confirmed.
Facilities 🍴 🍺 ♀ ♨ 🍴 ⛳
Location St George's Down (1.5m S off A3020)
Hotel ★★★57% Melville Hall Hotel, Melville St, SANDOWN ☎ (0983) 406526 33⇄ ℟

RYDE   Map 04 SZ59

Ryde ☎ (0983) 614809
Downland course with wide views over the Solent.
9 holes, 5287yds, Par 66, SSS 66.
Club membership 375.
Visitors may not play Wed afternoons & Sun mornings.
Societies must contact in writing.
Green Fees not confirmed.
Facilities ⊗ ⅶ 🍴 🍺 ♀ ♨ 🍴
Location Binstead Rd (1m W on A3054)
Hotel ★★65% Biskra House Beach Hotel, 17 Saint Thomas's St, RYDE
☎ (0983) 67913 9⇄ ℟

SANDOWN   Map 04 SZ58

Shanklin & Sandown ☎ (0983) 403217
Heathland course.
18 holes, 6000yds, Par 70, SSS 68, Course record 65.
Club membership 720.
Visitors must be member of a recognised club with a handicap certificate. Must contact in advance.
Societies limited bookings; telephone in advance.
Green Fees £20/25.
Facilities ⊗ & ⅶ by prior arrangement
🍴 🍺 ♀ ♨ 🍴 ⛳ ℣ Peter Hammond.
Location Fairway, Lake (1m NW)
Hotel ★★★59% Cliff Tops Hotel, Park Rd, SHANKLIN ☎ (0983) 863262 88⇄ ℟

VENTNOR   Map 04 SZ57

Ventnor ☎ (0983) 853326
Downland course subject to wind. Fine seascapes.
9 holes, 5752yds, Par 70, SSS 68, Course record 73.
Club membership 200.
Visitors may not play Fri noon-3.30pm or Sun mornings.
Societies must contact in advance.
Green Fees not confirmed.
Facilities 🍴 🍺 ♀ ♨ ⛳

Leisure pool table.
Location Steep Hill Down Rd, Upper Ventnor (1m NW off B3327)
Hotel ★★★62% Ventnor Towers Hotel, Madeira Rd, VENTNOR ☎ (0983) 852277 27rm(26⇄ ℟)

WILTSHIRE

BISHOPS CANNINGS   Map 04 SU06

North Wilts ☎ (038086) 627
High, downland course with fine views.
18 holes, 6484yds, Par 72, SSS 71, Course record 67.
Club membership 800.
Visitors welcome, a handicap certificate is required at weekends.
Societies must book in advance.
Green Fees £25 per day; £18 per round (£30 weekends, £15 after 4pm).
Facilities ⊗ ⅶ 🍴 🍺 ♀ ♨ 🍴 ℣ Graham Laing.
Leisure practice grounds.
Location 2m NW
Hotel ★★★62% Bear Hotel, Market Place, DEVIZES ☎ (0380) 722444 24⇄ ℟

CASTLE COMBE   Map 03 ST87

Castle Combe ☎ Chippenham (0249) 782982
Opened in 1992 and set in one of the finest locations in England, this 18-hole Peter Alliss/Clive Clark course was designed to marry neatly with the surrounding conservation area.
18 holes, 6340yds, Par 72, Course record 68.
Club membership 730.
Visitors must contact in advance, must have handicap certificate, limited at weekends.
Societies contact in advance.
Green Fees £28 (£32.50 weekends & bank holidays).
Facilities ⊗ ⅶ 🍴 🍺 ♀ ♨ 🍴 ℣ Christine Langford.
Leisure snooker.
Location 5m NW of Chippenham
Hotel ★★64% White Hart Inn, FORD
☎ (0249) 782213 3℟ Annexe8⇄ ℟

CHIPPENHAM   Map 03 ST97

Chippenham ☎ (0249) 652040
Easy walking on downland course. Testing holes at 1st and 15th.
18 holes, 5559yds, Par 69, SSS 67.
Club membership 650.
Visitors must contact in advance and have a handicap certificate.
Societies must contact in writing; handicap certificates required.
Green Fees £18 per day (£24 weekends & bank holidays).
Facilities ⊗ ⅶ & 🍴 (ex Mon) 🍺 ♀ ♨ 🍴 ⛳ ℣ Bill Creamer.
Location Malmesbury Rd (1.5m N on A429)
Hotel ★★★★⚜79% Manor House Hotel, CASTLE COMBE ☎ (0249) 782206
12⇄ ℟ Annexe24⇄ ℟

DURNFORD, GREAT
Map 04 SU13

High Post ☎ Middle Woodford (072273) 356
An interesting downland course on Wiltshire chalk with
good turf and splendid views over the southern area of
Salisbury Plain. The par 3, 17th and the two-shot 18th
require good judgement.
18 holes, 6297yds, Par 70, SSS 70, Course record 64.
Club membership 600.
Visitors a handicap certificate is required at
weekends. Must contact in advance.
Societies welcome except weekends.
Green Fees not confirmed.
Facilities ⊗ ⅲ Ⅼ ☟ ♀ ☂ ☎ (Anthony John Harman.
Location 1.75m SE on A345
Hotel ★★★70% Rose & Crown Hotel, Harnham
Rd, Harnham, SALISBURY
☎ (0722) 327908 28➪ ⁿ

HIGHWORTH
Map 04 SU29

Highworth Community Golf Centre
☎ Swindon (0793) 766014
Public downland course, situated in a high position affording
good views.
9 holes, 3120yds, Par 35, SSS 35.
Visitors no restrictions.
Societies must telephone in advance.
Green Fees £4.60 (£5.70 weekends).
Facilities ☟ ☂ ☎ ⁿ⫯ (Mark Toombs.
Location Swindon Rd
Hotel ★★★62% Forte Crest Hotel, Oxford Rd,
Stratton St Margaret, SWINDON
☎ (0793) 831333 94➪ ⁿ

KINGSDOWN
Map 03 ST86

Kingsdown ☎ Bath (0225) 742530
Fairly flat, open downland course with very sparse tree cover
but surrounding wood.
18 holes, 6445yds, Par 72, SSS 71, Course record 66.
Club membership 620.
Visitors welcome except at weekends. Must contact in
advance & handicap certificate required.
Societies apply by letter.
Green Fees £22 per day.
Facilities ⊗ ⅲ Ⅼ ☟ ♀ ☂ ☎ (Andrew Butler.
Location W side of village
Hotel ★★65% Methuen Arms Hotel, High St,
CORSHAM ☎ (0249) 714867
19➪ ⁿ Annexe6 ➪ ⁿ

MARLBOROUGH
Map 04 SU16

Marlborough ☎ (0672) 512147
Downland course open to prevailing wind. Extensive views.
18 holes, 6526yds, Par 72, SSS 71.
Club membership 920.
Visitors restricted at certain times; must have a handicap
certificate at weekends. Must contact in advance.
Societies must telephone in advance.
Green Fees £29 per day; £19.50 per round (£40 weekends).

Facilities ⊗ ⅲ by prior arrangement Ⅼ ☟ ♀ ☂ ☎ (
W McAdams.
Location The Common (N side of town centre on A345)
Hotel ★★★60% Castle & Ball Hotel, High St,
MARLBOROUGH
☎ (0672) 515201 36➪

OGBOURNE ST GEORGE
Map 04 SU27

Swindon ☎ (067284) 327
Downland turf and magnificent greens.
18 holes, 6226yds, Par 71, SSS 70, Course record 66.
Club membership 800.
Visitors welcome weekdays only, handicap certificate
required. Must contact in advance.
Societies must apply in advance.
Green Fees not confirmed.
Facilities ⊗ Ⅼ ☟ ♀ ☂ ☎ (Colin Harraway.
Leisure practice ground.
Location N side of village on A3459
Hotel ★★★62% Forte Crest Hotel, Oxford Rd,
Stratton St Margaret, SWINDON
☎ (0793) 831333 94➪ ⁿ

SALISBURY
Map 04 SU12

Salisbury & South Wilts ☎ (0722) 742645
Gently undulating parkland course in country setting with
panoramic views of the cathedral and surrounding country.
Main Course: 18 holes, 6528yds, Par 70, SSS 71.
Old Course: 18 holes, 6177yds, Par 70, SSS 70.
Club membership 1010.
Visitors welcome except for competitions days. Must
contact in advance.
Societies apply in writing.
Green Fees 18 hole course: £25 per day (£40 weekends). 9
hole: £12 per day (£15 weekends).
Facilities ⊗ ⅲ Ⅼ ☟ ♀ ☂ ☎ ⁿ⫯ (Gary Emerson.
Leisure snooker.
Location Netherhampton (2m W on A3094)
Hotel ★★★70% Rose & Crown Hotel, Harnham Rd,
Harnham, SALISBURY
☎ (0722) 327908 28➪ ⁿ

SWINDON
Map 04 SU18

Broome Manor Golf Complex ☎ (0793) 532403
Two courses and a 20-bay floodlit driving range. Parkland
with water hazards, open fairways and short cut rough.
Walking is easy on gentle slopes.
*18 holes, 6359yds, Par 71, SSS 70 or 9 holes, 2745yds, Par
66, SSS 67.*
Club membership 1300.
Visitors must contact in advance.
Societies welcome Mon-Thu only.
Green Fees not confirmed.
Facilities ⊗ ⅲ Ⅼ ☟ ♀ ☂ ☎ ⁿ⫯ (Barry Sandry.
Leisure driving range.
Location Pipers Way (1.75m SE of town centre off
B4006)
Hotel ★★★62% Forte Crest Hotel, Oxford Rd,
Stratton St Margaret, SWINDON
☎ (0793) 831333 94➪ ⁿ

UPAVON — Map 04 SU15

RAF Upavon ☎ Stonehenge (0980) 630787
Downland course set on sides of valley, with some wind affecting play. The 2nd, 9th, 11th and 18th are all par 3 to small greens.
18 holes, 5116mtrs, Par 69, SSS 67, Course record 66.
Club membership 350.

Visitors	must contact in advance but may not play before noon on Sun.
Societies	contact in advance.
Green Fees	£14 per day (£17 weekends).
Facilities	ⓑ ♥ ♀ ⚐ ⌂ ⏽
Location	York Rd (2m E on A342)
Hotel	★★★62% Bear Hotel, Market Place, DEVIZES ☎ (0380) 722444 24⇄ ⏽

WARMINSTER — Map 03 ST84

West Wilts ☎ (0985) 212702
A hilltop course among the Wiltshire downs without trees and somewhat windswept. First-class springy turf with many interesting holes.
18 holes, 5709yds, Par 70, SSS 68.
Club membership 600.

Visitors	with member only weekends, handicap certificate required. Must contact in advance.
Societies	apply by letter.
Green Fees	not confirmed.
Facilities	⊗ (ex Tue) ⏝ (ex Sun-Tue) ⓑ ♥ ♀ ⚐ ⌂ ⏽ John G Jacobs.
Location	Elm Hill (N side of town centre off A350)
Hotel	★★★★♨68% Bishopstrow House Hotel, WARMINSTER ☎ (0985) 212312 32⇄ ⏽

WOOTTON BASSETT — Map 04 SU08

Wootton Bassett ☎ Swindon (0793) 849999
A Peter Alliss/Clive Clark design set in rolling Wiltshire courntryside. A number of lakes add a challenge for both low and high handicappers.
18 holes, 6634yds, Par 73, Course record 71.
Club membership 730.

Visitors	must have handicap certificate and contact in advance; limited at weekends.
Societies	contact in advance.
Green Fees	£20 (£25 weekends & bank holidays).
Facilities	⊗ ⏝ ⓑ ♥ ♀ ⚐ ⌂ ⏽ ⏽ Chris Smith.
Location	Leave M4 at junc 16, on A3102
Hotel	★★★66% Marsh Farm Hotel, Coped Hall, WOOTTON BASSETT ☎ (0793) 848044 4⇄ ⏽ Annexe24⇄ ⏽

> *Remember* – unless stated otherwise, two-ball matches should have precedence over and be entitled to pass any three- or four-ball match and any match playing a whole round may pass a match playing a shorter round

CHANNEL ISLANDS

● ALDERNEY ●

ALDERNEY — Map 16

Alderney ☎ (0481) 822835 & 823609
Undulating seaside course with sea on all sides and offering magnificent views from its high tees and greens. Course designed by Frank Pennink.
9 holes, 2528yds, Par 32, SSS 65.
Club membership 560.

Visitors	may not play before 10am at weekends.
Societies	must contact in advance.
Green Fees	£15 per day (£20 weekends).
Facilities	⊗ ⏝ by prior arrangement ⓑ ♥ ♀ ⚐ ⌂ ⏽
Leisure	bowling green & boules pitch.
Location	Route des Carrières (1m E of St Annes)
Hotel	★★66% Inchalla Hotel, St Anne, ALDERNEY ☎ (0481) 823220 11rm(9⇄)

● GUERNSEY ●

L'ANCRESSE VALE — Map 16

Royal Guernsey ☎ (0481) 47022
Not quite as old as its neighbour Royal Jersey, Royal Guernsey is a sporting course which was re-designed after World War II by Mackenzie Ross, who has many fine courses to his credit. It is a pleasant links, well-maintained, and administered by the States of Guernsey in the form of the States Tourist Committee. The 8th hole, a good par 4, requires an accurate second shot to the green set amongst the gorse and thick rough. The 18th, with lively views, needs a strong shot to reach the green well down below. The course is windy, with hard walking. There is a junior section.
18 holes, 6206yds, Par 70, SSS 70, Course record 64.
Club membership 1500.

Visitors	must have a handicap certificate; may not play on Thu & Sat afternoons & Sun.
Societies	Oct-Apr; must telephone in advance.
Green Fees	£25 per day/round.
Facilities	⊗ ⏝ ⓑ ♥ (lunch & dinner Mon-Sat only). ♀ ⚐ ⌂ ⏽ ⏽ Norman Wood.
Leisure	snooker.
Location	3m N of St Peter Port
Hotel	★★★67% St Pierre Park Hotel, Rohais, ST PETER PORT ☎ (0481) 728282 135⇄ ⏽

ST PETER PORT — Map 16

St Pierre Park Golf Club ☎ (0481) 727039 & 728282
Par 3 parkland course with delightful setting, with lakes, streams and many tricky holes.
9 holes, 2511yds, Par 54, SSS 48.
Club membership 290.

Visitors	no restrictions.
Societies	must contact in advance.
Green Fees	£10 per 9 holes. £15 per 18 holes.
Facilities	⊗ ▥ ♀ ☎ ┭ ⊨
Leisure	hard tennis courts, heated indoor swimming pool, snooker, sauna, solarium, gymnasium, croquet & petanque.
Location	Rohais (1m W off Rohais Rd)
Hotel	★★★★67% St Pierre Park Hotel, Rohais, ST PETER PORT ☎ (0481) 728282 135⇋ ⋔

JERSEY

GROUVILLE　　　　　　　　　　　Map 16

Royal Jersey ☎ Jersey (0534) 54416
A seaside links, historic because of its age: its centenary was celebrated in 1978. It is also famous for the fact that Britain's greatest golfer, Harry Vardon, was born in a little cottage on the edge of the course and learned his golf here.
18 holes, 6059yds, Par 70, SSS 70, Course record 64.
Club membership 1364.

Visitors	restricted to 10am-noon & 2pm-4pm
Societies	welcome Mon-Fri.
Green Fees	£30 per round (£35 weekends & bank holidays).
Facilities	⊗ ▥ � ▥ ♀ ☎ ┭ ⋔ Tommy Horton.
Leisure	snooker.
Location	4m E of St Helier off coast rd
Hotel	★★★★(red)▲▲ Longueville Manor Hotel, ST SAVIOUR ☎ (0534) 25501 32⇋ ⋔

LA MOYE　　　　　　　　　　　　Map 16

La Moye ☎ Jersey (0534) 43401
Seaside championship links course (venue for the Jersey Open) situated in an exposed position on the south western corner of the island overlooking St Ouens Bay. Offers spectacular views, two start points, full course all year - no temporary greens.
18 holes, 6705yds, Par 72, SSS 72.
Club membership 1300.

Visitors	must contact in advance and have a handicap certificate.
Societies	must contact in advance.
Green Fees	£55 per day (lunch incl); £35 per round (£40 weekends).
Facilities	☎ ┭ ⋔
Leisure	snooker.
Location	W side of village off A13
Hotel	★★★67% Les Arches Hotel, Archirondel Bay, ARCHIRONDEL ☎ (0534) 53839 54⇋ ⋔

ST CLEMENT　　　　　　　　　　Map 16

St Clement ☎ Jersey (0534) 21938
Very tight moorland course. Holes cross over fairways, impossible to play to scratch. Suitable for middle to high handicaps.
9 holes, 2244yds, Par 30.
Club membership 500.

Visitors	must contact in advance.
Green Fees	not confirmed.
Facilities	☎
Leisure	hard tennis courts.
Location	Jersey Recreation Grounds (E side of St Helier on A5)
Hotel	★★★★(red)▲▲ Longueville Manor Hotel, ST SAVIOUR ☎ (0534) 25501 32⇋ ⋔

ISLE OF MAN

CASTLETOWN　　　　　　　Map 06 SC26

Castletown Golf Links ☎ (0624) 822201
Set on the Langness Peninsula, this superb Championship course is surrounded on three sides by the sea, and holds many surprises from its Championship tees. The hotel offers many leisure facilities.
18 holes, 6713yds, Par 72, SSS 73.
Club membership 350.

Visitors	must book tee one month in advance unless a hotel resident.
Societies	must telephone in advance.
Green Fees	not confirmed.
Facilities	⊗ ▥ ▥ ▥ ♀ ☎ ┭ ⊨ ⋔ Murray Crowe.
Leisure	heated indoor swimming pool, fishing, snooker, sauna, solarium, putting green & croquet.
Location	Fort Island, Derbyhaven
Hotel	★★★66% Castletown Golf Links Hotel, Fort Island, CASTLETOWN ☎ (0624) 822201 58⇋ ⋔

DOUGLAS　　　　　　　　　Map 06 SC37

Pulrose ☎ (0624) 675952
Hilly, mainly moorland course under the control of Douglas Corporation.
18 holes, 6080yds, Par 70, SSS 69.
Club membership 430.

Visitors	no restrictions.
Green Fees	not confirmed.
Facilities	♀ ☎ ┭ ⋔
Location	1m W off A1
Hotel	★★★70% The Empress Hotel, Central Promenade, DOUGLAS ☎ (0624) 661155 102⇋ ⋔

ONCHAN　　　　　　　　　　Map 06 SC47

King Edward Bay Golf & Country Club
☎ Douglas (0624) 620430
Club plays over King Edward Bay course. Hilly seaside links course with natural hazards and good views.
18 holes, 5457yds, Par 67, SSS 66, Course record 62.
Club membership 470.

Visitors	must have a handicap certificate.
Societies	must contact in advance.
Green Fees	£8 per day (£10 weekends & bank holidays).
Facilities	⊗ ▥ ▥ ▥ ♀ ☎ ┭ ⋔ Donald Jones.
Leisure	snooker, sauna, solarium.
Location	Howstrake, Groudle Rd (E side of town off A11)
Hotel	★★★65% Sefton Hotel, Harris Promenade, DOUGLAS ☎ (0624) 626011 80⇋ ⋔

PEEL
Map 06 SC28

Peel ☎ (062484) 2227 or 3456
Moorland course, with natural hazards and easy walking.
Good views. 11th hole is a par 4, dog-leg.
18 holes, 5914yds, Par 69, SSS 68.
Club membership 600.
Visitors   not before 10.30am weekends & bank holidays.
   Must have a handicap certificate.
Societies   must contact in advance.
Green Fees £13 per day (£17 weekends & bank holidays).
Facilities   ⊗ ⊪ by prior arrangement � ☞ ♀ ♨ 🖭
Leisure   snooker.
Location   Rheast Ln (SE side of town centre on A1)
Hotel   ★★★70% The Empress Hotel, Central
   Promenade, DOUGLAS
   ☎ (0624) 661155 102⇔ ʀ

PORT ERIN
Map 06 SC16

Rowany ☎ (0624) 834108 or 837072
Undulating seaside course with testing later holes.
18 holes, 5840yds, Par 70, SSS 69, Course record 67.
Club membership 600.
Visitors   must contact in advance & have handicap
   certificate.
Societies   weekends only; must contact in advance.
Green Fees £12 per day (£17 weekends & bank holidays).
Facilities   ⊗ ⊪ by prior arrangement ▮呂 ☞ ♀ ♨ 🖭 ʀ
   Callum Wilson.
Leisure   pool table & darts.
Location   Rowany Dr (N side of village off A32)
Hotel   ★★★66% Castletown Golf Links Hotel, Fort
   Island, CASTLETOWN
   ☎ (0624) 822201 58⇔ ʀ

RAMSEY
Map 06 SC49

Ramsey ☎ (0624) 812244
Parkland course, with easy walking. Windy. Good views.
Testing holes: 1st, par 5; 18th, par 3.
18 holes, 5657yds, Par 69, SSS 67.
Club membership 1000.
Visitors   restricted Tue mornings, Sat & Sun.
Societies   not Sat & Sun; must contact in writing.
Green Fees Winter: £10 per day (£12 weekends); summer:
   £15 per day (£18 weekends).
Facilities   ⊗ ⊪ (Thu-Sat only) ▮呂 ☞ ♀ ♨ 🖭 ♈ ʀ
   Peter Lowrey.
Leisure   snooker.
Location   Brookfield (SW side of town)
Hotel   ★★★★56% Grand Island Hotel, Bride Rd,
   RAMSEY
   ☎ (0624) 812455 54⇔ ʀ

> Each golf-course entry has a recommended
> AA-appointed hotel. For a wider choice of
> places to stay, consult *AA Hotels in Britain
> and Ireland* and *AA Inspected Bed and
> Breakfast in Britain and Ireland* available
> from your local book shop or AA shops

WALES

CLWYD

ABERGELE
Map 06 SH97

Abergele & Pensarn ☎ (0745) 824034
A beautiful parkland course with views of the Irish Sea and
Gwyrch Castle. There are splendid finishing holes, a testing
par 5, 16th; a 185 yd, 17th to an elevated green, and a superb
par 5 18th with out of bounds just behind the green.
18 holes, 6520yds, Par 72, SSS 71.
Club membership 1200.
Visitors   restricted Tue.
Societies   must contact in writing.
Green Fees £21 per day (£26 weekends & bank holidays).
Facilities   ⊗ ⊪ ▮呂 ☞ ♀ ♨ 🖭 ʀ Iain R Runcie.
Leisure   snooker.
Location   Tan-y-Goppa Rd (0.5m W off A547/A55)
Hotel   ★★63% Kinmel Manor Hotel, St Georges Rd,
   ABERGELE ☎ (0745) 832014 42⇔ ʀ

BRYNFORD
Map 07 SJ17

Holywell ☎ Holywell (0352) 710040 & 713937
Exposed moorland course, with bracken and gorse flanking
undulating fairways. 720 ft above sea level.
18 holes, 6005yds, Par 70, SSS 70, Course record 70.
Club membership 500.
Visitors   with member only weekend & bank holidays.
Societies   must have handicaps, telephone in advance.
Green Fees £12 per day (£18 weekends & bank holidays).
Facilities   ⊗ ⊪ ▮呂 ☞ (no catering Mon) ♀ ♨ 🖭 ʀ
   Martin Carty.
Leisure   snooker.
Location   Brynford (1.25m SW off B5121)
Hotel   ★★64% Stamford Gate Hotel, Halkyn Rd,
   HOLYWELL
   ☎ (0352) 712942 & 712968 12⇔ ʀ

CHIRK
SJ23

Chirk Golf & Country Club ☎ (0691) 774407
Overlooked by the National Trust's Chirk Castle, is a
championship-standard 18-hole course with a 664 yard, par 5
at the 9th - one of the longest in Europe. Also a 9-hole course,
driving range and golf academy.
*Canal Course: 18 holes, 6956yds, Par 72, SSS 74, Course
record 71.*
Mine Rock: 9 holes, 1141yds, Par 27, Course record 24.
Club membership 475.
Visitors   advisable to contact in advance. Some times
   restricted to members.
Societies   must telephone for provisonal booking.
Green Fees 18 holes: £20 per day; £13 per round (£25/£17
   weekends). 9 holes: £4 per round (£5 weekends).
Facilities   ⊗ ⊪ ▮呂 ☞ ♀ ♨ 🖭 ♈ ʀ James Waugh.
Leisure   15 bay driving range, canal boat marina.
Location   5m N of Oswestry
Hotel   ★★★62% Bryn Howel Hotel & Restaurant,
   LLANGOLLEN ☎ (0978) 860331 38⇔ ʀ

COLWYN BAY · Map 06 SH87

Old Colwyn ☎ (0492) 515581
Hilly, meadowland course with sheep and cattle grazing on it in parts.
9 holes, 5000yds, Par 68, SSS 66.
Club membership 300.
Visitors no restrictions.
Societies must contact in advance.
Green Fees £10 per day (£15 weekends and bank holidays).
Facilities ⊗ ⊪ ⅃ ♥ ♀ (weekends) ⛄
Location Woodland Av, Old Colwyn (E side of town centre on B5383)
Hotel ★★69% Hopeside Hotel, Princes Dr, West End, COLWYN BAY
☎ (0492) 533244 19⇆ ⋔

DENBIGH · Map 06 SJ06

Denbigh ☎ (0745) 814159
Parkland course, giving a testing and varied game. Good views.
18 holes, 5581yds, Par 68, SSS 67, Course record 64.
Club membership 750.
Visitors may not play before 9.30am weekdays or 10.30am weekends.
Societies must telephone in advance.
Green Fees £18 per day; £15 per round (£24/£20 weekend & bank holidays).
Facilities ⊗ ⊪ ⅃ ♥ ♀ ⛄ 🏠 ⋔ ⌇ M D Jones.
Leisure snooker.
Location Henllan Rd (1.5m NW on B5382)
Hotel ★★63% Kinmel Manor Hotel, St Georges Rd, ABERGELE
☎ (0745) 832014 42⇆ ⋔

FLINT · Map 07 SJ27

Flint ☎ (0352) 732327
Parkland course incorporating woods and streams. Excellent views of Dee estuary.
9 holes, 5953yds, Par 69, SSS 69, Course record 65.
Club membership 330.
Visitors with member only at weekends.
Societies apply in advance.
Green Fees £10 per day.
Facilities ⊗ ⊪ ⅃ ♥ (catering by arrangement) ♀ ⛄
Leisure hard tennis courts, snooker.
Location Cornist Park (1m W)
Hotel ★★★64% New Chequers Country House Hotel, Chester Rd, NORTHOP HALL
☎ (0244) 816181 27⇆ ⋔

HAWARDEN · Map 07 SJ36

Hawarden ☎ (0244) 531447
Parkland course with comfortable walking and good views.
9 holes, 5630yds, Par 68, SSS 67.
Club membership 430.
Visitors with member or by appointment. Must contact in advance and have a handicap certificate.
Societies apply in writing.
Green Fees £15 per round.

Facilities ⊗ ⊪ ⅃ ♥ ♀ ⛄ 🏠
Location Groomsdale Ln (W side of town off B5125)
Hotel ★★★64% New Chequers Country House Hotel, Chester Rd, NORTHOP HALL
☎ (0244) 816181 27⇆ ⋔

LLANGOLLEN · Map 07 SJ24

Vale of Llangollen ☎ (0978) 860040
Parkland course, set in superb scenery by the River Dee.
18 holes, 6661yds, Par 72, SSS 72.
Club membership 660.
Visitors must contact in advance. Restricted club competition days.
Societies apply in writing.
Green Fees £20 per day (£23 weekends & bank holidays).
Facilities ♀ ⛄ 🏠 ⋔ ⌇
Location Holyhead Rd (1.5m E on A5)
Hotel ★★★62% Bryn Howel Hotel & Restaurant, LLANGOLLEN ☎ (0978) 860331 38⇆ ⋔

MOLD · Map 07 SJ26

Old Padeswood ☎ Buckley (0244) 547401
Meadowland course, undulating in parts.
18 holes, 6639yds, Par 72, SSS 72.
Club membership 600.
Visitors welcome, subject to tee availability.
Societies must contact in advance.
Green Fees £16 per day (£20 weekends).
Facilities ⊗ & ⊪ by prior arrangement ⅃ ♥ ♀ ⛄ 🏠 ⋔ ⌇ Tony Davies.
Leisure fishing, riding.
Location Station Rd, Padeswood (3m SE off A5118)
Hotel ★★★64% New Chequers Country House Hotel, Chester Rd, NORTHOP HALL
☎ (0244) 816181 27⇆ ⋔

Padeswood & Buckley ☎ (0244) 550537
Gently undulating parkland course, with natural hazards and good views of the Welsh Hills.
18 holes, 5823yds, Par 68, SSS 68, Course record 66.
Club membership 600.
Visitors Sat & Sun by arrangement.
Societies must contact in advance.
Green Fees not confirmed.
Facilities ⊗ ⊪ ⅃ ♥ ♀ ⛄ 🏠 ⋔ ⌇ David Ashton.
Location The Caia, Station Ln (3m SE off A5118)
Hotel ★★★64% New Chequers Country House Hotel, Chester Rd, NORTHOP HALL
☎ (0244) 816181 27⇆ ⋔

PANTYMWYN · Map 07 SJ16

Mold ☎ (0352) 740318
Meadowland course with some hard walking and natural hazards. Fine views.
18 holes, 5548yds, Par 67, SSS 67.
Club membership 600.
Visitors may not play on captains day, or when county matches are held.
Societies apply in writing.
Green Fees £16 per day (£21 per round weekends and bank holidays). ▶

Facilities ⊗ ⅷ by prior arrangement 🍴 🍺 ♀ ⚲ 🏠 ⛳ ⬥ Martin Carty.
Location E side of village
Hotel ★★★64% New Chequers Country House Hotel, Chester Rd, NORTHOP HALL ☎ (0244) 816181 27⇄ ⬥

PRESTATYN　　　Map 06 SJ08

Prestatyn ☎ (0745) 854320
Very flat seaside links exposed to stiff breeze. Testing holes: 9th, par 4, bounded on 3 sides by water; 10th, par 4; 16th, par 4.
18 holes, 6792yds, Par 72, SSS 73, Course record 68.
Club membership 650.
Visitors welcome except Sat & Tue mornings. Must contact in advance & have handicap certificate.
Societies must contact in advance.
Green Fees not confirmed.
Facilities ⊗ ⅷ 🍴 🍺 ♀ ⚲ 🏠 ⛳ ⬥ Malcolm Staton.
Leisure snooker.
Location Marine Rd East (0.5m N off A548)
Hotel ★★63% Kinmel Manor Hotel, St Georges Rd, ABERGELE ☎ (0745) 832014 42⇄ ⬥

St Melyd ☎ (0745) 854405
Parkland course with good views of mountains and Irish Sea. Testing 1st hole (423 yds) par 4. 18 tees.
9 holes, 5829yds, Par 68, SSS 68, Course record 65.
Club membership 400.
Visitors must contact in advance.
Societies must telephone in advance.
Green Fees £14 per day (£18 weekends).
Facilities ⊗ ⅷ 🍴 🍺 (contact steward) ♀ ⚲ 🏠 ⬥ Ian Worsley.
Leisure snooker.
Location The Paddock, Meliden Rd (0.5m S on A547)
Hotel ★★★61% Oriel House Hotel, Upper Denbigh Rd, ST ASAPH ☎ (0745) 582716 19⇄ ⬥

RHUDDLAN　　　Map 06 SJ07

Rhuddlan ☎ (0745) 590217
Attractive, gently undulating parkland course with good views. Well bunkered with trees and water hazards.
18 holes, 6482yds, Par 71, SSS 71.
Club membership 953.
Visitors must contact in advance & have handicap certificate. Sun with member only.
Societies must contact in advance.
Green Fees £20 per day (£25 Sat & bank holidays).
Facilities ⊗ ⅷ (in season) 🍴 & 🍺 (in season) ♀ ⚲ 🏠 ⛳ ⬥ Ian Worsley.
Leisure snooker.
Location Meliden Rd (E side of town on A547)
Hotel ★★★61% Oriel House Hotel, Upper Denbigh Rd, ST ASAPH ☎ (0745) 582716 19⇄ ⬥

RHYL　　　Map 06 SJ08

Rhyl ☎ (0745) 353171
Seaside course.
9 holes, 3109yds, Par 35, SSS 35.
Club membership 350.

Visitors restricted Sun in summer. Must contact in advance.
Societies must contact in advance.
Green Fees not confirmed.
Facilities ⊗ ⅷ 🍴 🍺 ♀ ⚲ 🏠 ⛳
Leisure snooker.
Location Coast Rd (1m E on A548)
Hotel ★★★61% Oriel House Hotel, Upper Denbigh Rd, ST ASAPH ☎ (0745) 582716 19⇄ ⬥

RUTHIN　　　Map 07 SJ15

Ruthin-Pwllglas ☎ (0824) 703427
Hilly parkland course in elevated position with panoramic views. Stiff climb to 3rd and 9th holes.
10 holes, 5362yds, Par 66, SSS 66, Course record 66.
Club membership 380.
Visitors welcome except for competition days.
Societies apply in writing.
Green Fees £10 per day (£15 weekends & bank holidays).
Facilities ⊗ & ⅷ by prior arrangement ⚲
Location Pwllglas (2.5m S off A494)
Hotel ★★★63% Ruthin Castle, RUTHIN ☎ (08242) 2664 58⇄ ⬥

WREXHAM　　　Map 07 SJ35

Wrexham ☎ (0978) 261033
Inland, sandy course with easy walking. Testing dog-legged 7th hole (par 4), and short 14th hole (par 3) with full carry to green.
18 holes, 6078yds, Par 70, SSS 69, Course record 65.
Club membership 650.
Visitors may not play competition days, and are advised to contact in advance.
Societies welcome except for Tue, Wed & weekends.
Green Fees £17 per day (£22 weekends).
Facilities ⊗ ⅷ 🍴 🍺 ♀ ⚲ 🏠 ⛳ ⬥ David Larvin.
Leisure snooker.
Location Holt Rd (1.75m NE on A534)
Hotel ★★★64% Wynnstay Arms, High Street/Yorke St, WREXHAM ☎ (0978) 291010 76⇄ ⬥

DYFED

ABERYSTWYTH　　　Map 06 SN58

Aberystwyth ☎ (0970) 615104
Undulating meadowland course. Testing holes: 16th (The Loop) par 3; 17th, par 4; 18th, par 3. Good views over Cardigan Bay.
18 holes, 6150yds, Par 70, SSS 70.
Club membership 400.
Visitors must contact in advance at weekends & bank holidays. Must have an introduction from own club.
Societies must contact in advance.
Green Fees £18 per day; £15 per round (£20/£18 weekends).
Facilities ⊗ ⅷ 🍴 🍺 ♀ ⚲ 🏠 ⛳ ⬥
Location Brynymor Rd (N side of town)
Hotel ★★67% Belle Vue Royal Hotel, Marine Ter, ABERYSTWYTH ☎ (0970) 617558 37rm(30⇄ ⬥)

BORTH   Map 06 SN69

Borth & Ynslas ☎ (0970) 871202
Seaside links, over 100 years old, with strong winds at times. Some narrow fairways.
18 holes, 6116yds, Par 69, SSS 70, Course record 65.
Club membership 300.
Visitors   may not play before 11am or between 1.30-2.30pm at weekends.
Societies   apply in writing or telephone (0970) 828462.
Green Fees £15 per weekday (Apr-Oct). £20 in Aug.
Facilities ⊗ &)▥ (Etr-Sep) 🍴 ♀ 👤 🏠 ⛳ ⚑
Location   0.5m N on B4353
Hotel   ★★63% Four Seasons Hotel, 50-54 Portland St, ABERYSTWYTH ☎ (0970) 612120 14rm(11 ⇌ ╟)

BURRY PORT   Map 02 SN40

Ashburnham ☎ (05546) 2269
This course has a lot of variety. In the main it is of the seaside type although the holes in front of the clubhouse are of an inland character. They are, however, good holes which make a very interesting finish. Course record holder, Sam Torrance.
18 holes, 6916yds, Par 72, SSS 73, Course record 67.
Club membership 750.
Visitors   special times available. Must contact in advance and have an introduction from own club.
Societies   apply in writing.
Green Fees not confirmed.
Facilities ⊗)▥ 🍴 🍺 ♀ 👤 🏠 ⛳ ⚑ Robert Ryder.
Leisure   pool table.
Location   Cliffe Ter (W side of town on B4311)
Hotel   ★★★60% Diplomat Hotel, Felinfoel, LLANELLI ☎ (0554) 756156 23⇌╟ Annexe8⇌╟

CARDIGAN   Map 02 SN14

Cardigan ☎ (0239) 612035
A links course, very dry in winter, with wide fairways, light rough and gorse. Every hole overlooks the sea.
18 holes, 6641yds, Par 72, SSS 72.
Club membership 500.
Visitors   may not play between 1-2pm. Must have a handicap certificate
Societies   must telephone in advance.
Green Fees £15 per day (£20 weekends and bank holidays).
Facilities ⊗)▥ 🍴 🍺 ♀ 👤 🏠 ⛳ ⚑ Colin Parsons.
Leisure   squash.
Location   Gwbert-on Sea (3m N off B4548)
Hotel   ★★★56% Cliff Hotel, GWBERT ☎ (0239) 613241 75⇌╟

CARMARTHEN   Map 02 SN42

Carmarthen ☎ (026787) 588
Hilltop course with good views.
18 holes, 6210yds, Par 71, SSS 71, Course record 68.
Club membership 700.
Visitors   no restrictions.
Societies   must contact in advance.

Green Fees £15 per day (£20 weekends & bank holidays).
Facilities ⊗ &)▥ (ex Wed) 🍺 🍴 ♀ 👤 🏠 ⛳ ⚑ Pat Gillis.
Location   Blaenycoed Rd (4m NW)
Hotel   ★★★63% The Ivy Bush Royal, Spilman St, CARMARTHEN ☎ (0267) 235111 78⇌╟

HAVERFORDWEST   Map 02 SM91

Haverfordwest ☎ (0437) 764523
Parkland course in attractive surroundings.
18 holes, 6005yds, Par 70, SSS 69.
Club membership 720.
Visitors   must contact in advance. Restricted Wed & Thu.
Societies   must telephone in advance & confirm in writing.
Green Fees £16 per round (£23 weekends).
Facilities ⊗)▥ 🍺 🍴 ♀ 👤 🏠 ⛳ ⚑ Alex Pile.
Location   Arnolds Down (1m E on A40)
Hotel   ★★61% Hotel Mariners, Mariners Square, HAVERFORDWEST ☎ (0437) 763353 32rm(31⇌ ╟)

LLANDYBIE   Map 02 SN61

Glynhir ☎ (0269) 850472
Parkland course with good views, latter holes close to Upper Loughor River. The 14th is a 394-yd dog leg.
18 holes, 6090yds, Par 69, SSS 69, Course record 66.
Club membership 700.
Visitors   with member only weekends. No visitors Sun. Must contact in advance and have a handicap certificate.   ▶

The Mill at Glynhir AA ★★
Ashley Courtenay

BWRDD CROESO CYMRU
WALES TOURIST BOARD

♛♛♛

LLANDYBIE, NR. AMMANFORD, DYFED SA18 2TE
Telephone: (0269) 850672

Originally a XVIIth-century mill, now converted to a small secluded luxury hotel. Extensive views over River Loughor valley and adjacent **18-hole golf course – free to residents. Own practice area.** Indoor swimming pool. All rooms with private spa/bath/shower and colour TV. Ideal for touring Brecons and SW Wales as well as walking and pony trekking.
Alas no under 11's.

Societies welcome weekdays only. Must apply in writing.
Green Fees £15 per day (£20 weekends & bank holidays).
Facilities ⊗ ⅲ ⅇ ■ ⊻ ⅰ ⅰⅉ ⅰ Ian Roberts.
Location Glynhir Rd (2m NE)
Hotel ★★67% Mill at Glynhir, Glyn-Hir, Llandybie,
AMMANFORD ☎ (0269) 850672
9⇄ Annexe2⇄ ▮

LLANGYBI
Map 02 SN65

Cilgwyn ☎ (057045) 286
Picturesque parkland course in secluded valley, with natural
hazards of ponds, stream and woodland.
9 holes, 5309yds, Par 68, SSS 67, Course record 67.
Club membership 260.
Visitors no restrictions
Societies must telephone in advance and confirm in
writing
Green Fees £14 per day ; £60 per week.
Facilities ⊗ ⅲ ⅇ ■ ⊻ ⅋ ⅰⅉ
Leisure pool table.
Location 0.5m NW off A485
Hotel ★★★♨67% Falcondale Country House Hotel,
LAMPETER ☎ (0570) 422910 19⇄ ▮

LLANRHYSTUD
Map 06 SN56

Penrhos Golf & Country Club ☎ Llanon (0974) 202999
Beautifully scenic course incorporating five lakes and
spectacular coastal and inland views. Many leisure facilities.
18 holes, 6641yds, Par 72, SSS 72.
Club membership 300.
Visitors must contact in advance and should have a
handicap certificate.
Societies apply in writing.
Green Fees £18 per day; £12 per round (£24/£18 weekends
& bank holidays).
Facilities ⅲ (weekends) ⅇ ■ ⊻ ⅋ ⅰⅉ ⅰ Paul
Diamond.
Leisure hard tennis courts, heated indoor swimming
pool, fishing, sauna, solarium, gymnasium,
bowls, shooting.
Location 0.5m SE on B4337
Hotel ★★★♨66% Conrah Hotel, Ffosrhydygaled,
Chancery, ABERYSTWYTH
☎ (0970) 617941 11rm(9⇄ ▮) Annexe9⇄ ▮

LLANSTEFFAN
Map 02 SN31

Llansteffan ☎ (026783) 526
A Pay and Play downland course with superb views of the sea
and Gower Coast.
9 holes, 2165yds, Par 30, Course record 33.
Visitors no restrictions.
Societies must contact in advance.
Green Fees £3 per 9 holes.
Facilities catering facilities under construction. ⅰ ⅰⅉ
Leisure bowling green, croquet.
Location S of Carmarthen off B4312
Hotel ★★66% Forge Restaurant & Motel, ST CLEARS
☎ (0994) 230300 Annexe18⇄ ▮

MILFORD HAVEN
Map 02 SM90

Milford Haven ☎ (0646) 692368
Parkland course with excellent greens and views of the
Milford Haven waterway.
18 holes, 6030yds, Par 71, SSS 70.
Club membership 450.
Visitors no restrictions, advisable to contact in advance.
Societies telephone to book.
Green Fees £13 per round (£18 weekends & bank holidays).
Facilities ⊗ & ⅲ by prior arrangement (ex Tue)
ⅇ ■ ⊻ ⅋ ⅰ ⅰⅉ Stephen Laidler.
Location Woodbine House, Hubberstone (1.5m W)
Hotel ★★63% Lord Nelson Hotel, Hamilton Ter,
MILFORD HAVEN ☎ (0646) 695341 32⇄ ▮

NEWPORT
Map 02 SN03

Newport (Pemb) ☎ (0239) 820244
Seaside links course, with easy walking and good view of the
Preselli Hills and Newport Bay.
9 holes, 5815yds, Par 70, SSS 69, Course record 62.
Club membership 220.
Visitors no restrictions.
Societies must telephone in advance.
Green Fees £12.50 per day; £8 per round.
Facilities ⊗ ⅲ ⅇ ■ ⊻ ⅋ ⅰ ⅰⅉ ⅰ Colin Parsons.
Location The Golf Club (1.25m N)
Hotel ★★63% Cartref Hotel, 15-19 High St,
FISHGUARD ☎ (0348) 872430
12rm(10⇄ ▮)

PEMBROKE DOCK
Map 02 SM90

South Pembrokeshire ☎ (0646) 683817
Parkland course overlooking the Cleddau River.
9 holes, 5804yds, Par 70, SSS 69.
Club membership 350.
Visitors must contact in advance, restricted weekends &
club competitions.
Societies apply in writing.
Green Fees £10 per day.
Facilities ⅇ ■ ⊻ ⅋
Leisure snooker.
Location Defensible Barracks (SW side of town centre
off B4322)
Hotel ★★58% Old Kings Arms, Main St, PEMBROKE
☎ (0646) 683611 21⇄

ST DAVID'S
Map 02 SM72

St David's City ☎ (0437) 720312
Links course with alternative tees for 18 holes. Panoramic
views of St David's Head and Ramsey Island.
9 holes, 5961yds, Par 70, SSS 70, Course record 67.
Club membership 200.
Visitors welcome. No sharing of golf bags.
Societies must telephone in advance.
Green Fees £11 per day.
Facilities ⅋
Location Whitesands Bay (2m W overlooking
Whitesands Bay)
Hotel ★★★64% Warpool Court Hotel, ST DAVID'S
☎ (0437) 720300 25⇄ ▮

TENBY
Map 02 SN10

Tenby ☎ (0834) 842978
A fine old seaside links, with sea views and natural
hazards providing good golf.
18 holes, 6232yds, Par 69, SSS 71.
Club membership 650.
Visitors　subject to competition & tee reservation.
　　　　　　Must produce handicap certificate.
Societies　must telephone in advance.
Green Fees　£18 per day (£22.50 weekends & bank
　　　　　　holidays).
Facilities　⊗ ⊞ ⿃ ♥ ♀ � 🛏 (Terry Mountford.
Leisure　snooker.
Location　The Burrows
Hotel　★★★65% Atlantic Hotel, Esplanade,
　　　　　TENBY ☎ (0834) 842881 & 844176
　　　　　42⇄ ♠

GWENT

ABERGAVENNY
Map 03 SO21

Monmouthshire ☎ (0873) 853171
This parkland course is very picturesque, with the
beautifully wooded River Usk running alongside. There
are a number of par 3 holes and a testing par 4 at the
15th.
18 holes, 5961yds, Par 72, SSS 69.
Club membership 700.
Visitors　must play with member at weekends. Must
　　　　　　contact in advance & have handicap
　　　　　　certificate.
Societies　must contact in writing.
Green Fees　not confirmed.
Facilities　⊗ ⊞ ⿃ ♥ ♀ � 🛏 ⚐ (Philip Worthing.
Leisure　fishing.
Location　Gypsy Ln, LLanfoist (2m S off B4269)
Hotel　★★★★64% Craigendarroch Hotel &
　　　　　Country Club, Braemar Rd, BALLATER
　　　　　☎ (03397) 55858 50⇄ ♠

BETTWS NEWYDD
Map 03 SO30

Alice Springs ☎ Nantyderry (0873) 880772 & 880708
Two 18-hole undulating parkland courses set back to back
with magnificent views of the Usk Valley. The Queen's
course has testing 7th and 15th holes. The King's Course
which opened in summer 1992, is 6662yds long.
*Queens: 18 holes, 6041yds, Par 67, SSS 69, Course record
65.*
Kings: 18 holes, 6662yds, Par 72, SSS 71.
Club membership 350.
Visitors　should contact the club in advance for
　　　　　　weekend play.
Societies　must telephone in advance.
Green Fees　£12.50 per 18 holes (both courses).
Facilities　⊗ & ⊞ ⿃ ♥ ♀ ⿻ 🛏 (Jim Howard.
Hotel　★★73% Glen-yr-Afon Hotel, Pontypool Rd,
　　　　　USK ☎ (0291) 672302 & 673202
　　　　　27rm(26⇄ ♠)

BLACKWOOD
Map 03 ST19

Blackwood ☎ (0495) 223152
Heathland course with sand bunkers. Undulating, with hard
walking. Testing 2nd hole par 4. Good views.
9 holes, 5304yds, Par 66, SSS 66.
Club membership 250.
Visitors　must contact in advance & have handicap
　　　　　　certificate. Must play with member at weekends
　　　　　　& bank holidays.
Societies　may not play weekends & bank holidays.
Green Fees　not confirmed.
Facilities　ዾ
Location　Cwmgelli (0.75m N off A4048)
Hotel　★★★53% Maes Manor Hotel, BLACKWOOD
　　　　　☎ (0495) 224551 & 220011 8⇄Annexe14⇄

CAERWENT
Map 03 ST49

Dewstow ☎ Caldicot (0291) 430444
A newly-established, picturesque parkland course with
spectacular views over the Severn estuary towards Bristol.
Testing holes include the Par three 7th, which is approached
over water, some 50 feet lower than the tee. There is also a
26-bay floodlit driving range.
18 holes, 6100yds, Par 72, SSS 70, Course record 74.
Club membership 500.
Visitors　may book two days in advance.
Societies　apply in writing or telephone secretary.
Green Fees　not confirmed.
Facilities　⊗ ⊞ ⿃ ♥ ♀ ⿻ 🛏 ⚐ (Mark Kedward.
Leisure　floodlit golf range.
Location　0.5m S of A48 at Caerwent
Hotel　★★★69% St Pierre Hotel, Golf & Country
　　　　　Club, St Pierre Park, CHEPSTOW
　　　　　☎ (0291) 625261 106⇄ ♠ Annexe41⇄ ♠

CHEPSTOW
Map 03 ST59

St Pierre Hotel Golf and Country Club
☎ (0291) 625261
Parkland/meadowland championship course. There are
two golf courses, the Old and the Mathern. The Old is
home to the Epson Grand Prix of Europe, and is one of
Britain's major courses. Its long par 5, 12th hole of 545
yds, tests even the finest golfers. St Pierre, with its
delightful 14th-century mansion was discovered over 30
years ago by retired businessman Bill Graham. He said 'I
saw this deer park almost by accident. I liked the mature
trees and the atmosphere of the place - so I bought it!'
With Ken Cotton and golf coach Bill Cox, they
transformed the mansion into a club house and the park
into two golf courses that became famous and staged
professional tournaments within a very short time.
Today the courses attract many visitors. The club
professional Renton Doig and his staff can tell stories of
many well-known stars doing well, and of one Arwyn
Griffiths who arrived on the 18th tee needing a par 3 for
an amazing round of 63. This hole must be played over
water and, unhappily for Mr Griffiths, he took an 11.
Although shattered at failing to establish a record he still
won the competition and was able to celebrate at the
excellent 19th hole.　　　　　　　　　　　　　▶

Old Course: 18 holes, 6700yds, Par 71, SSS 73.
Mathern Course: 18 holes, 5762yds, Par 68, SSS 68.
Club membership 900.

Visitors	must contact in advance & have handicap certificate.
Societies	must make an advance reservation.
Green Fees	not confirmed.
Facilities	⊗ ⁜ ⬩ ▣ ♀ ♨ 🝰 ⍎ 🚻 ℓ Renton Doig.
Leisure	hard tennis courts, heated indoor swimming pool, squash, snooker, sauna, solarium, gymnasium, badminton, crown bowling & croquet.
Location	St Pierre Park (3m SW off A48)
Hotel	★★★69% St Pierre Hotel, Golf & Country Club, St Pierre Park, CHEPSTOW ☎ (0291) 625261 106⇔ ℝAnnexe41⇔ ℝ

CWMBRAN   Map 03 ST29

Pontnewydd ☎ (06333) 2170
Mountainside course, with hard walking. Good views across the Severn Estuary.
10 holes, 5353yds, Par 68, SSS 67, Course record 63.
Club membership 250.

Visitors	must play with member weekends & bank holidays.
Green Fees	not confirmed.
Facilities	♀ ⬩
Location	Maesgwyn Farm, West Pontnewydd (N side of town centre)
Hotel	★★★67% Kings Hotel, High St, NEWPORT ☎ (0633) 842020 47⇔ ℝ

LLANWERN   Map 03 ST38

Llanwern ☎ (0633) 412029
Two parkland courses.
New Course: 18 holes, 6115yds, Par 70, SSS 69.
Old Course: 9 holes, 5237yds, Par 67, SSS 67.
Club membership 850.

Visitors	must be a member of a recognised golf club.
Societies	must contact in writing.
Green Fees	£20 per day (Mon-Fri).
Facilities	⊗ ⁜ ⬩ ▣ ♀ ⬩ 🝰 ℓ Stephen Price.
Leisure	snooker.
Location	Tennyson Av (0.5m S off A455)
Hotel	★★★★65% Stakis Cardiff-Newport Country Court Hotel, Chepstow Rd, Langstone, NEWPORT ☎ (0633) 413737 141⇔ ℝ

MONMOUTH   Map 03 SO51

Monmouth ☎ (0600) 712212
Parkland course in scenic setting. High, undulating land with good views. Testing 1st and 4th holes.
18 holes, 5698yds, Par 69, SSS 67.
Club membership 500.

Visitors	no restricions.
Societies	Mon-Fri only, telephone in advance.
Green Fees	£15 per day.
Facilities	⊗ ⁜ ⬩ ▣ ♀ (Mon-Fri only) ⬩ 🝰
Location	Leasebrook Ln (1.5m NE off A40)
Hotel	★★★58% Kings Head Hotel, Agincourt Square, MONMOUTH ☎ (0600) 712177 29rm(27⇔ ℝ)

Rolls of Monmouth ☎ (0600) 715353
A hilly and challenging parkland course encompassing several lakes and ponds and surrounded by woodland. Set within a beautiful private estate complete with listed mansion.
18 holes, 6723yds, Par 72, SSS 72, Course record 68.
Club membership 200.

Visitors	must contact in advance and may not play on open days.
Societies	must contact in advance.
Green Fees	£28 per day (£33 weekends & bank holidays).
Facilities	⊗ ⁜ ⬩ ▣ ♀ ⬩ 🝰 🝰
Location	The Hendre (4m W on B4233)
Hotel	★★★58% Kings Head Hotel, Agincourt Square, MONMOUTH ☎ (0600) 712177 29rm(27⇔ ℝ)

NANTYGLO   Map 03 SO11

West Monmouthshire ☎ (0495) 310233
Mountain and heathland course with picturesque views, hard walking and natural hazards. Testing 3rd hole, par 5, and 7th hole, par 4.
18 holes, 6118yds, Par 71, SSS 69.
Club membership 700.

Visitors	welcome, must be guest of member for play on Sun.
Societies	must telephone 1 week in advance.
Green Fees	£12 per day (Mon-Sat).
Facilities	⊗ & ⁜ by prior arrangement ⬩ ▣ ♀ ⬩ 🝰 🝰
Location	Pond Rd (0.25m W off A467)
Hotel	★★★57% Angel Hotel, Cross St, ABERGAVENNY ☎ (0873) 857121 29⇔ ℝ

NEWPORT   Map 03 ST38

Newport ☎ (0633) 896794 & 892643
An undulating parkland course, part-wooded. The 2nd hole is surrounded by bunkers - a difficult hole. The 11th hole is a bogey 4 and the fairway runs through an avenue of trees, making a straight drive preferable. Set 300ft above sea level, it offers fine views.
18 holes, 6431yds, Par 72, SSS 71, Course record 65.
Club membership 700.

Visitors	must contact in advance & have handicap certificate. With member only on Sat.
Societies	must contact in writing.
Green Fees	£30 per day (£40 Sun).
Facilities	⊗ ⁜ ⬩ ▣ ♀ ⬩ 🝰 🝰 ℓ Roy Skuse.
Location	Great Oak, Rogerstone (3m NW of city centre off B4591)
Hotel	★★★★63% Celtic Manor Hotel, Coldra Woods, NEWPORT ☎ (0633) 413000 73⇔ ℝ

Tredegar Park ☎ (0633) 895219
A parkland course with River Ebbw and streams as natural hazards. The ground is very flat with narrow fairways and small greens. The 17th hole (par 3) is played on to a plateau where many players spoil their medal round.
18 holes, 6095yds, Par 71, SSS 70, Course record 67.
Club membership 800.

Visitors	must be a member of a recognised golf club. Must contact in advance and have an introduction from own club.
Societies	must contact in advance.
Green Fees	not confirmed.
Facilities	⊗ ⅢⅢ ⅃ 🍺 ⚲ ♨ 🏠 ♈ (Mervyn Morgan.
Leisure	snooker.
Location	Bassaleg Rd (2m SW off A467 exit 276 of M4)
Hotel	★★★67% Kings Hotel, High St, NEWPORT ☎ (0633) 842020 47⇄ 🐾

PONTYPOOL   Map 03 SO20

Pontypool ☎ (0495) 763655
Undulating, mountain course with magnificent views.
18 holes, 6046yds, Par 69, SSS 69.
Club membership 600.

Visitors	must have a handicap certificate. Must contact in advance and have an introduction from own club.
Societies	must contact secretary in advance.
Green Fees	not confirmed.
Facilities	⊗ ⅢⅢ ⅃ 🍺 ⚲ ♨ 🏠 ♈ (Jim Howard.
Leisure	snooker, pratice area.
Location	Trevethin (1.5m N off A4043)
Hotel	★★73% Glen-yr-Afon Hotel, Pontypool Rd, USK ☎ (0291) 672302 & 673202 27rm(26⇄ 🐾)

TREDEGAR   Map 03 SO10

Tredegar and Rhymney ☎ Rhymney (0685) 840743
Mountain course with lovely views.
9 holes, 5504yds, Par 68.
Club membership 194.

Visitors	no restrictions.
Societies	must contact in writing.
Green Fees	£10 per day (£12.50 weekends).
Facilities	⅃ 🍺 ⚲ ♨
Location	Cwmtysswg, Rhymney (1.75m SW on B4256)
Hotel	★★68% Tregenna Hotel, Park Ter, MERTHYR TYDFIL ☎ (0685) 723627 & 382055 14⇄ 🐾 Annexe7⇄ 🐾

GWYNEDD

ABERDOVEY   Map 06 SN69

Aberdovey ☎ (0654) 767210
A beautiful championship course at the mouth of the Dovey estuary, Aberdovey has all the true characteristics of a seaside links. It has some fine holes among them the 3rd, the 12th, an especially good short hole, and the 15th. There are some striking views to be had from the course.
18 holes, 6445yds, Par 71, SSS 71.
Club membership 750.

Visitors	members have priority between 8-10am & 12.30-2pm.

Societies	apply in writing to the secretary.
Green Fees	£21 per day; £19 per round (£31/£21 weekends).
Facilities	⊗ ⅢⅢ by prior arrangement ⅃ 🍺 ⚲ ♨ 🏠 (John Davies.
Leisure	snooker.
Location	0.5m W on A493
Hotel	★★★67% Trefeddian Hotel, ABERDOVEY ☎ (0654) 767213 46⇄ 🐾

ABERSOCH   Map 06 SH32

Abersoch ☎ (0758) 712622
Seaside links, with five parkland holes.
18 holes, 5994yds, Par 69, SSS 69.
Club membership 700.

Visitors	must have a handicap certificate.
Societies	must apply in writing.
Green Fees	not confirmed.
Facilities	⊗ ⅢⅢ ⅃ 🍺 ⚲ ♨
Location	S side of village
Hotel	★★★63% Abersoch Harbour Hotel, ABERSOCH ☎ (0758) 712406 9⇄ 🐾 Annexe5⇄ 🐾

ANGLESEY, ISLE OF   Map 06

Golf courses on the island of Anglesey are listed alphabetically under Anglesey, Isle of

AMLWCH   Map 06 SH49

Bull Bay ☎ (0407) 830960
Pleasant seaside course with natural meadow, rock, gorse and wind hazards. Views from all tees across Irish Sea to Isle of Man.
18 holes, 6132yds, Par 70, SSS 70.
Club membership 800.

Visitors	must have handicap certificate at weekends.
Societies	apply in writing.
Green Fees	£20 per day; £15 per round (£25/20 weekends).
Facilities	⊗ ⅢⅢ ⅃ 🍺 (limited catering Tue) ⚲ ♨ 🏠 (Neil Dunroe.
Location	1m NW on A5025
Hotel	★★54% Trecastell Hotel, Bull Bay, AMLWCH ☎ (0407) 830651 12rm(8⇄3 🐾)

BEAUMARIS   Map 06 SH67

Baron Hill ☎ (0286) 810231
Undulating course with natural hazards of rock and gorse. Testing 3rd and 4th holes (par 4's).
9 holes, 5062mtrs, Par 68, SSS 67.
Club membership 400.

Visitors	no restrictions.
Societies	apply in writing.
Green Fees	£12 per day.
Facilities	♨
Location	1m SW off A545
Hotel	★★66% Bishopsgate House Hotel, 54 Castle St, BEAUMARIS ☎ (0248) 810302 10⇄ 🐾

HOLYHEAD   Map 06 SH28

Holyhead ☎ (0407) 763279
Treeless, undulating seaside course which provides a
varied and testing game, particularly in a south wind. The
fairways are bordered by gorse, heather and rugged
outcrops of rock. Accuracy from most tees is paramount
as there are 43 fairway and greenside bunkers and lakes.
Designed by James Braid. Indoor driving range.
18 holes, 6056yds, Par 70, SSS 70, Course record 63.
Club membership 1309.

Visitors	must contact in advance & have handicap certificate.
Societies	must telephone in advance.
Green Fees	£20 per day; £17 per round (£25/£20 weekends).
Facilities	⊗ ⅷ ⅎ ⅊ (limited catering Mon) ⅊⅃⅄⅀ƒ Paul Capper.
Leisure	snooker, indoor driving range.
Location	Trearddur Bay (1.25m S on B4545)
Hotel	★★★70% Trearddur Bay Hotel, TREARDDUR BAY ☎ (0407) 860301 27rm(20⇄)

LLANGEFNI   Map 06 SH47

Llangefni (Public) ☎ (0248) 722193
Picturesque parkland course designed by Hawtree & Son.
9 holes, 1342yds, Par 28, SSS 28.

Visitors	no restrictions.
Societies	must contact in advance.
Facilities	⅃⅄ƒƒ
Location	1.5m off A5
Hotel	★★60% Anglesey Arms, MENAI BRIDGE ☎ (0248) 712305 17rm(10⇄6 ⅋)

RHOSNEIGR   Map 06 SH37

Anglesey ☎ (0407) 811202
Links course, low and fairly level with sand dunes and tidal river.
18 holes, 5713yds, Par 68, SSS 68.
Club membership 400.

Visitors	welcome, some times are reserved for members.
Societies	apply in writing.
Green Fees	£12.50 per day (£15 weekends & bank holidays).
Facilities	⊗ ⅷ by prior arrangement ⅊ ⅊⅃⅄⅀ƒ Paul Lovell.
Leisure	darts, pool table, golf practice ground.
Location	Station Rd (NE side of village on A4080)
Hotel	★★★70% Trearddur Bay Hotel, TREARDDUR BAY ☎ (0407) 860301 27rm(20⇄)

BALA   Map 06 SH93

Bala ☎ (0678) 520359
Mountainous course with natural hazards.
10 holes, 5980yds, Par 66, SSS 64.
Club membership 250.

Visitors	must telephone in advance for weekends & bank holidays.
Societies	must telephone in advance.
Green Fees	£10 per day (£10 per round weekends).
Facilities	⅃ (ex Wed winter) ⅊ ⅊⅄⅀ƒ
Leisure	snooker.

Location	Penlan (0.5m SW off A494)
Hotel	★★61% Plas Coch Hotel, High St, BALA ☎ (0678) 520309 10⇄ ⅋

BANGOR   Map 06 SH57

St Deiniol ☎ (0248) 353098
Elevated parkland course with panoramic views of
Snowdonia, Menai Straits, and Anglesey.
18 holes, 5068mtrs, Par 68, SSS 67.
Club membership 500.

Visitors	restricted weekends.
Societies	must contact in writing.
Green Fees	£10 (£15 weekends).
Facilities	⊗ ⅷ ⅃ ⅊ ⅊⅄⅀
Leisure	snooker.
Location	Penybryn (E side of town centre off A5122)
Hotel	★★74% Menai Court Hotel, Craig y Don Rd, BANGOR ☎ (0248) 354200 12⇄ ⅋

BEAUMARIS   Map 06 SH67

*See under **Anglesey, Isle of***

BETWS-Y-COED   Map 06 SH75

Betws-y-Coed ☎ (0690) 710556
Attractive parkland course set between two rivers in
Snowdonia National Park.
9 holes, 4996yds, Par 64, SSS 64.
Club membership 350.

Visitors	no restrictions.
Societies	welcome.
Green Fees	not confirmed.
Facilities	⊗ ⅷ ⅃ ⅊ ⅊⅄
Location	NE side of village off A5
Hotel	★★★66% Royal Oak, Holyhead Rd, BETWS-Y-COED ☎ (0690) 710219 27⇄ ⅋

CAERNARFON   Map 06 SH46

Caernarfon ☎ (0286) 673783 & 678359
Parkland course with gentle gradients.
18 holes, 5870yds, Par 69, SSS 69.
Club membership 745.

Visitors	may not play competition days.
Societies	must apply in advance.
Green Fees	£15 per day (£18 weekends).
Facilities	⊗ ⅷ ⅃ ⅊ ⅊⅄
Location	Llanfaglan (1.75m SW)
Hotel	★★65% Stables Hotel, LLANWNDA ☎ (0286) 830711 & 830935 Annexe14⇄ ⅋

CONWY   Map 06 SH77

Conwy (Caernarvonshire)
☎ Aberconwy (0492) 592423
This course close by the old town of Conwy is a real
seaside links with gorse, rushes, sandhills and fine old
turf. There are plenty of natural hazards, the gorse
providing more than its share. The course has a
spectacular setting between sea and mountains.
18 holes, 6647yds, Par 72, SSS 73.
Club membership 960.

Visitors	must have a certified club handicap. Restricted weekends & competitions.
Societies	must contact in advance.
Green Fees	£22 per day (£27 weekends & bank holidays).
Facilities	⊗ (ex Tue) 〲 (ex Mon and Tue) ⓑ (ex Tue) ♨ 𝖞 ⚐ ⚘ 🏠 ⟨ Peter Lees.
Location	The Morfa (1m W of town centre on A55)
Hotel	★★66% Bryn Cregin Garden Hotel, Ty Mawr Rd, DEGANWY ☏ (0492) 585266 17⇄ 🐾

CRICCIETH   Map 06 SH43

Criccieth ☏ (0766) 522154
Hilly course on Lleyn Peninsula. Good views.
18 holes, 5787yds, Par 69, SSS 68, Course record 65.
Club membership 234.

Visitors	no restrictions.
Societies	no restrictions.
Green Fees	not confirmed.
Facilities	⊗ 〲 ⓑ 🏠 𝖞 ⚘ 🏠
Location	Ednyfed Hill (1m NE)
Hotel	★★★⚑⚑67% Bron Eifion Country House Hotel, CRICCIETH ☏ (0766) 522385 19⇄ 🐾

DOLGELLAU   Map 06 SH71

Dolgellau ☏ (0341) 422603
Undulating parkland course. Good views of mountains and Mawddach estuary.
9 holes, 4671yds, Par 66, SSS 63.
Club membership 280.

Visitors	may not play on Sat.
Societies	must contact in advance.
Green Fees	£12 (£14 weekends & bank holidays).
Facilities	⊗ ⓑ 𝖞 ⚐ ⚘ 🏠
Location	Pencefn Rd (0.5m N)
Hotel	★★63% Royal Ship Hotel, Queens Square, DOLGELLAU ☏ (0341) 422209 24rm(13 ⇄4 🐾)

FFESTINIOG   Map 06 SH74

Ffestiniog ☏ (076676) 2637
Moorland course set in Snowdonia National Park.
9 holes, 4570yds, Par 68, SSS 66.
Club membership 150.

Visitors	welcome except during competitions.
Societies	must telephone in advance.
Green Fees	£8 per day.
Facilities	⚘
Location	Y Cefn (1m E on B4391)
Hotel	★★(red)⚑⚑ Maes y Neuadd Hotel, TALSARNAU ☏ (0766) 780200 12⇄ 🐾Annexe4⇄ 🐾

HARLECH   Map 06 SH53

Royal St Davids ☏ (0766) 780361
Championship links, with easy walking and natural hazards.
18 holes, 6427yds, Par 69, SSS 71.
Club membership 750.

Visitors	must be member of recognised golf club & hold current handicap certificate.
Societies	apply in writing.
Green Fees	£23 per day (£25 weekends & bank holidays).
Facilities	⊗ 〲 ⓑ 𝖞 ⚐ ⚘ 🏠 ⟨ John Barnett.
Location	W side of town on A496
Hotel	★★61% Ty Mawr Hotel, LLANBEDR ☏ (034123) 440 10⇄ 🐾

HOLYHEAD   Map 06 SH28

See under Anglesey, Isle of

LLANDUDNO   Map 06 SH78

Llandudno (Maesdu) ☏ (0492) 76450
Part links, part parkland, this championship course starts and finishes on one side of the main road, the remaining holes, more seaside in nature, being played on the other side. The holes are pleasantly undulating and present a pretty picture when the gorse is in bloom. Often windy, this varied and testing course is not for beginners.
18 holes, 6161yds, Par 70, SSS 70.
Club membership 1100.

Visitors	welcome although some times are restricted. Must be member of a club with handicap certificate.
Societies	must apply in advance, must be members of a recognised golf club.
Green Fees	£20 per day (£25 weekends & bank holidays).
Facilities	⊗ 〲 ⓑ 𝖞 ⚐ ⚘ 🏠 ⚐ ⟨ Simon Boulden.
Leisure	snooker.
Location	Hospital Rd (S side of town centre on A546)
Hotel	★★★66% Imperial Hotel, The Promenade, LLANDUDNO ☏ (0492) 877466 100 ⇄ 🐾

North Wales ☏ (0492) 875325
Challenging seaside links with superb views of Anglesey and Snowdonia.
18 holes, 6132yds, Par 71, SSS 69, Course record 65.
Club membership 750.

Visitors	must contact in advance & have handicap certificate, some times are restricted weekdays & weekends.
Societies	must telephone in advance.
Green Fees	£20 per day (£25 weekends & bank holidays).
Facilities	⊗ 〲 ⓑ 𝖞 ⚐ ⚘ 🏠 ⚐ ⟨ Richard Bradbury.
Leisure	snooker, practice ground.
Location	72 Bryniau Rd, West Shore (W side of town on A546)
Hotel	★★(red) St Tudno Hotel, Promenade, LLANDUDNO ☏ (0492) 874411 21⇄ 🐾

Rhos-on-Sea ☏ Colwyn Bay (0492) 549641
Seaside course, with easy walking and panoramic views.
18 holes, 6064yds, Par 69, SSS 69.
Club membership 400.

Visitors	must contact in advance.
Societies	booking essential, telephone in advance.
Green Fees	£15 per day (£20 weekends).
Facilities	⊗ 〲 by prior arrangement ⓑ 𝖞 ⚐ ⚘ 🏠 ⟨ ▶

Leisure snooker.
Location Penrhyn Bay (0.5m W off A546)
Hotel ★★★64% Gogarth Abbey Hotel, West Shore, LLANDUDNO ☎ (0492) 876211 40◁ ♣

LLANFAIRFECHAN   Map 06 SH67

Llanfairfechan ☎ (0248) 680144
Hillside course with panoramic views of coast.
9 holes, 3119yds, Par 54, SSS 57, Course record 53.
Club membership 350.
Visitors no restrictions.
Societies apply in writing to the secretary.
Green Fees £6 per day (£10 weekends).
Facilities ᗊ ♀ ⚘
Location Fford Llannerch (W side of town on A55)
Hotel ★★★65% Sychnant Pass Hotel, Sychnant Pass Rd, CONWY ☎ (0492) 596868 & 596869 13◁ ♣

LLANGEFNI   Map 06 SH47

See under Anglesey, Isle of

MORFA NEFYN   Map 06 SH24

Nefyn & District ☎ (0758) 720218
Seaside course, with parkland fairways and good views.
Testing golf along cliff edge. Large clubhouse with
excellent facilities. Course record holder Ian Woosnam.
18 holes, 6301yds, Par 72, SSS 71, Course record 67.
Club membership 800.
Visitors must have a handicap certificate.
Societies apply in writing to the secretary.
Green Fees £22.50 per day; £17.50 per round (£30/£25 weekends & bank holidays).
Facilities ⊗ ⍭ ᗊ ♥ ♀ ⚘ 🏮ℓ
Leisure snooker.
Location 0.75m NW
Hotel ★★58% Linksway Hotel, MORFA NEFYN ☎ (0758) 720258 26rm(11◁10 ♣)

PENMAENMAWR   Map 06 SH77

Penmaenmawr ☎ (0492) 623330
Hilly course with magnificent views across the bay to
Llandudno and Anglesey. Dry-stone wall natural hazards.
9 holes, 5306yds, Par 67, SSS 66.
Club membership 600.
Visitors no restrictions.
Societies must telephone in advance.
Green Fees not confirmed.
Facilities ♥ ♀ ⚘
Leisure bowling, darts, pool table.
Location Cae Maen Pavilion (1.5m NE off A55)
Hotel ★★58% Lion Hotel, Y Maes, CRICCIETH ☎ (0766) 522460 35rm(30◁ ♣)

PORTHMADOG   Map 06 SH53

Porthmadog ☎ (0766) 514124 & 513828
Seaside links,very interesting but with easy walking and good
views.
18 holes, 6240yds, Par 70, SSS 70.
Club membership 900.

Visitors must contact in advance.
Societies must apply in writing.
Green Fees not confirmed.
Facilities ⊗ ⍭ ᗊ ♥ ♀ ⚘ 🏮ℓ Peter Bright.
Leisure snooker.
Location Morfa Bychan (1.5m SW)
Hotel ★★62% Plas Isa Hotel, Porthmadog Rd, CRICCIETH ☎ (0766) 522443 14◁ ♣

PWLLHELI   Map 06 SH33

Pwllheli ☎ (0758) 612520
Easy walking on flat seaside course with outstanding views of
Snowdon, Cader Idris and Cardigan Bay.
18 holes, 6091yds, Par 69, SSS 69, Course record 66.
Club membership 880.
Visitors restricted Tue,Thu & weekends.
Societies must telephone in advance.
Green Fees £20 per day (£25 weekends & bank holidays).
Facilities ⊗ ⍭ ᗊ ♥ ♀ ⚘ 🏮ℓ G D Verity.
Leisure snooker.
Location Golf Rd (0.5m SW off A497)
Hotel ★60% Caeau Capel Hotel, Rhodfar Mor, NEFYN ☎ (0758) 720240 14rm(10 ♣)Annexe5◁ ♣

RHOSNEIGR   Map 06 SH37

See under Anglesey, Isle of

MID GLAMORGAN

ABERDARE   Map 03 SO00

Aberdare ☎ (0685) 871188 & 872797
Mountain course with parkland features overlooking Cynon
Valley.
18 holes, 5875yds, Par 69, SSS 69, Course record 63.
Club membership 550.
Visitors must contact in advance & have handicap certificate but may only play on Sat with member.
Societies must contact by phone & confirm in writing.
Green Fees £14 per day (£18 Sun & bank holidays).
Facilities ⊗ ⍭ ᗊ ♥ by prior arrangement ♀ ⚘ 🏮ℓ A W Palmer.
Leisure snooker.
Location Abernant (0.75m E)
Hotel ★★★53% Maes Manor Hotel, BLACKWOOD ☎ (0495) 224551 & 220011 8◁Annexe14◁

BARGOED   Map 03 ST19

Bargoed ☎ (0443) 830143
Mountain parkland course, testing par 4, 13th hole.
18 holes, 5836yds, Par 70, SSS 70.
Club membership 500.
Visitors must play with member at weekends.
Societies must contact in advance.
Green Fees £15 per day/round.
Facilities ⊗ ⍭ by prior arrangement ᗊ ♥ ♀ ⚘
Location Heolddu (NW side of town)
Hotel ★★★53% Maes Manor Hotel, BLACKWOOD ☎ (0495) 224551 & 220011 8 ◁Annexe14 ◁

BRIDGEND
Map 03 SS97

Southerndown ☎ (0656) 880476
Downland championship course with rolling fairways and fast greens. The par-3 5th is played across a valley and the 18th, with its split level fairway, is a demanding finishing hole. Superb views.
18 holes, 6615yds, Par 70, SSS 73, Course record 64.
Club membership 720.
Visitors   must contact in advance & have handicap certificate. With member only Sun (Oct-Mar).
Societies   must contact in advance.
Green Fees £24 per day; £18 per round (£30/£25 weekends) (Rounds played afternoons only).
Facilities ⊗ ⅲ by prior arrangement ⓑ ⬛ ♀ ⚘ ⛴ ℓ D G McMonagle.
Leisure   snooker.
Location   Ewenny (3m SW on B4524)
Hotel   ★★★65% Heronston Hotel, Ewenny, BRIDGEND ☎ (0656) 668811 76 ⇄ ☈
Additional ★★★72% Coed-y-Mwstwr Hotel,
Hotel   Coychurch, BRIDGEND
☎ (0656) 860621 24⇄ ☈

CAERPHILLY
Map 03 ST18

Caerphilly ☎ (0222) 883481 & 86344
Undulating mountain course with woodland. Good views especially from 10th hole, 700 ft above sea level.
14 holes, 6028yds, Par 73, SSS 71, Course record 67.
Club membership 792.

Coed-y-Mwstwr

An elegant late-Victorian mansion, tastefully converted into a Luxury Hotel and Restaurant for the discerning.
In the 17 acre grounds are a swimming pool and tennis court; the hotel also has a snooker room.
The focal point of the Hotel is undoubtedly the oak-panelled Restaurant, renowned for its Good food, fine wine and friendly attentive service. 2½ miles from exit 35 off M4. Turn off on to A473 towards Bridgend – approx 1 mile turn right into Coychurch Village Centre – well signposted from Fina filling station.

**AT COYCHURCH, Nr. BRIDGEND,
MID-GLAMORGAN CR35 6AF.
Tel: (0656) 860621**

Visitors   must contact in advance & have a handicap certificate & membership of a recognised golf club. May only play with member at weekends & bank holidays.
Societies   must contact in advance.
Green Fees £18 per day.
Facilities ♀ ⚘ ⛴ ℓ Richard Barter.
Leisure   snooker, billiards/snooker.
Location   Pencapel Mountain Rd (0.5m S on A469)
Hotel   ★★★70% Manor Parc Country Hotel & Restaurant, Thornhill Rd, Thornhill, CARDIFF ☎ (0222) 693723 12⇄ ☈

Castell Heights ☎ (0222) 886666
'Pay as you play' parkland courses.
Castell Heights: 9 holes, 2700yds, Par 34, SSS 32, Course record 31.
Mountain Lakes: 18 holes, 6500yds, Par 72, SSS 73, Course record 69.
Club membership 700.
Visitors   no restrictions.
Societies   must contact in advance.
Green Fees not confirmed.
Facilities ⊗ ⅲ ⓑ ⬛ ♀ ⚘ ⛴ ⅋ ℓ Sion Bebb.
Leisure   driving range.
Location   Blaengwynlais (2m SW)
Hotel   ★★★70% Manor Parc Country Hotel & Restaurant, Thornhill Rd, Thornhill, CARDIFF ☎ (0222) 693723 12⇄ ☈

CREIGIAU (CREIYIAU)
Map 03 ST08

Creigiau ☎ Cardiff (0222) 890263
Downland course, with small greens.
18 holes, 5979yds, Par 70, SSS 69.
Club membership 850.
Visitors   must be a member of a recognised golf club. Must play with member at weekends.
Societies   must contact in writing.
Green Fees £21 per day.
Facilities ⊗ ⅲ ⓑ ⬛ ♀ ⚘ ⛴ ℓ Mark Maddison.
Location   6m NW of Cardiff on A4119
Hotel   ★★★65% Forte Crest Hotel, Castle St, CARDIFF ☎ (0222) 388681 155⇄ ☈

MAESTEG
Map 03 SS89

Maesteg ☎ (0656) 732037
Reasonably flat hill-top course with scenic views.
18 holes, 5900yds, Par 70, SSS 69, Course record 64.
Club membership 700.
Visitors   must be a member of a recognised golf club & have a handicap certificate.
Societies   weekdays only. Must contact in advance.
Green Fees £15 per day (£20 weekends & bank holidays).
Facilities ⊗ ⅲ by prior arrangement ⓑ ⬛ ♀ ⚘ ⛴ ℓ W Evans.
Location   Mount Pleasant, Neath Rd (0.5m W off B4282)
Hotel   ★★★60% Aberavan Beach Hotel, PORT TALBOT ☎ (0639) 884949 52⇄

For an explanation of symbols and abbreviations, see page 11

MAESYCWMMER
Map 03 ST19

Bryn Meadows ☎ Blackwood (0495) 225590
A heavily wooded parkland course with panoramic views of
the Brecon Beacons.
18 holes, 6132yds, Par 72, SSS 69, Course record 68.
Club membership 540.
Visitors	may not play Sun mornings. Must contact in advance.
Societies	Tue & Thu only.
Green Fees	not confirmed.
Facilities	⊗ ⍾ ⤵ ♥ ♀ ⚲ ⌂ ↑ ◤ ¢ Bruce Hunter.
Leisure	heated indoor swimming pool, sauna, gymnasium.
Location	The Bryn (on the A4048 Blackwood to Ystrad Mynach rd)
Hotel	★★★53% Maes Manor Hotel, BLACKWOOD ☎ (0495) 224551 & 220011 8⇋Annexe14⇋

MERTHYR TYDFIL
Map 03 SO00

Merthyr Tydfil (Cilanws) ☎ (0685) 723308
Mountain-top course with good views and water hazards.
Requires accuracy off the tee.
11 holes, 5956yds, Par 70, SSS 69, Course record 66.
Club membership 200.
Visitors	may not play on Sun.
Societies	must contact in writing.
Green Fees	£10 (£12 weekends).
Facilities	♀
Location	Cilsanws, Cefn Coed (2m NW off A470)
Hotel	★★62% Nant Ddu Lodge, Cwm Taf, NR BRECON ☎ (0685) 379111 15⇋ ⁿ

Morlais Castle ☎ (0685) 722822
Beautiful moorland course in National Park adjacent to
Brecon Beacons. Rocky terrain off the fairways makes for a
testing game.
18 holes, 6320yds, Par 71, SSS 71.
Club membership 400.
Visitors	must contact in advance for weekends.
Societies	weekdays only; must telephone in advance & confirm in writing.
Green Fees	£14 (£16 weekends).
Facilities	⊗ ⍾ by prior arrangement ⤵ ♥ ♀ ⚲
Location	Pant, Dowlais (2.5m N off A465)
Hotel	★★62% Nant Ddu Lodge, Cwm Taf, NR BRECON ☎ (0685) 379111 15⇋ ⁿ

MOUNTAIN ASH
Map 03 ST09

Mountain Ash ☎ (0443) 472265
Mountain course.
18 holes, 5553yds, Par 69, SSS 68, Course record 63.
Club membership 600.
Visitors	must play with member at weekends and must have a handicap certificate.
Societies	must contact in writing.
Green Fees	£18 per day.
Facilities	⊗ ⍾ ⤵ ♥ (ex Mon) ♀ (Mon only in winter) ⚲ ⌂ ¢
Location	Cefnpennar (1m NW off A4059)
Hotel	★★62% Nant Ddu Lodge, Cwm Taf, NR BRECON ☎ (0685) 379111 15⇋ ⁿ

NELSON
Map 03 ST19

Whitehall ☎ (0443) 740245
Windy hilltop course. Testing 4th hole (225 yds) par 3, and
6th hole (402 yds) par 4. Pleasant views.
9 holes, 5666yds, Par 69, SSS 68, Course record 62.
Club membership 300.
Visitors	must be a member of a recognised golf club & have a handicap certificate. Must contact in advance to play at weekends.
Societies	must contact in writing 4 weeks in advance.
Green Fees	not confirmed.
Facilities	⊗ ⍾ ⤵ ♥ ♀ ⚲
Location	The Pavilion (2m W off A470)
Hotel	★★★62% Llechwen Hall Hotel, Llanfabon, PONTYPRIDD ☎ (0443) 742050 11⇋ ⁿ

PENRHYS
Map 03 ST09

Rhondda ☎ Tonypandy (0443) 441384
Mountain course with good views.
18 holes, 6206yds, Par 70, SSS 70, Course record 67.
Club membership 700.
Visitors	restricted Sun
Societies	must contact in advance.
Green Fees	£15 (£20 weekends & bank holidays).
Facilities	⊗ ⍾ ⤵ ♥ ♀ ⚲ ⌂ ¢ Rhys Davies.
Leisure	snooker.
Location	Golf Club House (0.5m W off B4512)
Hotel	★★57% Wyndham Hotel, Dunraven Place, BRIDGEND ☎ (0656) 652080 & 657431 28rm(25⇋)

PONTYPRIDD
Map 03 ST09

Pontypridd ☎ (0443) 409904 & 402359
Well-wooded mountain course with springy turf. Good views
of the Rhondda Valleys and coast.
18 holes, 5648yds, Par 69, SSS 68.
Club membership 800.
Visitors	must play with member on weekends & bank holidays. Must have a handicap certificate.
Societies	weekdays only. Must apply in writing.
Green Fees	£17 per day.
Facilities	⊗ ⍾ by prior arrangement ⤵ ♥ ♀ ⚲ ⌂ ¢
Leisure	snooker.
Location	Ty Gwyn Rd (E side of town centre off A470)
Hotel	★★★65% Forte Crest Hotel, Castle St, CARDIFF ☎ (0222) 388681 155⇋ ⁿ

PORTHCAWL
Map 03 SS87

Royal Porthcawl ☎ (0656) 782251
This championship-standard heathland/downland links
course is always in sight of the sea, and has hosted many
major tournaments.
18 holes, 6409yds, Par 72, SSS 73.
Club membership 800.
Visitors	must contact in advanced & have handicap certificate. Restricted at weekends & bank holidays.
Societies	must contact in writing.

Green Fees on application.
Facilities ⊗ ┣ ▆ ♀ 🛆 📧 ⛳ ₵ Peter Evans.
Location 1.5m NW of town centre
Hotel ★★★60% Seabank Hotel, The Promenade,
PORTHCAWL ☎ (0656) 782261 64⇆ 🐾

PYLE
Map 03 SS88

Pyle & Kenfig ☎ Porthcawl (065678) 3093
Links and downland course, with sand-dunes. Easy walking.
Often windy.
18 holes, 6081mtrs, Par 71, SSS 73.
Club membership 1089.
Visitors must play with member at weekends. Must have
a handicap certificate.
Societies weekdays only. Must contact in advance.
Green Fees not confirmed.
Facilities ⊗ ∭ by prior arrangement ┣ ▆ ♀ 🛆 📧 ₵
Robert Evans.
Location Waun-Y-Mer (S side of Pyle off A4229)
Hotel ★★★60% Seabank Hotel, The Promenade,
PORTHCAWL ☎ (0656) 782261 64⇆ 🐾

TALBOT GREEN
Map 03 ST08

Llantrisant & Pontyclun ☎ Llantrisant (0443) 222148
Parkland course.
12 holes, 5712yds, Par 68, SSS 68.
Club membership 600.
Visitors must have a club membership card & handicap
certificate and should be accompanied by a
member.
Societies apply in writing.
Green Fees not confirmed.
Facilities ⊗ ┣ ▆ ♀ 🛆 📧 ⛳ ₵ Nick Watson.
Location Llanelry Rd (N side of village off A473)
Hotel ★★57% Wyndham Hotel, Dunraven Place,
BRIDGEND ☎ (0656) 652080 & 657431
28rm(25⇆)

POWYS

BRECON
Map 03 SO02

Brecon ☎ (0874) 622004
Parkland course, with easy walking. Natural hazards include
two rivers on its boundary. Good river and mountain scenery.
9 holes, 5218yds, Par 66, SSS 66, Course record 61.
Club membership 420.
Visitors restricted on competition days.
Societies must contact in writing.
Green Fees not confirmed.
Facilities ⊗ & ∭ by prior arrangement ┣ ♀ 🛆
Location Newton Park (0.75m W of town centre on A40)
Hotel ★★63% Castle of Brecon Hotel, Castle Square,
BRECON ☎ (0874) 624611
37⇆ 🐾Annexe12 🐾

Cradoc ☎ (0874) 623658
Parkland with wooded areas, lakes and spectacular views
over the Brecon Beacons. Challenging golf.
18 holes, 6301yds, Par 71, SSS 71, Course record 65.
Club membership 700.
Visitors must contact in advance. Restricted on Sun.
Societies must contact 7 days in advance.
Green Fees £17 (£20 weekends & bank holidays).
Facilities ⊗ & ∭ (ex Mon) ┣ ▆ ♀ 🛆 📧 ₵ Douglas
Beattie.
Location Penoyre Park, Cradoc (2m NW)
Hotel ★★63% Castle of Brecon Hotel, Castle Square,
BRECON ☎ (0874) 624611
37⇆ 🐾Annexe12 🐾

CAERSWS
Map 06 SO09

Maesmawr ☎ (0686) 688303
A 9-hole, Par 3 course with sand bunkers and three ponds.
9 holes, 2554yds, Par 54, SSS 54, Course record 63.
Club membership 85.
Visitors restricted during competition time.
Societies telephone in advance.
Green Fees £6 per day (£8 weekends).
Facilities ▆ ♀ 🛆 📧 ⛳
Leisure 12 bay floodlit driving range.
Location Mid Wales Golf Centre (6m W of Newtown)
Hotel ★★63% Elephant & Castle, Broad St,
NEWTOWN
☎ (0686) 626271 25⇆ 🐾 Annexe11⇆ 🐾

KNIGHTON
Map 07 SO27

Knighton ☎ (0547) 528646
Hill course with hard walking.
9 holes, 5320yds, Par 68, SSS 66, Course record 60.
Club membership 150.
Visitors may not play on Sun afternoons.
Societies must contact in advance.
Green Fees £8 per round (£10 weekends).
Facilities ♀ 🛆
Location Frydd Wood (0.5m S off B4355)
Hotel ★★68% Radnorshire Arms Hotel, High St,
PRESTEIGNE ☎ (0544) 267406
8⇆ 🐾 Annexe8⇆ 🐾

LLANDRINDOD WELLS
Map 03 SO06

Llandrindod Wells ☎ (0597) 822010 & 823873
Moorland course, designed by Harry Vardon, with easy
walking and panoramic views. One of the highest courses in
Wales. (1,100 ft above sea level).
18 holes, 5759yds, Par 68, SSS 67.
Club membership 650.
Visitors no restrictions.
Societies must telephone in advance.
Green Fees £12 weekdays (£18 weekends).
Facilities ⊗ ∭ ┣ ▆ (no catering Tue) ♀ 🛆 📧 ⛳
Location 1m SE off A483
Hotel ★★★62% Hotel Metropole, Temple St,
LLANDRINDOD WELLS
☎ (0597) 823700 121⇆ 🐾

LLANGATTOCK   Map 03 SO21

Old Rectory ☎ (0873) 810373
Sheltered course with easy walking.
9 holes, 2225yds, Par 53, SSS 54 or 53yds.
Club membership 200.
Visitors   no restrictions.
Green Fees not confirmed.
Facilities ♀△
Leisure   swimming pool.
Location   SW of village
Hotel   ★★♣♣70% Gliffaes Country House Hotel,
                CRICKHOWELL ☎ (0874) 730371
                19rm(15⇌3 ♠) Annexe3⇌ ♠

LLANIDLOES   Map 06 SN98

St Idloes ☎ (05512) 2559
Hill-course, slightly undulating but walking is easy. Good
views.
9 holes, 5320yds, Par 66, SSS 66, Course record 59.
Club membership 350.
Visitors   may not play on Sun mornings. Must have a
                handicap certificate.
Societies   must contact in advance.
Green Fees £10 per round (£12 weekends).
Facilities ⊗ ♣ ♥ (catering by prior arrangement). ♀△
Location   Penrhallt (1m N off B4569)
Hotel   ★★69% Glansevern Arms Hotel, Pant Mawr,
                LLANGURIG ☎ (05515) 240 7⇌ ♠

MACHYNLLETH   Map 06 SH70

Machynlleth ☎ (0654) 702000
Lowland course with mostly natural hazards.
9 holes, 5726yds, Par 68, SSS 67, Course record 66.
Club membership 247.
Visitors   may not play during competitions & Thu 1-2pm.
Societies   must contact in advance.
Green Fees not confirmed.
Facilities △♠
Location   Ffordd Drenewydd (0.5m E off A489)
Hotel   ★★64% Wynnstay Arms Hotel, Maengwyn St,
                MACHYNLLETH ☎ (0654) 702941 20⇌ ♠

NEWTOWN   Map 07 SO19

St Giles ☎ (0686) 625844
Inland country course with easy walking. Testing 2nd hole,
par 3, and 4th hole, par 4. River Severn skirts four holes.
9 holes, 5936yds, Par 70, SSS 68, Course record 63.
Club membership 400.
Visitors   restricted Thu & Sat afternoons & Sun
                mornings. Must have a handicap certificate.
Societies   must contact in advance.
Green Fees £12.50 per day (£15 weekends & bank holidays).
Facilities ⊗ ♥ ♣ ♥ (No catering Mon) ♀(ex Mon) △
                ♠♥♦ D P Owen.
Leisure   fishing.
Location   Pool Rd (0.5m NE on A483)
Hotel   ★★63% Elephant & Castle, Broad St,
                NEWTOWN ☎ (0686) 626271
                25⇌ ♠ Annexe11⇌ ♠

WELSHPOOL   Map 07 SJ20

Welshpool ☎ Castle Caerinion (0938) 83249
Undulating heathland course with bracing air. Testing holes
are 2nd (par 5), 14th (par 3), 17th (par 3).
18 holes, 5708yds, Par 70, SSS 69.
Club membership 550.
Visitors   must contact in advance.
Societies   must book in advance.
Green Fees £8 (£15 weekends & bank holidays).
Facilities ⊗ & ♥ by prior arrangement ♣ ♥ ♀△ ♠
Location   Golfa Hill (3m W off A458)
Hotel   ★★65% Royal Oak Hotel, WELSHPOOL
                ☎ (0938) 552217 24⇌ ♠

● SOUTH GLAMORGAN ●

BARRY   Map 03 ST16

Brynhill ☎ (0446) 720277 & 735061
Meadowland course with some hard walking. Prevailing west
wind.
18 holes, 6077yds, Par 71, SSS 69.
Club membership 500.
Visitors   must have a handicap certificate. May not play
                on Sun.
Societies   weekdays only.
Green Fees £20 per round.
Facilities ⊗ ♥ ♣ ♥ ♀△ ♠♦ Peter Fountain.
Leisure   snooker.
Location   Port Rd (1.25m N on B4050)
Hotel   ★★★56% Mount Sorrell Hotel, Porthkerry Rd,
                BARRY ☎ (0446) 740069 45⇌ ♠

St Andrews Major
A new 9-hole, Pay and Play course with 6 Par 4s and 1 Par 5.
9 holes, 3100yds, Par 35.
Club membership 500.
Visitors   must have own clubs and be appropriately
                dressed including golf shoes.
Societies   contact in advance.
Green Fees £6 per 9 holes (£8 weekends).
Facilities ⊗ ♥ (summer only) ♣ ♥ ♀△ ♠♦♦
Location   Coldbrook Rd, Argae Ln, nr Cadoxton (off
                Barry new link road)
Hotel   ★★★♣♣74% Egerton Grey Country House
                Hotel, Porthkerry, BARRY
                ☎ (0446) 711666 10⇌ ♠

CARDIFF   Map 03 ST17

Cardiff ☎ (0222) 753320
Parkland course, where trees form natural hazards. Interesting
variety of holes, mostly bunkered.
18 holes, 6016yds, Par 70, SSS 70, Course record 66.
Club membership 930.
Visitors   must play with member at weekends.
Societies   Thu only.
Green Fees not confirmed.
Facilities ⊗ ♥ ♣ ♥ ♀△ ♠♦ Terry Hanson.

Location Sherborne Av, Cyncoed (3m N of city centre)
Hotel ★★★63% Forte Posthouse, Pentwyn Rd,
Pentwyn, CARDIFF
☎ (0222) 731212 142⇆ ⚑

Llanishen ☎ (0222) 755078
Mountain course, with hard walking overlooking the Bristol
Channel.
18 holes, 5296yds, Par 68, SSS 66, Course record 64.
Club membership 900.
Visitors must play with member at weekends & bank
holidays. Must contact in advance and have a
handicap certificate.
Societies Thu only.
Green Fees £22 per round.
Facilities ⊗ ⅲ ⅃ ♥ ♀ ⚖ ⌂ (R A Jones.
Leisure snooker.
Location Cwm Lisvane (5m N of city centre off A469)
Hotel ★★★63% Forte Posthouse, Pentwyn Rd,
Pentwyn, CARDIFF
☎ (0222) 731212 142⇆ ⚑

Peterstone ☎ (0633) 680009
Parkland course with abundant water features and several
long drives (15th, 601yds).
18 holes, 6600yds, Par 71, SSS 70.
Club membership 735.
Visitors must have a handicap certificate and be a
member of a club. Contact in advance with letter
from club.
Societies must apply in advance.
Green Fees £17.50 per 18 holes (£22.50 weekends).
Facilities ⊗ ⅲ ⅃ ♥ ♀ ⚖ ⌂ (Michael Pycroft.
Leisure fishing, snooker.
Location Peterstone, Wentloog (SW Newport,A48
Castleton,through Marshfield)
Hotel ★★★61% Wentloog Resort Hotel, CASTLETON
☎ (0633) 680591 55⇆ ⚑

Radyr ☎ (0222) 842408
Hillside, parkland course which can be windy. Good views.
18 holes, 6031yds, Par 69, SSS 70, Course record 63.
Club membership 870.
Visitors must play with member at weekends. Must
contact in advance and have an introduction
from own club.
Societies must contact in advance.
Green Fees not confirmed.
Facilities ⊗ ⅲ ⅃ ♥ ♀ ⚖ ⌂ (Steve Gough.
Leisure snooker.
Location Drysgol Rd, Radyr (4.5m NW of city centre off
A4119)
Hotel ★★★★56% Park Hotel, Park Place, CARDIFF
☎ (0222) 383471 119⇆ ⚑

St Mellons ☎ (0633) 680408
This parkland course comprises quite a few par-3 holes
and provides some testing golf. It is indeed a challenge to
the single handicap golfer. The 12th hole runs over a
stream, making an accurate drive virtually essential.
18 holes, 6080yds, Par 70, SSS 70.
Club membership 800.
Visitors must contact in advance & have handicap
certificate. With member only at weekends.
Societies must telephone in advance.

Green Fees not confirmed.
Facilities ⊗ ⅲ ⅃ ♥ ♀ ⚖ ⌂ (
Location St Mellons (5m NE off A48)
Hotel ★★★63% Forte Posthouse, Pentwyn Rd,
Pentwyn, CARDIFF
☎ (0222) 731212 142 ⇆ ⚑

Whitchurch ☎ (0222) 620985
Well manicured parkland course, with easy walking.
18 holes, 6319yds, Par 71, SSS 70, Course record 62.
Club membership 1000.
Visitors must have a handicap certificate. Restricted Sat
(Apr-Oct), Sun (Oct-Apr).
Societies Thu only. Must contact in writing.
Green Fees £23 (£30 weekends & bank holidays).
Facilities ⊗ & ⅲ by prior arrangement
⅃ ♥ ♀ ⚖ ⌂ ⚑ (E Clark.
Location Whitchurch (4m N of city centre on A470)
Hotel ★★★★56% Park Hotel, Park Place, CARDIFF
☎ (0222) 383471 119⇆ ⚑

DINAS POWIS
Map 03 ST17

Dinas Powis ☎ (0222) 512727
Parkland/downland course with views over the Bristol
Channel and the seaside resort of Barry.
18 holes, 5377yds, Par 67, SSS 66, Course record 65.
Club membership 620.
Visitors must play with member at weekends. Must have
an introduction from own club.
Societies must contact in advance.
Green Fees not confirmed.
Facilities ⊗ ⅲ ⅃ ♥ ♀ ⚖ ⌂ (G Bennett.
Location Old High Walls (NW side of village)
Hotel ★★★56% Mount Sorrell Hotel, Porthkerry Rd,
BARRY ☎ (0446) 740069 45⇆ ⚑

PENARTH
Map 03 ST17

Glamorganshire ☎ Cardiff (0222) 701185
Parkland course, overlooking the Bristol Channel.
18 holes, 6181yds, Par 70, SSS 70.
Club membership 1000.
Visitors must be a member of a recognised golf club &
have a handicap certificate. May not play on
competition & society days. Must contact in
advance.
Societies Mon, Wed-Fri only. Must contact in advance.
Green Fees £24 per day.
Facilities ⊗ ⅲ by prior arrangement ⅃ ♥ ♀ ⚖ ⌂ (
Andrew Kerr Smith.
Leisure squash, snooker.
Location Lavernock Rd (S side of town centre on B4267)
Hotel ★65% Walton House Hotel, 37 Victoria Rd,
PENARTH ☎ (0222) 707782 13rm(11⇆ ⚑)

WENVOE
Map 03 ST17

Wenvoe Castle ☎ Cardiff (0222) 594371
Parkland course which is hilly for first 9 holes. Lake, situated
280 yds from tee at 10th hole, is a hazard.
18 holes, 6422yds, Par 72, SSS 71, Course record 68.
Club membership 600.

▶

Visitors must be a member of a recognised golf club & have a handicap certificate. Must play with member at weekends. Must contact in advance and have an introduction from own club.
Societies must contact in writing.
Green Fees not confirmed.
Facilities ⊗ ⵜ ⴱ ⴱ ⵙ ⴷ ⴼ R J Wyer.
Location 1m S off A4050
Hotel ★★★65% Forte Crest Hotel, Castle St, CARDIFF ☎ (0222) 388681 155⇄ ♠

WEST GLAMORGAN

CLYDACH   Map 03 SN60

Inco ☎ (0792) 844216
Flat meadowland course.
12 holes, 6303yds, Par 71, SSS 70.
Club membership 300.
Visitors no restrictions.
Societies must contact in advance.
Green Fees £11/15 per round.
Facilities ⴱ ⵙ ⴷ
Location 0.75m SE on B4291
Hotel ★★62% Oak Tree Parc Hotel, Birchgrove Rd, BIRCHGROVE ☎ (0792) 817781 10⇄ ♠

GLYNNEATH   Map 03 SN80

Glynneath ☎ (0639) 720452
Attractive hillside golf overlooking the Vale of Neath. Reasonably level farmland/wooded course.
18 holes, 5560yds, Par 68, SSS 67, Course record 66.
Club membership 580.
Visitors restricted starting times at weekend.
Societies welcome mid-week. Must book in advance.
Green Fees £15 per day; £12 per round (£18 per day weekends).
Facilities ⴱ ⴱ ⵙ ⴷ ⴺ
Leisure snooker.
Location Pen-y-graig, Pontneathvaughan (2m NE on B4242)
Hotel ★★62% Oak Tree Parc Hotel, Birchgrove Rd, BIRCHGROVE ☎ (0792) 817781 10⇄ ♠

NEATH   Map 03 SS79

Neath ☎ (0639) 643615
Mountain course, with spectacular views. Testing holes: 10th par 4; 12th par 5; 15th par 4.
18 holes, 6492yds, Par 72, SSS 72.
Club membership 700.
Visitors with member only weekends & bank holidays.
Societies should either telephone or write in advance.
Green Fees £17 per day.
Facilities ⊗ ⵜ ⴱ ⴱ ⵙ ⴷ ⴺ ⴼ ⴼ E M Bennett.
Leisure snooker.
Location Cadoxton (2m NE off A4230)
Hotel ★★64% Castle Hotel, The Parade, NEATH ☎ (0639) 641119 & 643581 28⇄ ♠

Swansea Bay ☎ Skewen (0792) 814153
Fairly level seaside links with part-sand dunes.
18 holes, 6605yds, Par 72, SSS 70.
Club membership 500.
Visitors must have a handicap certificate.
Societies must book in advance.
Green Fees £16 per day (£22 weekends & bank holidays).
Facilities ⊗ ⵜ by prior arrangement ⴱ ⴱ ⵙ ⴷ ⴼ Mike Day.
Leisure riding, snooker.
Location Jersey Marine (4m SW off A48)
Hotel ★★64% Castle Hotel, The Parade, NEATH ☎ (0639) 641119 & 643581 28⇄ ♠

PONTARDAWE   Map 03 SN70

Pontardawe ☎ (0792) 863118
Meadowland course situated on plateau 600 ft above sea-level with good views over Bristol Channel and Brecon Beacons.
18 holes, 6162yds, Par 70, SSS 70.
Club membership 700.
Visitors must contact in advance, but may not play on weekends.
Societies welcome weekdays by prior arrangement.
Green Fees £16.50 per round.
Facilities ⊗ ⵜ by prior arrangement ⴱ ⴱ ⵙ ⴷ ⴼ Gary Hopkins.
Leisure snooker.
Location Cefn Llan (N side of town centre M4 junc 45 off A406)
Hotel ★★62% Oak Tree Parc Hotel, Birchgrove Rd, BIRCHGROVE ☎ (0792) 817781 10⇄ ♠

SOUTHGATE   Map 02 SS58

Pennard ☎ Bishopston (044128) 3131
Undulating, cliff-top seaside links with good coastal views.
18 holes, 6289yds, Par 71, SSS 71, Course record 66.
Club membership 779.
Visitors a handicap certificate is required.
Societies welcome except weekends & bank holidays, must apply by letter.
Green Fees not confirmed.
Facilities ⊗ & ⵜ by prior arrangement ⴱ ⴱ ⵙ (times vary) ⴷ ⴺ ⴻ ⴼ M V Bennett.
Leisure squash, snooker.
Location 2 Southgate Rd (NW side of village)
Hotel ★71% Windsor Lodge Hotel, Mount Pleasant, SWANSEA ☎ (0792) 642158 & 652744 19rm(11⇄4 ♠)

SWANSEA   Map 03 SS69

Clyne ☎ (0792) 401989
Moorland course, very open to the wind and with grazing rights for local commoners.
18 holes, 6323yds, Par 70, SSS 71, Course record 64.
Club membership 800.
Visitors must be member of a club with handicap certificate and contact in advance.
Societies must telephone in advance.
Green Fees not confirmed.
Facilities ⊗ ⵜ ⴱ ⴱ (no catering Mon) ⵙ ⴷ ⴺ ⴼ Mark Bevan.

Leisure snooker, practice facilities.
Location 120 Owls Lodge Ln, The Mayals, Blackpyl (3.5m SW on B4436 off A4067)
Hotel ★★67% Langland Court, Langland Court Rd, LANGLAND ☎ (0792) 361545 16⇌ 🐾Annexe5⇌ 🐾

Langland Bay ☎ (0792) 366023
Parkland course overlooking Gower coast. The par 4, 6th is an uphill dog-leg open to the wind, and the par 3, 16th (151 yds) is aptly named 'Death or Glory'.
18 holes, 5830yds, Par 70, SSS 70.
Club membership 850.
Visitors no restrictions.
Societies must telephone in advance.
Green Fees not confirmed.
Facilities ⊗ ⅏ 🝙 💺 ♀ 🝘 🝙 🛈
Location Langland Bay (6m W on A4067)
Hotel ★★67% Langland Court, Langland Court Rd, LANGLAND ☎ (0792) 361545 16⇌ 🐾 Annexe5⇌ 🐾

Morriston ☎ (0792) 796528
Pleasant parkland course.
18 holes, 5800yds, Par 68, SSS 68.
Club membership 580.
Visitors must have handicap certificate.
Societies apply in writing.
Green Fees £18 per day (£25 weekends & bank holidays).
Facilities ⊗ ⅏ 🝙 ♀ 🝘 🝙 🛈 🛈 D A Rees.
Location 160 Clasemont Rd (5m N on A48)
Hotel ★★62% Oak Tree Parc Hotel, Birchgrove Rd, BIRCHGROVE ☎ (0792) 817781 10⇌ 🐾

UPPER KILLAY   Map 02 SS59

Fairwood Park ☎ Swansea (0792) 203648
Championship parkland course on Gower coast with good views and easy walking.
18 holes, 6741yds, Par 72, SSS 72, Course record 67.
Club membership 720.
Visitors welcome except when championship or club matches are being held. Must contact in advance.
Societies must contact in advance.
Green Fees £20 per day (£25 weekends & bank holidays).
Facilities ⊗ ⅏ 🝙 💺 ♀ 🝘 🝙 🛈 🛈 Mark Evans.
Leisure snooker.
Location Blackhills Ln (1.5m S off A4118)
Hotel ★71% Windsor Lodge Hotel, Mount Pleasant, SWANSEA ☎ (0792) 642158 & 652744 19rm(11⇌4 🐾)

YSTALYFERA   Map 03 SN70

Palleg ☎ (0639) 842193
Heathland course liable to become heavy going after winter rain.
9 holes, 6400yds, Par 72, SSS 72.
Club membership 200.
Visitors restricted Sat (Apr-Sep) & Sun mornings in winter.
Societies must contact two months in advance.
Green Fees £10 per round (£15 weekends & bank holidays).
Facilities ⊗ (Sun only) 🝙 (Thu & Sat) ♀ (ex Mon) 🜔
Location Lower Cwm-twrch (1.5m N off A4068)
Hotel ★★62% Oak Tree Parc Hotel, Birchgrove Rd, BIRCHGROVE ☎ (0792) 817781 10⇌ 🐾

SCOTLAND

•

BORDERS

•

COLDSTREAM   Map 12 NT83

Hirsel ☎ (0890) 882678 & 882626
Parkland course, with hard walking and sheltered trees. Testing 3rd and 6th holes. A further 9 holes have been developed and are due to be fully functional from end of 1993.
9 holes, 5830yds, Par 70, SSS 68.
Club membership 475.
Visitors restricted during competitions.
Societies contact for details.
Green Fees £10 per day (£15 weekends & bank holidays).
Facilities ⊗ 🝙 💺 (Apr-May, daily ex Tue, Jun-Sep daily) ♀ (Apr-Sep) 🜔 🝙 🛈
Location Kelso Rd (SW side of town off A678)
Hotel ★★★66% Ednam House Hotel, Bridge St, KELSO ☎ (0573) 224168 32⇌ 🐾

DUNS   Map 12 NT75

Duns ☎ (0361) 82717
Interesting upland course, with natural hazards of water and hilly slopes. Views south to the Cheviot Hills.
9 holes, 5826yds, Par 68, SSS 68, Course record 66.
Club membership 295.
Visitors welcome except competition days & Tue evenings.
Societies apply in writing.
Green Fees £10 per day/round (£5 Nov-15 Mar).
Facilities 🝙 (in season) ♀ (in season) 🜔
Location Longformacus Rd (1m W off A6105)
Hotel ★★★61% Turret House Hotel, Etal Rd, Tweedmouth, BERWICK-UPON-TWEED ☎ (0289) 330808 13⇌ 🐾

EYEMOUTH   Map 12 NT96

Eyemouth ☎ (08907) 50551
With the exception of a steep climb to the 1st tee, this is a compact, flat and popular seaside course. Fast smooth greens and fine views are typified by the 15th, played from an elevated tee to a green on a peninsula over a North Sea inlet.
9 holes, 4608mtrs, Par 66, SSS 65, Course record 60.
Club membership 250.
Visitors may not play before 10.30am Sat or noon Sun.
Societies apply in writing.
Green Fees not confirmed.
Facilities ♀ (evenings) 🜔 🝙 🛈 Craig Maltman.
Leisure snooker.
Location Gunsgreen House (E side of town)
Hotel ★★★61% Turret House Hotel, Etal Rd, Tweedmouth, BERWICK-UPON-TWEED ☎ (0289) 330808 13⇌ 🐾

GALASHIELS

Map 12 NT43

Galashiels ☎ (0896) 3724
Hillside course, superb views from the top; 10th hole very steep.
18 holes, 5185yds, Par 67, SSS 66, Course record 63.
Club membership 290.
Visitors no restrictions.
Societies must contact in advance.
Green Fees £12 per day; £8 per round (£16/£12 weekends).
Facilities ⊗ ⅃ ■ ♀ ♨
Location Ladhope Recreation Ground (N side of town centre off A7)
Hotel ★★★67% Kingsknowes Hotel, Selkirk Rd, GALASHIELS ☎ (0896) 58375 11rm(10⇔ ⁀)

Torwoodlee ☎ (0896) 2260
Parkland course with natural hazards designed by James Braid. Testing 3rd hole (par 3).
9 holes, 5720yds, Par 68, SSS 68, Course record 64.
Club membership 300.
Visitors may not play Sat & Thu after 1pm.
Societies must contact in advance.
Green Fees £12 per day; £10 per round (£18/£14 weekends).
Facilities ⊗ Ⅲ⅃ ■ ♀ ♨ ⊟
Location 1.75m NW off A7
Hotel ★★★59% Burt's Hotel, The Square, MELROSE ☎ (089682) 2285 21⇔ ⁀

HAWICK

Map 12 NT51

Hawick ☎ (0450) 72293
Hill course with good views.
18 holes, 5929yds, Par 68, SSS 69, Course record 63.
Club membership 690.
Visitors by arrangement at weekends.
Societies must contact in writing.
Green Fees not confirmed.
Facilities ⊗ Ⅲ⅃ ■ (all catering by arrangement) ♀ by arrangement ⊟ ⁀
Location Vertish Hill (SW side of town)
Hotel ★★71% Kirklands Hotel, West Stewart Place, HAWICK ☎ (0450) 72263 5⇔ ⁀ Annexe7⇔ ⁀

INNERLEITHEN

Map 11 NT33

Innerleithen ☎ (0896) 830951
Moorland course, with easy walking. Burns and rivers are natural hazards. Testing 5th hole (100 yds) par 3.
9 holes, 2992yds, Par 68, SSS 69, Course record 67.
Club membership 260.
Visitors no restrictions.
Societies must contact in writing.
Green Fees £8 per day (£10 weekends).
Facilities ♀ ♨
Location Leithen Water, Leithen Rd (1.5m N on B709)
Hotel ★★★▲57% Tweed Valley Hotel & Restaurant, Galashiels Rd, WALKERBURN ☎ (089687) 636 15⇔ ⁀

JEDBURGH

Map 12 NT62

Jedburgh ☎ (08356) 3587
Undulating parkland course, windy, with young trees.
9 holes, 5760yds, Par 68, SSS 67.
Club membership 265.
Visitors restricted at weekends during competitions.
Societies must contact at least one month in advance.
Green Fees not confirmed.
Facilities ⊗ Ⅲ⅃ ■ (catering weekends only) ♀ ♨ ⊟
Location Dunion Rd (1m W on B6358)
Hotel ★★71% Kirklands Hotel, West Stewart Place, HAWICK ☎ (0450) 72263 5⇔ ⁀ Annexe7⇔ ⁀

KELSO

Map 12 NT73

Kelso ☎ (0573) 223009
Parkland course. Easy walking.
18 holes, 6061yds, Par 70, SSS 69.
Club membership 450.
Visitors restricted weekends & Mon-Fri 9-9.30am & 1-1.30pm.
Societies apply in writing.
Green Fees £18 per day; £12 per round (£25/£16 weekends).
Facilities ⊗ Ⅲ⅃ (all by arrangement) ■ ♀ ♨ ⊟
Location Racecourse Rd (N side of town centre off B6461)
Hotel ★★★58% Cross Keys Hotel, 36-37 The Square, KELSO ☎ (0573) 223303 24⇔ ⁀

LAUDER

Map 12 NT54

Lauder ☎ (0578) 722526
Inland course and practice area on gently sloping hill.
9 holes, 3001yds, Par 72, SSS 70, Course record 70.
Club membership 150.
Visitors restricted Wed 4.30-5.30pm and Sun before noon.
Societies telephone in advance.
Green Fees 18 holes £6 (£7 weekends).
Facilities ♨
Location Galashiels Rd (on Galashiels Rd, off A68,.5m from Lauder)
Hotel ★★69% Buccleuch Arms Hotel, The Green, ST BOSWELLS ☎ (0835) 22243 19rm(17⇔ ⁀)

MELROSE

Map 12 NT53

Melrose ☎ (089682) 2855
Undulating tree-lined fairways with spendid views.
9 holes, 5579yds, Par 70, SSS 68, Course record 61.
Club membership 390.
Visitors may not play on Sat or after 4pm, Apr-Oct.
Societies must telephone in advance.
Green Fees £12 per round/day.
Facilities Catering by arrangement ♀ ♨
Location Dingleton (S side of town centre on B6359)
Hotel ★★★59% Burt's Hotel, The Square, MELROSE ☎ (089682) 2285 21⇔ ⁀

MINTO
Map 12 NT52

Minto ☎ Denholm (045087) 220
Pleasant, undulating parkland course featuring mature trees and panoramic views of Scottish Border country. Short but quite testing.
18 holes, 5460yds, Par 68, SSS 68, Course record 66.
Club membership 600.
Visitors	may not play before 10.15am & 3.15pm Sat-Sun or during a club medal competition. Handicap certificate required.
Societies	must contact in writing.
Green Fees	£18 per day; £12 per round (£25/£18 weekends & bank holidays).
Facilities	⊗ ⅲ by prior arrangement ┗ ▉ (limited catering Thu) ♀ △ 🖘
Location	Denholm (S side of village)
Hotel	★★71% Kirklands Hotel, West Stewart Place, HAWICK ☎ (0450) 72263 5⇄ ⋒ Annexe7⇄ ⋒

NEWCASTLETON
Map 12 NY48

Newcastleton ☎ Liddesdale (03873) 75257
Hill course.
9 holes, 5748yds, Par 70, SSS 68.
Visitors	restricted competition days.
Societies	must contact in advance.
Green Fees	£6 per day/round.
Facilities	△
Location	Holm Hill (W side of village)
Hotel	★★56% Eskdale Hotel, Market Place, LANGHOLM ☎ (03873) 80357 & 81178 16rm(3⇄7 ⋒)

PEEBLES
Map 11 NT24

Peebles Municipal ☎ (0721) 20197
Parkland course with fine views.
18 holes, 6137yds, Par 70, SSS 70.
Club membership 600.
Visitors	advised to contact for weekends, 3 ball play only.
Societies	must be pre-booked with deposit.
Green Fees	£18 per day; £12 per round (£25/£18 weekends).
Facilities	⊗ ⅲ ┗ ▉ (no catering Tue) ♀ △ 🖘
Location	Kirkland St (W side of town centre off A72)
Hotel	★★★50% The Tontine, High St, PEEBLES ☎ (0721) 20892 37⇄ ⋒

ST BOSWELLS
Map 12 NT53

St Boswells ☎ (0835) 22359
Attractive parkland course by the banks of the River Tweed; easy walking.
9 holes, 2625yds, Par 66, SSS 65.
Club membership 310.
Visitors	play restricted after 4pm & on competition days.
Societies	must apply in writing.
Green Fees	£10 per day/round.
Facilities	▉ △
Leisure	fishing.
Location	N side of village off B6404
Hotel	★★69% Buccleuch Arms Hotel, The Green, ST BOSWELLS ☎ (0835) 22243 19rm(17⇄ ⋒)

BUCCLEUCH ARMS HOTEL ★★
St. Boswells Scotland
Tel: St. Boswells 0835 22243 Fax No 0835 23965

Whether you find your relaxation in active or more passive pursuits. The Buccleuch Arms Hotel is ideally suited for your purpose. Situated in the heart of the Borders beside the village green this former coaching inn has seventeen en-suite bedrooms all furnished to a high standard. The elegant Garden Room Restaurant with à la carte and table d'hôte menus, plus lounge bar with log fires in winter, serving lunches and bar suppers daily, or relax in our elegant lounge with an after dinner drink. The Borders can boast of fourteen golf courses five of which are eighteen hole and The Buccleuch is within a twelve mile radius of eleven of them including the picturesque course at St. Boswells.
Contact Sue Dodds or Louise Johnston
for further information.

SELKIRK
Map 12 NT42

Selkirk ☎ (0750) 20427
Pleasant moorland course set around Selkirk Hill. Unrivalled views.
9 holes, 5620yds, Par 68, SSS 67, Course record 60.
Club membership 364.
Visitors	may not play Mon evening, competition/match days.
Societies	must telephone in advance.
Green Fees	£10 per day.
Facilities	△
Location	Selkirk Hills (1m S on A7)
Hotel	★★61% Heatherlie House Hotel, Heatherlie Park, SELKIRK ☎ (0750) 21200 7rm(6 ⋒)

WEST LINTON
Map 11 NT15

West Linton ☎ (0968) 60970
Moorland course with beautiful views of Pentland Hills.
18 holes, 5864yds, Par 68, SSS 68, Course record 63.
Club membership 600.
Visitors	may not play on competition days & before 1pm weekends.
Societies	must contact in writing.
Green Fees	£20 per day; £14 per round (£22 per round weekends).
Facilities	⊗ (ex Tue) ┗ (ex Thu) ▉ ♀ △ 🖘 ⎷ Ricky Forrest.
Location	NW side of village off A702
Hotel	★★★50% The Tontine, High St, PEEBLES ☎ (0721) 20892 37⇄ ⋒

CENTRAL

ABERFOYLE   Map 11 NN50

Aberfoyle ☎ (08772) 493
Scenic heathland course with mountain views.
18 holes, 5210yds, Par 66, SSS 66.
Club membership 665.
Visitors   may not tee off before 10.30am Sat & Sun.
Societies   must contact in advance.
Green Fees   £16 per day; £12 per round (£24 per day; £16
                  per round weekends).
Facilities   ⊗ ⅶ Ⅼ ♥ ♀ ⚲ ↑
Location   Braeval (1m E on A81)
Hotel   ★★★♨67% Roman Camp Hotel, CALLANDER
                  ☎ (0877) 30003 14⇄ ↑

ALLOA   Map 11 NS89

Alloa ☎ (0259) 722745
Undulating, wooded parkland course.
18 holes, 6230yds, Par 70, SSS 70, Course record 63.
Club membership 750.
Visitors   no restrictions.
Societies   may not play at weekends.
Green Fees   £20 per day; £12 per round (£24 per day after
                  11.30am; £15 per round after 2pm weekends).
Facilities   ⊗ ⅶ Ⅼ ♥ ♀ ⚲ 🏠 ↑ ⚑ Bill Bennett.
Leisure   snooker.
Location   Schawpark, Sauchie (1.5m NE on A908)
Hotel   ★★★63% Royal Hotel, Henderson St, BRIDGE
                  OF ALLAN ☎ (0786) 832284 32⇄ ↑

Braehead ☎ (0259) 722078
Attactive parkland course at the foot of the Ochil Hills, and
offering spectacular views.
18 holes, 6041yds, Par 70, SSS 69, Course record 64.
Club membership 800.
Visitors   advisable to contact in advance.
Societies   must contact in advance.
Green Fees   £18 per day; £12 per round (£24/£18 weekends).
Facilities   ⊗ ⅶ Ⅼ ♥ ♀ ⚲ 🏠 ↑ ⚑ Paul Brookes.
Location   Cambus (1.5m NE on A908)
Hotel   ★★57% King Robert Hotel, Glasgow Rd,
                  Bannockburn, STIRLING
                  ☎ (0786) 811666 53⇄ ↑

BONNYBRIDGE   Map 11 NS88

Bonnybridge ☎ (0324) 812822
Testing heathland course, with tightly guarded greens. Easy
walking.
9 holes, 6060yds, Par 72, SSS 69.
Club membership 325.
Visitors   must contact in advance and be accompanied by
                  member.
Societies   must contact in advance.
Green Fees   not confirmed.
Facilities   ⊗ ⅶ Ⅼ & ♥ by prior arrangement ♀ ⚲ 🏠
Location   Larbert Rd (1m NE off A883)
Hotel   ★★★67% Inchyra Grange Hotel, Grange Rd,
                  POLMONT
                  ☎ (0324) 711911 43⇄ ↑

BRIDGE OF ALLAN   Map 11 NS79

Bridge of Allan ☎ (0786) 832332
Parkland course, very hilly with good views of Stirling Castle
and beyond to the Trossachs. Testing 1st hole, 221 yds (par 3)
uphill 6 ft wall 25 yds before green.
9 holes, 4932yds, Par 66, SSS 65, Course record 62.
Club membership 400.
Visitors   restricted Sat.
Societies   must contact in advance.
Green Fees   not confirmed.
Facilities   Catering at weekends or by arrangement ♀ ⚲
Leisure   pool table.
Location   Sunnylaw (0.5m N off A9)
Hotel   ★★★63% Royal Hotel, Henderson St, BRIDGE
                  OF ALLAN ☎ (0786) 832284 32⇄ ↑

CALLANDER   Map 11 NN60

Callander ☎ (0877) 30090
Parkland course, with fairly tightly guarded greens. Designed
by Tom Morris Snr and overlooked by the Trossachs.
18 holes, 5125yds, Par 66, SSS 66, Course record 61.
Club membership 580.
Visitors   must have handicap certificate to play Wed & Sun.
Societies   apply in writing.
Green Fees   not confirmed.
Facilities   ⊗ ⅶ Ⅼ ♥ ♀ ⚲ 🏠 ↑ ⚑ William Kelly.
Location   Aveland Rd (E side of town off A84)
Hotel   ★★★♨67% Roman Camp Hotel, CALLANDER
                  ☎ (0877) 30003 14⇄ ↑

DOLLAR   Map 11 NS99

Dollar ☎ (0259) 42400
Compact hillside course.
18 holes, 5144yds, Par 68, SSS 66.
Club membership 450.
Visitors   no restrictions
Societies   must contact in advance.
Green Fees   £11 per day; £7 per round (£15 per day
                  weekends).
Facilities   ⊗ ⅶ Ⅼ ♥ ♀ ⚲ ↑
Leisure   snooker.
Location   Brewlands House (0.5m N off A91)
Hotel   ★★57% King Robert Hotel, Glasgow Rd,
                  Bannockburn, STIRLING
                  ☎ (0786) 811666 53⇄ ↑

DRYMEN   Map 11 NS48

Buchanan Castle ☎ (0360) 60307
Parkland course, with easy walking and good views.
18 holes, 6086yds, Par 70, SSS 69.
Club membership 830.
Visitors   must be accompanied by member, contact in
                  advance and have an introduction from own club.
Societies   must contact in advance.
Green Fees   not confirmed.
Facilities   ⊗ & ⅶ by prior arrangement ⅬWell ♥ ♀ ⚲ 🏠 ↑
                  ⚑ Charles Dernie.
Location   1m W
Hotel   ★★★66% Buchanan Highland Hotel, DRYMEN
                  ☎ (0360) 60588 51⇄ ↑

DUNBLANE
Map 11 NN70

Dunblane New Golf Club ☎ (0786) 823711
Well maintained parkland course, with reasonably hard
walking. Testing 6th and 9th holes.
18 holes, 5876yds, Par 69, SSS 68, Course record 64.
Club membership 800.
Visitors may play 9.30am-noon & 2.30-4pm Mon-Fri.
Must contact in advance.
Societies welcome Mon & Thu, contact in advance.
Green Fees £24 per day; £16 per round.
Facilities ⊗ ⨯ ﬗ ⅃ ♥ ♀ ⚲ 🏠 ⚑ ⟨ R M Jamieson.
Location Perth Rd (E side of town on A9)
Hotel ★★★(red)⚘ Cromlix House Hotel, Kinbuck,
DUNBLANE ☎ (0786) 822125 14⇥ ⚐

FALKIRK
Map 11 NS88

Falkirk ☎ (0324) 611061
Parkland course with trees, gorse and streams.
18 holes, 6282yds, Par 71, SSS 69, Course record 66.
Club membership 800.
Visitors with member only at weekends.
Societies telephone (0324) 612219 in advance.
Green Fees not confirmed.
Facilities ⊗ ⨯ ﬗ ﬗ ♥ ♀ ⚲ 🏠
Location Stirling Rd, Camelon (1.5m W on A9)
Hotel ★★★62% Stakis Falkirk Park Hotel, Camelon
Rd, FALKIRK ☎ (0324) 28331 55⇥ ⚐

KILLIN
Map 11 NN53

Killin ☎ (0567) 820312
Parkland course with good views. Glorious setting.
9 holes, 5200yds, Par 66, SSS 65.
Club membership 250.
Visitors may not play competition days.
Societies apply in writing.
Green Fees not confirmed.
Facilities ⚲ 🏠 ⚑
Location 1m N on A827
Hotel ★★64% Falls of Dochart Hotel, Main St,
KILLIN ☎ (05672) 237
due to change to (0567) 820237 9rm(1⇥5 ⚐)

LARBERT
Map 11 NS88

Falkirk Tryst ☎ (0324) 562415 & 562054
Moorland course, fairly level with trees and broom, well-
bunkered. Winds can affect play.
18 holes, 6053yds, Par 70, SSS 69, Course record 64.
Club membership 900.
Visitors with member only weekend & bank holidays.
Societies apply in writing.
Green Fees £16 per day; £11 per round.
Facilities ⊗ ⨯ (Sat evening only) ﬗ ♥ ♀ ⚲ 🏠 ⟨
Steven Dunsmore.
Location 86 Burnhead Rd (1m NE off A88/B905)
Hotel ★★★67% Inchyra Grange Hotel, Grange Rd,
POLMONT ☎ (0324) 711911 43⇥ ⚐

Glenbervie Clubhouse ☎ (0324) 562605
Parkland course with good views.
18 holes, 6469yds, Par 71, SSS 71.
Club membership 600.
Visitors must contact in advance, restricted at weekends.
Societies apply in writing.
Green Fees £30 per day; £20 per round.
Facilities ⊗ ⨯ ﬗ ﬗ ♥ ♀ ⚲ 🏠 ⟨
Location Stirling Rd (2m NW on A9)
Hotel ★★★62% Stakis Falkirk Park Hotel, Camelon
Rd, FALKIRK ☎ (0324) 28331 55⇥ ⚐

MUCKHART
Map 11 NO00

Muckhart ☎ (0259) 781423
Scenic heathland/downland course.
18 holes, 6192yds, Par 71, SSS 70.
Club membership 850.
Visitors welcome except weekends before 9.45am &
between noon-2.30pm. Must contact in advance.
Societies must telephone in advance.
Green Fees £18 per day; £12.50 per round (£22/£18
weekends).
Facilities ⊗ ⨯ ﬗ ﬗ ♥ ♀ ⚲ 🏠 ⟨ Keith Salmoni.
Location SW of village off A91
Hotel ★★★67% Green Hotel, 2 The Muirs, KINROSS
☎ (0577) 63467 47⇥ ⚐

POLMONT
Map 11 NS97

Grangemouth ☎ (0324) 711500
Windy parkland course. Testing holes: 3rd, 4th (par 4's); 5th
(par 5); 7th (par 3) 216 yds over reservoir (elevated green);
8th, 9th, 18th (par 4's).
18 holes, 6314yds, Par 71, SSS 71.
Club membership 700.
Visitors must contact in advance.
Societies must contact in writing.
Green Fees not confirmed.
Facilities ⊗ ⨯ ﬗ ﬗ ♥ ♀ ⚲ 🏠 ⟨
Leisure pool tables.
Location Polmont Hill (on unclass rd 0.5m N of M9 junc 4)
Hotel ★★★67% Inchyra Grange Hotel, Grange Rd,
POLMONT ☎ (0324) 711911 43⇥ ⚐

Polmont ☎ (0324) 711277
Parkland course, hilly with few bunkers. Views of the River
Forth and Ochil Hills.
9 holes, 3031yds, Par 36.
Club membership 200.
Visitors restricted Sat.
Societies must telephone in advance.
Green Fees not confirmed.
Location Manuelrigg, Maddiston (E side of village off
A803)
Hotel ★★★67% Inchyra Grange Hotel, Grange Rd,
POLMONT ☎ (0324) 711911 43⇥ ⚐

STIRLING
Map 11 NS79

Stirling ☎ (0786) 64098
Undulating parkland course with magnificent views. Testing
15th, 'Cotton's Fancy', 384 yds (par 4).
18 holes, 6438yds, Par 72, SSS 71, Course record 65.
Club membership 950.

Visitors may not play Sat & restricted Sun.
Societies must telephone in advance.
Green Fees not confirmed.
Facilities ⊗)Ⅲ by prior arrangement ዬ ♥ ♀ (all day) ᕦ
🖻 ℂ Ian Collins.
Location Queens Rd (W side of town on B8051)
Hotel ★★57% King Robert Hotel, Glasgow Rd,
Bannockburn, STIRLING ☎ (0786) 811666
53➪ ℝ

TILLICOULTRY
Map 11 NS99

Tillicoultry ☎ (0259) 51337 & 50124
Parkland course at foot of the Ochil Hills entailing some hard
walking.
18 holes, 5358yds, Par 68, SSS 66.
Club membership 400.
Visitors welcome except during club competitions.
Societies apply in writing.
Green Fees £8 per round (£13.50 weekends).
Facilities ⊗)Ⅲ by prior arrangement ዬ ♥ ♀ ᕦ
Location Alva Rd
Hotel ★★★63% Royal Hotel, Henderson St, BRIDGE
OF ALLAN ☎ (0786) 832284 32➪ ℝ

DUMFRIES & GALLOWAY

CASTLE DOUGLAS
Map 11 NX76

Castle Douglas ☎ (0556) 2801
Parkland course, one severe hill.
9 holes, 2704yds, Par 34, SSS 33.
Club membership 500.
Visitors welcome except Tue & Thu after 4pm & Sun
during competitions.
Societies apply by writing.
Green Fees £10 per day/round.
Facilities ዬ (weekdays) ♥ (Jun-Aug only) ♀ ᕦ
Location Abercromby Rd (W side of town)
Hotel ★★69% Douglas Arms, King St, CASTLE
DOUGLAS ☎ (0556) 2231 22rm(15➪ ℝ)

COLVEND
Map 11 NX85

Colvend ☎ Rockcliffe (055663) 398
Picturesque and challenging course on Solway coast. Superb
views.
9 holes, 2322yds, Par 66, SSS 63, Course record 63.
Club membership 480.
Visitors restricted Tue, Thu & weekends in summer.
Societies must telephone in advance.
Green Fees £10 per day/round.
Facilities ⊗)Ⅲ ዬ (catering daily Apr-Sep) ♥ (Oct-Mar)
♀ (weekends only) ᕦ ⚑
Location Sandyhills (6m from Dalbeattie on A710 Solway
Coast Rd)
Hotel ★★67% Clonyard House Hotel, COLVEND
☎ (055663) 372 15➪ ℝ

CUMMERTREES
Map 11 NY16

Powfoot ☎ (04617) 227
The hills of Cumbria, away beyond the Solway Firth, and
from time to time a sight of the Isle of Man, make
playing at this delightfully compact semi-links seaside
course a scenic treat. Lovely holes include the 2nd, the
8th and the 11th.
18 holes, 6283yds, Par 71, SSS 70, Course record 65.
Club membership 820.
Visitors may not play Sat & only after 2.45pm on
Sun. Must contact in advance.
Societies must book at least one week in advance.
Green Fees £15 per round (£16 Sun after 2.45pm).
Facilities ⊗)Ⅲ ዬ ♥ ♀ ᕦ 🖻 ℂ Gareth Dick.
Location 0.5m off B724
Hotel ★★64% Golf Hotel, Links Av, POWFOOT
☎ (04617) 254 19rm(11➪ ℝ)

DUMFRIES
Map 11 NX97

Dumfries & County ☎ (0387) 53585
Parkland course alongside River Nith, with views over the
Queensberry Hills.
18 holes, 5928yds, Par 69, SSS 68.
Club membership 600.
Visitors must contact in advance but may not play on Sat
during Mar-Oct.
Societies apply in writing.
Green Fees £21.00 per day (£25 weekends).
Facilities ⊗)Ⅲ ዬ ♥ ♀ ᕦ 🖻 ⚑ ℂ Gordon Gray.
Location Edinburgh Rd (1m NE off A701)
Hotel ★★★63% Station Hotel, 49 Lovers Walk,
DUMFRIES ☎ (0387) 54316 32➪ ℝ

Dumfries & Galloway ☎ (0387) 63848
Parkland course.
18 holes, 5803yds, Par 68, SSS 68.
Club membership 800.
Visitors may not play on competition days.
Societies apply in writing.
Green Fees £16 per day/round (£20 weekends).
Facilities ⊗)Ⅲ by prior arrangement ዬ ♥ ♀ ᕦ 🖻 ⚑ ℂ
Joe Fergusson.
Leisure snooker.
Location 2 Laurieston Av (W side of town centre on A75)
Hotel ★★★63% Station Hotel, 49 Lovers Walk,
DUMFRIES ☎ (0387) 54316 32➪ ℝ

GATEHOUSE-OF-FLEET
Map 11 NX55

Gatehouse ☎ (0557) 814734
Set against a background of rolling hills with scenic views of
Fleet Bay and the Solway Firth.
9 holes, 2398yds, Par 66, SSS 63.
Club membership 280.
Visitors no restrictions.
Societies telephone (0557) 814459 in advance.
Green Fees £10 per day/round.
Facilities ᕦ
Location Laurieston Rd (N side of village)
Hotel ★★★62% Murray Arms Hotel, GATEHOUSE
OF FLEET ☎ (0557) 814207
12➪ ℝ Annexe1➪ ℝ

DUMFRIES & GALLOWAY

GLENLUCE
Map 10 NX15

Wigtownshire County ☎ (05813) 420
Seaside links course on the shores of Luce Bay, easy walking.
18 holes, 5411yds, Par 70, SSS 66.
Club membership 350.
Visitors may not play on Wed evenings.
Societies must telephone (05813) 589 in advance.
Green Fees £16 per day ; £12 per round (£18/£14
weekends).
Facilities ⊗ ⫘ ⅃ ⊑ ♥ ♀ ⚲ 🖻
Leisure pool table.
Location Mains of Park (1.5m W off A75)
Hotel ★★★★68% North West Castle Hotel,
STRANRAER ☎ (0776) 4413
72⇄ 👣

GRETNA
Map 11 NY36

Gretna ☎ (0461) 38464
A nice parkland course on gentle hills. Opened in 1991, it
offers a good test of skill.
9 holes, 3215yds, Par 72, SSS 71.
Club membership 250.
Visitors no restrictions.
Societies telephone in advance.
Green Fees £10 per day; £5 per 9 holes.
Facilities ⅃ ♥ ♀ ⚲
Location Kirtle View (.5m W of Gretna on
B721,signposted)
Hotel ★★68% Solway Lodge Hotel, Annan Rd,
GRETNA ☎ (0461) 38266
3⇄ 👣 Annexe7⇄ 👣

KIRKCUDBRIGHT
Map 11 NX65

Kirkcudbright ☎ (0557) 30314
Parkland course. Hilly, with hard walking. Good views.
18 holes, 5598yds, Par 67, SSS 67.
Club membership 500.
Visitors welcome except during club competitions.
Societies apply in writing to Secretary.
Green Fees not confirmed.
Facilities ⊗ ⫘ ⅃ ♥ (no catering Mon) ♀ ⚲
Location Stirling Crescent (NE side of town off A711)
Hotel ★★66% Selkirk Arms Hotel, Old High St,
KIRKCUDBRIGHT ☎ (0557) 30402
14⇄ 👣 Annexe1⇄ 👣

LANGHOLM
Map 11 NY38

Langholm ☎ (03873) 80265
Hillside course with fine views, hard walking.
9 holes, 5744yds, Par 70, SSS 68, Course record 65.
Club membership 130.
Visitors restricted Sat.
Societies apply in writing or telephone in advance.
Green Fees £10 per day/round.
Location Whitaside (E side of village off A7)
Hotel ★★56% Eskdale Hotel, Market Place,
LANGHOLM ☎ (03873) 80357 & 81178
16rm(3⇄7 👣)

LOCHMABEN
Map 11 NY08

Lochmaben ☎ (0387) 810552
Comfortable-walking parkland course between two lochs
with fine old trees and fast greens all year round.
9 holes, 5304yds, Par 66, SSS 66, Course record 60.
Club membership 550.
Visitors restricted weekdays & during competitions.
Societies must contact in advance.
Green Fees £12 per day (£14 weekends).
Facilities ⊗ ⫘ by prior arrangement ⅃ ♥ ♀ ⚲
Leisure fishing, snooker.
Location Castlehill Gate (S side of village off A709)
Hotel ★★★66% Dryfesdale Hotel, LOCKERBIE
☎ (05762) 2427 due to change to
(0576) 202427 15⇄ 👣

LOCKERBIE
Map 11 NY18

Lockerbie ☎ (0576) 20462
Parkland course with fine views and featuring the only pond
hole in Dumfriesshire.
18 holes, 5418yds, Par 67, SSS 66.
Club membership 627.
Visitors no restrictions.
Societies must contact in advance.
Green Fees not confirmed.
Facilities ⊗ ⫘ ⅃ ♥ ♀ ⚲
Location Corrie Rd (E side of town centre off B7068)
Hotel ★★★66% Dryfesdale Hotel, LOCKERBIE
☎ (05762) 2427 due to change to
(0576) 202427 15⇄ 👣

MOFFAT
Map 11 NT00

Moffat ☎ (0683) 20020
Scenic moorland course overlooking the town, with
panoramic views.
18 holes, 5218yds, Par 69, SSS 66, Course record 60.
Club membership 375.
Visitors restricted Wed afternoons.
Societies must contact in advance.
Green Fees £16 per day (£24 weekends & bank holidays).
Facilities ⊗ ⫘ ⅃ ⊑ ♥ ♀ ⚲ 🖻 ⚑
Leisure snooker, darts, table tennis, pool table.
Location Coatshill (1m SW off A701)
Hotel ★★★65% Moffat House Hotel, High St,
MOFFAT ☎ (0683) 20039
16⇄ 👣Annexe4⇄ 👣

MONREITH
Map 10 NX34

St Medan ☎ Port William (09887) 358
Links course with panoramic views of the Solway and Isle of Man.
9 holes, 4552yds, Par 64, SSS 62, Course record 60.
Club membership 300.
Visitors no restrictions.
Societies apply in writing.
Green Fees £10 per day; £14 per week; £6 per 9 holes.
Facilities ⊗ ⫘ ⅃ ⊑ ♥ ♀ ⚲ ⚑
Leisure pool table, video game.
Location 1m SE off A747
Hotel ★★★⚓63% Corsemalzie House Hotel, PORT
WILLIAM ☎ (098886) 254 14⇄ 👣

NEW GALLOWAY

Map 11 NT00

New Galloway ☎ (06442) 737
Set on the edge of the Galloway Hills and overlooking Loch
Ken, the course has excellent tees and first class greens.
9 holes, 4604yds, Par 63, SSS 63.
Club membership 266.
Visitors restricted on competition days.
Societies apply in writing.
Green Fees £10 per day.
Facilities ▉ ♀ ♤
Location S side of town on A762
Hotel ★★★67% Auchen Castle Hotel & Restaurant,
BEATTOCK ☎ (06833) 407
15↤ ☞ Annexe10 ☞

NEWTON STEWART

Map 10 NX46

Newton Stewart ☎ (0671) 2172
Parkland course in picturesque setting. Short but quite tight.
9 holes, 5362yds, Par 68, SSS 65.
Club membership 300.
Visitors telephone for details.
Societies must contact in advance.
Green Fees £12 per day (£15 weekends & bank holidays).
Facilities ⊗ ⅢⅡ ㉪ ▉ ♀ ♤ 🏠
Leisure pool table.
Location Kirroughtree Av, Minnigaff (0.5m N of town
centre)
Hotel ★★66% Creebridge House Hotel, NEWTON
STEWART ☎ (0671) 2121 18↤ ☞

PORTPATRICK

Map 10 NX05

Portpatrick ☎ (077681) 273
Seaside links-type course, set on cliffs overlooking the Irish
Sea, with magnificent views.
*Dunskey Course: 18 holes, 5771yds, Par 70, SSS 68, Course
record 64.*
Dinvin Course: 9 holes, 1504yds, Par 27.
Club membership 450.
Visitors welcome except for competition days. A
handicap certificate is required for 18 hole
course.
Societies must contact in advance.
Green Fees 18 holes: £20 per day; £13 per round (£24/£16
weekends) 9 holes: £10 per day; £5 per round.
Facilities ⊗ ⅢⅡ ㉪ ▉ ♀ (all day) ♤ 🏠 ⛳
Location Golf Course Rd (NW side of village)
Hotel ★★★66% Fernhill Golf Hotel,
PORTPATRICK ☎ (077681) 220
15rm(14↤ ☞) Annexe6rm(3↤1 ☞)

SANQUHAR

Map 11 NS70

Sanquhar ☎ (0659) 50577
Moorland course, fine views.
9 holes, 5144mtr, Par 70, SSS 68, Course record 66.
Club membership 180.
Visitors may not play competition days.
Societies apply in writing.
Green Fees not confirmed.
Facilities ⊗ ⅢⅡ ㉪ ▉ (all catering by prior
arrangement) ♤

Leisure snooker.
Location Euchan Golf Course (0.5m SW off A76)
Hotel ★★60% Mennockfoot Lodge Hotel, Mennock,
SANQUHAR ☎ (0659) 50382 & 50477
1↤ Annexe8↤ ☞

SOUTHERNESS

Map 11 NX95

Southerness ☎ Kirkbean (038788) 677
Natural links, Championship course with panoramic views.
Heather and bracken abound.
18 holes, 6564yds, Par 69, SSS 72, Course record 65.
Club membership 720.
Visitors some restricted times.
Societies must contact in advance.
Green Fees £23 per day (£30 weekends & bank holidays).
Facilities ⊗ ⅢⅡ ㉪ ▉ ♀ ♤
Location 3.5m S of Kirkbean off A710
Hotel ★★67% Clonyard House Hotel, COLVEND
☎ (055663) 372 15↤ ☞

STRANRAER

Map 10 NX06

Stranraer ☎ Leswalt (077687) 245
Parkland course with beautiful view of Lochryan.
18 holes, 6300yds, Par 70, SSS 71, Course record 66.
Club membership 550.
Visitors restricted at weekends. Must contact in advance.
Societies must telephone in advance.
Green Fees not confirmed.
Facilities ⊗ & ⅢⅡ by prior arrangement ㉪ ▉ ♀ ♤ 🏠
Leisure snooker.
Location Creachmore by Stranraer (2.5m NW on A718)
Hotel ★★★68% North West Castle Hotel,
STRANRAER ☎ (0776) 4413 72↤ ☞

THORNHILL

Map 11 NX89

Thornhill ☎ Dumfries (0848) 30546
Moorland/parkland course with fine views.
18 holes, 6011yds, Par 71, SSS 69.
Club membership 580.
Visitors no restrictions.
Societies must telephone in advance.
Green Fees not confirmed.
Facilities ㉪ ▉ ♀ ♤
Location Blacknest (1m E of town off A92)
Hotel ★★72% Trigony House Hotel, Closeburn,
THORNHILL ☎ (0848) 31211 9↤ ☞

WIGTOWN

Map 11 NX45

Wigtown & Bladnoch ☎ (09884) 3354
Slightly hilly parkland course with fine views over Wigtown
Bay to Galloway Hills.
9 holes, 5462yds, Par 68, SSS 67.
Club membership 180.
Visitors may not play competition days.
Societies apply in writing.
Green Fees £7 per day (£10 weekends per round).
Facilities ⊗ ㉪ ▉ ♀ ♤
Location Lightlands Ter (SW on A714)
Hotel ★★66% Creebridge House Hotel, NEWTON
STEWART ☎ (0671) 2121 18↤ ☞

FIFE

ABERDOUR   Map 11 NT18

Aberdour ☎ (0383) 860256
Parkland course with lovely views over Firth of Forth.
18 holes, 5460yds, Par 67, SSS 67, Course record 63.
Club membership 580.
Visitors   may play weekdays only and must contact in advance.
Societies   are advised to telephone in advance.
Green Fees £22 per day; £15 per round.
Facilities   ⊗ ⅏ ♨ ♥ ♀ ⚘ 🏠 ⚑ Gordon McCallum.
Location   Seaside Place (S side of village)
Hotel   ★★67% Woodside Hotel, High St, ABERDOUR
                ☎ (0383) 860328 21⇌ ⚑

ANSTRUTHER   Map 12 NO50

Anstruther ☎ (0333) 310956 & 312253
Seaside links course with some excellent par 3 holes; always in good condition.
9 holes, 4144mtrs, Par 62, SSS 63, Course record 62.
Club membership 600.
Visitors   advised to phone in advance.
Societies   welcome except Jun-Aug.
Green Fees £10 per round (£14 weekends and bank
              holidays).
Facilities   ⊗ ⅏ by prior arrangement ♨ ♥ (catering Jun-
              Aug) ♀ Jun-Aug ⚘
Location   Shore Rd, "Marsfield" (SW off A917)
Hotel   ★★59% Smugglers Inn, High St, ANSTRUTHER
                ☎ (0333) 310506 8⇌ ⚑

BURNTISLAND   Map 11 NT28

Burntisland Golf House Club ☎ (0592) 874093
This hill course has fine sea views.
18 holes, 5908yds, Par 69, SSS 69.
Club membership 780.
Visitors   no restrictions.
Societies   apply in writing.
Green Fees £21 per day; £15 per round (£35/£25 weekends).
Facilities   ⊗ ⅏ ♨ ♥ ♀ ⚘ 🏠 ⚑ Jacky Montgomery.
Location   Dodhead (1m E on B923)
Hotel   ★★★57% Dean Park Hotel, Chapel Level,
                KIRKCALDY ☎ (0592) 261635
                20⇌ ⚑ Annexe12 ⚑

COWDENBEATH   Map 11 NT19

Cowdenbeath ☎ (0383) 522928
A parkland-based 9-hole golf course.
Dora Course: 9 holes, 6552yds, Par 72, SSS 71, Course record 74.
Club membership 400.
Visitors   no restrictions.
Societies   must telephone in advance.
Green Fees £8 day ticket (£8.50 weekends).
Facilities   all catering by order ♀ ⚘ 🏠 ⚑
Location   Seco Place (6m E of Dunfermline)
Hotel   ★★67% Woodside Hotel, High St, ABERDOUR
                ☎ (0383) 860328 21⇌ ⚑

CRAIL   Map 12 NO60

Crail Golfing Society ☎ (0333) 50278
Perched on the edge of the North Sea on the very point of the golfing county of Fife, the Crail Golfing Society's course at Balcomie is picturesque and sporting. And here again golf history has been made for Crail Golfing Society began its life in 1786. The course is highly thought of by students of the game both for its testing holes and the stardard of its greens.
18 holes, 5720yds, Par 69, SSS 68.
Club membership 1100.
Visitors   must contact in advance, restricted 10am-
              noon & 2-4.30pm.
Societies   must telephone in advance.
Green Fees £24 per day; £16 per round (£30/£20
              weekends).
Facilities   ⊗ ⅏ ♨ ♥ ♀ ⚘ 🏠 ⚑ ⚑ Graheme Lennie.
Location   Balcomie Clubhouse, Fifeness (2m NE off
              A917)
Hotel   ★★62% Balcomie Links Hotel, Balcomie
                Rd, CRAIL ☎ (0333) 50237 11⇌ ⚑

CUPAR   Map 11 NO31

Cupar ☎ (0334) 53549
Hilly parkland course with fine views.
9 holes, 5500yds, Par 68, SSS 65, Course record 61.
Club membership 400.
Visitors   welcome except Sat.
Societies   must contact in advance.
Green Fees £10 per day (£12 Sun).
Facilities   ⊗ ♨ ♥ ♀ ⚘
Location   Hilltarvit (0.75m S off A92)
Hotel   ★★★69% Rufflets Country House & Garden
                Restaurant, Strathkinness Low Rd, ST
                ANDREWS ☎ (0334) 72594
                23⇌ ⚑ Annexe3⇌ ⚑

DUNFERMLINE   Map 11 NT08

Canmore ☎ (0383) 724969
Undulating parkland course affording excellent views.
18 holes, 5474yds, Par 67, SSS 66.
Club membership 620.
Visitors   no restrictions.
Green Fees not confirmed.
Facilities   ♀ ⚘ 🏠 ⚑
Location   Venturefair Av (1m N on A823)
Hotel   ★★★62% King Malcolm Thistle Hotel,
                Queensferry Rd, Wester Pitcorthie,
                DUNFERMLINE ☎ (0383) 722611 48⇌ ⚑

Dunfermline ☎ (0383) 723534
Gently undulating parkland course with interesting contours. Sixteenth-century clubhouse.
18 holes, 6237yds, Par 72, SSS 70, Course record 65.
Par 3 course: 9 holes, 1144yds, Par 27.
Club membership 675.
Visitors   welcome Mon-Fri. Must contact in advance.
Societies   must contact in advance.
Green Fees not confirmed.   ▶

Facilities	⊗ (ex Mon) ⭐ by prior arrangement 🏌 🍺 ⚲ ⚴ 🏠 Steve Craig.
Location	Pitfirrane, Crossford (2m W on A994)
Hotel	★★★62% King Malcolm Thistle Hotel, Queensferry Rd, Wester Pitcorthie, DUNFERMLINE ☎ (0383) 722611 48⇨ 🏃

Pitreavie ☎ (0383) 722591

Picturesque woodland course with panoramic view of the River Forth Valley. Testing golf.

18 holes, 6086yds, Par 70, SSS 69, Course record 65.

Club membership 700.

Visitors	welcome except for competition days.
Societies	must write or telephone in advance.
Green Fees	£18 per day; £13 per round (£24 per day weekends).
Facilities	⊗ ⭐ by prior arrangement 🏌 🍺 ⚲ ⚴ 🏠 🏃 Jim Forrester.
Leisure	pool table.
Location	Queensferry Rd (SE side of town on A823)
Hotel	★★★62% King Malcolm Thistle Hotel, Queensferry Rd, Wester Pitcorthie, DUNFERMLINE ☎ (0383) 722611 48⇨ 🏃

ELIE   Map 12 NO40

Golf House Club ☎ (0333) 330301

One of Scotland's most delightful holiday courses with panoramic views over the Firth of Forth. Some of the holes out towards the rocky coastline are splendid. This is the course which has produced many good professionals, including the immortal James Braid.

18 holes, 6241yds, Par 70, SSS 70, Course record 62.

Club membership 650.

Visitors	may not play before 10am; no parties at weekends.
Societies	mid week only, except Jun-Aug.
Green Fees	not confirmed.
Facilities	⊗ by prior arrangement 🏌 🍺 ⚲ ⚴ 🏠 🏃 Robin Wilson.
Location	W side of village off A917
Hotel	★★★66% Old Manor Hotel, Leven Rd, LUNDIN LINKS ☎ (0333) 320368 15⇨ 🏃

FALKLAND   Map 11 NO20

Falkland ☎ (0337) 57404

A flat, well kept course with excellent greens and views of East Lomond Hill and Falkland Palace.

9 holes, 5216yds, Par 68, SSS 65.

Club membership 325.

Visitors	parties must make prior arrangements.
Societies	must contact in advance.
Green Fees	£7 per day (£10 weekends); £25 per week.
Facilities	⊗ & ⭐ by prior arrangement 🏌 🍺 ⚲ ⚴
Location	The Myre (N side of town on A912)
Hotel	★★★69% Balgeddie House Hotel, Balgeddie Way, GLENROTHES ☎ (0592) 742511 18⇨ 🏃

> Entries with a shaded background identify courses that are considered to be particularly interesting

GLENROTHES   Map 11 NO20

Glenrothes ☎ (0592) 758686

Testing and hilly parkland course with burn crossed four times. Good views.

18 holes, 6444yds, Par 71, SSS 71.

Club membership 800.

Visitors	no restrictions.
Societies	telephone one month in advance.
Green Fees	£13 per day; £7.60 per round (£15/£10 weekends).
Facilities	⊗ ⭐ 🏌 🍺 🍺 ⚲ ⚴
Location	Golf Course Rd (W side of town off B921)
Hotel	★★★69% Balgeddie House Hotel, Balgeddie Way, GLENROTHES ☎ (0592) 742511 18⇨ 🏃

KINCARDINE   Map 11 NS98

Tulliallan ☎ (0259) 30396

Partially hilly parkland course with testing 3rd hole (par 4).

18 holes, 5982yds, Par 69, SSS 69.

Club membership 525.

Visitors	restricted at weekends.
Societies	may not play on Sat; must contact in advance.
Green Fees	not confirmed.
Facilities	⊗ ⭐ 🏌 🍺 🍺 ⚲ ⚴ 🏠 🏃 Steven Kelly.
Location	Alloa Rd (1m NW on A977)
Hotel	★★★67% Inchyra Grange Hotel, Grange Rd, POLMONT ☎ (0324) 711911 43⇨ 🏃

KINGHORN   Map 11 NT28

Kinghorn ☎ (0592) 890345

Municipal course, 300 ft above sea level with views over Firth of Forth and North Sea. Undulating and quite testing. Facilities shared by Kinghorn Ladies.

18 holes, 5269yds, Par 65, SSS 67.

Club membership 190.

Visitors	no restrictions.
Societies	must contact in writing.
Green Fees	not confirmed.
Facilities	⚲ ⚴
Location	Macduff Cres (S side of town on A921)
Hotel	★★★57% Dean Park Hotel, Chapel Level, KIRKCALDY ☎ (0592) 261635 20⇨ 🏃Annexe12 🏃

KIRKCALDY   Map 11 NT29

Dunnikier Park ☎ (0592) 261599

Parkland, rolling fairways, not heavily bunkered, views of Firth of Forth.

18 holes, 6601yds, Par 72, SSS 72.

Club membership 600.

Visitors	no restrictions.
Societies	apply in writing to the Secretary.
Green Fees	£12 day; £9 round (£18/12 weekends).
Facilities	⊗ (ex Mon-Tue during Oct-Mar) ⭐ 🏌 🍺 ⚲ ⚴ 🏠 🏃
Location	Dunnikier Way (2m N off A988)
Hotel	★★★57% Dean Park Hotel, Chapel Level, KIRKCALDY ☎ (0592) 261635 20⇨ 🏃 Annexe12 🏃

Kirkcaldy ☎ (0592) 260370
Parkland course.
18 holes, 6004yds, Par 71, SSS 70, Course record 67.
Club membership 725.
Visitors may not play Sat. Must contact in advance.
Societies apply in writing to the Secretary.
Green Fees not confirmed.
Facilities Paul Hodgson.
Location Balwearie Rd (SW side of town off A910)
Hotel ★★★57% Dean Park Hotel, Chapel Level, KIRKCALDY
☎ (0592) 261635 20 Annexe12

LADYBANK Map 11 NO30

Ladybank ☎ (0337) 30814
Picturesque parkland/heathland course, popular with visitors. Qualifying course for the British Open.
18 holes, 6641yds, Par 71, SSS 72, Course record 66.
Club membership 800.
Visitors must contact in advance.
Societies must telephone or write in advance.
Green Fees £32 per day; £24 per round (£35/£26 weekends).
Facilities Martin Gray.
Location Annsmuir (N side of village off B9129)
Hotel ★★63% Lomond Hills Hotel, Parliament Square, FREUCHIE ☎ (0337) 57329 & 57498 25
Additional Hotel ★★★58% Fernie Castle Hotel, LETHAM ☎ (033781) 381 15

Fernie Castle Hotel

Set in the heart of Fife, the golfers' paradise, with Ladybank 2 miles, St Andrews 12 miles and many superb courses including: Carnoustie, Downfield, Elie, Lundin Links, Monifieth and Scotscraig within easy striking distance.

Fernie Castle is the ideal centre for your golfing holiday.

15 comfortable en suite bedrooms, stylish public rooms and the unique 14th century dungeon bar "The Keep" complement our creative Scottish menus and warm welcome to ensure your total relaxation after a hard days golf.

Complete golf packages with special tariff available; please contact us for details.

AA ★★★
STB Commended

Letham • Nr. Cupar • Fife KY7 7RU
Tel: (033 781) 381 • Fax: (033 781) 422

LESLIE Map 11 NO20

Leslie ☎ Glenrothes (0592) 620040
Challenging parkland course.
9 holes, 2470yds, Par 62, SSS 64, Course record 59.
Club membership 200.
Visitors no restrictions.
Societies must apply to the Secretary.
Green Fees £6 per day (£8 weekends).
Facilities & by prior arrangement
Location Balsillie Laws (N side of town off A911)
Hotel ★★★69% Balgeddie House Hotel, Balgeddie Way, GLENROTHES
☎ (0592) 742511 18

LEUCHARS Map 12 NO42

St Michael's ☎ (0334) 839365
Parkland course with open views over Fife and Tayside.
9 holes, 5158yds, Par 70, SSS 66, Course record 64.
Club membership 550.
Visitors may not play on Sun before 1pm.
Societies must apply in writing.
Green Fees £12 per day.
Facilities
Location NW side of village on A919
Hotel ★★63% Lomond Hills Hotel, Parliament Square, FREUCHIE
☎ (0337) 57329 & 57498 25

LEVEN Map 11 NO30

Leven Golfing Society ☎ (0333) 426096
Plays over Leven Links - typical links course.
18 holes, 6435yds, Par 71, SSS 71, Course record 63.
Club membership 700.
Visitors start times restricted, phone for details.
Societies apply in writing.
Green Fees £26 per day; £18 per round (£36/£24 weekends).
Facilities George Finlayson.
Leisure snooker.
Location Links Rd
Hotel ★★★66% Old Manor Hotel, Leven Rd, LUNDIN LINKS
☎ (0333) 320368 15

Leven Thistle ☎ (0333) 26397
Leven has the classic ingredients which make up a golf links in Scotland; undulating fairways with hills and hallows, out of bounds and a 'burn' or stream. A top class championship links course used for British Open final qualifying stages, it has fine views over Largo Bay.
18 holes, 6434yds, Par 71, SSS 71, Course record 64.
Club membership 400.
Visitors parties may not play on Sat.
Societies must telephone 1 month in advance.
Green Fees not confirmed.
Facilities & by prior arrangement G Finlayson.
Leisure pool table, carpet bowls, darts.
Location 3 Balfour St
Hotel ★★★66% Old Manor Hotel, Leven Rd, LUNDIN LINKS
☎ (0333) 320368 15

LOCHGELLY
Map 11 NT19

Lochgelly ☎ (0592) 780174
Parkland course with easy walking and often windy.
18 holes, 5491yds, Par 68, SSS 67.
Club membership 600.
Visitors no restrictions.
Societies must apply in writing.
Green Fees not confirmed.
Facilities (catering during season, weekends
and Fri) ♀ ♨
Location Cartmore Rd (W side of town off A910)
Hotel ★★★57% Dean Park Hotel, Chapel Level,
KIRKCALDY ☎ (0592) 261635
20⇥ ♞ Annexe12 ♞

Lochore Meadows ☎ Ballingry (0592) 860086
Lochside course with natural stream running through, and
woodland nearby. Country park offers many leisure facilities.
9 holes, 5554yds, Par 72, SSS 71, Course record 68.
Club membership 200.
Visitors no restrictions.
Societies must contact in advance.
Green Fees not confirmed.
Facilities ⊗ ৳ ♥ ♨
Leisure fishing, riding.
Location Lochore Meadows Country Park, Crosshill (2m
N off B920)
Hotel ★★★67% Green Hotel, 2 The Muirs, KINROSS
☎ (0577) 63467 47⇥ ♞

LUNDIN LINKS
Map 12 NO40

Lundin ☎ (0333) 320202
The Leven Links and the course of the Lundin Club
adjoin each other. The course is part seaside and part
inland. The holes are excellent but those which can be
described as seaside holes have a very different nature
from the inland style ones..
18 holes, 6377yds, Par 71, SSS 71, Course record 65.
Club membership 850.
Visitors with member only on Sun.
Societies apply in writing.
Green Fees not confirmed.
Facilities ⊗ & 〴 (Tue-Fri) ৳ (Mon-Fri) ♥ ♀♨〔
D K Webster.
Location Golf Rd (W side of village off A915)
Hotel ★★★66% Old Manor Hotel, Leven Rd,
LUNDIN LINKS
☎ (0333) 320368 15⇥ ♞

Lundin Ladies ☎ (0333) 320022
Short, lowland course with Roman stones on the second
fairway, and coastal views.
9 holes, 4730yds, Par 68, SSS 67, Course record 67.
Club membership 300.
Visitors no restrictions.
Societies apply to Secretary.
Green Fees £6 (£7.50 weekends).
Facilities ♨
Location Woodilea Rd (W side of village off A915)
Hotel ★★★66% Old Manor Hotel, Leven Rd,
LUNDIN LINKS
☎ (0333) 320368 15⇥ ♞

MARKINCH
Map 11 NO20

Balbirnie Park ☎ Glenrothes (0592) 752006
Scenic parkland course with several interesting holes.
18 holes, 6210yds, Par 71, SSS 70, Course record 66.
Club membership 800.
Visitors must contact in advance.
Societies apply in writing or telephone Mon-Fri, 9am-
1pm.
Green Fees £25 per day; £18 per round (£32 per day; £26
per round weekends).
Facilities (catering by prior arrangement) ♀ ♨
Location 2m W of Glenrothes
Hotel ★★★★♨67% Balbirnie House, Balbirnie Park,
MARKINCH ☎ (0592) 610066 30⇥ ♞

Remember – prior to playing a stroke or
making a practise swing, the players should
ensure that no one is standing close by and
that no one should move, talk or stand close
to or directly behind the ball or the hole
when a player is addressing the ball or
making a stroke

ST ANDREWS
Map 12 NO51

British Golf Museum ☎ (0334)78880 (Situated opposite Royal & Ancient Golf Club) Tells the fascinating history of golf. Highly visual displays are complemented by the use of visitor-activated touch screens throughout the galleries. Exhibits take the visitor from the misty origins of the game to the present day. You will see amazing images, fascinating collections of clubs, balls, fashion and memorabilia, two period workshops and historic documents. An audio-visual theatre shows historic golfing moments. Shop. **Open:** May-Oct, daily 10 00-17 30; Nov, 10 00-16 00 closed Wed; Dec-Feb, 11 00-15 00 closed Tue & Wed (Closed 25-26 Dec); Mar-Apr, 10 00-17 00, closed Wed. Hours may vary during major St Andrews Golfing events. ☎ to confirm. *Admission:*There is a charge. ☎ for details.

ST ANDREWS LINKS See page 245

SALINE
Map 11 NT09

Saline ☎ (0383) 852591
Hillside course with panoramic view of the Forth Valley.
9 holes, 5302yds, Par 68, SSS 66, Course record 65.
Club membership 350.

Visitors	may not play Sat.
Societies	telephone one week in advance.
Green Fees	£9 per day (£11 Sun).
Facilities	⊗ & ᛟ by prior arrangement ᛚ ♉ ♀ ᛉ
Location	Kinneddar Hill (.5m E at junc B913/914)
Hotel	★★★62% King Malcolm Thistle Hotel, Queensferry Rd, Wester Pitcorthie, DUNFERMLINE ☎ (0383) 722611 48⇆ ℟

TAYPORT
Map 12 NO42

Scotscraig ☎ Dundee (0382) 552515
A rather tight course on downland-type turf with an abundance of gorse. The sheltered position of this Open qualifying course ensures good weather throughout the year.
18 holes, 6496yds, Par 71, SSS 71, Course record 61.
Club membership 650.

Visitors	restricted at weekends. Must contact in advance
Societies	apply in writing.
Green Fees	on application.
Facilities	⊗ & ᛟ by prior arrangement ᛚ ♉ ♀ ᛉ ☎ ᛏ
Location	Golf Rd (S side of village off B945)
Hotel	★★★65% The Queen's Hotel, 160 Nethergate, DUNDEE ☎ (0382) 22515 47 ⇆ ℟

THORNTON   Map 11 NT29

Thornton ☎ Glenrothes (0592) 771111
Undulating and fairly difficult parkland course.
18 holes, 5878yds, Par 70, SSS 69, Course record 65.
Club membership 650.
Visitors   restricted at weekends before 10am & between
                 12.30-2.30pm.
Societies   apply in advance.
Green Fees   £17 per day; £11 per round (£25/£16 weekends).
Facilities   ⊗ ⅢⅢ 陆 ♥ (Apr-Oct) ♀ (Apr-Oct) 占 🏠
Location   Station Rd (1m E of town off A92)
Hotel   ★★★69% Balgeddie House Hotel, Balgeddie
                 Way, GLENROTHES ☎ (0592) 742511 18⇌ ₨

GRAMPIAN

ABERDEEN   Map 15 NJ90

Balnagask ☎ (0224) 876407
Links course.
18 holes, 5486mtrs, SSS 69.
Visitors   no restrictions.
Societies   must contact in advance.
Facilities   ♀ 占
Location   St Fitticks Rd (2m E of city centre)
Hotel   ★★★64% Caledonian Thistle Hotel, 10 Union
                 Ter, ABERDEEN ☎ (0224) 640233 80⇌ ₨

Bon Accord ☎ (0224) 633464
Links coastal course. Municipal course used by three clubs.
18 holes, 6433yds, Par 72, SSS 71.
Club membership 800.
Visitors   no restrictions.
Societies   welcome.
Green Fees   not confirmed.
Facilities   ⊗ 陆 ♥ ♀ 🏠
Leisure   snooker.
Location   19 Golf Rd (0.75 NE of city centre)
Hotel   ★★★64% Caledonian Thistle Hotel, 10 Union
                 Ter, ABERDEEN ☎ (0224) 640233 80⇌ ₨

Deeside ☎ (0224) 867697
Scenic parkland course.
18 holes, 6000yds, Par 69, SSS 69, Course record 64.
Club membership 600.
Visitors   must contact in advance but may not play on Sat
                 before 4pm & medal days.
Societies   Thu only by arrangement.
Green Fees   £20 per round.
Facilities   ⊗ 陆 ♥ ♀ 占 🏠 ⌁ F J Coutts.
Leisure   snooker.
Location   Bielside (3m W of city centre off A93)
Hotel   ★★★68% Ardoe House, Blairs, South
                 Deeside Rd, ABERDEEN
                 ☎ (0224) 867355 71⇌ ₨

Hazelhead Public ☎ No telephone
A tree-lined course.
18 holes, 6595yds, Par 70, SSS 70.
Visitors   no restrictions.
Societies   must contact in advance.

Green Fees not confirmed.
Facilities   占 🏠 ⌁
Location   Hazelhead (4m W of city centre off A944)
Hotel   ★★★68% Ardoe House, Blairs, South
                 Deeside Rd, ABERDEEN
                 ☎ (0224) 867355 71⇌ ₨

Murcar ☎ (0224) 704370
Seaside links course, prevailing NE wind, hard-walking.
Testing 4th and 14th holes.
18 holes, 5809yds, Par 69, SSS 68, Course record 65.
Club membership 830.
Visitors   may not play Wed afternoon, Sat all day & Sun
                 mornings. Must contact in advance & have either
                 a letter of introduction or handicap certificate.
Societies   apply in writing.
Green Fees   £20 per day; £16 per round (£22.50 per round
                 Sun & bank holidays).
Facilities   ⊗ & ⅢⅢ (ex Tue) 陆 ♥ ♀ 占 🏠 ⌁ Alan White.
Leisure   grass tennis courts.
Location   Bridge of Don (5m NE of city centre off A92)
Hotel   ★★★66% The Craighaar, Waterton Rd,
                 Bucksburn, ABERDEEN
                 ☎ (0224) 712275 53⇌ ₨

Nigg Bay ☎ (0224) 871286
Seaside course, hard walking. Plays over Balnagask Course.
18 holes, 5984yds, Par 69, SSS 69.
Club membership 800.
Visitors   must be accompanied by member.
Societies   must contact in advance.
Green Fees   not confirmed.
Facilities   ♀ 占
Location   St Fitticks Rd
Hotel   ★★★64% Caledonian Thistle Hotel, 10 Union
                 Ter, ABERDEEN ☎ (0224) 640233 80⇌ ₨

Northern ☎ (0224) 636440
Exposed and windy seaside course, testing 10th hole. One of
three clubs playing over King's Links municipal course.
18 holes, Par 72, SSS 72.
Club membership 1000.
Visitors   no restrictions.
Societies   must contact in advance.
Green Fees   not confirmed.
Facilities   ♀ 占
Location   22 Gold Rd (adjacent to beach)
Hotel   ★★★64% Caledonian Thistle Hotel, 10 Union
                 Ter, ABERDEEN ☎ (0224) 640233 80⇌ ₨

Royal Aberdeen ☎ (0224) 702571
Championship links course. Windy, easy walking.
*Balgownie: 18 holes, 6372yds, Par 70, SSS 71, Course
record 64.*
Silverburn: 18 holes, 4066yds, Par 64, SSS 60.
Club membership 640.
Visitors   may not play before 3.30pm Sat. Must contact in
                 advance and have an introduction from own club.
Societies   must telephone in advance.
Green Fees   not confirmed.
Facilities   ⊗ ⅢⅢ by prior arrangement 陆 ♥ ♀ (all day)
                 占 🏠 ⌁ ⌁ Ronnie MacAskill.
Location   Balgownie, Bridge of Don (2.5m N of city
                 centre off A92)
Hotel   ★★★64% Caledonian Thistle Hotel, 10 Union
                 Ter, ABERDEEN ☎ (0224) 640233 80⇌ ₨

St Andrews Links

St Andrews ☎ (0334) 75757   Map 12 N051

John Ingham writes: If golf has a mother, then without doubt it is St Andrews, the most famous links in all the world. Sir Winston Churchill is said to have claimed golf was invented by the Devil, and if this is so then the famous Old Course must be the Devil's playground. How can one reconcile these two thoughts; the birthplace and mother of the game - and yet the very Devil of a test?

The great Bobby Jones started by hating St Andrews and shredded his card into a hundred pieces, letting it blow in the wind. But eventually he came to love the place, and earn the affection of all golf. However you view St Andrews, you cannot ignore it. That master shot-maker from America, Sam Snead, took one look and claimed they should plant cattle fodder on the bumpy acres. Gary Player once said it should be towed out to sea, and sunk. But Jack Nicklaus loved it so much that when he won an Open title here, he threw his putter into the air. And he went away, and copied several of the St Andrews features in other courses that now decorate this earth.

St Andrews is much more than an 18-hole test. It is a whole experience and a walk in history. Name the famous players of yesteryear, and they played here, taking divots from the very spot that you can also take divots - merely by paying for a ticket. You too can wander out with your clubs to conquer some holes, maybe, and to be brought to a humbling halt by others.

Jack Nicklaus won his most remarkable victory on this course, thanks to an historic missed putt of just 3 feet 6 inches by Doug Sanders, who had needed a final hole par 4 to win the 1970 Open Championship. The all-time course record is 62, shot by Curtis Strange in the 1987 Dunhill Cup. Surely nobody can ever beat that?

Visitors	must telephone in advance
Societies	must telephone in advance
Green fees	Old course: £40;
	New Course £18;
	Jubilee and Eden £16;
	Strathyrum £12
Facilities	⌂ 🖼 ⛳ (no bar)
Location	NW of town off the A91

90 holes. Old Course: 18 holes, 6566yds, Par 72, SSS 72
New (West Sands Rd): 18 holes, 6604yds, Par 71, SSS 72
Jubilee (West Sands Rd): 18 holes, 6284yds, Par 69, SSS 70
Eden (Dundee Rd): 18 holes, 6112yds, Par 70, SSS 69
Strathyrum (from Summer 1993): 18 holes, 5195yds, Par 69

WHERE TO STAY AND EAT NEARBY

HOTELS:

ST ANDREWS

★★★★(red)🏵 St Andrews Old Course, Old Station Rd.
☎ (0334) 74371. 125 ➭ ⛳.
Scottish & French cuisine

★★★🏵 70% St Andrews Golf, 40 The Scores.
☎ (0334) 72611. 23 ➭ ⛳
Scottish & French cuisine

★★★ 64% Scores, 76 The Scores
☎ (0334) 72451. 30 ➭ ⛳.
British & French cuisine

RESTAURANTS:

CUPAR
✕🏵🏵🏵 Ostlers Close, Bonnygate
☎ (0334) 55574
French & Swiss cuisine

PEAT INN
✕🏵🏵🏵The Peat Inn.
☎ (033484) 206 French cuisine

Westhill ☎ (0224) 740159
A highland course.
18 holes, 5921yds, Par 69, SSS 69.
Club membership 600.
Visitors   restricted Mon-Fri 4pm-7pm & Sat all day. Must
                 contact in advance.
Societies   must contact in advance.
Green Fees   £13 per day; £10 per round (£16/13 Sun and
                 bank holidays).
Facilities   ⊗ & 〉Ⅲ by prior arrangement ⅇ 🖤 ♀ ⅄ 🏠 ℓ
Location   Westhill Heights, Westhill, Skene (6m NW of
                 city centre off A944)
Hotel   ★★★61% Westhill Hotel, WESTHILL
                 ☎ (0224) 740388 38⇄ ↶Annexe14⇄ ↶

ABOYNE   Map 15 NO59

Aboyne ☎ (03398) 86328
Beautiful parkland with outstanding views. Two lochs on
course.
18 holes, 5910yds, Par 68, SSS 68.
Club membership 900.
Visitors   no restrictions.
Societies   prior booking essential.
Green Fees   not confirmed.
Facilities   ⊗ 〉Ⅲ ⅇ 🖤 ♀ ⅄ 🏠 ↶ℓ
Location   Formaston Park (E side of village, N of A93)
Hotel   ★★66% Birse Lodge Hotel, Charleston Rd,
                 ABOYNE ☎ (03398) 86253 & 86254 12⇄ ↶

ALFORD   Map 15 NJ51

Alford ☎ (09755) 62178
A flat parkland course in scenic coutryside. Divided into
sections by a road, a railway and a burn.
18 holes, 5290yds, Par 69, SSS 66.
Club membership 538.
Visitors   advisable to contact in advance.
Societies   must contact in advance.
Green Fees   £12 per day; £8 per round (£16/£12 weekends).
Facilities   ⊗ & 〉Ⅲ by prior arrangement ⅇ 🖤 ♀ ⅄
Location   Montgarrie Rd
Hotel   ★★★★♨82% Kildrummy Castle Hotel,
                 KILDRUMMY ☎ (09755) 71288 16⇄ ↶

AUCHINBLAE   Map 15 NO77

Auchinblae ☎ Laurencekirk (0561) 378869
Picturesque, small, undulating parkland course offering good
views.
9 holes, 2174yds, Par 32, SSS 30, Course record 60.
Club membership 78.
Visitors   restricted Wed & Fri evenings.
Societies   must telephone (0561) 320331 in advance.
Green Fees   £6 per round (£6.50 Sat; £7 Sun).
Location   0.5m NE
Hotel   ★★59% County Hotel, Arduthie Rd,
                 STONEHAVEN ☎ (0569) 64386 14⇄ ↶

If you know of a golf course that welcomes
visitors and is not already in this guide, we
should be grateful for information

BALLATER   Map 15 NO39

Ballater ☎ (03397) 55567
Moorland course with testing long holes and beautiful
scenery.
18 holes, 5638yds, Par 67, SSS 68, Course record 61.
Club membership 620.
Visitors   must phone Pro shop (03397) 55658 for
                 weekend play.
Societies   must telephone in advance.
Green Fees   £15 per round (£18 weekends).
Facilities   ⊗ 〉Ⅲ ⅇ 🖤 ♀ ⅄ 🏠 ↶ℓ Joe Blair.
Leisure   hard tennis courts, fishing, snooker, bowling
                 club & putting green.
Location   Victoria Rd (W side of town)
Hotel   ★★★65% Darroch Learg Hotel, Braemar Rd,
                 BALLATER ☎ (03397) 55443
                 15⇄ ↶ Annexe5⇄ ↶

BANCHORY   Map 15 NO69

Banchory ☎ (03302) 2365
Sheltered parkland course situated beside the River Dee, with
easy walking and woodland scenery. 11th and 12th holes are
testing.
18 holes, 5245yds, Par 67, SSS 66, Course record 60.
Club membership 1000.
Visitors   must contact in advance.
Societies   must book in advance.
Green Fees   £17.50 per day (£19.50 weekends).

Facilities ⊗ ⑂ & ⓛ (limited Nov-Mar) 🍺 ⓨ ♨ 🏠 ⛳ ⓕ
Charles Dernie.
Leisure snooker.
Location Kinneskie Rd (A93, 300 yds from W end of High St)
Hotel ★★★(red)♨♨ Banchory Lodge Hotel, BANCHORY ☎ (03302) 2625 23⇥ ⓘ

BANFF
Map 15 NJ66

Duff House Royal ☎ (0261) 812062
Well-manicured flat parkland, bounded by woodlands and River Deveron. Well bunkered and renowned for its large, two-tier greens.
18 holes, 6161yds, Par 68, SSS 69, Course record 63.
Club membership 1000.
Visitors a handicap certificate is preferred. Some time restrictions.
Societies must apply in writing.
Green Fees £15 per day; £11 per round (£21/£16 weekends).
Facilities ⊗ ⓛ 🍺 ⓨ ♨ 🏠 ⓕ R S Strachan.
Leisure snooker.
Location The Barnyards (0.5m S on A98)
Hotel ★★★57% Banff Springs Hotel, Golden Knowes Rd, BANFF ☎ (0261) 812881 30⇥ ⓘ

BRAEMAR
Map 15 NO19

Braemar ☎ (03397) 41618
Flat course, set amid beautiful countryside on Royal Deeside, with River Clunie running through several holes. The 2nd hole is one of the most testing in the area.
18 holes, 5000yds, Par 65, SSS 64, Course record 61.
Club membership 400.
Visitors are advised to book 24 hours in advance to play at weekends.
Societies must contact secretary in advance.
Green Fees £13 per day; £10 per round (£16 per day; £13 per round weekends).
Facilities ♨ 🏠 ⛳
Location Cluniebank Rd (0.5m S)
Hotel ★★★65% Invercauld Arms Hotel, BRAEMAR ☎ (03397) 41605 68⇥ ⓘ

BUCKIE
Map 15 NJ46

Buckpool ☎ (0542) 32236
Windy, seaside course, with easy walking. Overlooking Moray Firth, its fairways are lined by whin and broom.
18 holes, 6257yds, Par 70, SSS 70.
Club membership 300.
Visitors may not play on competition days.
Societies booking advisable.
Green Fees £10 per day; £6 per round (£15/10 weekends).
Facilities ⊗ ⑂ (high season) ⓛ 🍺 ⓨ ♨
Leisure squash, snooker.
Location Barhill Rd, Buckpool (W side of town off A990)
Hotel ★★61% Mill House Hotel, TYNET ☎ (05427) 233 15⇥ ⓘ

Strathlene ☎ (0542) 31798
Windy seaside course with magnificent view, offering testing golf, including difficult 4th (par 3).
18 holes, 5925yds, Par 69, SSS 68, Course record 65.
Club membership 350.

Visitors no restrictions.
Societies must telephone in advance.
Green Fees £12 per day; £10 per round (£15/12 weekends).
Facilities ⊗ ⓛ 🍺 ⓨ ♨ 🏠
Location Strathlene Rd (3m E on A942)
Hotel ★★61% Mill House Hotel, TYNET ☎ (05427) 233 15⇥ ⓘ

CAIRNBULG
Map 15 NK06

Inverallochy ☎ No telephone
Windy seaside links course with natural hazards, tricky par 3s and easy walking. Panoramic views of North Sea at every hole.
18 holes, 5137yds, Par 64, SSS 65.
Club membership 300.
Visitors no restrictions
Societies apply in writing.
Green Fees £8 per day (£10 weekends).
Facilities ⓛ (weekends) 🍺 (evenings and weekends)
Location 24 Shore St (E side of village off B9107)
Hotel ★★63% Tufted Duck Hotel, ST COMBS ☎ (03460) 582481 582482/3 18⇥ ⓘ

CRUDEN BAY
Map 15 NK03

Cruden Bay ☎ (0779) 812285
A seaside links which provides golf of a high order. It was designed by a master architect, Tom Simpson, and although changed somewhat from his original design it is still a great golf course. Magnificent views.
Cruden Bay: 18 holes, 6370yds, Par 70, SSS 71.
St Olaf: 9 holes, 4710yds, Par 64, SSS 62.
Club membership 1050.
Visitors restricted on Wed & may not play competition days.
Societies apply in writing.
Green Fees not confirmed.
Facilities ⊗ ⑂ by prior arrangement ⓛ 🍺 ⓨ ♨ 🏠 ⛳ ⓕ Robbie Stewart.
Location SW side of village on A975
Hotel ★★★67% Waterside Inn, Fraserburgh Rd, PETERHEAD ☎ (0779) 71121 70⇥ ⓘ Annexe40⇥ ⓘ

CULLEN
Map 15 NJ56

Cullen ☎ (0542) 40685
Interesting links on two levels with rocks and ravines offering some challenging holes. Spectacular scenery.
18 holes, 4610yds, Par 63, SSS 62, Course record 58.
Club membership 620.
Visitors no restrictions.
Societies apply in advance.
Green Fees £8 per day (£11 weekends).
Facilities ⊗ ⑂ by prior arrangement ⓛ 🍺 (catering Apr-Oct) ⓨ ♨
Location The Links (0.5m W off A98)
Hotel ★★61% Mill House Hotel, TYNET ☎ (05427) 233 15⇥ ⓘ

For an explanation of symbols and abbreviations, see page 11

DUFFTOWN
Map 15 NJ33

Dufftown ☎ (0340) 20325
A short and undulating inland course with good views. Highest hole over 1000 ft above sea level.
18 holes, 5308yds, Par 67, SSS 67.
Club membership 300.
Visitors Tue & Wed evening course not available until after 6pm.
Societies must contact in advance.
Green Fees £12 per day; £10 per round.
Facilities ⊗ ⋔ ๒ ♥ ♀ ♨ ᵀ
Location 0.75m SW off B9009
Hotel ★★★♨♨61% Rothes Glen Hotel, ROTHES ☎ (03403) 254 & 255 16rm(13➪)

ELGIN
Map 15 NJ26

Elgin ☎ (0343) 542338
Possibly the finest inland course in the north of Scotland, with undulating greens and compact holes that demand the highest accuracy. There are thirteen par 4's and one par 5 hole on its parkland layout.
18 holes, 6401yds, Par 69, SSS 71.
Club membership 906.
Visitors restricted until 10.05am at weekends. A handicap certificate is required. An advance telephone call is required if more than four people intend to play.
Societies contact in advance.
Green Fees £20 per day; £14 per round (£28/£20 weekends).
Facilities ⊗ ⋔ ๒ ♥ ♀ ♨ 🏠 ᵀ Ian P Rodger.
Leisure practice area.
Location Hardhillock, Birnie Rd, New Elgin (1m S off A941)
Hotel ★★★68% Mansfield House Hotel, Mayne Rd, ELGIN ☎ (0343) 540883 17➪ ฿

ELLON
Map 15 NJ93

McDonald ☎ (0358) 20576
Tight, parkland course with streams and a pond.
18 holes, 5986yds, Par 70, SSS 69.
Club membership 710.
Visitors no restrictions.
Green Fees not confirmed.
Facilities ♀ ♨
Location Hospital Rd (0.25m N on A948)
Hotel ★66% Meldrum Arms Hotel, The Square, OLD MELDRUM ☎ (06512) 2238 & 2505 7฿

FORRES
Map 14 NJ05

Forres ☎ (0309) 672949
An all-year parkland course laid on light, well-drained soil in wooded countryside. Walking is easy despite some hilly holes. A test for the best golfers.
18 holes, 6240yds, Par 70, SSS 69, Course record 63.
Club membership 950.
Visitors welcome although club competitions take priority. Weekends may be restricted in summer.

Societies must telephone 2-3 weeks in advance.
Green Fees £12 per day (£17 weekends).
Facilities ⊗ ⋔ ๒ ♥ ♀ ♨ 🏠 ᵀ ᶜ Sandy Aird.
Location Muiryshade (SE side of town centre off B9010)
Hotel ★★68% Ramnee Hotel, Victoria Rd, FORRES ☎ (0309) 672410 20➪ ฿

FRASERBURGH
Map 15 NJ96

Fraserburgh ☎ (0346) 518287
Testing seaside course.
18 holes, 6279yds, Par 70, SSS 70.
Club membership 700.
Visitors no restrictions.
Societies must contact in advance.
Green Fees £11 per day (£15 weekends); £44 per week.
Facilities ⊗ ⋔ ๒ ♥ (No catering Mon) ♀ ♨ 🏠 ᶜ Craig Stephen.
Location Corbie Hill (1m SE on B9033)
Hotel ★★63% Tufted Duck Hotel, ST COMBS ☎ (03460) 582481 582482/3 18➪ ฿

GARMOUTH
Map 15 NJ36

Garmouth & Kingston ☎ Spey Bay (034387) 388
Seaside course with several parkland holes and tidal waters. Naturally flat.
18 holes, 5656yds, Par 67, SSS 67, Course record 64.
Club membership 400.
Visitors restricted on competition days.
Societies must telephone in advance.
Green Fees £12 per day; £10 per round (£18/£14 weekends).
Facilities ⊗ ⋔ ๒ ♥ (catering May-Sep) ♀ ♨
Location In village on B9015
Hotel ★★★68% Mansfield House Hotel, Mayne Rd, ELGIN ☎ (0343) 540883 17➪ ฿

HOPEMAN
Map 15 NJ16

Hopeman ☎ (0343) 830578
Links-type course with beautiful views over the Moray Firth.
18 holes, 5511yds, Par 67, SSS 67, Course record 66.
Club membership 600.
Visitors restricted Tue 5pm-6pm & weekends.
Societies apply by letter 2 weeks in advance.
Green Fees £10 per day (£15 weekends).
Facilities ⊗ ⋔ by prior arrangement ๒ ♥ ♀ ♨ 🏠
Leisure pool table.
Location E side of village off B9012
Hotel ★★★68% Mansfield House Hotel, Mayne Rd, ELGIN ☎ (0343) 540883 17➪ ฿

HUNTLY
Map 15 NJ53

Huntly ☎ (0466) 792643
A parkland course lying between the Rivers Deveron and Bogie.
18 holes, 5399yds, Par 67, SSS 66.
Club membership 820.
Visitors may not play before 8am.
Societies must contact the secretary.

Green Fees £10 per day (£15 weekends); weekly ticket £50.
Facilities ⊗ ⍟ 🏌 & 🍺 by prior arrangement ⛳ 🏌 🏠
Leisure pool table.
Location Cooper Park (0.25m through School Arch N side of Huntly)
Hotel ★★★♨56% Castle Hotel, HUNTLY
☎ (0466) 792696 21rm(20⇄ ⥀)

INVERURIE   Map 15 NJ72

Inverurie ☎ (0467) 24080
Parkland course, part of which is exposed and windy, and part through wooded area.
18 holes, 5096yds, Par 66, SSS 65, Course record 60.
Club membership 585.
Visitors no restrictions.
Green Fees not confirmed.
Facilities ⛏ 🏠
Location Davah Wood, Blackhall Rd (W side of town off A96)
Hotel ★★★67% Strathburn Hotel, Burghmuir Dr, INVERURIE ☎ (0467) 24422 22⇄ ⥀

KEITH   Map 15 NJ45

Keith ☎ (05422) 2469
Parkland course, with natural hazards over first 9 holes. Testing 7th hole, 232 yds, par 3.
18 holes, 5780yds, Par 69, SSS 68, Course record 64.
Club membership 280.
Visitors no restrictions.
Societies must telephone in advance.
Green Fees not confirmed.
Facilities ⊗ 🏌 🍺 (all catering Jun-Aug) ⛳ 🏌
Location Fife Park (NW side of town centre off A96)
Hotel ★★★74% Craigellachie Hotel, CRAIGELLACHIE ☎ (0340) 881204 30⇄ ⥀

KEMNAY   Map 15 NJ71

Kemnay ☎ (0467) 42225
Undulating parkland course with superb views. A stream crosses four holes.
9 holes, 5502yds, Par 68, SSS 67, Course record 66.
Club membership 510.
Visitors may not play Mon, Tue & Thu evenings or before 11am on Sun.
Societies must telephone in advance.
Green Fees £8 per day (£10 weekends).
Facilities 🏌 🍺 ⛳ 🏌
Location Monymusk Rd (W side of village on B993)
Hotel ★★★61% Westhill Hotel, WESTHILL
☎ (0224) 740388 38⇄ ⥀Annexe14⇄ ⥀

LOSSIEMOUTH   Map 15 NJ27

Moray ☎ (0343) 812018
Two fine Scottish Championship links courses, known as Old and New (Moray), and situated on the Moray Firth where the weather is unusually mild.
Old Course: 18 holes, 6643yds, Par 71, SSS 72.
New Course: 18 holes, 6005yds, Par 69, SSS 69.
Club membership 1300.

Visitors must contact in advance, restricted at weekends.
Societies must contact in advance.
Green Fees not confirmed.
Facilities ⊗ ⍟ by prior arrangement 🏌 🍺 ⛳ 🏌 🏠 ℓ Alistair Thomson.
Location Stotfield Rd (N side of town)
Hotel ★★★73% Mansion House Hotel, The Haugh, ELGIN ☎ (0343) 548811 24⇄ ⥀

MACDUFF   Map 15 NJ76

Royal Tarlair ☎ (0261) 32897
Seaside clifftop course, can be windy. Testing 13th, 'Clivet' (par 3).
18 holes, 5866yds, Par 71, SSS 68, Course record 64.
Club membership 576.
Visitors no restrictions.
Societies apply in writing.
Green Fees Apr-Oct: £12 per day (£15 weekends). Nov-Mar: £6 per day (£8 weekends).
Facilities ⊗ ⍟ 🏌 🍺 ⛳ 🏌
Location Buchan St (0.75m E off A98)
Hotel ★★60% The Highland Haven, Shore St, MACDUFF ☎ (0261) 32408 20⇄ ⥀

NEWBURGH ON YTHAN   Map 15 NJ92

Newburgh on Ythan ☎ Newburgh (03586) 89438
Seaside course adjacent to bird sanctuary. Testing 550-yd dog leg (par 5).
9 holes, 6404yds, Par 72, SSS 70, Course record 69.
Club membership 300.
Visitors restricted Tue & Sat.
Societies must telephone in advance.
Green Fees not confirmed.
Location E side of village on A975
Hotel ★66% Meldrum Arms Hotel, The Square, OLD MELDRUM ☎ (06512) 2238 & 2505 7⥀

NEWMACHAR   Map 15 NJ81

Newmachar ☎ (0651) 863002
Championship-standard parkland course designed by Dave Thomas and opened in 1991. Several lakes affect five of the holes and there are well developed birch and Scots pine trees.
Hawkshill: 18 holes, 6605yds, Par 72, SSS 73, Course record 68.
Club membership 750.
Visitors must contact in advance & have handicap certificate, restricted at weekends.
Societies apply in writing.
Green Fees £24 per day; £16 per round (£30/£20 weekends).
Facilities ⊗ ⍟ 🏌 🍺 ⛳ 🏌 🏠 ℓ Glenn Taylor.
Location Swailend (2m N of Dyce, off A947)
Hotel ★★★67% Strathburn Hotel, Burghmuir Dr, INVERURIE ☎ (0467) 24422 22⇄ ⥀

OLD MELDRUM   Map 15 NJ82

Old Meldrum ☎ (0651) 872648
Parkland course with tree-lined fairways and superb views. There is a water feature at the par 3, 11th.
18 holes, 5442yds, Par 68, SSS 66, Course record 69.
Club membership 700.

▶

Visitors may not play during Club competitions. Must contact in advance.
Societies apply in writing
Green Fees £10 per day (£15 weekends); weekly ticket (Mon-Fri) £35.
Facilities ⊗ ⅷ ⅃ ☕ ♀ ⚐ ⚘
Location Kirkisrae (E side of village off A947)
Hotel ★66% Meldrum Arms Hotel, The Square, OLD MELDRUM
☎ (06512) 2238 & 2505 7✷

PETERHEAD   Map 15 NK14

Peterhead ☎ (0779) 72149
Natural links course bounded by the sea and the River Ugie.
Old Course: 18 holes, 6173yds, Par 70, SSS 70, Course record 64.
New Course: 9 holes, 2237yds, Par 62, SSS 62.
Club membership 550.
Visitors telephone for details.
Societies apply in writing.
Green Fees Old Course: £12 per day (£16 weekends). New Course: £5 per day.
Facilities ⊗ & ⅷ by prior arrangement ⅃ ☕ ♀ ⚘
Leisure pool table.
Location Craigewan Links (N side of town centre off A952)
Hotel ★★★67% Waterside Inn, Fraserburgh Rd, PETERHEAD ☎ (0779) 71121
70⇌ ✷ Annexe40⇌ ✷

PORTLETHEN   Map 15 NO99

Portlethen ☎ Aberdeen (0224) 782575
Set in pleasant parkland, this new course features mature trees and a stream which affects a number of holes.
18 holes, 6735yds, Par 72, SSS 72, Course record 66.
Club membership 650.
Visitors may not play prior to 3pm Sat.
Societies apply in writing.
Green Fees £15 per day; £10 per round (£15 per round weekends & bank holidays).
Facilities ⊗ ⅷ ⅃ ☕ ♀ ⚘ ⛁ ⚑ Muriel Thompson.
Leisure snooker, darts, pool table.
Location Badentoy Rd
Hotel ★★59% County Hotel, Arduthie Rd, STONEHAVEN
☎ (0569) 64386 14⇌ ✷

ROTHES   Map 15 NJ24

Rothes ☎ (03403) 443
A hilly course opened in 1990 on an elevated site overlooking the remains of Rothes castle.
9 holes, 4956yds, Par 68, SSS 64.
Club membership 300.
Visitors no restrictions.
Societies apply in advance.
Green Fees £6 (£8 weekends).
Facilities ⅃ (weekends or by arrangement) ♀ (evening & weekends) ⚘
Location Blackhall (9m S of Elgin on A941)
Hotel ★★★⚇61% Rothes Glen Hotel, ROTHES
☎ (03403) 254 & 255 16rm(13⇌)

SPEY BAY   Map 15 NJ36

Spey Bay ☎ Fochabers (0343) 820424
Seaside links course over gently undulating banks and well-drained ground. Good views along Moray coast. Driving range.
18 holes, 5736yds, Par 71, SSS 69, Course record 66.
Club membership 177.
Visitors telephone for details.
Societies must contact in advance.
Green Fees not confirmed.
Facilities ⊗ ⅃ ☕ ♀ ⚘ ⛁ ⚑ ⚐ ⛾
Leisure hard tennis courts, fishing, caravan site, putting & driving range.
Location 4.5m N of Fochabers on B9104
Hotel ★★61% Mill House Hotel, TYNET
☎ (05427) 233 15⇌ ✷

STONEHAVEN   Map 15 NO88

Stonehaven ☎ (0569) 62124
Challenging meadowland course overlooking sea with three gullies and splendid views.
18 holes, 5103yds, Par 66, SSS 65.
Club membership 840.
Visitors must contact in advance, restricted at weekends.
Societies must contact in advance.
Green Fees £13 per day (£18 weekends).
Facilities ⊗ ⅷ by prior arrangement ⅃ ☕ ♀ ⚘ ⛁
Leisure snooker.
Location Cowie (1m N off A92)
Hotel ★★59% County Hotel, Arduthie Rd, STONEHAVEN
☎ (0569) 64386 14⇌ ✷

TARLAND   Map 15 NJ40

Tarland ☎ (03398) 81413
Difficult upland course, but easy walking.
9 holes, 5816yds, Par 66, SSS 68.
Club membership 240.
Visitors welcome except for competition days. Advisable to contact in advance for weekends.
Societies must telephone in advance.
Green Fees not confirmed.
Facilities ⊗ ⅷ ⅃ ☕ ♀ ⚘
Location Aberdeen Rd (E side of village off B9119)
Hotel ★★66% Birse Lodge Hotel, Charleston Rd, ABOYNE ☎ (03398) 86253 & 86254
12⇌ ✷

TORPHINS   Map 15 NJ60

Torphins ☎ (03398) 82115
Heathland/parkland course built on a hill with views of the Cairngorms.
9 holes, 4684yds, Par 64, SSS 63, Course record 63.
Club membership 370.
Visitors must contact in advance. Restricted weekends, members only Tues after 5pm.
Societies must contact in writing.
Green Fees £8 per day (£10 weekends).
Facilities ⊗ (in summer) ⅃ (weekends, daily in summer) ☕ ⚘

| Location | Golf Rd (0.25m W of village off A980) |
| Hotel | ★★★64% Tor-na-Coille Hotel, BANCHORY ☎ (03302) 2242 24⇄ ⌐ |

TURRIFF

Map 15 NJ74

Turriff ☎ (0888) 62982
A well-maintained parkland course alongside the River Deveron in picturesque surroundings. Friendly clubhouse.
18 holes, 6145yds, Par 69, SSS 69, Course record 63.
Club membership 808.

Visitors	may not play before 10am weekends. Must contact in advance.
Societies	apply in writing to the secretary.
Green Fees	£15 per day; £12 per round (£20/£15 weekends).
Facilities	⊗ ᛘ by prior arrangement ᛒ ♥ ♀ ♨ 🖻 ⚲ ⸙ Robin Smith.
Location	Rosehall (1m W off B9024)
Hotel	★★★57% Banff Springs Hotel, Golden Knowes Rd, BANFF ☎ (0261) 812881 30⇄ ⌐

HIGHLAND

ALNESS

Map 14 NH66

Alness ☎ (0349) 883877
A short, but testing, parkland course with beautiful views over the Cromarty Firth and the Black Isle.
9 holes, 2606yds, Par 66, SSS 64, Course record 62.
Club membership 230.

Visitors	restricted during competitions.
Societies	must telephone in advance.
Green Fees	not confirmed.
Facilities	ᛒ ♥ ♀ ♨ ⸙
Location	Ardross Rd (0.5m N off A9)
Hotel	★★★63% Morangie House Hotel, Morangie Rd, TAIN ☎ (0862) 892281 13⇄ ⌐

BOAT OF GARTEN

Map 14 NH91

Boat of Garten ☎ (047983) 282
This parkland course was cut out from a silver birch forest though the fairways are adequately wide. There are natural hazards of broom and heather, good views and walking is easy. A round provides great variety.
18 holes, 5837yds, Par 69, SSS 69, Course record 67.
Club membership 400.

Visitors	must contact in advance and have a handicap certificate. Restricted weekdays 9.30am-5.30pm.
Societies	must telephone in advance.
Green Fees	£15 per day (£20 weekends).
Facilities	⊗ ᛒ ♥ ♀ ♨ 🖻
Leisure	hard tennis courts.
Location	E side of village
Hotel	★★★64% Boat Hotel, BOAT OF GARTEN ☎ (047983) 258 32⇄ ⌐

THE BOAT HOTEL

GOLF WEEKS AND TEE BREAKS

AA ★ ★ ★

Situated overlooking the beautiful but challenging Boat of Garten Golf Course - the 'Gleneagles' of the Highlands - the Boat Hotel offers you both Tuition and Competition Weeks with our resident Professionals, or, excellent value Tee Break holidays with golf on any of six local courses. Individual tuition available throughout the year.

For Golf Brochure Contact: Golf Desk, The Boat Hotel, Boat of Garten, Inverness-shire. PH24 3BH
Tel: 047 983 258 Fax: 047 983 414

BONAR BRIDGE

Map 14 NH69

Bonar Bridge-Ardgay ☎ Ardgay (08632) 750
Wooded moorland course with picturesque views of hills and loch.
9 holes, 4626yds, Par 66, SSS 63, Course record 66.
Club membership 240.

Visitors	restricted during competitions.
Societies	apply in advance.
Green Fees	£7.50 per day.
Facilities	ᛒ & ♥ (May-Sep) ⏃
Location	0.5m E
Hotel	★★66% Dornoch Castle Hotel, Castle St, DORNOCH ☎ (0862) 810216 4⇄ ⌐ Annexe13⇄ ⌐

BRORA

Map 14 NC90

Brora ☎ (0408) 621417
Typical seaside links with little rough and fine views. Some testing holes.
18 holes, 6110yds, Par 69, SSS 69.
Club membership 550.

Visitors	welcome except for competition days.
Societies	must contact in advance.
Green Fees	£15 per day.
Facilities	⊗ ᛘ ᛒ ♥ (meals Etr-Oct otherwise by prior arrangement) ♀ ⏃ 🖻 ⸙
Location	Golf Rd (E side of village) ▶

Hotel   ★★★56% The Links Hotel, Golf Rd, BRORA
       ☎ (0408) 621225 21⇋ ℝ
Additional   ★★62% Royal Marine Hotel, Golf Rd, BRORA
Hotel   ☎ (0408) 621252 11⇋ ℝ

CARRBRIDGE   Map 14 NH92

Carrbridge ☎ (047984) 623
Short part-parkland, part-moorland course with magnificent
views of the Cairngorms.
9 holes, 5300yds, Par 71, SSS 66.
Club membership 530.
Visitors   restricted Sun & competition days.
Societies   must contact in advance.
Green Fees £8-£10 per day.
Facilities   ⊗ ⅃ ☕ (catering Apr-Oct) ⚲ ⚑
Location   N side of village
Hotel   ★★★⚑⚑67% Muckrach Lodge Hotel, DULNAIN
       BRIDGE ☎ (047985) 257
       9⇋ ℝ Annexe2⇋ ℝ

DORNOCH   Map 14 NH78

Royal Dornoch ☎ (0862) 810219
Very challenging seaside championship links, designed
by Tom Morris and John Sutherland.
18 holes, 6591yds, Par 70, SSS 72, Course record 67.
Struie: 18 holes, 5321yds, Par 68, SSS 70.
Club membership 900.

Visitors	handicap of 24 for gentlemen (ladies 35). Must contact in advance and have a handicap certificate.
Societies	must telephone in advance.
Green Fees	£30 per round (£35 weekends).
Facilities	⊗ ⫴ ⮂ 🍽 ♀ ⛳ ⛳ ⛳ (W E Skinner.
Leisure	hard tennis courts, fishing, riding.
Location	Golf Rd (E side of town)
Hotel	★★66% Dornoch Castle Hotel, Castle St, DORNOCH ☎ (0862) 810216 4⇥ (Annexe13 ⇥ (

DURNESS   Map 14 NC46

Durness ☎ (0971) 511364
A 9-hole course set in tremendous scenery overlooking
Balnakeil Bay. Part links and part inland with water hazards.
Off alternative tees for second 9 holes giving surprising
variety. Tremendous last hole played across the sea to the
green over 100 yards away.
9 holes, 5545yds, Par 70, SSS 68, Course record 72.
Club membership 100.

Visitors	restricted 10am-noon on Sun.
Societies	must telephone in advance.
Green Fees	£8 per day.
Facilities	⊗ ⮂ 🍽 (catering Jun-Sep) ⛳ ⛳
Location	Balnakeil (1m W of village)
Hotel	★★★65% Kinlochbervie Hotel, KINLOCHBERVIE ☎ (0971) 521275 14⇥ (

FORT AUGUSTUS   Map 14 NH30

Fort Augustus ☎ (0320) 6460
Moorland course, with narrow fairways and good views.
Bordered by the tree-lined Caledonian Canal.
9 holes, 5454yds, Par 67, SSS 68, Course record 69.
Club membership 170.

Visitors	no restrictions.
Societies	welcome.
Green Fees	£10 per day.
Facilities	⮂ 🍽 ♀ ⛳ ⛳
Location	Markethill (1m SW on A82)
Hotel	★★61% Lovat Arms Hotel, FORT AUGUSTUS ☎ (0320) 6206 & 6204 21⇥ (

FORTROSE   Map 14 NH75

Fortrose & Rosemarkie ☎ (0381) 20733 & 20529
Seaside links course, set on a peninsula with sea on three
sides. Easy walking, good views. Designed by James Braid;
the club was founded in 1888.
18 holes, 5973yds, Par 71, SSS 69, Course record 64.
Club membership 750.

Visitors	restricted Sat & Sun 8.45-10.15am & 12.45-1.15pm.
Societies	must telephone in advance.
Green Fees	£17 per day; £12 per round (£17 per round weekends).
Facilities	⊗ ⫴ ⮂ 🍽 (by arrangement) ♀ ⛳ 🛍 ⛳ (Graham Philip.
Location	Ness Rd East (W side of town centre)
Hotel	★★★65% Priory Hotel, The Square, BEAULY ☎ (0463) 782309 22⇥ (

FORT WILLIAM   Map 14 NN17

Fort William ☎ (0397) 4464
Moorland course with fine views. Tees and greens very good,
but fairways can be very soft in wet weather.
18 holes, 5640yds, Par 70, SSS 68.
Club membership 200.

Visitors	no restrictions.
Societies	must contact in writing.
Green Fees	£8 per round; £10 per day.
Facilities	⮂ 🍽 ♀ ⛳ ⛳
Location	3m NE on A82
Hotel	★★★75% Moorings Hotel, Banavie, FORT WILLIAM ☎ (0397) 772797 21⇥ (Annexe3(

GAIRLOCH   Map 14 NG87

Gairloch ☎ (0445) 2407
Fine seaside course running along Gairloch Sands with good
views over the sea to Skye.
9 holes, 4577yds, Par 62, SSS 63.
Club membership 350.

Visitors	no restrictions.
Societies	must telephone in advance.
Green Fees	£10 per day.
Facilities	🍽 (Etr-Sep) ⛳ ⛳
Location	1m S on A832
Hotel	★★63% The Old Inn, Flowerdale, GAIRLOCH ☎ (0445) 2006 14⇥ (

GOLSPIE   Map 14 NH89

Golspie ☎ (0408) 633266
Founded in 1889, Golspie's seaside course offers easy
walking and natural hazards including beach heather and
whins. Spectacular scenery.
18 holes, 5836yds, Par 68, SSS 68.
Club membership 480.

Visitors	restricted on competition days.
Societies	must telephone in advance.
Green Fees	£15 per day/round.
Facilities	⊗ ⮂ 🍽 ♀ ⛳ 🛍
Location	Ferry Rd (0.5m S off A9)
Hotel	★★58% Golf Links Hotel, GOLSPIE ☎ (0408) 633408 9⇥ (

GRANTOWN-ON-SPEY   Map 14 NJ02

Grantown-on-Spey ☎ (0479) 2079 (summer) & 2715
Parkland and woodland course. Part easy walking, remainder
hilly. The 7th to 13th really sorts out the golfers.
18 holes, 5745yds, Par 70, SSS 67, Course record 60.
Club membership 500.

Visitors	restricted 8am-10am weekends.
Societies	telephone in advance, or write in winter.
Green Fees	£13 per day (£16 weekends).
Facilities	⊗ ⫴ ⮂ 🍽 (catering by prior arrangement) ♀ ⛳ 🛍 ⛳ (Bill Mitchell.
Location	Golf Course Rd (E side of town centre)
Hotel	★★63% Seafield Lodge Hotel, Woodside Av, GRANTOWN-ON-SPEY ☎ (0479) 2152 14⇥ (

HELMSDALE

Map 14 ND01

Helmsdale ☎ (04312) 240
Sheltered, undulating course following the line of the
Helmsdale River.
9 holes, 1825yds, Par 62, SSS 62.
Club membership 137.
Visitors   no restrictions.
Societies   apply in writing.
Green Fees not confirmed.
Facilities   ⚐
Location   Golf Rd (NW side of town on A896)
Hotel   ★★★56% The Links Hotel, Golf Rd, BRORA
☎ (0408) 621225 21➪ ♠

INVERGORDON

Map 14 NH76

Invergordon ☎ (0349) 852715
Fairly easy but windy parkland course, with good views over
Cromarty Firth. Very good greens. Clubhouse situated 1m
from course close to middle of town.
9 holes, 6028yds, Par 68, SSS 69, Course record 65.
Club membership 300.
Visitors   no restrictions.
Societies   must telephone in advance.
Green Fees not confirmed.
Facilities   ⬤ & ♨ (Sat only) ⚑ (Sat, Tue &
Thu eve) ⚐
Location   King George St (W side of town centre on B817)
Hotel   ★★66% Royal Hotel, Marine Ter, CROMARTY
☎ (03817) 217 10➪ ♠

INVERNESS

Map 14 NH64

Inverness ☎ (0463) 239882
Fairly flat parkland course with burn running through it.
Windy in winter.
18 holes, 6226yds, Par 69, SSS 70.
Club membership 1050.
Visitors   restricted at weekends.
Societies   must telephone in advance.
Green Fees £20 per day; £15 per round (£22/£18 weekends
& public holidays).
Facilities   ⊗ ⊪ ⬤ ♨ (all day in summer) ⚐ 📠 ⌐ ⌐
A P Thomson.
Location   Culcabock (1m S of town centre on B9006)
Hotel   ★★★★66% Kingsmills Hotel, Culcabock Rd,
INVERNESS ☎ (0463) 237166
73➪ ♠ Annexe6➪ ♠

Torvean ☎ (0463) 711434
Municipal parkland course, easy walking, good views.
18 holes, 5784yds, Par 69, SSS 68, Course record 65.
Club membership 403.
Visitors   must contact in advance, restricted on
competition days.
Societies   must telephone in advance.
Green Fees £8.50 per round (£9.50 weekends).
Facilities   ⬤ & ♨ (Apr-Oct) ⚐ 📠 ⌐
Location   Glenurquhart Rd (1.5m SW on A82)
Hotel   ★★(red)🏩 Dunain Park Hotel, INVERNESS
☎ (0463) 230512 12rm(10➪ ♠)

KINGUSSIE

Map 14 NH70

Kingussie ☎ (0540) 661374
Hilly upland course with natural hazards and magnificent
views. Stands about 1000ft above sea level at its highest
point, and the River Gynack comes into play on five holes.
18 holes, 5555yds, Par 66, SSS 67, Course record 64.
Club membership 700.
Visitors   no restrictions.
Societies   must telephone (0540) 661600 to book.
Green Fees £13.50 per day; £10.50 per round (£16.50 &
£12.50 weekends).
Facilities   ⊗ (Jun-Sep) ⬤ & ♨ (Apr-Oct)
⚑ (Apr-Oct) ⚐ 📠 ⌐
Location   Gynack Rd (0.25m N off A86)
Hotel   ★69% Osprey Hotel, Ruthven Rd, KINGUSSIE
☎ (0540) 661510 8rm(4➪ ♠)

LYBSTER

Map 15 ND23

Lybster
Picturesque, short heathland course, easy walking.
9 holes, 1896yds, Par 62, SSS 62.
Club membership 80.
Visitors   no restrictions.
Societies   must contact in advance.
Green Fees not confirmed.
Facilities   ⚐ ⌐
Location   Main St (E side of village)
Hotel   ★★63% Portland Arms, LYBSTER
☎ (05932) 208 19➪ ♠

MUIR OF ORD

Map 14 NH55

Muir of Ord ☎ (0463) 870825
Old established (1875), heathland course with tight fairways
and easy walking. Testing 11th, 'Castle Hill' (par 3).
18 holes, 5202yds, Par 67, SSS 65, Course record 61.
Club membership 700.
Visitors   not permitted during specified draw times for
medal tees.
Societies   apply in writing.
Green Fees £12 per round/day (£15 weekends).
Facilities   ⊗ ⊪ ⬤ ♨ ⚑ ⚐ 📠 ⌐ ⌐ Graham Vivers.
Leisure   snooker.
Location   Great North Rd (S side of village on A862)
Hotel   ★★★65% Priory Hotel, The Square, BEAULY
☎ (0463) 782309 22➪ ♠

NAIRN

Map 14 NH85

Nairn ☎ (0667) 53208
Championship, seaside links founded in 1887 and
extended by Tom Morris and James Braid. Opening holes
stretch out along the shoreline with the turn for home at
the 10th. Regularly chosen for national championships.
18 holes, 6722yds, Par 72, SSS 71, Course record 65.
Club membership 1066.
Visitors   restricted until 10.30am weekends.
Societies   telephone at least 6 weeks in advance.
Green Fees £35 per day; £25 per round (£40/£30
weekends). 9 hole course: £8 per day.

Facilities	⊗ ⫶⫶⫶ by prior arrangement ⮱ ⚑ ♀ ⚘ 🕿 ⛳ ⚑ Robin Fyfe.
Leisure	snooker, 9 hole course.
Location	Seabank Rd
Hotel	★★★★65% Golf View Hotel, Seabank Rd, NAIRN ☎ (0667) 52301 48 ⇄ ⚲

Nairn Dunbar ☎ (0667) 52741

Links course with sea views and testing gorse-and whin-lined fairways. Breezy at holes 6, 7 and 8. Testing hole: 'Long Peter' (527 yds).

18 holes, 6431yds, Par 71, SSS 71.
Club membership 700.

Visitors	must contact in advance & have handicap certificate.
Societies	must contact in advance.
Green Fees	£20 per day; £15 per round (£25/£20 weekends).
Facilities	⊗ ⫶⫶⫶ ⮱ ⚑ ♀ ⚘ 🕿 ⛳ ⚑ Brian Mason.
Location	Lochloy Rd (E side of town off A96)
Hotel	★★59% Carnach House Hotel, Delnies, NAIRN ☎ (0667) 52094 14rm(13 ⇄ ⚲)
Additional Hotel	★★64% Claymore House Hotel, 45 Seabank Rd, NAIRN ☎ (0667) 53731 12 ⇄ ⚲

NETHY BRIDGE   Map 14 NJ02

Abernethy ☎ (0479) 821305

Picturesque moorland course.

9 holes, 4986yds, Par 66, SSS 66.
Club membership 300.

★★

Scottish Tourist Board
HIGHLY COMMENDED

The Claymore House Hotel is proud to offer you the very highest of standards along with the warmest of welcomes during your stay in Nairn.

Newly re-opened after a total refurbishment, the hotel lets you enjoy the most luxurious of surroundings at a reasonable cost. All our bedrooms have en-suite bathroom, colour television, direct dial telephone, hairdryer and tea/coffee making facilities. The Hotel is run by golfers for golfers and with 25 golf courses within 1 hour this is truly golf's northern Mecca.

A short distance from Nairn's famous championship golf course we offer great value packages for the golfer and non-golfer alike, including courtesy car from Inverness rail or airports.

After a day out whether golfing or sight-seeing you can relax in our bar or restaurant where we serve Real Ale and Malt Whiskies with everything in between.

For further details: **Claymore House Hotel,**
Seabank Road, Nairn IV12 4EY
Tel: 0667-53731   Fax: 55290

Visitors	restricted during club matches.
Societies	must telephone in advance.
Green Fees	£8 per day (£12 weekends).
Facilities	⊗ ⮱ ♀ ⚘ ⛳
Location	N side of village on B970
Hotel	★★★⚑67% Muckrach Lodge Hotel, DULNAIN BRIDGE ☎ (047985) 257 9⇄ ⚲Annexe2⇄ ⚲

NEWTONMORE   Map 14 NN79

Newtonmore ☎ (05403) 328

Inland course beside the River Spey. Beautiful views and easy walking. Testing 17th hole (par 3).

18 holes, 5880yds, Par 70, SSS 68, Course record 64.
Club membership 450.

Visitors	must contact in advance.
Societies	apply in writing.
Green Fees	not confirmed.
Facilities	⊗ ⫶⫶⫶ ⮱ ⚑ (all catering Mar-Oct ex Tue) ♀ ⚘ 🕿 ⚑ Robert Henderson.
Location	Golf Course Rd (E side of town off A9)
Hotel	★★69% Columba House Hotel, Manse Rd, KINGUSSIE ☎ (0540) 661402 7⇄ ⚲

PORTMAHOMACK   Map 14 NH98

Tarbat ☎ (086287) 236

Picturesque links course with magnificent views.

9 holes, 5046yds, Par 66, SSS 65.
Club membership 180.

Visitors	no restrictions.
Societies	must telephone in advance.
Green Fees	£5 per day (£6 weekends).
Facilities	⮱ ⚘
Location	E side of village
Hotel	★★★56% Royal Hotel, High St, TAIN ☎ (0862) 892013 25rm(9⇄13 ⚲)

REAY   Map 15 NC96

Reay ☎ (084781) 288

Picturesque seaside links with natural hazards, following the contours of Sandside Bay. Tight and testing.

18 holes, 5884yds, Par 69, SSS 68, Course record 64.
Club membership 450.

Visitors	restricted competition days
Societies	apply in writing.
Green Fees	£10.
Facilities	⊗ (Jun-Sep) ⮱ (weekends) ⚑ ♀ ⚘
Location	0.5m E off A836
Hotel	★★62% Pentland Hotel, Princes St, THURSO ☎ (0847) 63202 53rm(28⇄11 ⚲)

STRATHPEFFER   Map 14 NH45

Strathpeffer Spa ☎ (0997) 421219

Upland course with many natural hazards (no sand bunkers), hard walking and fine views. Testing 3rd hole (par 3) across loch.

18 holes, 4792yds, Par 65, SSS 65, Course record 60.
Club membership 550.

Visitors	may not play during club competition times or until after 10am on Sun. ▶

Societies apply in writing.
Green Fees £15 per day; £10 per round (£18/12 weekends).
Facilities ⊗ ⓛ ▦ (no catering Mon) ♀ ♨ 🖝 ⚑
Location 0.25m N of village off A834
Hotel ★★64% Holly Lodge Hotel, STRATHPEFFER
☎ (0997) 21254 7rm(3⇄3 ℞)

TAIN
Map 14 NH78

Tain ☎ (0862) 892314
Heathland/links course with river affecting 3 holes; easy
walking, fine views.
18 holes, 6238yds, Par 70, SSS 70, Course record 62.
Club membership 600.
Visitors must contact in advance and may not play on
competition days.
Societies must book in advance.
Green Fees £12 per round (£18 weekends).
Facilities ⊗ ▦ ⓛ ▦ ♀ ♨ 🖝
Location Golf Links (E side of town centre off B9174)
Hotel ★★★56% Royal Hotel, High St, TAIN
☎ (0862) 892013 25rm(9⇄13 ℞)

THURSO
Map 15 ND16

Thurso ☎ (0847) 63807
Parkland course, windy, but with fine views of Dunnet Head
and the Orkney Islands.
18 holes, 5818yds, Par 69, SSS 69, Course record 63.
Club membership 366.
Visitors no restrictions.
Societies must telephone in advance.
Green Fees not confirmed.
Facilities ⊗ & ▦ (summer only) ⓛ ▦ ♀ ♨ 🖝 ⚑
Location Newlands of Geise (2m SW on B874)
Hotel ★★62% Pentland Hotel, Princes St, THURSO
☎ (0847) 63202 53rm(28⇄11 ℞)

WICK
Map 15 ND35

Wick ☎ (0955) 2726
Typical seaside links course, windy, easy walking.
18 holes, 5976yds, Par 69, SSS 69, Course record 63.
Club membership 352.
Visitors no restrictions.
Societies apply in writing or telephone in advance.
Green Fees £10 per day (£12 weekends).
Facilities ▦ ▦ ♀
Location Reiss (3.5m N off A9)
Hotel ★★58% Mackay's Hotel, Union St, WICK
☎ (0955) 2323 26rm(23⇄1 ℞)

● LOTHIAN ●

ABERLADY
Map 12 NT47

Kilspindie ☎ (08757) 358
Seaside course, short but tight and well-bunkered. Testing
holes: 2nd, 3rd, 4th and 7th.
18 holes, 5410yds, Par 69, SSS 66.
Club membership 600.
Visitors no restrictions.

Societies must contact in advance.
Green Fees not confirmed.
Facilities ⊗ high tea (Apr-Oct) ⓛ ▦ ♀ ♨ 🖝 ⚑
Graham J Sked.
Location W side of village off A198
Hotel ★★65% Kilspindie House Hotel, Main St,
ABERLADY ☎ (08757) 682 26⇄ ℞

Luffness New ☎ Gullane (0620) 843114 & 843336
Seaside course.
18 holes, 6122yds, Par 69, SSS 69, Course record 62.
Club membership 700.
Visitors must contact in advance but may not play at
weekends & bank holidays.
Societies must contact in writing.
Green Fees £35 per day; £25 per round.
Facilities ⊗ & ▦ by prior arrangement ▦ ♀ ♨ 🖝
Location 1m E on A198
Hotel ★★★(red)♣♣ Greywalls Hotel, Muirfield,
GULLANE ☎ (0620) 842144
17⇄ ℞ Annexe5⇄ ℞

BATHGATE
Map 11 NS96

Bathgate ☎ (0506) 630505
Moorland course. Easy walking. Testing 11th hole, par 3.
18 holes, 6328yds, Par 71, SSS 70, Course record 58.
Club membership 650.
Visitors must contact in advance & may not play on
competition days.
Societies must contact in advance.
Green Fees £20 per day; £15 per round (£25 per day
weekends).
Facilities ⊗ ▦ ▦ ⓛ ▦ ♀ ♨ 🖝 ⚑ Sandy Strachan.
Location Edinburgh Rd (E side of town off A89)
Hotel ★★★65% Houstoun House Hotel, UPHALL
☎ (0506) 853831 28⇄ ℞ Annexe2⇄

BONNYRIGG
Map 11 NT36

Broomieknowe ☎ 031-663 9317
Easy walking mature parkland course laid out by Ben Sayers
and extended by James Braid. Elevated site with excellent
views.
18 holes, 5754yds, Par 68, SSS 68, Course record 64.
Club membership 450.
Visitors restricted Wed, weekends & bank holidays; a
handicap certificate is preferred.
Societies must contact in writing and pay a deposit.
Green Fees £25 per day; £15 per round (£25 per round
weekends).
Facilities ⊗ ▦ & ▦ (ex Mon) ▦ ♀ ♨ 🖝 ⚑ ⚐ Mark
Patchett.
Location 36 Golf Course Rd (0.5m NE off B704)
Hotel ★★★58% Donmaree Hotel, 21 Mayfield
Gardens, EDINBURGH
☎ 031-667 3641 17⇄ ℞

BROXBURN
Map 11 NT07

Niddry Castle ☎ (0506) 891097
A 9-hole parkland course. While not very long, it requires
accurate golf to score well.
9 holes, 5514yds, Par 70, SSS 67, Course record 69.
Club membership 320.

Visitors advisable to contact at weekends, restricted
during competition time.
Societies must contact in advance.
Green Fees 18 holes £7.50 (£10 weekends).
Facilities ⓑ 🍴 🛇
Location Castle Rd, Winchburgh (9m W of Edinburgh off
junc 1)
Hotel ★★★60% Forth Bridges Moat House, Forth
Bridge, SOUTH QUEENSFERRY
☎ 031-331 1199 108⇔ ↸

DALKEITH   Map 11 NT36

Newbattle ☎ 031-663 2123
Undulating parkland course on three levels, surrounded by
woods.
18 holes, 6012yds, Par 69, SSS 69.
Club membership 650.
Visitors restricted before 4pm on weekdays; may not
play at weekends. Handicap certificate required.
Societies must contact in advance.
Green Fees £20 per day.
Facilities ⊗ ⓑ 🍴 ♀ 🛇 🏠 (David Torrance.
Location Abbey Rd (SW side of town off A68)
Hotel ★★64% Eskbank Motor Hotel, 29 Dalhousie
Rd, DALKEITH ☎ 031-663 3234
16⇔ ↸

DUNBAR   Map 12 NT67

Dunbar ☎ (0368) 62317
Another of Scotland's old links. It is said that it was
some Dunbar members who first took the game of golf to
the North of England. The club dates back to 1856. The
wind, if blowing from the sea, is a problem.
18 holes, 6426yds, Par 71, SSS 71, Course record 64.
Club membership 650.
Visitors must contact in advance.
Societies must contact in advance.
Green Fees £25 per day (£40 weekends).
Facilities ⊗ ⓜ ⓑ 🍴 ♀ (all day) 🛇 🏠 🍴 (
Derek Small.
Location East Links (.5m E off A1087)
Hotel ★★65% Bayswell Hotel, Bayswell Park,
DUNBAR ☎ (0368) 62225 13⇔ ↸

Winterfield ☎ (0368) 63562
Seaside course with superb views.
18 holes, 5220yds, SSS 64.
Club membership 200.
Visitors must contact in advance.
Green Fees not confirmed.
Facilities ♀ 🛇 🏠 🍴
Location North Rd (W side of town off A1087)
Hotel ★★65% Bayswell Hotel, Bayswell Park,
DUNBAR ☎ (0368) 62225 13 ⇔ ↸
Additional ★★63% Redheugh Hotel, Bayswell Park,
Hotel DUNBAR ☎ (0368) 62793
10⇔ ↸

> If visiting a brand new course, be sure to
> telephone before your visit to confirm the
> course information is correct

EDINBURGH   Map 11 NT27

Baberton ☎ 031-453 4911
Parkland course.
18 holes, 6098yds, Par 69, SSS 69, Course record 64.
Club membership 1000.
Visitors may not play at weekends.
Societies must contact in advance.
Green Fees not confirmed.
Facilities ⊗ ⓜ by prior arrangement ⓑ 🍴 ♀ 🛇 🏠 (
Kenneth Kelly.
Location Juniper Green (5m W of city centre off A70)
Hotel ★★★67% Bruntsfield Hotel, 69/74 Bruntsfield
Place, EDINBURGH ☎ 031-229 1393 50⇔ ↸

Braid Hills ☎ 031-447 6666
Municipal heathland course with good views of Edinburgh
and the Firth of Forth.
18 holes, 6172yds, Par 70, SSS 68 or 4832yds, Par 65.
Visitors may not play on Sat mornings.
Societies apply in writing to Leisure Management Unit,
Edinburgh District Council, 141 London Road,
Edinburgh.
Green Fees not confirmed.
Facilities 🛇 🏠 🍴 (J Boath.
Location Braid Hills Approach (2.5m S of city centre off
A702)
Hotel ★★★59% Braid Hills Hotel, 134 Braid Rd,
Braid Hills, EDINBURGH
☎ 031-447 8888 68⇔ ↸ ▶

Bruntsfield Links Golfing Society ☎ 031-336 1479

Parkland course with good views of Forth Estuary. 4th and 14th holes testing.
18 holes, 6407yds, Par 71, SSS 71, Course record 67.
Club membership 1000.

Visitors may not play at weekends. Must contact in advance and have an introduction from own club.
Societies must contact in advance.
Green Fees apply for details.
Facilities ⊗ ⫽ by prior arrangement ▦ ♀ 🕭 🏠 ₵
Location 32 Barnton Av, Davidsons-Mains (4m NW of city centre off A90)
Hotel ★★★63% Barnton Thistle Hotel, Queensferry Rd, Barnton, EDINBURGH ☎ 031-339 1144 50⇥ ♠

Carrick Vale ☎ 031-337 1096

Flat parkland course.
18 holes, 6299yds, Par 71, SSS 70, Course record 64.
Club membership 450.

Visitors must have an introduction from own club.
Green Fees not confirmed.
Location Carricknowe Municipal, Glendevon Park (3m W of city centre, S of A8)
Hotel ★★★64% Forte Posthouse, Corstorphine Rd, EDINBURGH ☎ 031-334 0390 200⇥ ♠

Craigmillar Park ☎ 031-667 0047

Parkland course, with good views.
18 holes, 5859yds, Par 70, SSS 68, Course record 65.
Club membership 520.

Visitors must play with member at weekends & after 3pm on weekdays.
Societies must contact in writing.
Green Fees £18 per day; £12.50 per round.
Facilities ⊗ ⫽ by prior arrangement ▧ ▦ ♀ 🕭 🏠 ⫽ ₵ Brian McGhee.
Location 1 Observatory Rd (2m S of city centre off A7)
Hotel ★★★58% Donmaree Hotel, 21 Mayfield Gardens, EDINBURGH ☎ 031-667 3641 17⇥ ♠

Dalmahoy Country ☎ 031-333 1845

Two upland courses, one Championship.
18 holes, 6664yds, Par 72, SSS 72.
Club membership 700.

Visitors must contact in advance.
Societies must telephone for details.
Facilities ♀ 🕭 🏠 ⫽ 🎏 ₵
Leisure squash.
Location Kirknewton (7m W of city centre on A71)
Hotel ★★★64% Forte Posthouse, Corstorphine Rd, EDINBURGH ☎ 031-334 0390 200⇥ ♠

Duddingston ☎ 031-661 7688

Parkland, semi-seaside course with burn as a natural hazard. Testing 11th hole. Easy walking and windy.
18 holes, 6647yds, Par 72, SSS 72, Course record 64.
Club membership 700.

Visitors may not play at weekends.
Societies Tue & Thu only. Must contact in advance.
Green Fees £26 per day; £20 per round.
Facilities ⊗ ⫽ by prior arrangement ▧ ▦ ♀ 🕭 🏠 ⫽ ₵ Alastair McLean.

Location Duddingston Rd West (2.5m SE of city centre off A1)
Hotel ★★★58% Donmaree Hotel, 21 Mayfield Gardens, EDINBURGH ☎ 031-667 3641 17⇥ ♠

Kingsknowe ☎ 031-441 1145

Hilly parkland course with prevailing SW winds.
18 holes, 5979yds, Par 69, SSS 69, Course record 64.
Club membership 705.

Visitors must contact in advance.
Societies may not play at weekends and must contact in advance.
Green Fees £20 per day; £16 per round (£25 per round weekends).
Facilities ⊗ 🕭 ▦ ♀ 🏠 🎏 ₵
Leisure snooker.
Location 326 Lanark Rd (4m SW of city centre on A70)
Hotel ★★★67% Bruntsfield Hotel, 69/74 Bruntsfield Place, EDINBURGH ☎ 031-229 1393 50⇥ ♠

Liberton ☎ 031-664 3009

Undulating, wooded parkland course.
18 holes, 5299yds, Par 67, SSS 67.
Club membership 650.

Visitors may only play before 5pm on Tue & Thu Apr-Sep. Must contact in advance.
Societies must contact in writing.
Green Fees not confirmed.
Facilities ⊗ ⫽ 🕭 ▦ ♀ 🏠 ₵ Iain Seath.
Location 297 Gilmerton Rd (3m SE of city centre on A7)
Hotel ★★57% Suffolk Hall Hotel, 10 Craigmillar Park, EDINBURGH ☎ 031-668 4333 12rm(11⇥ ♠)

Lothianburn ☎ 031-445 2206

Hillside course with a 'T' shaped wooded-area, situated in the Pentland foothills. Sheep on course. Testing in windy conditions.
18 holes, 5750yds, Par 71, SSS 69, Course record 63.
Club membership 800.

Visitors may not play on competition days.
Societies must contact in writing.
Green Fees £16 per day; £11 per round (£20 per day; £15 per round weekends).
Facilities ⊗ ⫽ 🕭 ▦ (no catering Wed)
♀ (ex Wed) 🏠 🎏 ₵ Paul Morton.
Location 106A Biggar Rd, Fairmilehead (4.5m S of city centre on A702)
Hotel ★★★59% Braid Hills Hotel, 134 Braid Rd, Braid Hills, EDINBURGH ☎ 031-447 8888 68⇥ ♠

Merchants of Edinburgh ☎ 031-447 1219

Testing hill course.
18 holes, 4889mtrs, Par 64, SSS 64, Course record 61.
Club membership 700.

Visitors must play with member at weekends.
Societies must contact in writing.
Green Fees not confirmed.
Facilities ⊗ & ⫽ (ex Wed and Thu) 🕭 ♀ 🏠 ₵ Craig Imlah.
Leisure snooker.
Location 10 Craighill Gardens (2m SW of city centre off A702)
Hotel ★★★59% Braid Hills Hotel, 134 Braid Rd, Braid Hills, EDINBURGH ☎ 031-447 8888 68⇥ ♠

Mortonhall ☎ 031-447 6974
Moorland course with views over Edinburgh.
18 holes, 6557yds, Par 72, SSS 71, Course record 66.
Club membership 650.
Visitors must have letter of introduction.
Societies may not play at weekends. Must contact in advance.
Green Fees £25 per day; £20 per round (£35/£30 weekends).
Facilities ⊗ (ex weekends & Mon) 🏌 🍺 ♀ ♣ 🏠 ⛳ ⛆
D B Horn.
Location Braid Rd (3m S of city centre off A702)
Hotel ★★★59% Braid Hills Hotel, 134 Braid Rd,
Braid Hills, EDINBURGH
☎ 031-447 8888 68⇥ ☏

Murrayfield ☎ 031-337 1009
Parkland course on the side of Corstorphine Hill, with fine views.
18 holes, 5725yds, Par 70, SSS 68, Course record 64.
Club membership 775.
Visitors may not play at weekends. Must be accompanied by member, contact in advance and have an introduction from own club.
Green Fees not confirmed.
Facilities ⊗ ⍊ by prior arrangement 🏌 🍺 ♀ ♣ 🏠 ⛳ ⛆
James Fisher.
Location 43 Murrayfield Rd (2m W of city centre off A8)
Hotel ★★★64% Forte Posthouse, Corstorphine Rd,
EDINBURGH ☎ 031-334 0390
200⇥ ☏

Portobello ☎ 031-669 4361
Public parkland course, easy walking.
9 holes, 2400yds, Par 32, SSS 32, Course record 62.
Club membership 70.
Visitors may not play Sat 8.30-10am & 12.30-2pm and on competition days.
Societies must contact in advance.
Green Fees £3 for 9 holes.
Facilities ⛳
Location Stanley St (3m E of city centre off A1)
Hotel ★★★58% Donmaree Hotel, 21 Mayfield Gardens, EDINBURGH ☎ 031-667 3641
17⇥ ☏

Prestonfield ☎ 031-667 1273
Parkland course with beautiful views.
18 holes, 6216yds, Par 70, SSS 70, Course record 62.
Club membership 800.
Visitors may not play between noon-1pm Sat & before 11.30am Sun
Societies must contact in advance.
Green Fees £25 per day; £17 per round (£25 per round; £32 per day weekends).
Facilities ♣ 🏠 ⛆
Location Priestfield Rd North (1.5m S of city centre off A68)
Hotel ★★★58% Donmaree Hotel, 21 Mayfield Gardens, EDINBURGH ☎ 031-667 3641
17⇥ ☏

Ravelston ☎ 031-332 2486
Parkland course.
9 holes, 5322yds, Par 66, SSS 66, Course record 66.
Club membership 610.

Visitors must contact in advance & have handicap certificate, but may not play at weekends & bank holidays.
Green Fees £12.50 per round.
Facilities 🏌 🍺 ♣
Location 24 Ravelston Dykes Rd (3m W of city centre off A90)
Hotel ★★★64% Forte Posthouse, Corstorphine Rd,
EDINBURGH ☎ 031-334 0390 200⇥ ☏

Royal Burgess ☎ 031-339 2075
No mention of golf clubs would be complete without mention of the Royal Burgess, which was instituted in 1735, thus being the oldest golfing society in the world. Its course is a pleasant parkland, and one with very much variety. A club which all those interested in the history of the game should visit.
18 holes, 6111yds, Par 68, SSS 69.
Club membership 620.
Visitors must contact in advance. Gentlemen only.
Societies must contact in advance.
Green Fees not confirmed.
Facilities ⊗ (Tue-Fri only) 🏌 🍺 ♀ ♣ 🏠 ⛳ ⛆
George Yuille.
Location 181 Whitehouse Rd, Barnton (5m W of city centre off A90)
Hotel ★★★63% Barnton Thistle Hotel, Queensferry Rd, Barnton, EDINBURGH
☎ 031-339 1144 50⇥ ☏

Silverknowes ☎ 031-336 3843
Public links course on coast overlooking the Firth of Forth.
18 holes, 6216yds, Par 71, SSS 70, Course record 66.
Club membership 500.
Visitors no restrictions.
Societies must contact in advance in writing.
Green Fees £6.60 per round.
Facilities 🏌 by prior arrangement ♀ by prior arrangement
Location Silverknowes, Parkway (4m NW of city centre N of A902)
Hotel ★★65% Murrayfield Hotel, 18 Corstorphine Rd,
EDINBURGH ☎ 031-337 1844
23⇥ ☏ Annexe10 ☏

Swanston ☎ 031-445 2239
Hillside course with steep climb at 12th & 13th holes.
18 holes, 5024yds, Par 66, SSS 65, Course record 63.
Club membership 500.
Visitors may not play on competition days. Must contact in advance.
Societies telephone for details.
Green Fees not confirmed.
Facilities ⊗ 🏌 🍺 ♀ ♣ 🏠 ⛆ Ian Seith.
Location 111 Swanston Rd, Fairmilehead (4m S of city centre off B701)
Hotel ★★★59% Braid Hills Hotel, 134 Braid Rd,
Braid Hills, EDINBURGH
☎ 031-447 8888 68 ⇥ ☏

Torphin Hill ☎ 031-441 1100
Beautiful hillside, heathland course, with fine views of Edinburgh and the Forth Estuary.
18 holes, 4597mtrs, Par 67, SSS 66.
Club membership 410.
Visitors must contact in advance but may not play on competition days. ▶

Societies must contact in advance.
Green Fees not confirmed.
Facilities ⊗ � ┺ 里 ♀ ⚐ ⚑ ⚑
Location Torphin Rd, Colinton (5m SW of city centre
S of A720)
Hotel ★★★59% Braid Hills Hotel, 134 Braid Rd,
Braid Hills, EDINBURGH
☎ 031-447 8888 68⇆ ☎

Turnhouse ☎ 031-539 5937 & 031-339 1014
Hilly, parkland/heathland course, good views.
18 holes, 6171yds, Par 69, SSS 69, Course record 63.
Club membership 750.
Visitors must be accompanied by a member & may not
play at weekends or on competition days.
Societies must contact in writing.
Green Fees £20 per day; £14 per round.
Facilities ⊗ � by prior arrangement ┺ 里 by prior
arrangement ♀ ⚐ ⚑ ⚑ ⚑ John Murray.
Location Turnhouse Rd (6m W of city centre N of A8)
Hotel ★★★63% Barnton Thistle Hotel, Queensferry
Rd, Barnton, EDINBURGH
☎ 031-339 1144 50⇆ ☎

FAULDHOUSE

Map 11 NS96

Greenburn ☎ (0501) 70292
Exposed rolling course with sparse tree cover. Water hazards
from a pond and a burn.
18 holes, 6200yds, Par 71, SSS 70, Course record 63.
Club membership 500.
Visitors must contact club in advance.
Societies by prior arrangement.
Green Fees £16.50 per day; £11 per round (£19.50/£13
weekends).
Facilities ⊗ � ┺ 里 ♀ ⚐ ⚑ ⚑ Howard Ferguson.
Location 6 Greenburn Rd (3m SW of Whitburn)
Hotel ★★60% Dreadnought Hotel, 17/19 Whitburn
Rd, BATHGATE
☎ (0506) 630791 19rm(18⇆ ☎)

GIFFORD

Map 12 NT56

Gifford ☎ (062081) 267 & 591
Parkland course, with easy walking.
9 holes, 6101yds, Par 71, SSS 69.
Club membership 504.
Visitors restricted Tue, Wed & weekends.
Green Fees £10 per day (£10 per round weekends).
Facilities ⚐
Location Calroust (1m SW off B6355)
Hotel ★★70% Tweeddale Arms Hotel, GIFFORD
☎ (062081) 240 15⇆ ☎

Each golf-course entry has a recommended
AA-appointed hotel. For a wider choice of
places to stay, consult *AA Hotels in Britain
and Ireland* and *AA Inspected Bed and
Breakfast in Britain and Ireland* available
from your local book shop or AA shops

GULLANE

Map 12 NT48

Gullane ☎ (0620) 843115
Gullane is a delightful village and one of Scotland's great
golf centres. Gullane club was formed in 1882. There are
three Gullane courses and the No 1 is of championship
standard. It differs from most Scottish courses in as much
as it is of the downland type and really quite hilly. The
first tee is literally in the village. The views from the top
of the course are magnificent and stretch far and wide in
every direction - in fact, it is said that 14 counties can be
seen from the highest spot.
Course No 1:: 18 holes, 6466yds, Par 71, SSS 71.
Course No 2:: 18 holes, 6219yds, Par 70, SSS 70.
Course No 3:: 18 holes, 5128yds, Par 65, SSS 65.
Club membership 1200.
Visitors must contact in advance.
Societies must contact in writing.
Green Fees not confirmed.
Facilities ⊗ � ┺ 里 ♀ ⚐ ⚑ ⚑ ⚑ J Hume.
Location On A198
Hotel ★★★(red)⚘ Greywalls Hotel, Muirfield,
GULLANE ☎ (0620) 842144
17⇆ ☎ Annexe5⇆ ☎

MUIRFIELD See page 261

(Honourable Company of Edinburgh Golfers)

HADDINGTON

Map 12 NT57

Haddington ☎ (062082) 3627
Inland course, tree-lined and bunkered, but not hilly.
18 holes, 6280yds, Par 71, SSS 70.
Club membership 600.
Visitors may not play between 7am-10am & noon-2pm at
weekends. Must contact in advance.
Societies must contact in advance; deposits required.
Green Fees £14 per day; £10 per round (£18/£13 weekends).
Facilities ⊗ � ┺ 里 (catering weekends only mid Oct-
Mar) ♀ ⚐ ⚑ ⚑ John Sandilands.
Leisure pool table.
Location Amisfield Park (E side off A613)
Hotel ★★70% Tweeddale Arms Hotel, GIFFORD
☎ (062081) 240 15⇆ ☎

LINLITHGOW

Map 11 NS97

Linlithgow ☎ (0506) 842585
Slightly hilly parkland course in beautiful setting.
18 holes, 5800yds, Par 70, SSS 68.
Club membership 400.
Visitors may not play Sat. Must book in advance Sun.
Societies must contact in writing.
Green Fees not confirmed.
Facilities ⊗ ┺ & 里 (in season except Tue) ♀ ⚐ ⚑ ⚑
Derek Smith.
Location Braehead (1m S off Bathgate Road off A803)
Hotel ★★★67% Inchyra Grange Hotel, Grange Rd,
POLMONT ☎ (0324) 711911 43⇆ ☎

For an explanation of symbols and
abbreviations, see page 11

Muirfield

(Honourable Company of Edinburgh Golfers)

Gullane ☎(062084) 2123. **Map 12 NT 48**

John Ingham writes: Ask an American superstar to name the best golf course in Great Britain, or maybe even in the entire world, and the likely answer will be Muirfield. It certainly features in the top ten of any meaningful selection.

Purely on shape and balance, the course has everything. Ask competitors in the Open Championship what they think of the last nine holes, and they will tell you it can wreck the stoutest heart. But ask Isoa Aoki of Japan what he thinks, and he will smile and maybe tell of his course record 63 here.

Established in 1744, it is just ten years older than the Royal & Ancient itself but not as old as Royal Blackheath. However, these dates show that Muirfield certainly has seniority and tradition. Quite simply, it is exclusive and entirely excellent. Muirfield has staged some outstanding Open Championships with one, I suspect, standing out in people's minds more than any other.

Back in 1972, Tony Jacklin was Europe's best player and looked set to prove it again at Muirfield when he had appeared to wear down Lee Trevino, the defending champion. At the 71st hole, Trevino seemed to be frittering away strokes as he mishit a shot downwind through the dry, fast, green. The next few minutes were truly hair-raising 'I was mad' recalled Trevino. 'My next shot from the bank was strictly a give-up one. And the ball went straight in the hole.' Jacklin had chipped up, well short. Then he missed his putt, turned for the return putt, and missed again. We all did mental arithmetic. Jacklin had blown it and when he bogeyed the last, furious at himself, he suddenly wasn't the winner - Trevino was.

Those of us who were there recall Trevino had holed one bunker shot, and chipped in three times. Muirfield looked on his brilliance with favour and sad Jacklin never won an Open again.

Membership 625

Visitors accepted on Tuesdays and Thursdays: also Friday mornings September-June. Must contact in advance

Societies telephone in advance. But also restricted to Tuesdays, Thursdays: and Friday mornings September-June

Green fees £64 per day; £48 per round

Facilities ⊗ 🍺 ♀ ⛄

Location Duncur Rd (off A198 on NE side of village)

18 holes, 6601 yards, Par 70, SSS 73

WHERE TO STAY AND EAT NEARBY

HOTELS:

ABERLADY
★★ 65% Kilspindie House, Main St. ☎(08757) 682. 26 ⇆ 🐾

GULLANE
★★★(red) ❀❀ ♨ Greywalls, Muirfield. ☎(0620) 842144. 17 ⇆ 🐾 Annexe 5 ⇆ 🐾

NORTH BERWICK
★★★ 65% The Marine, Cromwell Rd. ☎(0620) 2406. 83 ⇆ 🐾 International cuisine

★★ 62% Nether Abbey, 20 Dirleton Ave. ☎(0620) 2802. 16 (10 ⇆ 🐾)

★★ 63% Point Garry, West Bay Rd. ☎(0620) 2380. 16 (12 ⇆ 🐾) International cuisine

RESTAURANT:

GULLANE
✕❀❀❀ La Potinière, Main St. ☎(0620) 843214. French cuisine

West Lothian ☎ (0506) 826030
Hilly parkland course with superb views of River Forth.
18 holes, 6340yds, Par 71, SSS 71, Course record 64.
Club membership 500.
Visitors   may not play after 4pm midweek. Weekends by
          arrangement. Must contact in advance
Societies   must telephone in advance.
Green Fees £15 day ; £10 per round (£20/14 weekends).
Facilities   ⛬
Location   Airngath Hill (1m S off A706)
Hotel   ★★★67% Inchyra Grange Hotel, Grange Rd,
          POLMONT ☎ (0324) 711911 43⇆ 🐾

LIVINGSTON

Map 11 NT06

Deer Park Golf & Country Club ☎ (0506) 38843 & 31037
Long testing course, fairly flat, championship standard.
18 holes, 6636yds, Par 71, SSS 72.
Club membership 500.
Visitors   no restrictions.
Green Fees £14-£19 (£22-£31 weekends).
Facilities   ⊗ �)Ⓜ ⓑ 🍺 ♀ ⛬ ⛳ 🐾 ⓣ
Leisure   heated indoor swimming pool, squash, snooker,
          sauna, solarium, gymnasium.
Location   Golfcourse Rd (N side of town off A809)
Hotel   ★★★65% Houstoun House Hotel, UPHALL
          ☎ (0506) 853831 28⇆ 🐾 Annexe2⇆

Pumpherston ☎ (0506) 32869
Undulating parkland course with testing 6th hole (par 3), and
view of Pentland Hills.
9 holes, 5154yds, Par 64, SSS 65, Course record 61.
Club membership 350.
Visitors   must be accompanied by a member.
Societies   weekdays only. Must apply in writing.
Green Fees not confirmed.
Facilities   ⊗ �)Ⓜ ⓑ 🍺 ♀ ⛬
Location   Drumshoreland Rd, Pumpherston (1m E
          between A71 & A89)
Hotel   ★★★65% Houstoun House Hotel, UPHALL
          ☎ (0506) 853831 28⇆ 🐾 Annexe2⇆

LONGNIDDRY

Map 12 NT47

Longniddry ☎ (0875) 52141
Undulating seaside links and partial parkland course. One
of the numerous courses which stretch east from
Edinburgh right to Dunbar. The inward half is more open
and less testing than the wooded outward half.
18 holes, 6219yds, Par 68, SSS 70, Course record 63.
Club membership 950.
Visitors   must contact in advance & have a handicap
          certificate; must play with member at
          weekends but may not play on bank
          holidays or competition days.
Societies   must contact in writing.
Green Fees £32 per day; £22 per round.
Facilities   ⊗ �)Ⓜ ⓑ 🍺 ♀ ⛬ ⛳ 🐾 ⓣ John Gray.
Location   Links Rd (W side of village off A198)
Hotel   ★★65% Kilspindie House Hotel, Main St,
          ABERLADY ☎ (08757) 682 26⇆ 🐾

MUSSELBURGH

Map 11 NT37

Musselburgh ☎ 031-665 2005
Testing parkland course with natural hazards including trees
and a burn, easy walking.
18 holes, 6614yds, Par 71, SSS 72, Course record 64.
Club membership 700.
Visitors   must contact in advance. May not play before
          9.30am weekdays & before 10am weekends.
Societies   must contact in advance.
Green Fees £22 per day; £15 per round (£26/£19 weekends).
Facilities   ⊗ �)Ⓜ by prior arrangement ⓑ 🍺 ♀ (ex Tue)
          ⛬ 🏠 🐾 ⓣ Tom Stangoe.
Location   Monktonhall (1m S on B6415)
Hotel   ★★★58% Donmaree Hotel, 21 Mayfield
          Gardens, EDINBURGH
          ☎ 031-667 3641 17⇆ 🐾

Musselburgh Old Course ☎ 031-655 5438
A links type course.
9 holes, 2371yds, Par 33, SSS 33, Course record 67.
Club membership 70.
Visitors   may not play at weekends.
Societies   must contact in advance.
Green Fees not confirmed.
Facilities   ♀ ⛬
Location   Millhill (1m E of town off A1)
Hotel   ★★★58% Donmaree Hotel, 21 Mayfield
          Gardens, EDINBURGH
          ☎ 031-667 3641 17⇆ 🐾

NORTH BERWICK

Map 12 NT58

Glen ☎ (0620) 5288 & 2726
An interesting course with a good variety of holes. The views
of the town, the Firth of Forth and the Bass Rock are breath
taking.
18 holes, 6086yds, Par 69, SSS 69, Course record 64.
Club membership 500.
Visitors   booking advisable.
Societies   must telephone in advance.
Green Fees £16 per day; £11 per round (£20/£14 weekends).
Facilities   ⊗ ⛬)Ⓜ by prior arrangement ⓑ 🍺 ♀ ⛬ 🏠 🐾
Location   East Links, Tantallon Ter (E side of town centre)
Hotel   ★★62% Nether Abbey Hotel, 20 Dirleton Av,
          NORTH BERWICK ☎ (0620) 2802
          16rm(4⇆6 🐾)

North Berwick ☎ (0620) 2135
Another of East Lothian's famous courses, the links at
North Berwick is still popular. A classic championship
links, it has many hazards including the beach, streams,
bunkers, light rough and low walls. The great hole on the
course is the 15th, the famous 'Redan', selected for
televisions best 18 in the UK. Used by both the Tantallon
and Bass Rock Golf Clubs.
18 holes, 6315yds, Par 71, SSS 70, Course record 66.
Club membership 500.
Visitors   must contact in advance.
Societies   must contact in advance.
Green Fees Mar-Oct: £30 per day; £20 per round
          (£40/£30 weekends & public holidays).
          Nov-Feb £15 per day (£20 weekends &
          public holidays).

Facilities	⊗ ▥ by prior arrangement ⓑ ☲ ♀ ♨ 盒 ☝ (D Huish.
Location	New Clubhouse, Beach Rd (W side of town on A198)
Hotel	★★★65% The Marine Hotel, Cromwell Rd, NORTH BERWICK ☎ (0620) 2406 83⇄ ♠

PENICUIK   Map 11 NT25

Glencorse ☎ (0968) 677177
Picturesque parkland course with burn affecting ten holes.
Testing 5th hole (237 yds) par 3.
18 holes, 5205yds, Par 64, SSS 66.
Club membership 650.
Visitors   must contact in advance, restricted at weekends.
Societies   Tue-Thu only; must contact in advance.
Green Fees £20 per day; £15 per round.
Facilities   ⊗ ⓑ ☲ ♀ ♨ 盒 ☝ (Cliffe Jones.
Location   Milton Bridge (1.5m N on A701)
Hotel   ★★★59% Braid Hills Hotel, 134 Braid Rd, Braid Hills, EDINBURGH ☎ 031-447 8888 68⇄ ♠

PRESTONPANS   Map 11 NT37

Royal Musselburgh ☎ (0875) 810276
Tree-lined parkland course overlooking Firth of Forth.
18 holes, 6237yds, Par 70, SSS 70.
Club membership 900.
Visitors   must contact in advance, restricted Fri afternoons & weekends.
Societies   must contact in writing.
Green Fees £27.50 per day; £16.50 per round (£27.50 per round weekends).
Facilities   ⊗ ▥ by prior arrangement ⓑ ☲ ♀ ♨ 盒 ☝ (John Henderson.
Leisure   snooker.
Location   Prestongrange House (W side of town centre off A59)
Hotel   ★★65% Kilspindie House Hotel, Main St, ABERLADY ☎ (08757) 682 26⇄ ♠

RATHO   Map 11 NT17

Ratho Park ☎ 031-333 1252
Flat parkland course.
18 holes, 5900yds, Par 69, SSS 68, Course record 61.
Club membership 720.
Visitors   must contact in advance.
Societies   must contact in writing.
Green Fees not confirmed.
Facilities   ⊗ ▥ ⓑ ☲ ♀ ♨ 盒 (Alan Pate.
Leisure   snooker.
Location   0.75m E, N of A71
Hotel   ★★★64% Forte Posthouse, Corstorphine Rd, EDINBURGH ☎ 031-334 0390 200⇄ ♠

A golf course name printed in ***bold italics*** means we have been unable to verify information with the club's management for the current year

SOUTH QUEENSFERRY   Map 11 NT17

Dundas Parks ☎ 031-331 1416
Parkland course situated on the estate of Lady Jane Stewart-Clark, with excellent views. For 18 holes, the 9 are played twice.
9 holes, 6024yds, Par 70, SSS 69, Course record 66.
Club membership 500.
Visitors   must contact in advance.
Societies   must contact in advance.
Green Fees £8 per day.
Facilities   ♨
Leisure   practice ground, bunker & driving bay.
Location   Hope Cottage, Loch Rd (1m S on B8000)
Hotel   ★★★60% Forth Bridges Moat House, Forth Bridge, SOUTH QUEENSFERRY ☎ 031-331 1199 108⇄ ♠

UPHALL   Map 11 NT07

Uphall ☎ (0506) 856404
Windy parkland course, easy walking.
18 holes, 5567yds, Par 69, SSS 67.
Club membership 500.
Visitors   restricted weekends until 11am.
Green Fees not confirmed.
Facilities   ♀ ♨
Location   W side of village on A899
Hotel   ★★★65% Houstoun House Hotel, UPHALL ☎ (0506) 853831 28⇄ ♠ Annexe2⇄

WEST CALDER   Map 11 NT06

Harburn ☎ (0506) 871256
Moorland, reasonably flat.
18 holes, 5853yds, Par 69, SSS 68, Course record 62.
Club membership 600.
Visitors   may not play after 2.30pm.
Societies   must contact in writing.
Green Fees £18.50 per day; £12.50 per round (£25 per day; £18.50 per round weekends).
Facilities   ⊗ ⓑ ☲ (No catering Tue) ♀ ♨ 盒 (Stuart Crookston.
Hotel   ★★★65% Houstoun House Hotel, UPHALL ☎ (0506) 853831 28⇄ ♠ Annexe2⇄

WHITBURN   Map 11 NS96

Polkemmet Country Park ☎ (0501) 43905
Public parkland course surrounded by mature woodland and rhododendron bushes. 15-bay floodlit driving range.
9 holes, 2969mtrs, Par 37.
Visitors   no restrictions.
Societies   must contact in advance.
Green Fees not confirmed.
Facilities   ⊗ ▥ ⓑ ☲ ♀
Leisure   floodlit 15 bay driving range.
Location   2m W off B7066
Hotel   ★★★65% Houstoun House Hotel, UPHALL ☎ (0506) 853831 28⇄ ♠ Annexe2⇄

STRATHCLYDE

AIRDRIE
Map 11 NS76

Airdrie ☎ (0236) 762195
Picturesque parkland course with good views.
18 holes, 6004yds, Par 69, SSS 69.
Club membership 450.
Visitors   must contact in advance. With member only weekends & bank holidays.
Societies   apply in writing.
Green Fees £20 per day; £12 per round.
Facilities   ⊗ ⊪ ᕋ ᗑ ♀ ዲ ⌂ ℓ A McCloskey.
Leisure   snooker.
Location   Rochsoles (1m N on B802)
Hotel   ★★★64% Garfield House Hotel, Cumbernauld Rd, STEPPS ☎ 041-779 2111 27⇄ �

Easter Moffat ☎ (0236) 842878
Moorland/parkland course.
18 holes, 6221yds, Par 72, SSS 70, Course record 67.
Club membership 450.
Visitors   may only play on weekdays.
Societies   must contact in advance.
Green Fees not confirmed.
Facilities   ⊗ ⊪ by prior arrangement ᕋ and ᗑ (all day) ♀ ዲ ⌂ ℓ Brian Dunbar.
Location   Mansion House, Plains (2m E on old Edinburgh-Glasgow road)
Hotel   ★★★64% Garfield House Hotel, Cumbernauld Rd, STEPPS ☎ 041-779 2111 27⇄ ℝ

AYR
Map 10 NS32

Belleisle ☎ (0292) 441258
Parkland course with beautiful sea views. First-class conditions.
Belleisle Course: 18 holes, 6540yds, Par 70, SSS 71, Course record 63.
Seafield Course: 18 holes, 5498yds, Par 68, SSS 67, Course record 63.
Visitors   must contact in advance.
Societies   must contact in advance.
Green Fees Belleisle £15 per round; Seafield £10 per round. Daily ticket (one round per course) £22.
Facilities   ᗑ ♀ ዲ ⌂ ℱ ⋈ ℓ David Gemmell.
Leisure   children's animal menagerie.
Location   Belleisle Park (2m S on A719)
Hotel   ★★★59% Pickwick Hotel, 19 Racecourse Rd, AYR ☎ (0292) 260111 15⇄ ℝ

Dalmilling ☎ (0292) 263893
Meadowland course, with easy walking.
18 holes, 5752yds, Par 69, SSS 68.
Club membership 140.
Visitors   must contact in advance.
Societies   must contact in advance.
Green Fees £18 per day; £10 per round.
Facilities   ⊗ ⊪ ᕋ ᗑ ♀ ዲ ⌂ ℱ ℓ Philip Cheyney.
Location   Westwood Av (1.5m E of town centre off A719)
Hotel   ★★★60% Carlton Toby Hotel, PRESTWICK ☎ (0292) 76811 39⇄ ℝ

BALMORE
Map 11 NS57

Balmore ☎ (0360) 20240
Parkland course with fine views.
18 holes, 5516yds, Par 66, SSS 67.
Club membership 700.
Visitors   must be accompanied by member and contact in advance.
Societies   must contact in advance.
Green Fees not confirmed.
Facilities   ⊗ ⊪ ᕋ ᗑ ♀ ዲ ⌂
Location   N off A807
Hotel   ★★★65% Black Bull Thistle Hotel, Main St, MILNGAVIE ☎ 041-956 2291 27⇄ ℝ

BARASSIE
Map 10 NS33

Kilmarnock (Barassie) ☎ Troon (0292) 313920
A magnificent seaside course, relatively flat with much heather. The turf and greens are quite unequalled. The 15th is a testing par 3 at 220 yards.
18 holes, 6473yds, Par 71, SSS 71.
Club membership 500.
Visitors   with member only Wed & weekends. Restricted Mon, Tue, Thu & Fri afternoons. Must contact in advance.
Societies   must telephone in advance and confirm in writing.
Green Fees £25/£35 per day.
Facilities   ⊗ ⊪ by prior arrangement ᕋ ᗑ ♀ ዲ ⌂ ℱ ℓ W R Lockie.
Location   29 Hillhouse Rd (E side of village on B746)
Hotel   ★★★★ Marine Highland Hotel, TROON ☎ (0292) 314444 72⇄ ℝ

BARRHEAD
Map 11 NS45

Fereneze ☎ 041-881 1519
Hilly moorland course, with a good view at the end of a hard climb to the 3rd, then levels out.
18 holes, 5821yds, Par 70, SSS 68.
Club membership 700.
Visitors   must contact in advance but may not play at weekends.
Societies   apply in writing.
Green Fees £17.50 per day/round.
Facilities   ⊗ ⊪ ᕋ ᗑ ♀ ዲ ⌂ ℱ ℓ
Leisure   pool table.
Location   Fereneze Av (NW side of town off B774)
Hotel   ★★62% Dalmeny Park Country House, Lochlibo Rd, BARRHEAD ☎ 041-881 9211 18rm(3⇄10 ℝ)

BEARSDEN
Map 11 NS57

Bearsden ☎ 041-942 2351
Parkland course, with 16 greens and 11 teeing grounds. Easy walking and views over city.
9 holes, 6020yds, Par 68, SSS 69, Course record 67.
Club membership 550.
Visitors   must be accompanied by member and contact in advance.
Societies   apply by letter at least 1 month in advance.
Green Fees not confirmed.

Facilities ⊗ 🏃 ♦ ♀ ♿ 🏠
Location Thorn Rd (1m W off A809)
Hotel ★★★65% Black Bull Thistle Hotel, Main St, MILNGAVIE ☎ 041-956 2291 27⇔ ℜ

Douglas Park ☎ 041-942 2220
Parkland course with wide variety of holes.
18 holes, 5957yds, Par 69, SSS 69, Course record 64.
Club membership 900.
Visitors may not play Mon & Fri. Must be accompanied by member and contact in advance.
Societies must telephone in advance.
Green Fees not confirmed.
Facilities ⊗ 🌉 🏃 ♦ ♀ ♿ 🏠 ⚑ ℓ David Scott.
Location Hillfoot (E side of town on A81)
Hotel ★★★65% Black Bull Thistle Hotel, Main St, MILNGAVIE ☎ 041-956 2291 27⇔ ℜ

Glasgow ☎ 041-942 2011
One of the finest parkland courses in Scotland.
18 holes, 5968yds, Par 70, SSS 69.
Club membership 800.
Visitors must contact in advance & have handicap certificate.
Green Fees £35 per day; £30 per round.
Facilities ⊗ 🌉 🏃 & ♦ by prior arrangement ♀ (members guest only) ♿ 🏠 ⚑ ℓ J Steven.
Location Killermont (SE side off A81)
Hotel ★★★65% Black Bull Thistle Hotel, Main St, MILNGAVIE ☎ 041-956 2291 27⇔ ℜ

Windyhill ☎ 041-942 2349
Hard walking parkland/moorland course; testing 12th hole.
18 holes, 6254yds, Par 71, SSS 70, Course record 66.
Club membership 675.
Visitors may not play at weekends. Must contact in advance.
Societies must apply to secretary in writing.
Green Fees £15 per day.
Facilities ⊗ 🌉 🏃 ♦ ♀ ♿ 🏠 ℓ R Collinson.
Location Windyhill (2m NW off B8050)
Hotel ★★★65% Black Bull Thistle Hotel, Main St, MILNGAVIE ☎ 041-956 2291 27⇔ ℜ

BEITH   Map 10 NS35

Beith ☎ (05055) 3166
Hilly course, with panoramic views over 7 counties.
9 holes, 2559yds, Par 68, SSS 67.
Club membership 400.
Visitors may not play at weekends.
Societies apply in writing.
Green Fees £10 per day; £8 per round.
Facilities 🏃 ♦ ♀ ♿
Location Threepwood Rd (1.5m NE off A737)
Hotel ★★★♨75% Chapeltoun House Hotel, STEWARTON ☎ (0560) 82696 8⇔ ℜ

BELLSHILL   Map 11 NS76

Bellshill ☎ (0698) 745124
Parkland course.
18 holes, 6205yds, Par 70, SSS 70, Course record 68.
Club membership 600.

Visitors may not play between 4-7pm May-Aug.
Societies apply in writing in advance.
Green Fees not confirmed.
Facilities ⊗ 🌉 🏃 ♦ ♀ ♿
Location Community Rd, Orbiston (1m SE off A721)
Hotel ★★62% Silvertrees Hotel, Silverwells Crescent, BOTHWELL ☎ (0698) 852311 7⇔ ℜ Annexe19⇔ ℜ

BIGGAR   Map 11 NT03

Biggar ☎ (0899) 20618
Flat parkland course, easy walking and fine views.
18 holes, 5416yds, Par 67, SSS 66, Course record 65.
Club membership 200.
Visitors restricted at certain times. Must contact in advance. Smart casual wear required (no jeans).
Societies telephone (0899) 20319 to book in advance.
Green Fees £8.50 per day (£11.50 weekends).
Facilities ⊗ 🌉 🏃 ♦ ♀ ♿ 🏠
Leisure hard tennis courts, caravan park, childrens play area.
Location The Park, Broughton Rd (S side of town)
Hotel ★★★67% Peebles Hydro Hotel, PEEBLES ☎ (0721) 20602 137⇔ ℜ

BISHOPBRIGGS   Map 11 NS67

Bishopbriggs ☎ 041-772 1810
Parkland course with views to Campsie Hills.
18 holes, 6041yds, Par 69, SSS 69, Course record 63.
Club membership 600.
Visitors must be accompanied by member, contact in advance and have an introduction from own club.
Societies apply in writing to the Committee one month in advance.
Green Fees not confirmed.
Facilities ⊗ 🌉 🏃 ♦ ♀ ♿ 🏠
Leisure snooker.
Location Brackenbrae Rd (0.5m NW off A803)
Hotel ★★★65% Black Bull Thistle Hotel, Main St, MILNGAVIE ☎ 041-956 2291 27⇔ ℜ

Cawder ☎ 041-772 5167
Two parkland courses; Cawder Course is hilly, with 5th, 9th, 10th, 11th-testing holes. Keir Course is flat.
Cawder Course: 18 holes, 6295yds, Par 70, SSS 71.
Keir Course: 18 holes, 5877yds, Par 68, SSS 68.
Club membership 1150.
Visitors must contact in advance & may play on weekdays only.
Societies must contact in writing.
Green Fees not confirmed.
Facilities ⊗ 🌉 🏃 ♦ ♀ ♿ 🏠 ⚑ ℓ
Location Cadder Rd (1m NE off A803)
Hotel ★★★65% Black Bull Thistle Hotel, Main St, MILNGAVIE ☎ 041-956 2291 27⇔ ℜ

BISHOPTON   Map 10 NS47

Erskine ☎ (0505) 862302
Parkland course.
18 holes, 6287yds, Par 71, SSS 70.
Club membership 700.

►

Visitors must be accompanied by member and must have a handicap certificate.
Societies apply in writing.
Green Fees £20 per round; £30 day ticket.
Facilities ⊗ 🍴 🍺 ♀ ⚲ 🏠 ✆ Peter Thomson.
Location 0.75 NE off B815
Hotel ★★★65% Forte Posthouse Glasgow, North Barr, ERSKINE
🕿 041-812 0123 166⇄ 🏌

BONHILL   Map 10 NS37

Vale of Leven 🕿 Alexandria (0389) 52351
Hilly moorland course, tricky with many natural hazards - gorse, burns, trees. Overlooks Loch Lomond.
18 holes, 5162yds, Par 67, SSS 66, Course record 60.
Club membership 640.
Visitors may not play Sat Apr-Sep.
Societies apply to the secretary.
Green Fees £15 per day; £10 per round (£20/£12 weekends & holidays).
Facilities ⊗ 🍴 🍺 🍺 ♀ ⚲ 🏠
Location North Field Rd (E side of town off A813)
Hotel ★★66% Dumbuck Hotel, Glasgow Rd, DUMBARTON 🕿 (0389) 34336 22⇄ 🏌

BOTHWELL   Map 11 NS75

Bothwell Castle 🕿 (0698) 853177
Flat parkland course in residential area.
18 holes, 6243yds, Par 71, SSS 70.
Club membership 1200.
Visitors may only play Mon-Fri 9.30am-noon & 2-3.30pm.
Societies apply in writing.
Green Fees £25 per day; £18 per round.
Facilities ⊗ 🍴 🍺 🍺 ♀ ⚲ 🏠 ✆ W Walker.
Location Blantyre Rd (NW of village off B7071)
Hotel ★★62% Silvertrees Hotel, Silverwells Crescent, BOTHWELL 🕿 (0698) 852311
7⇄ 🏌 Annexe19⇄ 🏌

BRIDGE OF WEIR   Map 10 NS36

Ranfurly Castle 🕿 Johnston (0505) 612609 or 614795
A highly challenging, 240 acre, picturesque moorland course.
18 holes, 6284yds, Par 70, SSS 70, Course record 63.
Club membership 360.
Visitors weekdays only, must have a handicap certificate.
Societies Tues am only, apply in writing.
Green Fees £27 per day; £22 per round.
Facilities ⊗ & 🍴 by prior arrangement 🍺 🍺 ♀ ⚲ 🏠 ✆ Alistair Forrow.
Location The Clubhouse, Golf Rd (5m NW of Johnstone)
Hotel ★★★62% Bowfield Hotel & Country Club, Lands of Bowfield, HOWWOOD
🕿 (05057) 5225 12⇄ 🏌

BURNSIDE   Map 11 NS51

Blairbeth 🕿 041-634 3355
Parkland course.
18 holes, 5481yds, Par 70, SSS 67, Course record 64.
Club membership 400.

Visitors introduced by a member or by arrangement with Secretary.
Societies apply in writing.
Green Fees £14 per day.
Facilities ⊗ 🍴 🍺 🍺 ♀ ⚲
Location S off A749
Hotel ★★★63% Macdonald Thistle Hotel, Eastwood Toll, GIFFNOCK 🕿 041-638 2225 56⇄ 🏌

Cathkin Braes 🕿 041-634 6605
Moorland course, prevailing westerly wind, small loch hazard at 5th hole.
18 holes, 6208yds, Par 71, SSS 71.
Club membership 890.
Visitors must contact in advance & have handicap certificate but may not play at weekends.
Societies apply in writing.
Green Fees £25 per day; £16 per round.
Facilities ⊗ 🍴 🍺 🍺 (catering by arrangement) ♀ ⚲ 🏠 ✆ Stephen Bree.
Location Cathkin Rd (1m S on B759)
Hotel ★★61% Royal Hotel, 1 Glaisnock St, CUMNOCK 🕿 (0290) 20822 11rm(2⇄3 🏌)

CAMBUSLANG   Map 11 NS66

Cambuslang 🕿 041-641 3130
Parkland course.
9 holes, 6072yds, Par 70, SSS 69, Course record 65.
Club membership 200.
Visitors must contact in advance and have an introduction from own club.
Societies weekdays only; must contact in writing.
Green Fees not confirmed.
Facilities ⊗ 🍺 🍺 ♀ ⚲
Location Westburn Dr (0.25m N off A724)
Hotel ★★62% Silvertrees Hotel, Silverwells Crescent, BOTHWELL 🕿 (0698) 852311
7⇄ 🏌 Annexe19⇄ 🏌

CARDROSS   Map 10 NS37

Cardross 🕿 (0389) 841213
Undulating parkland course, testing with good views.
18 holes, 6496yds, Par 71, SSS 71, Course record 65.
Club membership 800.
Visitors may not play at weekends unless introduced by member.
Societies must contact in writing.
Green Fees not confirmed.
Facilities ⊗ 🍴 by prior arrangement 🍺 🍺 ♀ ⚲ 🏠 ✆ Robert Craig.
Location Main Rd (In centre of village on A814)
Hotel ★★★56% Commodore Toby Hotel, 112 West Clyde St, HELENSBURGH
🕿 (0436) 76924 45⇄

CARLUKE   Map 11 NS85

Carluke 🕿 (0555) 771070
Parkland course with views over the Clyde Valley. Testing 11th hole, par 3.
18 holes, 5811yds, Par 70, SSS 68, Course record 64.
Club membership 800.

Visitors	until 4pm weekdays only. Must contact in advance & have handicap certificate.
Societies	apply in writing.
Green Fees	£18 per day; £12 per round.
Facilities	⊗ ⫪ ᒪ (ex Thu) ⬤ ♀ ᎙ 🏠 ⊓ᵏ ʔ Andrew Brooks.
Location	Mauldslie Rd, Hallcraig (1m W off A73)
Hotel	★★★63% Popinjay Hotel, Lanark Rd, ROSEBANK ☎ (055586) 441 38🛏 🕭 Annexe5🛏 🕭

CARNWATH   Map 11 NS94

Carnwath ☎ (0555) 840251
Picturesque parkland course slightly hilly, with small greens calling for accuracy. Panoramic views.
18 holes, 5953yds, Par 70, SSS 69.
Club membership 470.

Visitors	restricted after 5pm, no visitors Sat.
Societies	apply in writing or telephone.
Green Fees	£17 per day (£20 Sun & bank holidays).
Facilities	catering by arrangement ♀ ᎙ 🏠
Location	1 Main St (W side of village on A70)
Hotel	★★★63% Popinjay Hotel, Lanark Rd, ROSEBANK ☎ (055586) 441 38🛏 🕭 Annexe5🛏 🕭

CARRADALE   Map 10 NR83

Carradale ☎ (05833) 387
Pleasant seaside course built on a promontory overlooking the Isle of Arran. Natural terrain and small greens are the most difficult natural hazards. Described as the most sporting 9-hole course in Scotland. Testing 7th hole (240 yds), par 3.
9 holes, 2387yds, Par 66, SSS 63, Course record 62.
Club membership 300.

Visitors	no restrictions
Societies	welcome.
Green Fees	£5 per day.
Facilities	᎙
Location	S side of village
Hotel	★★62% Royal Hotel, Main St, CAMPBELTOWN ☎ (0586) 52017 16rm(8🛏4 🕭)

CLARKSTON   Map 11 NS55

Cathcart Castle ☎ 041-638 0082
Tree-lined parkland course, with undulating terrain.
18 holes, 5832yds, Par 68, SSS 68, Course record 62.
Club membership 990.

Visitors	must have a letter of introduction from own club.
Societies	Tue & Thu only; must apply in writing.
Green Fees	£25 per day; £17 per round.
Facilities	⊗ ⫪ ᒪ ⬤ ♀ ᎙ 🏠 ʔ David Naylor.
Location	Mearns Rd (0.75m SW off A726)
Hotel	★★★63% Macdonald Thistle Hotel, Eastwood Toll, GIFFNOCK ☎ 041-638 2225 56🛏 🕭

> We make every effort to ensure that our information is accurate but details may change after we go to print

CLYDEBANK   Map 11 NS56

Clydebank & District ☎ Duntocher (0389) 73289
An undulating parkland course established in 1905 overlooking Clydebank.
18 holes, 5823yds, Par 68, SSS 68, Course record 64.
Club membership 825.

Visitors	handicap certificate is required. Round only, weekdays only.
Societies	must apply in writing.
Green Fees	£12 per round.
Facilities	⊗ ⫪ ᒪ ⬤ ♀ ᎙ ʔ David Pirie.
Location	Glasgow Rd, Hardgate (2m E of Erskine Bridge)
Hotel	★★★66% Patio Hotel, 1 South Av, Clydebank Business Park, CLYDEBANK ☎ 041-951 1133 80🛏 🕭

Clydebank Municipal ☎ 041-952 6372
Hilly, compact parkland course with tough finishing holes.
18 holes, 5349yds, Par 67, SSS 67.

Visitors	no restrictions.
Societies	contact in advance.
Green Fees	not confirmed.
Facilities	Cafeteria ᎙ 🏠 ʔ Richard Bowman.
Location	Overtoun Rd, Dalmur (2m NW of town centre)
Hotel	★★★64% Stakis Normandy Hotel, Inchinnan Rd, Renfrew, RENFREW ☎ 041-886 4100 141🛏 🕭

COATBRIDGE   Map 11 NS76

Drumpellier ☎ (0236) 24139
Parkland course.
18 holes, 6227yds, Par 71, SSS 70, Course record 62.
Club membership 700.

Visitors	must contact in advance and may not play weekends or public holidays.
Societies	telephone for details.
Green Fees	£25 per day; £18 per round.
Facilities	⊗ ⫪ ᒪ ⬤ ♀ ᎙ 🏠 ʔ Kenneth Hutton.
Leisure	pool table.
Location	Drumpellier Av (0.75m W off A89)
Hotel	★★★60% Bothwell Bridge Hotel, 89 Main St, BOTHWELL ☎ (0698) 852246 76🛏 🕭

CUMBERNAULD   Map 11 NS77

Dullatur ☎ (0236) 723230
Parkland course, with natural hazards and wind. Testing 17th hole, par 5.
18 holes, 6219yds, Par 70, SSS 70.
Club membership 656.

Visitors	may not play on competition days & must play with member at weekends. Must contact in advance.
Societies	must be in writing.
Green Fees	not confirmed.
Facilities	catering by arrangement ♀ ᎙ 🏠 ⊓ᵏ ʔ
Leisure	snooker.
Location	Dullatur (1.5m N)
Hotel	★★★62% Stakis Falkirk Park Hotel, Camelon Rd, FALKIRK ☎ (0324) 28331 55🛏 🕭

Palacerigg ☎ (0236) 734969
Parkland course.
18 holes, 6444yds, Par 72, SSS 71, Course record 65.
Club membership 400.
Visitors must contact in advance & have handicap
certificate but may not play at weekends.
Societies must contact in advance.
Green Fees £7.50 per round.
Facilities ⊗ ⫟ ⌫ ⬛ (catering Wed-Sun) ♀
Location Palacerigg Country Park (2m S)
Hotel ★★★62% Stakis Falkirk Park Hotel, Camelon
Rd, FALKIRK ☎ (0324) 28331 55⇥ ⟆

Westerwood Hotel Golf & Country Club
☎ (0236) 457171
Undulating parkland/woodland course designed by Dave
Thomas and Seve Ballesteros. Holes meander through silver
birch, firs, heaths and heathers, and the spectacular 15th, 'The
Waterfall', has its green set against a 40ft rockface. Buggie
track. Hotel facilities.
18 holes, 6721yds, Par 73, SSS 72.
Club membership 250.
Visitors no restrictions.
Societies by prior arrangement.
Green Fees £22.50 per round (£27.50 weekends).
Facilities ⊗ ⫟ ⌫ ⬛ ♀ ⌂ 🏠 ⫟ ⟆ ℂ Tony Smith.
Leisure hard tennis courts, heated indoor swimming
pool, snooker, solarium, gymnasium, driving
range, golf school & putting.
Location St Andrews Dr (adjacent to A80)
Hotel ★★★★69% Westerwood Hotel Golf And
Country Club, 1 St Andrews Dr, Westerwood,
CUMBERNAULD ☎ (0236) 457171 47⇥ ⟆

DUMBARTON Map 10 NS37

Dumbarton ☎ (0389) 32830
Flat parkland course.
18 holes, 5992yds, Par 71, SSS 69.
Club membership 500.
Visitors may not play weekends & public holidays.
Societies advance booking with secretary.
Green Fees £15 per day.
Facilities ⊗ & ⫟ by prior arrangement ♀ ⌂
Location Broadmeadow (0.25m N off A814)
Hotel ★★66% Dumbuck Hotel, Glasgow Rd,
DUMBARTON ☎ (0389) 34336 22⇥ ⟆

DUNOON Map 10 NS17

Cowal ☎ (0369) 5673
Moorland course. Panoramic views of Clyde Estuary and
surrounding hills.
18 holes, 6251yds, Par 70, SSS 70, Course record 63.
Club membership 550.
Visitors handicap certificate preferred or club
membership.
Societies must telephone in advance.
Green Fees £20 per day; £13 per round (£30/£20 weekends).
Facilities ⊗ ⫟ by prior arrangement ⌫ ⬛ ♀ ⌂ 🏠 ⟆ ℂ
Russell Weir.
Location Ardenslate Rd (1m N)
Hotel ★★76% Enmore Hotel, Marine Pde, Kirn,
DUNOON ☎ (0369) 2230 11⇥ ⟆

EAGLESHAM Map 11 NS55

Bonnyton ☎ (03553) 2781
Windy, moorland course.
18 holes, 6255yds, Par 72, SSS 71.
Club membership 950.
Visitors welcome weekdays only, must contact in
advance.
Societies must telephone in advance.
Green Fees not confirmed.
Facilities ⊗ ⫟ ⌫ ⬛ ♀ ⌂ 🏠 ⟆ ℂ Robert Crerar.
Location 0.25m SW off B764
Hotel ★★★61% Bruce Swallow Hotel, Cornwall St,
EAST KILBRIDE ☎ (03552) 29771 79⇥ ⟆

EAST KILBRIDE Map 11 NS65

East Kilbride ☎ (03552) 20913
Parkland and hill course. Very windy. Testing 7th, 9th and
14th holes.
18 holes, 6419yds, Par 71, SSS 71.
Club membership 800.
Visitors by appointment. Must be a member of
recognised golfing society.
Societies must telephone in advance & submit formal
application.
Green Fees £20 per day; £14 per round.
Facilities ⊗ ⫟ ⌫ ⬛ ♀ ⌂ 🏠 ⟆ ℂ A Taylor.
Location Chapelside Rd, Nerston (0.5m N off A7)
Hotel ★★★61% Bruce Swallow Hotel, Cornwall St,
EAST KILBRIDE ☎ (03552) 29771 79⇥ ⟆

Torrance House ☎ (03552) 48638
A parkland course.
18 holes, 6415yds, Par 72, SSS 69.
Club membership 1000.
Visitors welcome, may book up to six days in advance.
Green Fees £11 per round.
Facilities ⓑ ⬛ ♀ 🏠 (
Location Calderglen Country Park, Strathaven Rd (1.5m SE of Kilbride on A726)
Hotel ★★★61% Bruce Swallow Hotel, Cornwall St, EAST KILBRIDE ☎ (03552) 29771 79⇔ ⋒

GALSTON Map 11 NS53

Loudoun ☎ (0563) 821993
Pleasant, testing parkland course.
18 holes, 5600yds, Par 67, SSS 68, Course record 62.
Club membership 750.
Visitors must contact in advance. No play at weekends.
Societies must contact in advance.
Green Fees £25 per day; £15 per round.
Facilities ⓧ ⑪ ⓑ ⬛ ♀ 👟 🏠
Location Edinburgh Rd (NE side of town on A71)
Hotel ★★★64% Strathaven Hotel, Hamilton Rd, STRATHAVEN ☎ (0357) 21778 10⇔ ⋒

GARTCOSH Map 11 NS66

Mount Ellen ☎ (0236) 872277
Downland course with 73 bunkers. Testing hole: 10th ('Bedlay'), 156 yds, par 3.
18 holes, 5525yds, Par 68, SSS 68, Course record 60.
Club membership 500.
Visitors may play Mon-Fri 9am-4pm. Must contact in advance.
Societies must contact in advance.
Green Fees £11 per round.
Facilities ⓧ ⑪ ⓑ ⬛ ♀ 👟 🏠 (Iain Bilsborough.
Location 0.75m N off A752
Hotel ★★★64% Garfield House Hotel, Cumbernauld Rd, STEPPS ☎ 041-779 2111 27⇔ ⋒

GIRVAN Map 10 NX19

Brunston Castle ☎ Dailly (0465) 81471
Sheltered inland parkland course. A championship design by Donald Steel with picturesque summer greens all year. Also a driving range.
Burns: 18 holes, 6792yds, Par 72, SSS 72, Course record 70.
Club membership 200.
Visitors must contact in advance.
Societies must contact in advance.
Green Fees £30 per day; £20 per round (£35/£25 weekends).
Facilities ⓧ ⓑ ⬛ ♀ 👟 (Douglas W Smart.
Leisure fishing, driving range.
Location Dailly (6m SE of Turnberry)
Hotel ★★63% King's Arms Hotel, Dalrymple St, GIRVAN ☎ (0465) 3322 25⇔ ⋒

Girvan ☎ (0465) 4272
Municipal seaside and parkland course. Testing 17th hole (223-yds) uphill, par 3. Good views.
18 holes, 5098yds, Par 64, SSS 65.
Club membership 175.

Visitors no restrictions.
Societies may not play Jul & Aug.
Green Fees not confirmed.
Facilities ♀ 👟
Location Golf Course Rd (N side of town off A77)
Hotel ★★63% King's Arms Hotel, Dalrymple St, GIRVAN ☎ (0465) 3322 25⇔ ⋒

GLASGOW Map 11 NS56

Alexandra ☎ 041-556 3211
Parkland course, hilly with some woodland.
9 holes, 2800yds, Par 34.
Club membership 250.
Visitors no restrictions.
Societies no prior arrangement required.
Green Fees £1.70 per day (£2 weekends).
Facilities 👟
Location Alexandra Park, Alexandra Pde (2m E of city centre off M8/A8)
Hotel ★★★★60% Stakis Grosvenor Hotel, 1/10 Grosvenor Ter, Great Western Rd, GLASGOW ☎ 041-339 8811 95⇔ ⋒

Cowglen ☎ 041-632 0556
Parkland course with good views over Clyde valley to Campsie Hills.
18 holes, 5976yds, Par 69, SSS 69, Course record 63.
Club membership 775.
Visitors play on shorter course. Must contact in advance and have a handicap certificate.
Societies must telephone in advance.
Green Fees not confirmed.
Facilities ⓧ ⑪ ⓑ ⬛ ♀ 👟 🏠 (John McTear.
Location Barrhead Rd (4.5m SW of city centre on B762)
Hotel ★★★63% Macdonald Thistle Hotel, Eastwood Toll, GIFFNOCK ☎ 041-638 2225 56⇔ ⋒

Haggs Castle ☎ 041-427 1157
Wooded, parkland course where Scottish National Championships and the Glasgow and Scottish Open have been held. Quite difficult.
18 holes, 6464yds, Par 72, SSS 71.
Club membership 960.
Visitors may not play at weekends. Must contact in advance and have a handicap certificate.
Societies apply in writing in advance.
Green Fees £36 per day; £24 per round.
Facilities ⓧ ⑪ ⓑ ⬛ ♀ 👟 🏠 ⫟ (Jim McAlister.
Location 70 Dumbreck Rd, Dumbreck (2.5m SW of city centre on B768)
Hotel ★★★61% Sherbrooke Castle Hotel, 11 Sherbrooke Av, Pollokshields, GLASGOW ☎ 041-427 4227 10⇔ ⋒ Annexe11⇔ ⋒

Kirkhill ☎ 041-641 8499
Meadowland course designed by James Braid.
18 holes, 5889yds, Par 69, SSS 69, Course record 63.
Club membership 650.
Visitors must play with member at weekends. Must contact in advance.
Societies must contact in advance.
Green Fees not confirmed.
Facilities ⓧ (ex Mon) ⑪ by prior arrangement ⓑ (ex Mon and Thu) ⬛ ♀ 👟 ▶

Location Greenless Rd, Cambuslang (5m SE of city centre off A749)

Hotel ★★★60% Stuart Hotel, 2 Cornwall Way, EAST KILBRIDE ☎ (03552) 21161 39⇋ Ɽ

Knightswood Park ☎ 041-959 2131
Parkland course within easy reach of city. Two dog-legs.
9 holes, 2700yds, Par 33, SSS 33.
Club membership 60.
Visitors no restrictions.
Societies welcome.
Green Fees not confirmed.
Location Lincoln Av (4m W of city centre off A82)
Hotel ★★★58% Jurys Pond Hotel, Great Western Rd, GLASGOW ☎ 041-334 8161 134⇋ Ⱥ

Lethamhill ☎ 041-770 6220
Municipal parkland course.
18 holes, 5859yds, Par 70, SSS 68.
Visitors must have an introduction from own club.
Societies must contact in advance.
Facilities ♨
Location 1240 Cumbernauld Rd, Millerston (3m NE of city centre on A80)
Hotel ★★★64% Garfield House Hotel, Cumbernauld Rd, STEPPS ☎ 041-779 2111 27⇋ Ⱥ

Linn Park ☎ 041-637 5871
Municipal parkland course with six par 3's in outward half.
18 holes, 4952yds, Par 65, SSS 65, Course record 61.
Club membership 80.
Visitors no restrictions.
Green Fees not confirmed.
Facilities ♨
Location Simshill Rd (4m S of city centre off B766)
Hotel ★★★61% Bruce Swallow Hotel, Cornwall St, EAST KILBRIDE ☎ (03552) 29771 79⇋ Ⱥ

Pollok ☎ 041-632 1080
Parkland course with woods and river.
18 holes, 6257yds, Par 71, SSS 70, Course record 62.
Club membership 460.
Visitors must play with member at weekends. Must contact in advance and have a handicap certificate.
Societies Mon-Fri only; must contact in writing.
Green Fees £26 per round; £33 per day.
Facilities ⊗ 〗 by prior arrangement ⓛ ⬛ ♀ ♨
Location 90 Barrhead Rd (4m SW of city centre on A762)
Hotel ★★★65% Tinto Firs Thistle Hotel, 470 Kilmarnock Rd, GLASGOW ☎ 041-637 2353 28⇋ Ⱥ

Williamwood ☎ 041-637 1783
Inland course, fairly hilly with wooded areas, a small lake and pond.
18 holes, 5878yds, SSS 68, Course record 61.
Club membership 450.
Visitors must be introduced by and play with member.
Green Fees not confirmed.
Facilities ⊗ 〗 ⓛ ⬛ ♀ ⓑ ⱡ J Gardner.
Location Clarkston Rd (5m S of city centre on B767)
Hotel ★★★63% Macdonald Thistle Hotel, Eastwood Toll, GIFFNOCK ☎ 041-638 2225 56⇋ Ⱥ

GOUROCK
Map 10 NS27

Gourock ☎ (0475) 31001
Moorland course with hills and dells. Testing 8th hole, par 5. Magnificent views over Firth of Clyde.
18 holes, 6492yds, Par 73, SSS 71, Course record 64.
Club membership 720.
Visitors by introduction or with member.
Societies welcome weekdays, must contact in advance.
Green Fees not confirmed.
Facilities ⊗ 〗 ⓛ ⬛ ♀ ♨ ⓑ ⱡ Robert Collinson.
Location Cowal View (SW side of town off A770)
Hotel ★★★▲▲61% Manor Park Hotel, SKELMORLIE ☎ (0475) 520832 10⇋ ⱤAnnexe13⇋ Ⱥ

GREENOCK
Map 10 NS27

Greenock ☎ (0475) 20793
Testing moorland course with panoramic views of Clyde Estuary.
18 holes, 5838yds, Par 68, SSS 68.
Club membership 730.
Visitors may not play Sat. Must contact in advance and have a handicap certificate.
Societies must telephone in advance.
Green Fees not confirmed.
Facilities ⊗ 〗 ⓛ ⬛ (No catering Mon) ♀ ♨ ⓑ ⱡ Graham Ross.
Location Forsyth St (SW side of town off A770)
Hotel ★★★▲▲61% Manor Park Hotel, SKELMORLIE ☎ (0475) 520832 10⇋ ⱤAnnexe13⇋ Ⱥ

Whinhill ☎ (0475) 21064
Picturesque heathland public course.
18 holes, 5454yds, Par 66, SSS 68.
Visitors may only use club facilities with member.
Green Fees not confirmed.
Location Beith Rd (1.5m SW off B7054)
Hotel ★★★▲▲61% Manor Park Hotel, SKELMORLIE ☎ (0475) 520832 10⇋ Ⱥ Annexe13⇋ Ⱥ

HAMILTON
Map 11 NS75

Hamilton ☎ (0698) 282872
Beautiful parkland course.
18 holes, 6281yds, Par 70, SSS 70.
Club membership 480.
Visitors must be accompanied by member.
Green Fees not confirmed.
Facilities ♀ ♨ ⓑ ⱡ
Location Riccarton, Ferniegair (1.5m SE on A72)
Hotel ★★62% Silvertrees Hotel, Silverwells Crescent, BOTHWELL ☎ (0698) 852311 7⇋ Ⱥ Annexe19⇋ Ⱥ

Strathclyde Park ☎ (0698) 266155
Municipal parkland course.
9 holes, 3147yds, Par 36, SSS 70, Course record 67.
Club membership 180.
Visitors no restrictions.
Societies must contact in advance.
Green Fees not confirmed.
Facilities ⊗ 〗 ⓛ ⬛ ♀ ♨ ⓑ ⱡ Ken Davidson.
Leisure driving range.

Location   Mote Hill (N side of town off B7071)
Hotel   ★★62% Silvertrees Hotel, Silverwells Crescent,
               BOTHWELL ☎ (0698) 852311
               7⇥ ↟ Annexe19⇥ ↟

HELENSBURGH   Map 10 NS28

Helensburgh ☎ (0436) 74173
Sporting moorland course with superb views of Loch
Lomond and River Clyde.
18 holes, 6058yds, Par 69, SSS 69, Course record 64.
Club membership 850.
Visitors   may not play at weekends. Must contact in
                  advance.
Societies   must contact in writing.
Green Fees   not confirmed.
Facilities   ⴲ by prior arrangement ⅃ ⚐ ♀ ⚘ 🏠 ⛳ ℓ
                  Robert Farrell.
Location   25 East Abercromby St (NE side of town off
                  B832)
Hotel   ★★★56% Commodore Toby Hotel, 112 West
                  Clyde St, HELENSBURGH
                  ☎ (0436) 76924 45⇥

IRVINE   Map 10 NS33

Glasgow ☎ (0294) 311347
A lovely seaside links. The turf of the fairways and all
the greens is truly glorious and provides tireless play.
Established in 1787, this is the ninth oldest course in the
world and is a qualifying course for the Open
Championship.
18 holes, 6502yds, Par 71, SSS 72.
Club membership 1150.
Visitors   must contact in advance but may not play
                  mornings at weekends & bank holidays.
Societies   apply to secretary.
Green Fees   £33 per day; £27 per round (£30 afternoon
                  round weekends).
Facilities   ⴲ ⴲ by prior arrangement ⅃ ⚐ ♀ ⚘ 🏠
Location   Gailes (2m S off A737)
Hotel   ★★★★52% Hospitality Inn, Annick Rd,
                  Annickwater, IRVINE
                  ☎ (0294) 74272 128⇥ ↟

Irvine ☎ (0294) 78139
Testing links course; only two short holes.
18 holes, 6400yds, Par 71, SSS 71, Course record 65.
Club membership 450.
Visitors   may not play before 3pm Sat & Sun. Must
                  contact in advance.
Societies   are welcome weekdays, telephone (0294) 75979
                  to book in advance.
Green Fees   not confirmed.
Facilities   ⴲ ⴲ ⅃ ⚐ ♀ ⚘ 🏠 ℓ Keith Erskine.
Location   Bogside (N side of town off A737)
Hotel   ★★★★52% Hospitality Inn, Annick Rd,
                  Annickwater, IRVINE
                  ☎ (0294) 74272 128⇥ ↟

Irvine Ravenspark ☎ (0294) 79550
Parkland course.
18 holes, 6702yds, Par 71, SSS 71, Course record 66.
Club membership 400.
Visitors   may not play Sat 7am-2pm.

Societies   may not play Sat. Must telephone in advance.
Green Fees   £11 per day; £4.70 per round (£14 per round/day
                  weekends).
Facilities   ⴲ ⴲ ⅃ ⚐ (no catering Tue and Thu)
                  ♀ ⚘ 🏠 ℓ Peter Bond.
Location   N side of town on A737
Hotel   ★★★⬥⬥75% Chapeltoun House Hotel,
                  STEWARTON ☎ (0560) 82696 8⇥ ↟

Western Gailes ☎ (0294) 311649
A magnificent seaside links with glorious turf and
wonderful greens. The view is open across the Firth of
Clyde to the neighbouring islands. It is a well-balanced
course crossed by 3 burns. There are 2 par 5's, the 6th
and 14th, and the 11th is a testing 445-yd, par 4, dog-leg.
18 holes, 6664yds, Par 71, SSS 72.
Visitors   welcome Mon, Tue, Wed & Fri. Must
                  contact in advance.
Societies   must contact in advance.
Green Fees   not confirmed.
Facilities   ⴲ ⴲ by prior arrangement ⅃ ⚐ ♀ ⚘
Location   Gailes by Irvine (2m S off A737)
Hotel   ★★★★ Marine Highland Hotel, TROON
                  ☎ (0292) 314444 72⇥ ↟

JOHNSTONE   Map 10 NS46

Cochrane Castle ☎ (0505) 20146
Fairly hilly parkland course, wooded with two small streams
running through it.
18 holes, 6226yds, Par 70, SSS 70, Course record 66.
Club membership 580.
Visitors   may not play at weekends. Must contact in
                  advance.
Societies   may not play at weekends.
Green Fees   £20 per day; £15 per round.
Facilities   ⴲ ⴲ & ⅃ (ex Mon) ⚐ (no dinner Thu)
                  ♀ ⚘ 🏠 ℓ Stuart Campbell.
Location   Scott Av, Craigstone (0.5m W off A737)
Hotel   ★★★65% Glynhill Hotel & Leisure Club,
                  Paisley Rd, RENFREW
                  ☎ 041-886 5555 125⇥ ↟

Elderslie ☎ (0505) 22835
Parkland course, undulating, with good views.
18 holes, 6037yds, Par 70, SSS 69.
Club membership 700.
Visitors   may not play at weekends & bank holidays.
                  Must contact club in advance and have a
                  handicap certificate.
Societies   must contact in writing.
Green Fees   not confirmed.
Facilities   ⅃ ♀ ⚘ 🏠 ℓ
Leisure   snooker.
Location   63 Main Rd, Elderslie (E side of town on A737)
Hotel   ★★★65% Glynhill Hotel & Leisure Club,
                  Paisley Rd, RENFREW
                  ☎ 041-886 5555 125⇥ ↟

KILBIRNIE   Map 10 NS35

Kilbirnie Place ☎ (0505) 683398
Easy walking parkland course.
18 holes, 5400yds, Par 69, SSS 67.
Club membership 400.

▶

Visitors no restrictions.
Societies must contact in advance.
Green Fees not confirmed.
Facilities ⊗ ⓛ 🖤 ♀ ⚘
Location Largs Rd (1m W on A760)
Hotel ★★68% Elderslie Hotel, John St, Broomfields, LARGS ☎ (0475) 686460 25rm(9⇨4 🐾)

KILMACOLM   Map 10 NS36

Kilmacolm ☎ (050587) 2139
Moorland course, easy walking, fine views. Testing 7th, 13th and 14th holes.
18 holes, 5964yds, Par 69, SSS 68.
Club membership 800.
Visitors must contact in advance, restricted weekends.
Societies apply in writing.
Green Fees £24 per day; £18 per round.
Facilities ⊗ ⓛ 🖤 ♀ ⚘ 🏠 ⒧
Location Porterfield Rd (SE side of town off A761)
Hotel ★★★⚓68% Gleddoch House Hotel, LANGBANK ☎ (047554) 711 33⇨ 🐾

KILMARNOCK   Map 10 NS43

Annanhill ☎ (0563) 21644
Municipal, tree-lined parkland course played over by private clubs.
18 holes, 6269yds, Par 71, SSS 70, Course record 64.
Club membership 280.
Visitors restricted at weekends.
Societies must telephone in advance.
Green Fees not confirmed.
Facilities ⊗ (ex Tue & Thu) ⫟ ⓛ 🖤 ♀
Location Irvine Rd (1m W on A71)
Hotel ★★★⚓75% Chapeltoun House Hotel, STEWARTON ☎ (0560) 82696 8⇨ 🐾

Caprington ☎ (0563) 23702
Municipal parkland course.
18 holes, 5718yds, Par 69, SSS 68.
Club membership 400.
Visitors may not play on Fri afternoons. Must contact in advance and have an introduction from own club.
Green Fees not confirmed.
Facilities ♀ ⚘ 🏠 ⒧
Location Ayr Rd (1.5m S on B7038)
Hotel ★★★⚓75% Chapeltoun House Hotel, STEWARTON ☎ (0560) 82696 8⇨ 🐾

KILSYTH   Map 11 NS77

Kilsyth Lennox ☎ (0236) 822190
Hilly moorland course, hard walking. Course and facilities due to be revamped with 18-holes after a serious fire early in 1993. Course is open with a temporary clubhouse. The phone may be disconnected until late 1993 - contact in writing if necessary.
9 holes, 5944yds, Par 70, SSS 69, Course record 65.
Club membership 400.
Visitors must play with member at weekends.
Societies must contact in writing.
Green Fees £12 per day; £8 per round.

Facilities ⚘ 🏠
Location Tak Ma Doon Rd (N side of town off A803)
Hotel ★★★62% Kirkhouse Inn, STRATHBLANE ☎ (0360) 70621 15⇨ 🐾

KIRKINTILLOCH   Map 11 NS67

Hayston ☎ 041-776 1244
An undulating, tree-lined course with a sandy subsoil.
18 holes, 6042yds, Par 70, SSS 69.
Club membership 440.
Visitors must apply to secretary.
Societies apply in writing.
Green Fees £20 per day; £12 per round.
Facilities ⊗ ⫟ ⓛ 🖤 ♀ ⚘ 🏠 ⒧ Steven Barnett.
Location Campsie Rd (1m NW off A803)
Hotel ★★★62% Kirkhouse Inn, STRATHBLANE ☎ (0360) 70621 15⇨ 🐾

Kirkintilloch ☎ 041-776 1256
Parkland course in rural setting.
18 holes, 5269yds, Par 70, SSS 66.
Club membership 650.
Visitors must be introduced by member.
Societies apply in writing.
Green Fees £17 per day; £12 per round.
Facilities ⚘ 🏠
Location Campsie Rd (1m NW off A803)
Hotel ★★★62% Kirkhouse Inn, STRATHBLANE ☎ (0360) 70621 15⇨ 🐾

LANARK   Map 11 NS84

Lanark ☎ (0555) 663219
Chosen as one of the pre-qualifying tests for the Open Championship held at Lanark from 1977 to 1983. The address of the club, 'The Moor', gives some indication as to the kind of golf to be found there. Golf has been played at Lanark for well over a century and the Club dates from 1851.
18 holes, 6423yds, Par 70, SSS 71, Course record 62.
Club membership 850.
Visitors must contact in advance, restricted until 4pm weekdays only.
Societies may not play at weekends. Telephone in advance.
Green Fees £28 per day; £18 per round. 9 hole £3.50.
Facilities ⊗ & ⫟ (Apr-Oct) ⓛ 🖤 ♀ ⚘ 🏠 ⒤ ⒧
Location The Moor (E side of town centre off A73)
Hotel ★★★63% Popinjay Hotel, Lanark Rd, ROSEBANK ☎ (055586) 441 38⇨ 🐾 Annexe5⇨ 🐾

LANGBANK   Map 10 NS37

Gleddoch Golf and Country Club ☎ (047554) 304
Parkland and heathland course with other sporting facilities available to temporary members. Good views over Firth of Clyde.
18 holes, 5661yds, Par 68, SSS 67.
Club membership 600.
Visitors must contact in advance.
Societies must contact in advance.
Green Fees on application.
Facilities ⊗ ⫟ ⓛ 🖤 ♀ ⚘ 🏠 ⒤ ⒟ ⒧ Keith Campbell.

Leisure grass tennis courts, heated indoor swimming pool, squash, riding, snooker, sauna, archery, clay pigeon shooting.
Location B789-Old Greenock Road
Hotel ★★★♨68% Gleddoch House Hotel, LANGBANK ☎ (047554) 711 33⇌ ♪♠

LARGS   Map 10 NS25

Largs ☎ (0475) 673594
A parkland, tree-lined course with views to the Clyde coast and Arran Isles.
18 holes, 6220yds, Par 70, SSS 70.
Club membership 850.
Visitors may not play weekends & competition days. Must contact in advance.
Societies apply in writing.
Green Fees not confirmed.
Facilities ⊗ ℳ ⓑ ♥ ♀ ♨ 🛍 ♪♠ ⚑ Robert Collinson.
Location Irvine Rd (1m S of town centre on A78)
Hotel ★★68% Elderslie Hotel, John St, Broomfields, LARGS ☎ (0475) 686460 25rm(9⇌4 ♠)

Routenburn ☎ (0475) 673230
Heathland course with fine views over Firth of Clyde.
18 holes, 5675yds, Par 68, SSS 67.
Club membership 350.
Visitors no restrictions.
Green Fees not confirmed.
Facilities ♀ 🛍 🛍
Location Routenburn Rd (1m N off A78)
Hotel ★★★♨61% Manor Park Hotel, SKELMORLIE ☎ (0475) 520832 10⇌ ♠ Annexe13⇌ ♠

LARKHALL   Map 11 NS75

Larkhall ☎ (0698) 881113
Small, inland parkland course.
9 holes, 6700yds, Par 72, SSS 71, Course record 69.
Club membership 250.
Visitors restricted Tue & Sat.
Green Fees not confirmed.
Facilities ⓑ (weekends only) ♀
Location Burnhead Rd (E side of town on B7019)
Hotel ★★★63% Popinjay Hotel, Lanark Rd, ROSEBANK ☎ (055586) 441 38⇌ ♠ Annexe5⇌ ♠

LEADHILLS   Map 11 NS81

Leadhills ☎ (0659) 74222
A testing, hilly course with high winds. At 1500ft above sea level it has the privilege of being the is the highest golf course in Great Britain.
9 holes, 4354yds, Par 66, SSS 64.
Club membership 80.
Visitors no restrictions.
Societies must telephone in advance.
Green Fees £4 per day.
Location E side of village off B797
Hotel ★★60% Mennockfoot Lodge Hotel, Mennock, SANQUHAR ☎ (0659) 50382 & 50477 1⇌ ♠ Annexe8⇌ ♠

LENNOXTOWN   Map 11 NS67

Campsie ☎ (0360) 310244
Scenic hillside course.
18 holes, 5515yds, Par 70, SSS 67, Course record 65.
Club membership 560.
Visitors restricted after 4pm.
Societies must contact one month in advance.
Green Fees not confirmed.
Facilities ⊗ ℳ ⓑ ♥ ♀ 🛍 🛍
Location Crow Rd (.5m N on B822)
Hotel ★★★62% Kirkhouse Inn, STRATHBLANE ☎ (0360) 70621 15⇌ ♠

LENZIE   Map 11 NS67

Lenzie ☎ 041-776 1535
Pleasant moorland course.
18 holes, 5984yds, Par 69, SSS 69, Course record 64.
Club membership 800.
Visitors must have introduction by member or by prior arrangement with secretary.
Societies apply in writing.
Green Fees £20 per day; £12.50 per round.
Facilities ⊗ ℳ by prior arrangement ⓑ ♥ ♀ 🛍 🛍 ⚑ Jim McCallum.
Location 19 Crosshill Rd (S side of town on B819)
Hotel ★★★64% Garfield House Hotel, Cumbernauld Rd, STEPPS ☎ 041-779 2111 27⇌ ♠

LESMAHAGOW   Map 11 NS83

Holland Bush ☎ (0555) 893484
Fairly difficult, tree-lined municipal parkland and moorland course. 1st half is flat, while 2nd half is hilly. No bunkers.
18 holes, 6110yds, Par 72, SSS 70, Course record 63.
Club membership 500.
Visitors no restrictions.
Societies must contact in advance.
Green Fees not confirmed.
Facilities ⊗ ℳ ⓑ ♥ ♀ 🛍 🛍 ⚑ Ian Rae.
Location Acretophead
Hotel ★★★63% Popinjay Hotel, Lanark Rd, ROSEBANK ☎ (055586) 441 38⇌ ♠ Annexe5⇌ ♠

LOCHWINNOCH   Map 10 NS35

Lochwinnoch ☎ (0505) 842153
Parkland course, slightly hilly in middle, with testing golf. Overlooks bird sanctuary and boating loch.
18 holes, 6243yds, Par 71, SSS 70, Course record 67.
Club membership 650.
Visitors may not play at weekends & restricted during competition days.
Societies apply in writing to club administrator.
Green Fees £20 per round/day.
Facilities ⊗ ℳ ⓑ ♥ ♀ 🛍 🛍 ⚑ Gerry Reilly.
Location Burnfoot Rd (W side of town off A760)
Hotel ★★68% Elderslie Hotel, John St, Broomfields, LARGS ☎ (0475) 686460 25rm(9⇌4 ♠)

MACHRIHANISH

Map 10 NR62

Machrihanish ☎ (058681) 213
Magnificent seaside links of championship status. The
1st holes is the famous drive across the Atlantic. Sandy
soil allows for play all year round. Large greens, easy
walking, windy. Fishing.
18 holes, 6228yds, Par 70, SSS 70.
Club membership 850.
Visitors   no restrictions.
Societies   apply in writing.
Green Fees   £20 per day Mon-Sun; £15 per round Mon-
                 Fri.
Facilities   ⊗ ℳ ⌫ 🍺 by prior arrangement 🍴 🛆 🏠 ⌂
                 Kenneth Campbell.
Location   5m W of Campbeltown on B843
Hotel   ★★63% Seafield Hotel, Kilkerran Rd,
                 CAMPBELTOWN ☎ (0586) 54385
                 3⌂ Annexe6 ⌂

MAUCHLINE

Map 11 NS42

Ballochmyle ☎ (0290) 50469
Wooded parkland course.
18 holes, 5952yds, Par 70, SSS 69, Course record 65.
Club membership 840.
Visitors   may not play on Sat.
Societies   apply in writing.
Green Fees   not confirmed.
Facilities   ⊗ ℳ ⌫ 🍺 🍴 🛆 🏠
Leisure   squash, snooker.
Location   Ballochmyle (1m SE on B705)
Hotel   ★★61% Royal Hotel, 1 Glaisnock St,
                 CUMNOCK ☎ (0290) 20822 11rm(2⇄3 ⌂)

MAYBOLE

Map 10 NS20

Maybole Municipal
Hilly parkland course.
9 holes, 2635yds, Par 33, SSS 65, Course record 64.
Club membership 100.
Visitors   no restrictions.
Societies   must contact in advance.
Green Fees   not confirmed.
Location   Memorial Park
Hotel   ★★★69% Malin Court, TURNBERRY
                 ☎ (0655) 31457 8⌂

MILNGAVIE

Map 11 NS57

Clober ☎ 041-956 1685
Parkland course. Testing 5th hole, par 3.
18 holes, 5042yds, Par 65, SSS 65.
Club membership 600.
Visitors   may not play before 4.30pm Mon-Thu and
                 before 4pm Fri & last Tue in month (Mar-Sep).
                 Must play with member weekends and bank
                 holidays.
Societies   must contact in advance.
Green Fees   £9 per round.
Facilities   ⊗ ℳ ⌫ 🍺 🍴 🏠
Location   Craigton Rd (NW side of town)
Hotel   ★★★65% Black Bull Thistle Hotel, Main St,
                 MILNGAVIE ☎ 041-956 2291 27⇄ ⌂

Dougalston ☎ 041-956 5750
Tree-lined with water features.
18 holes, 6683yds, Par 72, SSS 71.
Visitors   must contact in advance.
Societies   must contact in advance.
Green Fees   not confirmed.
Facilities   ⊗ ℳ ⌫ 🍺 🍴 🛆 ⌐
Location   Strathblane Rd (NE side of town on A81)
Hotel   ★★★65% Black Bull Thistle Hotel, Main St,
                 MILNGAVIE ☎ 041-956 2291 27⇄ ⌂

Hilton Park ☎ 041-956 4657
Moorland courses set amidst magnificent scenery.
Hilton: 18 holes, 6007yds, Par 70, SSS 70.
Allander: 18 holes, 5374yards, Par 69, SSS 67.
Club membership 1200.
Visitors   must contact in advance but may not play at
                 weekends.
Societies   weekdays only by prior arrangement.
Green Fees   £18 per round; £25 two rounds.
Facilities   ⊗ ℳ ⌫ 🍺 🍴 🛆 🏠 ⌐ ⌂
Location   Stockiemuir Rd (3m NW on A809)
Hotel   ★★★65% Black Bull Thistle Hotel,
                 Main St, MILNGAVIE
                 ☎ 041-956 2291 27⇄ ⌂

Milngavie ☎ 041-956 1619
Moorland course, hard walking, sometimes windy, good
views. Testing 1st and 4th holes (par 4).
18 holes, 5818yds, Par 68, SSS 68, Course record 64.
Club membership 700.
Visitors   must contact in advance.
Societies   apply in writing.
Green Fees   not confirmed.
Facilities   ⊗ ℳ ⌫ 🍺 🍴 🛆
Location   Laigh Park (1.25m N)
Hotel   ★★★65% Black Bull Thistle Hotel,
                 Main St, MILNGAVIE
                 ☎ 041-956 2291 27⇄ ⌂

MOTHERWELL

Map 11 NS75

Colville Park ☎ (0698) 263017
Parkland course. First nine, tree-lined, second nine, more
exposed. Testing 10th hole par 3, 16th hole par 4.
18 holes, 6265yds, Par 71, SSS 70.
Club membership 790.
Visitors   with member only except for parties. Must
                 contact in advance in writing.
Societies   weekdays only, apply in writing.
Green Fees   £20 per day.
Facilities   ⊗ ℳ ⌫ 🍺 🍴 🛆 🏠
Leisure   2 bowling greens, sailing, fishing club.
Location   New Jerviston House, Jerviston Estate (1.25m
                 NE on A723)
Hotel   ★★62% Silvertrees Hotel, Silverwells Crescent,
                 BOTHWELL ☎ (0698) 852311
                 7⇄ ⌂ Annexe19⇄ ⌂

MUIRHEAD

Map 11 NS66

Crow Wood ☎ 041-779 4954
Parkland course.
18 holes, 6249yds, Par 71, SSS 70, Course record 62.
Club membership 700.

Visitors	must contact in advance but may not play at weekends & bank holidays.
Societies	maximum 32, apply in writing.
Green Fees	£16 per round.
Facilities	⊗ ⫟ by prior arrangement ⤬ ⬛ ♀ ⚲ 🏠 (
Leisure	snooker.
Location	Garnkirk House (.5m W on A80)
Hotel	★★★64% Garfield House Hotel, Cumbernauld Rd, STEPPS ☎ 041-779 2111 27⇔ ⁀

NEW CUMNOCK   Map 11 NS61

New Cumnock ☎ (0290) 32037
Parkland course.
9 holes, 5176yds, Par 68, SSS 65, Course record 62.
Club membership 240.

Visitors	restricted on Sun competition days; not before 4pm.
Societies	apply in writing to the Secretary, 23 Castlemains Avenue, New Cumnock.
Green Fees	£8 per day.
Facilities	⚲
Location	Lochhill (0.75m N on A76)
Hotel	★★61% Royal Hotel, 1 Glaisnock St, CUMNOCK ☎ (0290) 20822 11rm(2⇔3 ⁀)

NEWTON MEARNS   Map 11 NS55

East Renfrewshire ☎ Loganswell (03555) 258
Undulating moorland with loch; prevailing SW wind.
18 holes, 6097yds, Par 70, SSS 70.
Club membership 500.

Visitors	must contact in advance.
Societies	must contact in advance.
Green Fees	not confirmed.
Facilities	⊗ ⫟ ⤬ ⬛ ♀ ⚲ 🏠 (
Location	Pilmuir (3m SW on A77)
Hotel	★★★63% Macdonald Thistle Hotel, Eastwood Toll, GIFFNOCK ☎ 041-638 2225 56⇔ ⁀

Eastwood ☎ Loganswell (03555) 261
Moorland course.
18 holes, 5864yds, Par 68, SSS 68.
Club membership 900.

Visitors	welcome by appointment.
Societies	must contact in advance.
Green Fees	£26 per day; £18 per round.
Facilities	⊗ ⫟ ⤬ ⬛ ♀ ⚲ 🏠 (Stephen Campbell.
Leisure	pool table.
Location	Muirshield (2.5m S on A77)
Hotel	★★★63% Macdonald Thistle Hotel, Eastwood Toll, GIFFNOCK ☎ 041-638 2225 56⇔ ⁀

Whitecraigs ☎ 041-639 4530
Beautiful parkland course.
18 holes, 6230yds, Par 70, SSS 70.
Club membership 1150.

Visitors	must contact in advance and have a handicap certificate.
Societies	apply in writing.
Green Fees	not confirmed.
Facilities	⊗ ⫟ ⤬ ⬛ ♀ ⚲ 🏠 (W Watson.
Location	72 Ayr Rd (1.5m NE on A77)
Hotel	★★★63% Macdonald Thistle Hotel, Eastwood Toll, GIFFNOCK ☎ 041-638 2225 56⇔ ⁀

OBAN   Map 10 NM83

Glencruitten ☎ (0631) 62868
There is plenty of space and considerable variety of hole on this downland course - popular with holidaymakers. In a beautiful, isolated situation, the course is hilly and testing, particularly the 1st and 12th, par 4's, and 10th and 15th, par 3's.
18 holes, 4250yds, Par 61, SSS 63.
Club membership 620.

Visitors	restricted Thu & Sat.
Societies	must contact in writing.
Green Fees	not confirmed.
Facilities	⊗ ⫟ ⤬ ⬛ ♀ ⚲ 🏠 ⳾ (
Location	Glencruitten Rd (NE side of town centre off A816)
Hotel	★★★56% Caledonian Hotel, Station Square, OBAN ☎ (0631) 63133 70⇔

PAISLEY   Map 11 NS46

Barshaw ☎ 041-889 2908
Municipal parkland course.
18 holes, 5703yds, Par 68, SSS 67.
Club membership 77.

Visitors	no restrictions.
Green Fees	not confirmed.
Facilities	⚲
Location	Barshaw Park (1m E off A737)
Hotel	★★★65% Glynhill Hotel & Leisure Club, Paisley Rd, RENFREW ☎ 041-886 5555 125⇔ ⁀

Paisley ☎ 041-884 3903
Moorland course, windy but with good views.
18 holes, 6220yds, Par 70, SSS 70.
Club membership 700.

Visitors	must contact in advance & have handicap certificate.
Societies	apply in writing.
Green Fees	£24 per day; £16 per round.
Facilities	⊗ ⫟ ⤬ ⬛ ♀ ⚲ 🏠 (Grant Gilmour.
Leisure	snooker.
Location	Braehead (S side of town off B774)
Hotel	★★★65% Glynhill Hotel & Leisure Club, Paisley Rd, RENFREW ☎ 041-886 5555 125⇔ ⁀

Ralston ☎ 041-882 1349
Parkland course.
18 holes, 6071yds, Par 71, SSS 69.
Club membership 750.

Visitors	must be accompanied by member.
Green Fees	not confirmed.
Facilities	♀ ⚲ 🏠
Location	Strathmore Av, Ralston (2m E off A737)
Hotel	★★★62% Swallow Hotel, 517 Paisley Rd West, GLASGOW ☎ 041-427 3146 119⇔ ⁀

Remember – replace all divots, and repair ball-marks or damage by spikes on completion of the hole

PORT GLASGOW

Map 10 NS37

Port Glasgow ☎ (0475) 704181
A moorland course set on a hilltop overlooking the Clyde, with magnificent views to the Cowal hills.
18 holes, 5712yds, Par 68, SSS 68, Course record 63.
Club membership 390.
Visitors may not play on Sat. Must contact in advance.
Societies apply in writing.
Green Fees not confirmed.
Facilities ⊗ 洲 ⓑ 🖤 (catering on request) ♀
Location Devol Rd (1m S)
Hotel ★★★♨68% Gleddoch House Hotel,
LANGBANK
☎ (047554) 711 33⇌ ℝ

PRESTWICK

Map 10 NS32

Prestwick ☎ (0292) 77404
Seaside links with natural hazards and fine views.
18 holes, 6544yds, Par 71, SSS 72.
Club membership 606.
Visitors restricted Thu; may not play at weekends.
Must contact in advance and have a
handicap certificate.
Societies must contact in writing.
Green Fees £50 before 12.30pm, £30 from 2.40pm.
Facilities ⊗ (summer) ⓑ 🖤 ♀ ♨ ⓕ 🝙 ℓ
F C Rennie.
Location 2 Links Rd (In town centre off A79)
Hotel ★★62% Parkstone Hotel, Esplanade,
PRESTWICK
☎ (0292) 77286 15⇌ ℝ

Prestwick St Cuthbert ☎ (0292) 77101
Parkland course with easy walking, natural hazards and sometimes windy.
18 holes, 6470yds, Par 71, SSS 71.
Club membership 820.
Visitors must contact in advance but may not play at
weekends & bank holidays.
Societies apply in writing.
Green Fees £24 per day; £18 per round.
Facilities ⊗ & 洲 (ex Thu) ⓑ 🖤 ♀ ♨
Location East Rd (0.5m E of town centre off A77)
Hotel ★★62% St Nicholas Hotel, 41 Ayr Rd,
PRESTWICK ☎ (0292) 79568
17rm(13⇌ ℝ)

Prestwick St Nicholas ☎ (0292) 77608
Seaside links course with whins, heather and tight fairways. It provides easy walking and has an unrestricted view of the Firth of Clyde.
18 holes, 5952yds, Par 69, SSS 69, Course record 63.
Club membership 700.
Visitors except weekends & public holidays. Must
contact in advance.
Societies must contact in advance.
Green Fees £30 per day; £18 per round.
Facilities ⊗ 洲 ⓑ 🖤 ♀ ♨ 🝙 ⓕ ℓ Stewart Smith.
Location Grangemuir Rd (S side of town off A79)
Hotel ★★62% Parkstone Hotel, Esplanade,
PRESTWICK
☎ (0292) 77286 15⇌ ℝ

RENFREW

Map 11 NS46

Renfrew ☎ (041886) 6692
Tree-lined parkland course.
18 holes, 6818yds, Par 72, SSS 73, Course record 67.
Club membership 700.
Visitors must be accompanied by member, contact in
advance and have an introduction from own
club.
Green Fees not confirmed.
Facilities ⊗ 洲 ⓑ 🖤 ♀ ♨ 🝙
Location Blythswood Estate, Inchinnan Rd
(0.75m W off A8)
Hotel ★★★64% Stakis Normandy Hotel, Inchinnan
Rd, Renfrew, RENFREW
☎ 041-886 4100 141⇌ ℝ

SHOTTS

Map 11 NS86

Shotts ☎ (0501) 820431 & 826628
Moorland course.
18 holes, 6125yds, Par 70, SSS 70, Course record 63.
Club membership 900.
Visitors welcome weekdays, must contact in advance.
Societies apply by letter, weekdays only.
Green Fees £14 per day; low season £10 per round.
Facilities ⊗ 洲 ⓑ 🖤 ♀ (all day) ♨ 🝙 ⓕ James Forrester.
Location Blairhead (2m from M8 off Benhar Road)
Hotel ★★★63% Popinjay Hotel, Lanark Rd,
ROSEBANK ☎ (055586) 441
38⇌ ℝ Annexe5⇌ ℝ

SKELMORLIE

Map 10 NS16

Skelmorlie ☎ (0475) 520152
Parkland/moorland course with magnificent views over Firth of Clyde. Designed by James Braid, the club celebrated its centenary in 1991. The first five holes are played twice.
18 holes, 5056yds, Par 64, SSS 65.
Club membership 400.
Visitors must contact in advance, restricted Sat.
Societies apply in writing to the secretary.
Green Fees £20 for two rounds including meals (£25 Sun).
Facilities ⊗ 洲 ⓑ (all by arrangement) 🖤 ♀ ♨ ⓕ
Leisure fishing.
Location Beithglass (E side of village off A78)
Hotel ★★★♨61% Manor Park Hotel, SKELMORLIE
☎ (0475) 520832 10⇌ ℝ Annexe13⇌ ℝ

SOUTHEND

Map 10 NR60

Dunaverty ☎ (058683) 677
Undulating, seaside course.
18 holes, 4597yds, SSS 63, Course record 59.
Club membership 250.
Visitors no restrictions.
Societies apply in writing.
Green Fees £12 per day; £8 per round.
Facilities ⊗ & 🖤 by prior arrangement ♨ 🝙
Location 10m S of Campbeltown on B842
Hotel ★★62% Royal Hotel, Main St,
CAMPBELTOWN ☎ (0586) 52017
16rm(8⇌4 ℝ)

MALIN·COURT

Turnberry

PRO, AMATEUR OR NOVICE, WE'VE GOT THE BEST CLUBS FOR YOU!

Wedged on the Ayrshire coast in the heart of Burns Country overlooking the Firth of Clyde and the Isle of Arran we have many **links** with the world of golf which put us above **par**.

Not only are we a **3-wood** shot from Turnberry's Championship course, the venue for the 1994 British Open, it's only a short **drive** to the newly opened Brunston Castle course and many other local clubs where you can get a **slice** of the action.

AA
★★★

For further information about our golfing holidays, please contact:

HIGHLY COMMENDED

MALIN COURT HOTEL AND RESTAURANT
TURNBERRY, GIRVAN, AYRSHIRE KA26 9PB
TELEPHONE: 0655 31457/8 FACSIMILE: 0655 31072

STEVENSTON   Map 10 NS24

Ardeer ☎ (0294) 64542
Parkland course with natural hazards.
18 holes, 6500yds, Par 72, SSS 72, Course record 64.
Club membership 560.
Visitors   may not play Sat.
Societies   must contact in advance.
Green Fees £18 per day; £10 per round (£24/£14 Sun).
Facilities   ⊗ ⅷ ⅃ ♥ ♀ ⚲ 🖿
Leisure   snooker.
Location   Greenhead (0.5m N off A78)
Hotel   ★★★★52% Hospitality Inn, Annick Rd, Annickwater, IRVINE
           ☎ (0294) 74272 128⇥ 📞

STRATHAVEN   Map 11 NS64

Strathaven ☎ (0357) 20421
Gently undulating, tree-lined, Championship parkland course with panoramic views over town and Avon valley.
18 holes, 6206yds, Par 71, SSS 70, Course record 63.
Club membership 950.
Visitors   welcome weekdays only. Must contact in advance.
Societies   Tue only.
Green Fees £25 per day; £17.50 per round.
Facilities   ⊗ ⅷ ⅃ ♥ ♀ ⚲ 🖿 ℓ M McCrorie.
Location   Overton Av, Glasgow Rd (NE side of town on A726)
Hotel   ★★★60% Stuart Hotel, 2 Cornwall Way, EAST KILBRIDE ☎ (03552) 21161 39⇥ 📞

TARBERT   Map 10 NR86

Tarbert ☎ (0880) 820565
Beautiful moorland course. Four fairways crossed by streams.
9 holes, 4460yds, Par 66, SSS 64.
Club membership 110.
Visitors   may not play competition days.
Societies   apply in writing.
Green Fees £6 per 18 holes; £4 per 9 holes; £8 per day.
Facilities   ♀ (Sat & Sun)
Location   1m W on B8024
Hotel   ★★★61% Stonefield Castle Hotel, TARBERT,
           ☎ (0880) 820836 33rm(30⇥2 📞)

TIGHNABRUAICH   Map 10 NR97

Kyles of Bute ☎ (0700) 811601
Moorland course which is hilly and exposed to wind. Good views of the Kyles of Bute.
9 holes, 4778yds, Par 66, SSS 64.
Club membership 160.
Visitors   no restrictions.
Societies   must give 3 weeks prior notice.
Green Fees not confirmed.
Facilities   ♥ ⚲
Location   1.25m S off B8000
Hotel   ★★71% Kilfinan Hotel, KILFINAN
           ☎ (070082) 201 11⇥

TROON   Map 10 NS33

ROYAL TROON See page 279

Troon Municipal ☎ (0292) 312464
Three links courses, two championship.
Lochgreen course: 18 holes, 6785yds, par 74, sss 73, course record 66.
Darley: 18 holes, 6501yds, par 71, sss 71, course record 65.
fullerton: 18 holes, 4822yds, par 64, sss 63, course record 59.
Club membership 3000.
Visitors   must contact in advance.
Societies   apply in writing.
Green fees not confirmed.
Facilities   ⊗ ⅷ ⅃ ♥ ♀ ⚲ 🖿 ℐ ℓ Gordon McKinley.
Location   harling dr (100yds from railway station)
Hotel   ★★59% Ardneil Hotel, 51 Saint Meddans St, TROON
           ☎ (0292) 311611 9rm(3⇥4 📞)

TURNBERRY   Map 10 NS20

TURNBERRY HOTEL GOLF COURSES See page 281

A golf course name printed in ***bold italics*** means we have been unable to verify information with the club's management for the current year

UDDINGSTON   Map 11 NS66

Calderbraes ☎ (0698) 813425
Parkland course with good view of Clyde Valley. Testing 4th
hole (par 4), hard uphill.
9 holes, 5046yds, Par 66, SSS 67.
Club membership 230.
Visitors   weekdays before 5pm.
Societies   welcome.
Green Fees   £10 per day or round.
Facilities   ⊗ ⅲ ᛚ 🍺 ♀ 🖰
Location   57 Roundknowe Rd (1.5m NW off A74)
Hotel   ★★64% Redstones Hotel, 8-10 Glasgow Rd,
               UDDINGSTON ☎ (0698) 813774 & 814843
               18rm(16⇌ ♠)

UPLAWMOOR   Map 10 NS45

Caldwell ☎ (050585) 329
Parkland course.
18 holes, 6046yds, Par 71, SSS 69.
Club membership 600.
Visitors   restricted weekends & bank holidays. Must
               contact in advance.
Societies   apply in writing.
Green Fees   £24 per day; £16 per round.
Facilities   ⊗ ᛚ 🍺 ♀ 🖰 🖰 ℓ Stephen Forbes.
Location   0.5m SW A736
Hotel   ★★62% Dalmeny Park Country House,
               Lochlibo Rd, BARRHEAD
               ☎ 041-881 9211 18rm(3⇌10 ♠)

WEST KILBRIDE   Map 10 NS24

West Kilbride ☎ (0294) 823911
Seaside links course on Firth of Clyde, with fine view of Isle
of Arran from every hole.
18 holes, 5974yds, Par 70, SSS 69, Course record 63.
Club membership 960.
Visitors   may not play at weekends. Must have a handicap
               certificate.
Societies   Tue & Thu only; must contact in advance.
Green Fees   not confirmed.
Facilities   ⊗ ⅲ by prior arrangement ᛚ 🍺 ♀ 🖰 🖰 ℓ
               Gregor Howie.
Location   Fullerton Dr (W side of town off A78)
Hotel   ★★68% Elderslie Hotel, John St, Broomfields,
               LARGS ☎ (0475) 686460 25rm(9⇌4 ♠)

WISHAW   Map 11 NS75

Wishaw ☎ (0698) 372869
Parkland course with many tree-lined areas. Bunkers protect
17 of the 18 greens.
18 holes, 6051yds, Par 69, SSS 69, Course record 63.
Club membership 980.
Visitors   welcome midweek before 5pm, Sun after
               10.30am, not Sat.
Societies   apply by letter 4 weeks in advance.
Green Fees   £12 per round; £20 per day (£25 per day Sun).
Facilities   ⊗ ⅲ ᛚ 🍺 ♀ 🖰 🖰 ℓ John Campbell.
Location   55 Cleland Rd (NW side of town off A721)
Hotel   ★★★63% Popinjay Hotel, Lanark Rd, ROSEBANK
               ☎ (055586) 441 38⇌ ♠ Annexe5⇌ ♠

TAYSIDE

ABERFELDY   Map 14 NN84

Aberfeldy ☎ (0887) 820535
Flat, parkland course, situated by River Tay near the famous
Wade Bridge and Black Watch Monument.
9 holes, 5466yds, Par 67, SSS 67.
Club membership 250.
Visitors   are advised to book in advance and must do so at
               weekends Jun-Aug.
Societies   must contact in advance.
Green Fees   £10 per 18 holes; £6 per 9 holes.
Facilities   ᛚ 🍺 ♀ 🖰 🖰
Location   Taybridge Rd (N side of town centre)
Hotel   ★★63% Weem Hotel, Weem, ABERFELDY
               ☎ (0887) 820381 14⇌ ♠

ALYTH   Map 15 NO24

Alyth ☎ (08283) 2268
Windy, heathland course with easy walking.
18 holes, 6226yds, Par 70, SSS 70, Course record 66.
Club membership 850.
Visitors   must contact in advance.
Societies   must contact in advance.
Green Fees   not confirmed.
Facilities   ⊗ high tea ⅲ by prior arrangement ᛚ 🍺 ♀ 🖰
               🖰 ℓ Tom Melville.
Location   Pitcrocknie (1m E on B954)
Hotel   ★★▲66% Altamount House Hotel, Coupar
               Angus Rd, BLAIRGOWRIE
               ☎ (0250) 873512 & 873814 7 ⇌ ♠

ARBROATH   Map 12 NO64

Arbroath Artisan ☎ (0241) 75837
Municipal seaside links course, with bunkers guarding
greens. Played upon by Arbroath Artisan Club.
18 holes, 6090yds, Par 70, SSS 69.
Club membership 600.
Visitors   no restrictions.
Societies   must telephone in advance; deposit required.
Green Fees   not confirmed.
Facilities   ⊗ ᛚ 🍺 ♀ 🖰 🖰 ♈ ℓ Lindsay Ewart.
Location   Elliot (2m SW on A92)
Hotel   ★★61% Hotel Seaforth, Dundee Rd,
               ARBROATH ☎ (0241) 72232 20⇌ ♠

Letham Grange ☎ (024189) 373
Two courses of great variety. Old Course is set in wooded
estate with attractive lochs and burns. New Course is shorter
and less arduous but deceptive.
Old Course: 18 holes, 6614yds, Par 73, SSS 73.
New Course: 18 holes, 5528yds, Par 68, SSS 68.
Club membership 780.
Visitors   restricted Tue & weekends on Old Course. Must
               contact in advance.
Societies   must contact in advance.
Green Fees   Old Course: £30 per day; £20 per round (£25 per
               round weekends). New Course: £18 per day; £12
               per round (£15 weekends).   ▶

*R*oyal *T*roon

Troon ☎ **(0292) 311555**   **Map 10 NS33**

John Ingham writes: When Jack Nicklaus first played Royal Troon in the 1962 Open, he was 22 and hit the ball a long way. At that time Nicklaus told me 'There are only two holes that I might not reach with my second shot. My favourite shot is the drive, which I hit up to 350 yards. Just before I swing,' he said, 'all my concentration is directed on one thing and that is to give the ball as big a hit - and as square a hit - as I physically can.'

While sheer length from the back tees at Royal Troon is a great advantage, bearing in mind the full course measures 7097 yards, where you hit the ball is more important than how far. The reason is that this championship links-type course is peppered with bunkers not visible from the tee.

That particular Open was won by Arnold Palmer, in those days a longish hitter as well. However, Palmer also had a delightful putting touch, essential for Royal Troon greens, which can prove hard to read.

Royal Troon is one of the finest links in the world and in an American list appears at number 36. Created in 1878, it was then mercifully free of jumbo jets from nearby Prestwick and has provided entertaining and testing golf for players from all over the world. Greg Norman holds the record with a 10-under-par round of 64. A round which put him in a tie for the 1989 Open which he lost to Mark Calcavecchia.

In the 1960s I played a round at this grand links with the late Henry Longhurst, a good club single figure man who had once won the German Amateur championship. To my best drives, lashed in the breeze, he would just hiss 'Wrong line' and, sure enough, when we got up the fairway, the ball would be submerged in soft sand. In fact I'm told there are 365 bunkers, one for every day of the year!

The Marine Highland hotel is on the edge of the course and, as there are 22 other courses in the area, this makes a great place for a holiday.

So great is Royal Troon, in fact, that the Royal and Ancient has announced that the 1997 Open will again be staged there - for the seventh time since 1923!

Membership 500 (male only)

Visitors may not play Wednesdays, Fridays, weekends and public holidays. Must have handicap certificate. Must contact in advance and have a letter of introduction from own club. Ladies and under 18s may only play on the Portland

Societies apply in writing

Green fees £75 per day inc meals

Facilities ⊗ ▥ (Fri & Sat) ⓫ ♟ ♀ ⌓ 🏠 ⚐ ⌁ (R B Anderson)

Location Craigend Rd (S side of town on B749)

36 holes. Old Course: 18 holes, 7067 yds, Par 73, SSS 74, course record 64 (Greg Norman) Portland: 18 holes, 6386yds, Par 71, SSS 71, course record 6 (W. Cunningham)

WHERE TO STAY AND EAT NEARBY

HOTEL

TROON

★★★ ⊛⊛ ▲▲ 74% Lochgreen House, Monktenhill Rd, Southwood ☎(0292)313343. 7 ⇆ ⌂

★★★★ 63% Marine Highland. ☎ (0292) 314444, 72 ⇆ ⌂. International cuisine

★★★ ⊛⊛ 69% Highgrove House ☎ (0292) 312511. 9 ⇆ ⌂. French cuisine

★★★ 66% Piersland House, Craigend Rd. ☎ (0292) 314747. 15 ⇆ ⌂ Annexe 4 ⇆. British & Continental cuisine

Facilities ⊗ ∭ ⓑ ▦ ♀ ⚘ 🖅 ⌇ 🏌 ⌘ David F G Scott.
Leisure curling rink in winter.
Location Colliston (4m N on A993)
Hotel ★★★66% Letham Grange Hotel, Colliston,
ARBROATH ☎ (024189) 373 19⇥

AUCHTERARDER   Map 11 NN91

Auchterarder ☎ (0764) 662804
Parkland course with easy walking.
18 holes, 5757yds, Par 69, SSS 68, Course record 65.
Club membership 650.
Visitors restricted on competition days. Must contact in
advance,
Societies must contact 2 months in advance.
Green Fees £18 per day; £13 per round (£26 per day; £19
per round weekends).
Facilities ⊗ ∭ ▦ ♀ ⚘ 🖅 🏌 ⌇ Gavin Baxter.
Location Orchil Rd (0.75m SW on A824)
Hotel ★★★★★(red) The Gleneagles Hotel,
AUCHTERARDER ☎ (0764) 62231 236⇥ ⋔

Gleneagles Hotel ☎ (0764) 663543
Famous moorland courses designed by James Braid. The
King's has heather and gorse threatening wayward shots;
The Queen's is more heavily wooded with a variety of
dog-leg holes and the Loch-an-Eerie to negotiate.
Sumptuous hotel offers unrivalled sports and leisure
activities. Course record holder on King's Course is Ian
Woosnam. The new championship Monarchs Course,
designed by Jack Nicklaus, was opened at the end of
1992.
*Kings Course: 18 holes, 6471yds, Par 70, SSS 71, Course
record 62.*
Queens Course: 18 holes, 5965yds, Par 68, SSS 69.
Wee Course: 9 holes, 1481yds, Par 27.
Monarch Course: 18 holes, 6551yds, Par 72.
Visitors must be hotel residents or the guest of a club
member. A handicap certificate is not
required. Must contact in advance.
Societies must be resident in the hotel.
Green Fees not confirmed.
Facilities ⊗ ∭ ⓑ ▦ (catering available to hotel
guests) ♀ ⚘ 🖅 🏌 ⌇ 🏌 Ian Marchbank.
Leisure hard and grass tennis courts, heated indoor
swimming pool, squash, fishing, riding,
snooker, sauna, solarium, gymnasium,
croquet, bowls, pitch & putt & cycling.
Location 2m SW of A823
Hotel ★★★★★(red) The Gleneagles Hotel,
AUCHTERARDER
☎ (0764) 62231 236⇥ ⋔

BARRY   Map 12 NO53

Panmure ☎ (0241) 53120
A nerve-testing, adventurous course set amongst
sandhills - its hazards belie the quiet nature of the
opening holes. This tight links has been used as a
qualifying course for the Open Championship, and
features Ben Hogan's favourite hole, the dog-leg 6th,
which heralds the toughest stretch, around the turn.
18 holes, 6317yds, Par 70, SSS 70, Course record 62.
Club membership 650.

Visitors must play with member on Sat.
Societies must contact secretary in advance.
Green Fees £30 per day; £20 per round.
Facilities ⊗ ∭ ⓑ ▦ ♀ ⚘ 🖅 ⌇ Andew Cullen.
Location Burnside Rd (S side of village off A930)
Hotel ★★62% Glencoe Hotel, Links Pde,
CARNOUSTIE ☎ (0241) 53273
11rm(3⇥5 ⋔)

BLAIR ATHOLL   Map 14 NN86

Blair Atholl ☎ (0796) 481407
Parkland course, river runs alongside 3 holes, easy walking.
9 holes, 5710yds, Par 70, SSS 69.
Club membership 400.
Visitors no restrictions.
Societies must contact in advance.
Green Fees £9 per day (£10 weekends).
Facilities ⓑ ▦ ♀ ⚘ 🖅
Location 0.5m S off B8079
Hotel ★★63% Atholl Arms Hotel, BLAIR ATHOLL
☎ (0796) 481205 30⇥ ⋔

BLAIRGOWRIE   Map 15 NO14

Blairgowrie ☎ (0250) 872622
Two 18-hole heathland courses, also a 9-hole course.
Rosemount Course: 18 holes, 6588yds, Par 72, SSS 72.
Lansdowne Course: 18 holes, 6895yds, Par 72, SSS 73.
Wee Course: 9 holes, 4654yds, Par 64, SSS 63.
Club membership 1200. ▶

⊂urnberry ℋotel Golf ℂourses

Turnberry ☎ (0655) 31000   **Map 10 NS20**

*J*ohn Ingham writes: The hotel is sumptuous, the Ailsa and Arran courses beneath it are total magic. The air reaches down into your inner lung and of all places in Scotland, Turnberry has to be among the finest.

Turnberry is delightfully off the beaten track and, although the courses are principally for residents of the hotel, if you wish to fly in, then Prestwick Airport is only seventeen miles from the first tee. What makes the place so desirable is the warmness of the welcome and, course professional Bob Jamieson will tell you, this is literally so on occasions, as the links is on the friendliest of gulf streams.

The Ailsa course has been the venue for the Open in 1977 and 1986 and will be hosting it again in 1994. It was here in the 1977 Open, that Jack Nicklaus put up such a brave fight against Tom Watson. Then, in 1986, we had a wondrous victory from Greg Norman. He has fond memories of Turnberry, where a few hours after the prize-giving he was able to sit with his wife on the edge of the great links, drinking champagne, and watching the moon roll round the pure white lighthouse out by the 9th green.

Without any doubt, Turnberry is the stuff of dreams and you must go there if you possibly can.

Visitors	must contact in advance as the golf courses are principally for residents of the hotel
Societies	contact in advance as courses are principally for residents of the hotel
Green fees	Arran Course £25; Ailsa Course £75 - includes a round on Arran Residents: Arran Course £15; Ailsa Course £45 -includes a round on Arran;
Facilities	✕ ⽧ ⯑ ⯑ ⯑ 𝄞 ⯑ ⯑ 𝄐 ℓ (R SJamieson)
Leisure	tennis (hardcourt), indoor-heated swimming pool, squash, snooker, sauna, solarium, gymnasium, treatment rooms
Location	N side of village, on A719

36 holes. Ailsa Course: 18 holes, 6408 yds, Par 69, SSS 72, Course record 63 (Greg Norman & Maric Hayes) Arran Course: 18 holes, 6249yds, Par 69, SSS 70. Course record 65 (E Macintosh/C Ronald/S McGregor)

WHERE TO STAY AND EAT NEARBY

HOTELS:

GIRVAN
★★ 63% King's Arms, Dalrymple St. ☎ (0465) 3322. 25 ⇌ ↶.
Scottish & French cuisine

MAYBOLE
★★⊛ Ladyburn. ☎ Crosshill (06554) 585. 8(7 ⇌ ↶)

TURNBERRY
★★★★★⊛ 73% Turnberry Hotel and Golf Courses. ☎ (0655) 31000. 132 ⇌ ↶
Scottish & French cuisine

★★★ 69% Malin Court.
☎ (0655) 31457. 8 ⇌ ↶

Visitors must contact in advance & have handicap
certificate, restricted Wed, Fri & weekends.
Societies must contact in writing.
Green Fees Rosemount & Lansdowne £40 per day; £30
per round (£34 per round weekends).
Facilities ⊗ ⊞ ⓛ ⬛ ♀ ⚐ ⛋ ⛳ ⛴ Gordon Kinnoch.
Location Rosemount (2m S off A93)
Hotel ★★★▲♣77% Kinloch House Hotel,
BLAIRGOWRIE ☎ (0250884) 237 21⇄ ⋔

BRECHIN   Map 15 NO56

Brechin ☎ (03562) 2383
Rolling parkland course, with easy walking and good views
of Strathmore Valley and Grampian Mountains.
18 holes, 6100yds, Par 70, SSS 69.
Club membership 650.
Visitors may not play at weekends when competitions are
being held.
Societies must contact in advance.
Green Fees £16 per day; £11 per round (£25/£16 weekends
& bank holidays).
Facilities ⊗ ⊞ ⓛ ⬛ ♀ ⚐ ⛋ ⛳ ⛴ S Rennie.
Leisure squash, pool table.
Location Trinity (1m N on B966)
Hotel ★★56% Northern Hotel, Clerk St, BRECHIN
☎ (03562) 2156 & 5505 17rm(4⇄11 ⋔)

CARNOUSTIE   Map 12 NO53

CARNOUSTIE GOLF LINKS See page 283

COMRIE   Map 11 NN72

Comrie ☎ (0764) 670055
Scenic highland course.
9 holes, 5250yds, Par 70, SSS 69.
Club membership 400.
Visitors restricted Mon & Tue evenings.
Societies must contact in advance.
Green Fees £8 per day (£12 weekends).
Facilities ⬛ ⚐ ⛳
Location E side of village off A85
Hotel ★★60% Royal Hotel, Melville Square, COMRIE
☎ (0764) 670200 9rm(8⇄)

CRIEFF   Map 11 NN82

Crieff ☎ (0764) 652909
This course is what you might call 'up and down' but the
turf is beautiful and the highland air fresh and
invigorating. There are views from the course over
Strathearn. Of the two courses the Ferntower is the more
challenging. Both parkland, the Dornock has one water
hazard.
*Ferntower: 18 holes, 6402yds, Par 71, SSS 71, Course
record 66.*
Dornock: 9 holes, 4772yds, Par 64, SSS 63.
Club membership 570.

Visitors must have a handicap certificate. Must
contact in advance.
Societies must contact in advance.
Green Fees not confirmed.
Facilities ⊗ ⊞ ⓛ ⬛ ♀ ⚐ ⛋ ⛳ ⛴ D Murchie & J M
Stark.
Location Perth Rd (0.5m NE on A85)
Hotel ★★68% Murray Park Hotel, Connaught
Ter, CRIEFF ☎ (0764) 3731 13⇄

DUNDEE   Map 11 NO43

Caird Park ☎ (0382) 453606
Municipal parkland course.
18 holes, 6281yds, Par 72, SSS 70.
Club membership 400.
Visitors no restrictions.
Green Fees not confirmed.
Facilities ♀ ⚐ ⛴
Location Mains Loan (1.5m N of city centre off A972)
Hotel ★★★65% The Queen's Hotel, 160 Nethergate,
DUNDEE ☎ (0382) 22515 47⇄ ⋔

Camperdown ☎ (0382) 621145
Parkland course. Testing 2nd hole.
18 holes, 5999yds, Par 71, SSS 69.
Club membership 600.
Visitors must contact in advance.
Societies must contact in advance.
Green Fees not confirmed.   ▶

$\mathcal{C}$arnoustie $\mathcal{G}$olf $\mathcal{L}$inks

Carnoustie ☎ (0241) 53789　　　　**Map 12 NO53**

John Ingham writes: You love it, or hate it - but you respect it. Carnoustie can be a graveyard. Simply standing up to the buffeting is bad enough, but those closing holes, across the Barry Burn (or into it) are a prospect which can gnaw at the mind. The burn twists through the links like an angry serpent and has to be crossed no fewer than seven times.

Back in 1953 they came to see Ben Hogan play in the Open Championship. This little man from Texas had a magic about him, and the huge terrifying links, the dread of any short hitter, certainly promised to be a platform on which to examine the finest golfer of his day, and maybe of any day.

Not since 1860 had any golfer won the Open on his first attempt. Certainly Hogan hadn't come to this awesome place for the money which, in those days, was a pittance. He had come to prove he was the best player in the world. That was pressure!

When Mr Hogan saw the 'Stone Age' course, dating back to the birth of the game, he was shocked because it lacked trees and colour, and looked drab. But he beat the 7200-yard monster course for the 1953 Championship, which was, as they say, something else.

'Winning the British Open at Carnoustie gave me my greatest pleasure' he told the *Fort Worth Star-Telegram*. 'Certainly the other victories were pleasurable, but none gave me the feeling, the desire to perform, that gripped me in Scotland'.

Sadly, Hogan never returned and then the great links was taken from the Open Championship rota. Today there are hopes it may be re-instated.

Visitors	must contact club in advance. Restricted hours during week. Must have a handicap certificate for Championship course
Societies	prior arrangement required either in writing or by telephone
Green fees	Championship: £60 per day; £34 per round
	Burnside: £20 per day; £13 per round
	Buddon Links: £12 per day; £8 per round. Combination day tickets: Championship & Burnside £40.50
	Championship & Buddon Links £38 Burnside & Buddon Links £17
Facilities	⌂
Location	Links Parade (SW side of town, off A930)

54 holes. Championship Course: 18 holes, 6936 yds, Par 72, SSS 74, Course record 65 (Tom Watson). Burnside Course: 18 holes, 6020 yds, Par 68, SSS 69. Buddon Links: 18 holes, 5196 yds, Par 66, SSS 66

WHERE TO STAY AND EAT NEARBY

HOTELS:

ARBROATH
★★★ ✿✿ 66% Letham Grange, Colliston, ☎ Gowanbank (024189) 373 19 ⇋. International cuisine

CARNOUSTIE
★★ 62% Carlogie House, Carlogie Rd ☎ (0241) 53185. 11 ⇋ 🔥 Scottish & French cuisine

★★62% Glencoe, Links Pde. ☎ (0241) 53273. 11(8 ⇋ 🔥) Scottish & French cuisine

LETHAM
★★★ ⚘⚘ 58% Fernie Castle. ☎ (033781) 381. 15 ⇋ 🔥

RESTAURANT:

INVERKEILOR
✗ ✿ Gordon's, Homewood House, Main St. ☎ (02413) 364 Scottish & French cuisine

Facilities ⌂ 🏠 ℂ
Leisure hard tennis courts, riding.
Location Camperdown House, Camperdown Park (3m
NW of city centre off A923)
Hotel ★★★62% Angus Thistle Hotel, 101 Marketgait,
DUNDEE ☎ (0382) 26874 58⇄ ℝ

Downfield ☎ (0382) 825595
A fine inland course of recent Championship rating set in
undulating woodland to the north of Dundee. The Gelly
burn provides a hazard for several holes.
18 holes, 6804yds, Par 73, SSS 73.
Club membership 742.
Visitors must telephone 0382 89246 for start time on
day of play.
Societies must contact in advance.
Green Fees £36 per day; £24 per round.
Facilities ⊗ 🏶 ⓑ 🍺 ♀ ⌂ 🏠 ℸ ℂ Colin Waddell.
Leisure snooker.
Location Turnberry Av (N of city centre off A923)
Hotel ★★★62% Angus Thistle Hotel, 101
Marketgait, DUNDEE
☎ (0382) 26874 58⇄ ℝ

DUNKELD

Map 11 NO04

Dunkeld & Birnam ☎ (0350) 727524
Interesting heathland course with spectacular views of
surrounding countryside.
9 holes, 5264yds, Par 68, SSS 66.
Club membership 300.
Visitors may not play on competition days.
Societies must telephone in advance.
Green Fees on application.
Facilities ⊗ 🏶 ⓑ (food by arrangement) 🍺 ♀ ⌂ 🏠 ℸ
Location Fungarth (1m N of village on A923)
Hotel ★★★★67% Stakis Dunkeld House Resort
Hotel, DUNKELD ☎ (0350) 727771 92⇄

DUNNING

Map 11 NO01

Dunning ☎ (0764) 684312 & 684747
Parkland course.
9 holes, 4836yds, Par 66, SSS 64.
Club membership 580.
Visitors may not play on Sat before 4pm or Sun before
1pm. With member only after 5pm Mon-Fri.
Green Fees £7 per day.
Facilities 🍺 ⌂
Location Rollo Park (Off A9 NW)
Hotel ★★★59% Stakis Perth City Mills Hotel, West
Mill St, PERTH ☎ (0738) 28281 76⇄ ℝ

EDZELL

Map 15 NO66

Edzell ☎ (0356) 647283
This delightful course is situated in the foothills of the
Scottish Highlands and provides good golf as well as
conveying to everyone who plays there a feeling of peace
and quiet. The village of Edzell is one of the most
picturesque in Scotland.
18 holes, 6348yds, Par 71, SSS 70, Course record 65.
Club membership 910.

Visitors restricted at certain times. Must have a
handicap certificate.
Societies must contact in advance.
Green Fees £22.50 per day; £15 per round (£30 per day;
£20 per round weekends & bank holidays).
Facilities ⊗ 🏶 ⓑ 🍺 ♀ ⌂ 🏠 ℸ ℂ A J Webster.
Location S side of village on B966
Hotel ★★★60% Glenesk Hotel, High St, EDZELL
☎ (0356) 648319 25rm(23⇄ ℝ)

FORFAR

Map 15 NO45

Forfar ☎ (0307) 62120 & 63773
Moorland course with wooded, undulating fairways and fine
views.
18 holes, 5522mtrs, Par 69, SSS 69, Course record 64.
Club membership 850.
Visitors no restrictions.
Societies must contact in advance.
Green Fees £20 per day (£25 weekends & bank holidays).
Facilities ⊗ 🏶 ⓑ 🍺 ♀ ⌂ 🏠 ℂ Peter McNiven.
Location Cunninghill, Arbroath Rd (1m E on A932)
Hotel ★★★♣64% Idvies House Hotel, Letham,
FORFAR ☎ (030781) 787
due to change to (0307) 818787 10⇄ ℝ

GLENSHEE (SPITTAL OF)

Map 15 NO16

Dalmunzie ☎ Glenshee (0250) 885224
Well maintained Highland course with difficult walking.
Testing 5th hole. Small but good greens.
9 holes, 2035yds, Par 30, SSS 30.
Club membership 50.
Visitors restricted Sun 10.30-11.30am.
Societies must contact by telephone.
Green Fees £8 per day; £5 per round.
Facilities ⊗ 🏶 by prior arrangement 🍺 ♀ ℸ 🛏
Leisure hard tennis courts, fishing, stalking & shooting.
Location Dalmunzie Estate (2m NW of Spittal of
Glenshee)
Hotel ★★★♣65% Dalmunzie House Hotel, GLENSHEE
☎ (0250) 885224 18rm(16⇄ ℝ)

KENMORE

Map 14 NN74

Kenmore ☎ Aberfeldy (0887) 830226
Testing course in mildly undulating natural terrain. Beautiful
views in tranquil setting by Loch Tay..
9 holes, 6052yds, Par 70, SSS 69, Course record 71.
Club membership 150.
Visitors restricted Thur evenings and during club
competitions.
Societies apply in writing.
Green Fees £10 per 18 holes (£11 weekends).
Facilities ⊗ 🏶 ⓑ 🍺 ♀ ⌂ 🏠 ℸ 🛏
Location Taymouth Holiday Centre
Hotel ★★64% Fortingall Hotel, FORTINGALL
☎ (0887) 830367 & 830368 9rm(8⇄ ℝ)

Taymouth Castle ☎ (08873) 228
Parkland course set amidst beautiful mountain and loch
scenery. Easy walking. Fishing.
18 holes, 6066yds, Par 69, SSS 69, Course record 63.
Club membership 200.

Visitors	must contact in advance.
Societies	must telephone in advance.
Green Fees	not confirmed.
Facilities	Alex Marshall.
Leisure	fishing.
Location	1m E on A827
Hotel	★★64% Fortingall Hotel, FORTINGALL ☎ (0887) 830367 & 830368 9rm(8)

KINROSS Map 11 NO10

Green Hotel ☎ (0577) 863407
Two interesting and picturesque parkland courses, with easy walking.
Red Course: 18 holes, 6257yds, Par 72, SSS 70.
Blue Course: 18 holes, 6456yds, Par 71, SSS 71.
Club membership 450.

Visitors	must contact in advance.
Societies	must contact in advance.
Green Fees	not confirmed.
Facilities	Stuart Gerrachty.
Leisure	heated indoor swimming pool, squash, fishing, sauna, solarium, gymnasium.
Location	NE side of town on B996
Hotel	★★★67% Green Hotel, 2 The Muirs, KINROSS ☎ (0577) 63467 47

Kinross Beeches Park ☎ (0577) 862237
Parkland course on the banks of Loch Leven.
18 holes, 6124yds, Par 70, SSS 70.
Club membership 540.

Visitors	no restrictions.
Green Fees	not confirmed.
Facilities	
Location	NE side of town on B996
Hotel	★★★67% Green Hotel, 2 The Muirs, KINROSS ☎ (0577) 63467 47

KIRRIEMUIR Map 15 NO35

Kirriemuir ☎ (0575) 73317
Parkland and heathland course set at the foot of the Angus glens, with good view.
18 holes, 5553yds, Par 68, SSS 67, Course record 62.
Club membership 600.

Visitors	must play with member at weekends.
Societies	must telephone in advance.
Green Fees	£18 per day; £13.50 per round.
Facilities	A Caira.
Location	Northmuir (1m N off B955)
Hotel	★★★73% Castleton House Hotel, GLAMIS ☎ (030784) 340 6

MILNATHORT Map 11 NO10

Milnathort ☎ Kinross (0577) 864069
Undulating parkland course.
9 holes, 5969yds, Par 71, SSS 69, Course record 65.
Club membership 400.

Visitors	must contact in advance.
Societies	must contact in writing; deposit required.
Green Fees	£10 per day (£15 weekends).
Facilities	& by prior arrangement
Location	South St (S side of town on A922)
Hotel	★★★67% Green Hotel, 2 The Muirs, KINROSS ☎ (0577) 63467 47

MONIFIETH Map 12 NO43

Monifieth ☎ (0382) 532767
The chief of the two courses at Monifieth is the Medal Course. It has been one of the qualifying venues for the Open Championship on more than one occasion. A seaside links, but divided from the sand dunes by a railway which provides the principal hazard for the first few holes. The 10th hole is outstanding, the 17th is excellent and there is a delightful finishing hole. The other course here is the Ashludie, and both are played over by a number of clubs who share the links.
Medal Course: 18 holes, 6651yds, Par 71, SSS 72.
Ashludie Course: 18 holes, 5123yds, SSS 64.
Club membership 1500.

Visitors	must contact in advance. Restricted to after 2pm Sat & after 10am Sun.
Societies	must contact in advance.
Green Fees	Medal Course: £32 per day; £22 per round (£36/£24 weekends). Ashludie Course: £20 per day; £14 per round (£22/£15 weekends).
Facilities	Ian McLeod.
Location	The Links (NE side of town on A930)
Hotel	★★62% Carlogie House Hotel, Carlogie Rd, CARNOUSTIE ☎ (0241) 53185 11

THE IDEAL
GREEN
FOR GOLFERS
JUST A SHORT IRON FROM THE FRONT DOOR YOU WILL FIND THE FIRST TEES OF OUR OWN TWO SCENIC GOLF COURSES. BOTH OFFER AN ENJOYABLE AND STIMULATING CHALLENGE WHETHER YOU'RE A HOLIDAY GOLFER OR LOW HANDICAP PLAYER.
OUR 47 MODERN SPACIOUS BEDROOMS ARE ALL WELL APPOINTED AND INCLUDE SATELLITE TV. INDOOR LEISURE COMPLEX FEATURES INDOOR POOL, SAUNA, SOLARIUM, SQUASH COURT AND FITNESS AREA. OVER 50 OTHER GREAT COURSES WITHIN AN HOUR'S EASY DRIVE INCLUDING ST. ANDREWS, GLENEAGLES AND CARNOUSTIE.
★★★

THE GREEN
HOTEL
2 The Muirs, Kinross, Scotland, KY13 7AS.
Tel: (0577) 863467. Fax: (0577) 863180

MONTROSE

Map 15 NO75

Montrose Links Trust ☎ (0674) 72932
The links at Montrose like many others in Scotland are on commonland and are shared by three clubs. The Medal course at Montrose - the fifth oldest in the world - is typical of Scottish seaside links, with narrow, undulating fairways and problems from the first hole to the last. The Broomfield course is flatter and easier.
Medal Course: 18 holes, 6443yds, Par 71, SSS 71, Course record 64.
Broomfield Course: 18 holes, 4815yds, Par 66, SSS 63.
Club membership 1155.

Visitors	may not play on the Medal Course on Sat & before 10am on Sun. Must have a handicap certificate for medal Course.
Societies	must telephone at least 7 days in advance.
Green Fees	not confirmed.
Facilities	⊗ ⅢⓁⒷ ♥ ♀ △ 🏠 ⚲ (Kevin Stables.
Location	Traill Dr (NE side of town off A92)
Hotel	★★★61% Park Hotel, 61 John St, MONTROSE ☎ (0674) 73415 59rm(48⇄5 ⚲)

MUTHILL

Map 11 NN81

Muthill ☎ (076481) 523
Parkland course with fine views. Not too hilly, tight with narrow fairways.
9 holes, 4700yds, Par 66, SSS 63, Course record 61.
Club membership 400.

Visitors	restricted on match nights.
Green Fees	£8 per day (£12 weekends).
Facilities	♥ (summer only) △
Location	Peat Rd (W side of village off A822)
Hotel	★★68% Murray Park Hotel, Connaught Ter, CRIEFF ☎ (0764) 3731 13⇄

PERTH

Map 11 NO12

Craigie Hill ☎ (0738) 22644
Slightly hilly, parkland course. Good views over Perth.
18 holes, 5379yds, Par 66, SSS 66, Course record 60.
Club membership 610.

Visitors	must contact in advance but may not play on Sat.
Societies	must contact in writing.
Green Fees	£15 per day (£20 Sun).
Facilities	⊗ (ex Thu) Ⅲ (ex Mon & Thu) Ⓛ ♥ ♀ △ 🏠(
Location	Cherrybank (1m SW of city centre off A952)
Hotel	★★★59% Stakis Perth City Mills Hotel, West Mill St, PERTH ☎ (0738) 28281 76⇄ ⚲

King James VI ☎ (0738) 25170
Parkland course, situated on island in the middle of River Tay. Easy walking.
18 holes, 6026yds, Par 70, SSS 69, Course record 62.
Club membership 675.

Visitors	must contact in advance but may not play on Sat.
Societies	may not play on Sat. Must contact in writing.
Green Fees	£20 per day; £13 per round (£27/£15 weekends after 10am).
Facilities	⊗ Ⅲ Ⓛ ♥ ♀ △ 🏠(Tony Coles.
Location	Moncrieffe Island (SE side of city centre)
Hotel	★★★60% Queens Hotel, Leonard St, PERTH ☎ (0738) 25471 50rm(40⇄9 ⚲)

Murrayshall Country House Hotel
☎ New Scone (0738) 51171
This course is laid out in 130 acres of parkland with tree-lined fairways. Hotel and driving range.
18 holes, 6446yds, Par 73, SSS 71, Course record 68.
Club membership 300.

Visitors	must contact in advance.
Societies	must contact in advance.
Green Fees	not confirmed.
Facilities	⊗ Ⅲ Ⓛ ♥ ♀ △ 🏠 ⚲ ⋈ (Neil Macintosh.
Leisure	hard tennis courts, driving range, putting green, croquet.
Location	Murrayshall, Scone (E side of village off A94)
Hotel	★★★59% The Royal George, Tay St, PERTH ☎ (0738) 24455 42⇄ ⚲
Additional Hotel	★★★64% Newton House Hotel, Glencarse, PERTH ☎ (073886) 250 10⇄ ⚲

PITLOCHRY

Map 14 NN95

Pitlochry ☎ (0796) 2792
A varied and interesting heathland course with fine views and posing many problems. Its SSS permits few errors in its achievement.
18 holes, 5811yds, Par 69, SSS 68.
Club membership 400.

Visitors	may not play before 9.30am.
Societies	must contact in writing.
Green Fees	£14 per day (£17 weekends).

Facilities	⊗ ※ by prior arrangement
	⬚ ♥ ♀ ⚑ ⛴ ℉ George Hampton.
Location	Pitlochry Estate Office (N side of town off A924)
Hotel	★★★♨71% Pine Trees Hotel, Strathview Ter, PITLOCHRY
	☎ (0796) 472121 20rm(19➩ ℝ)

ST FILLANS

Map 11 NN62

St Fillans ☎ (076485) 312
Fairly flat, beautiful parkland course. Wonderfully rich in flora, animal and bird life.
9 holes, 5680yds, Par 69, SSS 68, Course record 66.
Club membership 400.

Visitors	may not play on Sat mornings.
Societies	may not play in Jul & Aug. Booking fee required.
Green Fees	not confirmed.
Facilities	⊗ ⬚ ♥ ♀ ⚑ ℉
Leisure	fishing.
Location	E side of village off A85
Hotel	★★★66% The Four Seasons Hotel, ST FILLANS
	☎ (076485) 333
	due to change to (0764) 685333 12➩ ℝ

SCOTTISH ISLANDS

ARRAN, ISLE OF

BLACKWATERFOOT

Map 10 NR82

Shiskine ☎ Shiskine (077086) 226
Unique 12-hole links course with gorgeous outlook to the Mull of Kintyre.
12 holes, 2990yds, Par 42, SSS 42.

Visitors	no restrictions.
Societies	must contact in writing.
Green Fees	not confirmed.
Facilities	⊗ ♥ ♀ ⚑
Leisure	hard tennis courts, all weather bowling green.
Location	Shore Rd (W side of village off A841)
Hotel	★★63% The Lagg Hotel, Kilmory, BRODICK
	☎ (077087) 255 15➩ ℝ

BRODICK

Map 10 NS03

Brodick ☎ (0770) 2349 due to change to 302349
Short seaside course, very flat.
18 holes, 4405yds, Par 62, SSS 62, Course record 61.
Club membership 552.

Visitors	must contact in advance but may not play on competition days.
Societies	must contact in advance.
Green Fees	£11 per day; £8 per round (£12/£9 weekends).
Facilities	⬚ ♀ ⚑ ⛴ ℉ Peter McCalla.
Location	N side of village
Hotel	★★★74% Auchrannie Country House Hotel, BRODICK ☎ (0770) 2234 & 2235 28➩ ℝ

CORRIE

Map 10 NS04

Corrie ☎ (0770) 810223
A heathland course on the coast with beautiful mountain scenery.
9 holes, 3896yds, Par 62, SSS 61, Course record 60.
Club membership 220.

Visitors	restricted Sat when medal games played.
Societies	must contact in advance.
Green Fees	£6 per day.
Facilities	⊗ ※ ⬚ ♥ ⚑ ℉
Location	Sannox (2m N on A841)
Hotel	★★★74% Auchrannie Country House Hotel, BRODICK ☎ (0770) 2234 & 2235 28➩ ℝ

LAMLASH

Map 10 NS03

Lamlash ☎ (0770) 600296
Undulating heathland course with magnificent views of the mountains and sea.
18 holes, 4611yds, Par 64, SSS 63, Course record 62.
Club membership 400.

Visitors	no restrictions.
Societies	must contact in writing.
Green Fees	£8 per day (£10 weekends).
Facilities	⊗ ※ ⬚ ♥ ♀ ⚑ ⛴ ℉
Location	0.75m N on A841
Hotel	★★67% Glenisle Hotel, LAMLASH ☎ (0770) 600559 & 600258 13➩ ℝ

LOCHRANZA

Map 10 NR95

Lochranza ☎ (077083) 273
Level parkland course by the sea. River crosses four holes. Nine large greens, 18 tees.
9 holes, 5569yds, Par 69, SSS 70, Course record 78.

Visitors	no restrictions; course closed Oct-mid May.
Societies	must telephone in advance.
Green Fees	not confirmed.
Facilities	⊗ ♥ ⚑
Hotel	★★63% The Lagg Hotel, Kilmory, BRODICK ☎ (077087) 255 15➩ ℝ

MACHRIE

Map 10 NR83

Machrie Bay ☎ Brodick (077084) 261
Fairly flat seaside course. Designed at turn of century by William Fernie.
9 holes, 2143yds, Par 32.
Club membership 225.

Visitors	no restrictions.
Societies	must contact in advance.
Green Fees	£5 per day/round.
Facilities	♥ (Apr-Sep)
Leisure	hard tennis courts.
Location	9m W of Brodick via String Rd
Hotel	★★63% The Lagg Hotel, Kilmory, BRODICK ☎ (077087) 255 15➩ ℝ

Use the AA *Hotels* or *Bed and Breakfast*
Guides to extend your choice of
accommodation

WHITING BAY   Map 10 NS02

Whiting Bay ☎ (07707) 487
Heathland course.
18 holes, 4405yds, Par 63, SSS 63.
Club membership 290.
Visitors   no restrictions.
Green Fees not confirmed.
Facilities   ♀
Location   NW side of village off A841
Hotel   ★★63% The Lagg Hotel, Kilmory, BRODICK
                 ☎ (077087) 255 15⇦ 🐾

BUTE, ISLE OF

KINGARTH   Map 10 NS05

Kingarth ☎ Kilchattan Bay (070083) 648
Flat seaside course with good fenced greens.
9 holes, 2497yds, Par 64, SSS 64, Course record 65.
Club membership 120.
Visitors   restricted Sat until after 12.30pm.
Societies   apply in advance.
Green Fees £5 per day.
Facilities   △
Location   Kingarth, Rothesay (1m W off A844)
Hotel   ★59% St Ebba Hotel, 37 Mountstuart Rd,
                 Craigmore, ROTHESAY
                 ☎ (0700) 502683 11⇦ 🐾

PORT BANNATYNE   Map 10 NS06

Port Bannatyne ☎ (0700) 2009
Seaside hill course with panoramic views. Difficult hole: 4th
(par 3).
13 holes, 4730yds, Par 68, SSS 63, Course record 61.
Club membership 200.
Visitors   no restrictions.
Societies   must telephone in advance.
Green Fees £7.50 per day.
Facilities   △
Location   Bannatyne Mains Rd (W side of village off
                 A844)
Hotel   ★59% St Ebba Hotel, 37 Mountstuart Rd,
                 Craigmore, ROTHESAY
                 ☎ (0700) 502683 11⇦ 🐾

ROTHESAY   Map 10 NS06

Rothesay ☎ (0700) 3554 & 2244
A scenic island course designed by James Braid and Ben
Sayers.
18 holes, 5043yds, Par 69, SSS 65.
Club membership 350.
Visitors   pre-booking essential for weekends, telephone
                 professional.
Societies   contact in advance, booking essential at
                 weekends.
Green Fees £11 daily (£17 weekends).

Facilities   ⊗ ⅲ ℟ ☕ (catering Apr-Sep only) ♀ △ 📦 ⋔
                 ☪ James Dougal.
Location   Canada Hill (off road to Kingarth)
Hotel   ★59% St Ebba Hotel, 37 Mountstuart Rd,
                 Craigmore, ROTHESAY
                 ☎ (0700) 502683 11⇦ 🐾

COLONSAY, ISLE OF

SCALASAIG   Map 10 NR39

Colonsay ☎ Colonsay (09512) 316
Traditional links course on natural machair (hard wearing
short grass), challenging, primitive. Colonsay Hotel, 2 miles
away, is the headquarters of the club, offering
accommodation and facilities.
18 holes, 4775yds, Par 72, SSS 72.
Club membership 120.
Visitors   no restrictions.
Societies   apply in writing.
Green Fees not confirmed.
Facilities   ⋔
Location   2m W on A870
Hotel   ★74% Colonsay Hotel, SCALASAIG
                 ☎ (09512) 316 10rm(1⇦7 🐾) Annexe1rm

ISLAY, ISLE OF

PORT ELLEN   Map 10 NR34

Machrie Hotel ☎ (0496) 2310
Championship links course opened in 1891, where golf's first
£100 Open Championship was played in 1901. Fine turf and
many blind holes. Par 4.
18 holes, 6226yds, Par 71, SSS 70, Course record 66.
Visitors   must be member of a recognised golf club and
                 have a handicap certificate.
Societies   must contact in advance.
Green Fees not confirmed.
Facilities   ⊗ ⅲ ℟ ☕ ♀ 📦 ⋔ ⋈
Leisure   fishing, riding, snooker, clay pigeon shooting.
Location   Machrie (4m N off A846)
Hotel   ★★58% Lochside Hotel, 19 Shore St,
                 BOWMORE ☎ (049681) 244 7rm(4⇦ 🐾)

LEWIS, ISLE OF

STORNOWAY   Map 13 NB43

Stornoway ☎ (0851) 702240
Picturesque, tree-lined parkland course, fine views. The 11th
hole, 'Dardanelles' - most difficult par 5.
18 holes, 5178yds, Par 68, SSS 66.
Club membership 200.
Visitors   may not play on Sun.
Societies   must contact the secretary in writing.
Green Fees £10 per day.

Facilities
Location Lady Lever Park (N side of town centre off
A857)
Hotel ★★★66% Caberfeidh Hotel, STORNOWAY
☎ (0851) 702604 46➪ ♦

MULL, ISLE OF

CRAIGNURE — Map 10 NM73

Craignure ☎ (06802) 370
A flat links course, overlooking the sea.
9 holes, 2218mtrs, Par 64, SSS 64.
Club membership 70.
Visitors may not play on competition days.
Societies must contact in advance.
Green Fees £6 per day.
Facilities ♨
Location Scallastle (1m N on A849)
Hotel ★★★65% Western Isles Hotel, TOBERMORY
☎ (0688) 2012 27➪ ♦

TOBERMORY — Map 13 NM55

Tobermory ☎ (0688) 2020
Hilly seaside cliff-top course. No sand-bunkers, hard
walking, superb views over the Sound of Mull. Testing 3rd
hole (par 3).
9 holes, 4474yds, Par 64, SSS 64, Course record 67.
Club membership 100.
Visitors no restrictions.
Societies must contact in advance.
Green Fees £9 per day/round; £30 per week.
Facilities ♨ ♦
Location 0.5m N off A848
Hotel ★56% Mishnish Hotel, Main St, TOBERMORY
☎ (0688) 2009 12rm(7➪2 ♦)

ORKNEY

KIRKWALL — Map 16 HY41

Orkney ☎ (0856) 872457
Open parkland course with few hazards and superb views
over Kirkwall and Islands.
18 holes, 5406yds, Par 70, SSS 68, Course record 65.
Club membership 380.
Visitors may not play on competition days.
Societies advance contact preferred.
Green Fees £10 per day; £35 per week; £50 per fortnight.
Facilities ♨ & ♨ (lunchtime) ♀ ♨ ♦
Location Grainbank (0.5m W off A965)
Hotel ★★61% Ayre Hotel, Ayre Rd, KIRKWALL
☎ (0856) 873001 34rm(30➪ ♦)

> We make every effort to ensure that our
> information is accurate but details may
> change after we go to print

STROMNESS — Map 16 HY20

Stromness ☎ (0856) 850772
Testing parkland/seaside course with easy walking. Beautiful
holiday course with magnificent views of Scapa Flow.
18 holes, 4762yds, Par 65, SSS 64, Course record 61.
Club membership 250.
Visitors no restrictions.
Societies must contact in advance.
Green Fees £8 per day.
Facilities ♀ (evenings only) ♨ ♦
Leisure hard tennis courts, bowls & putting.
Location S side of town centre off A965
Hotel ★★61% Ayre Hotel, Ayre Rd, KIRKWALL
☎ (0856) 873001 34rm(30➪ ♦)

WESTRAY — Map 16 HY44

Westray ☎ (08577) 373
Interesting, picturesque seaside course, easy walking.
9 holes, 2405yds, Par 33.
Visitors may not play on Sun.
Green Fees not confirmed.
Facilities ♦
Location 1m NW of Pierowall off B9066
Hotel ★★61% Ayre Hotel, Ayre Rd, KIRKWALL
☎ (0856) 873001 34rm(30➪ ♦)

SHETLAND

LERWICK — Map 16 HU44

Dale ☎ Gott (059584) 369
Challenging moorland course, hard walking. A burn runs the
full length of the course and provides a natural hazard.
Testing holes include the 3rd (par 4), 5th (par 4).
18 holes, 5776yds, Par 68, SSS 70.
Club membership 370.
Visitors restricted on competition days.
Societies must contact in advance.
Green Fees £8 per day.
Facilities ♀ ♨
Location PO Box 18 (4m N on A970)
Hotel ★★★58% Lerwick Hotel, South Rd, LERWICK
☎ (0595) 2166 31➪ ♦

WHALSAY, ISLAND OF — Map 16 HU56

Whalsay ☎ Symbister (08066) 452
The most northerly golf course in Britain, with a large part of
it running round the coastline, offering spectacular holes in an
exposed but highly scenic setting. There are no cut fairways
as yet, these are defined by marker posts, with preferred lies
in operation all year round.
18 holes, 6009yds, Par 70, SSS 70, Course record 69.
Club membership 100.
Visitors are advised to telephone, and on arrival on
Whalsay call at the shop by the harbour.
Societies welcome.
Green Fees £5 per day. ▶

Facilities ⛳
Location Skaw Taing
Hotel ★★★♨67% Busta House Hotel, BRAE
☎ (080622) 506 20🛏 ☔

SKYE, ISLE OF

SCONSER
Map 13 NG53

Isle of Skye ☎ (0478) 3235
Seaside course, often windy, splendid views.
9 holes, 4796yds, Par 66, SSS 63, Course record 62.
Club membership 210.
Visitors welcome except Wed 5-6.30pm & Sat 9.30-10.30am.
Societies welcome.
Green Fees £7 per day.
Facilities ⛳
Location 0.5m E of village on A850
Hotel ★★55% Broadford Hotel, BROADFORD
☎ (0471) 822204 & 822205 20🛏 ☔
Annexe9🛏 ☔

SOUTH UIST, ISLE OF

ASKERNISH
Map 13 NF72

Askernish ☎ No telephone
Golfers play on machair (hard-wearing short grass), close to the Atlantic shore.
9 holes, 5312yds, Par 68, SSS 67.
Club membership 20.
Visitors no restrictions.
Societies welcome.
Green Fees £5 per day; £3.50 per round.
Facilities 🎯
Location Lochboisdale (5m NW of Lochboisdale off A865 via ferry)
Hotel ★★62% Isle of Barra Hotel, Tangusdale Beach, TANGUSDALE ☎ (08714) 383 30🛏

NORTHERN IRELAND

CO ANTRIM

ANTRIM
Map 01 D5

Massereene ☎ (08494) 28096
The first nine holes are parkland, while the second, adjacent to the shore of Lough Neagh, have more of a links character with sandy ground.
18 holes, 6614yds, Par 72, SSS 71.
Club membership 800.

Visitors welcome except for Sat which is competition day.
Societies apply in writing.
Green Fees £16 per day (£20 weekends).
Facilities ⊗ 🍴 🍺 ♥ ♀ ⚒ 🏌 ☔ 🎯 Jim Smyth.
Leisure snooker, indoor bowling in winter.
Location 51 Lough Rd (1m SW of town)
Hotel ★★★62% Adair Arms Hotel, Ballymoney Rd, BALLYMENA
☎ (0266) 653674 39🛏 ☔

BALLYCASTLE
Map 01 D6

Ballycastle ☎ (02657) 62536
An unusual mixture of terrain beside the sea, with magnificent views from all parts. The first five holes are inland type; the middle holes on the Warren are links type and the rest, on high ground, are heath type.
18 holes, 5177mtrs, Par 71, SSS 68.
Club membership 865.
Visitors are welcome during the week.
Societies apply in writing.
Green Fees £12 per day (£17 per round weekends).
Facilities ⊗ & 🍴 by prior arrangement 🍺 ♥ ♀ ⚒ 🎯 Trevor Stewart.
Leisure snooker.
Location Cushendall Rd
Hotel ★★56% Thornlea Hotel, 6 Coast Rd, CUSHENDALL
☎ (02667) 71223 13rm(1🛏11 ☔)

BALLYCLARE
Map 01 D5

Ballyclare ☎ (09603) 22696
Parkland course with lots of trees and shrubs and water hazards provided by the river, streams and lakes.
18 holes, 5745mtrs, Par 71, SSS 72.
Club membership 980.
Visitors may not play on Thu or weekends before 3pm.
Societies must contact in writing.
Green Fees £12 per round (£18 weekends & bank holidays).
Facilities ⊗ 🍺 ♥ ♀ ⚒
Leisure snooker.
Location 25 Springdale Rd (1.5m N)
Hotel ★★★69% Stormont Hotel, 587 Upper Newtonards Rd, BELFAST
☎ (0232) 658621 106🛏 ☔

BALLYGALLY
Map 01 D5

Cairndhu ☎ Larne (0574) 583248
Built on a hilly headland, this course is both testing and scenic, with wonderful coastal views.
18 holes, 5598mtrs, Par 70, SSS 69.
Club membership 875.
Visitors may not play on Sat.
Societies must contact in writing.
Green Fees not confirmed.
Facilities ⊗ 🍴 🍺 ♥ ♀ ⚒ 🏌 🎯 Robert Walker.
Leisure snooker.
Location 192 Coast Rd (4m N of Larne on coast road)
Hotel ★★★55% Ballygally Castle Hotel, 274 Coast Rd, BALLYGALLY
☎ (0574) 583212 30🛏

BALLYMENA   Map 01 D5

Ballymena ☎ (0266) 861487
Parkland course of level heathland with plenty of bunkers.
18 holes, 5654yds, Par 68, SSS 67.
Visitors   may not play on Tue or Sat.
Societies   must contact in advance.
Green Fees not confirmed.
Facilities   ⊗ ⅏ ⅃ ♀ ⚐ ⛴ James Gallagher.
Leisure   snooker, bowling green.
Location   128 Raceview Rd (2m E on A42)
Hotel   ★★★62% Adair Arms Hotel, Ballymoney Rd,
         BALLYMENA
         ☎ (0266) 653674   39⇌ ☞

CARRICKFERGUS   Map 01 D5

Carrickfergus ☎ (09603) 63713 & 51803
Parkland course, fairly level but nevetheless demanding, with
a notorious water hazard at the 1st. Well maintained and with
nice views.
18 holes, 5759yds, Par 68, SSS 68, Course record 63.
Club membership 815.
Visitors   no restrictions.
Societies   must contact in advance.
Green Fees £13 (£18 weekends & bank holidays).
Facilities   ⊗ ⅏ ⅃ ♀ ⚐ ⛴ T Raymond
         Stevenson.
Leisure   snooker.
Location   25 North Rd (9m NE of Belfast on A2)
Hotel   ★★★54% Chimney Corner Hotel, 630 Antrim
         Rd, NEWTOWNABBEY
         ☎ (0232) 844925 & 844851   63⇌ ☞

CUSHENDALL   Map 01 D6

Cushendall ☎ (02667) 71318
Scenic course with spectacular views over the Sea of Moyle
and Red Bay to the Mull of Kintyre. The River Dall winds
through the course, coming into play in seven of the nine
holes.
9 holes, 4386mtrs, Par 66, SSS 63.
Club membership 714.
Visitors   restricted on Sun.
Societies   must contact in writing.
Green Fees £9 per day (£11 weekends & bank holidays).
Facilities   ⊗ ⅏ & ⅃ by prior arrangement ♥ ♀ ⚐
Location   21 Shore Rd
Hotel   ★★56% Thornlea Hotel, 6 Coast Rd,
         CUSHENDALL
         ☎ (02667) 71223   13rm(1⇌11 ☞)

LARNE   Map 01 D5

Larne ☎ Islandmagee (09603) 82228
An exposed part links, part heathland course offering a good
test, particularly on the last three holes along the sea shore.
9 holes, 6066yds, Par 70, SSS 69, Course record 66.
Club membership 450.
Visitors   may not play on Sat before 5.30pm.
Societies   apply in writing.
Green Fees £8 (£15 Sun & public holidays).
Facilities   ⊗ ⅏ by prior arrangement
         ⅃ ♥ (meals Apr-Sep only) ♀ ⚐

Leisure   snooker, indoor bowling.
Location   54 Ferris Bay Rd, Islandmagee
Hotel   ★★★55% Ballygally Castle Hotel, 274 Coast
         Rd, BALLYGALLY ☎ (0574) 583212   30⇌

LISBURN   Map 01 D5

Lisburn ☎ (0846) 677216
Meadowland course, fairly level, with plenty of trees and
shrubs. Challenging last three holes.
18 holes, 6572yds, Par 72, SSS 72, Course record 64.
Club membership 1000.
Visitors   must play with member at weekends.
Societies   must contact in writing.
Green Fees not confirmed.
Facilities   ⊗ ⅏ ♥ ♀ ⚐ ⛴ ⛴ B R Campbell.
Leisure   snooker.
Location   Blaris Lodge, 68 Eglantine Rd (2m from town
         on A1)
Hotel   ★★★69% Stormont Hotel, 587 Upper
         Newtonards Rd, BELFAST
         ☎ (0232) 658621   106⇌ ☞

PORTRUSH   Map 01 C6

ROYAL PORTRUSH See page 293

WHITEHEAD   Map 01 D5

Whitehead ☎ (09603) 53631
Undulating parkland course with magnificent sea views.
18 holes, 6426yds, Par 72, SSS 71.
Visitors   may not play on Sat. Must play with member on
         Sun.
Societies   must contact in advance.
Green Fees not confirmed.
Facilities   ⊗ ⅏ ♀
Leisure   snooker.
Location   McCrae's Brae (0.5m N)
Hotel   ★★★54% Chimney Corner Hotel, 630 Antrim
         Rd, NEWTOWNABBEY
         ☎ (0232) 844925 & 844851   63⇌ ☞

CO ARMAGH

ARMAGH   Map 01 C5

County Armagh ☎ (0861) 522501
Mature parkland course with excellent views of Armagh city
and its surroundings.
18 holes, 5641mtrs, Par 70, SSS 69, Course record 65.
Club membership 1000.
Visitors   may not play noon-3pm on Sat or noon-2pm on
         Sun. Must contact in advance.
Societies   must contact in writing.
Green Fees not confirmed.   ▶

We make every effort to ensure that our
information is accurate but details may
change after we go to print

Facilities	⊗ ⊪ ⅄ & ⬛ (all ex Mon) ⚲ ⚘ 🏠 (Alan Rankin.
Leisure	snooker.
Location	The Demesne (On the Newry road)
Hotel	★★★69% Stormont Hotel, 587 Upper Newtonards Rd, BELFAST ☎ (0232) 658621 106⇥ ℞

LURGAN   Map 01 D5

Craigavon Golf & Ski Centre ☎ (0762) 326606
Parkland course with a lake and stream providing water hazards.
18 holes, 6496yds, Par 72, SSS 72.

Visitors	no restrictions.
Societies	must contact in advance.
Green Fees	£8 per day (£11 weekends).
Facilities	⊗ ⊪ ⬛ ⅄ ⚘ (Des Paul.
Leisure	putting green, floodlit driving range.
Location	Turmoyra Ln (2m N at Silverwood off the M1)
Hotel	★★★69% Stormont Hotel, 587 Upper Newtonards Rd, BELFAST ☎ (0232) 658621 106⇥ ℞

Lurgan ☎ (0762) 322087
Testing parkland course bordering Lurgan Park Lake with a need for accurate shots.
18 holes, 5836mtrs, Par 70, SSS 70, Course record 65.
Club membership 800.

Visitors	may not play Wed & Sat.
Societies	must contact in writing.
Green Fees	£15 (£20 weekends & bank holidays).
Facilities	⊗ ⊪ ⅄ ⚲ ⚘ 🏠 (Des Paul.
Leisure	snooker, putting green, practice area.
Location	The Demesne (0.5m from town centre near Lurgan Park)
Hotel	★★★69% Stormont Hotel, 587 Upper Newtonards Rd, BELFAST ☎ (0232) 658621 106⇥ ℞

PORTADOWN   Map 01 D5

Portadown ☎ (0762) 355356
Well wooded parkland course on the banks of the River Bann, which features among the water hazards.
18 holes, 5621mtrs, Par 70, SSS 70, Course record 65.
Club membership 1014.

Visitors	may not play on Tue & Sat.
Societies	must contact in advance.
Green Fees	£15 per round (£18 weekends & bank holidays).
Facilities	⊗ ⊪ ⅄ ⚲ ⚘ 🏠 (Paul Stevenson.
Leisure	squash, snooker, indoor bowling.
Location	192 Gilfrod Rd (SE via A59)
Hotel	★★★69% Stormont Hotel, 587 Upper Newtonards Rd, BELFAST ☎ (0232) 658621 106⇥ ℞

TANDRAGEE   Map 01 D5

Tandragee ☎ (0762) 841272
Pleasant hilly parkland with mature trees.
18 holes, 5519mtrs, Par 69, SSS 67.
Club membership 1085.

Visitors	may not play Thu & Fri afternoon or on Sat & Sun before 2pm unless by prior arrangement.
Societies	Mar-Sep; must contact in writing.
Green Fees	£10 per day/round (£15 Sun & public holidays).
Facilities	⊗ ⊪ ⅄ ⬛ (no catering Mon, Oct-Mar) ⚲ ⚘ 🏠 ⚘ (John Black.
Leisure	snooker, sauna, gymnasium.
Location	Markethill Rd
Hotel	★★★✦67% Ballynahinch Castle, BALLYNAHINCH ☎ (095) 31006 & 31086 28⇥ ℞

BELFAST

BELFAST   Map 01 D5

Balmoral ☎ (0232) 381514
Parkland course, mainly level, with tree-lined fairways and a stream providing a water hazard.
18 holes, 6238yds, Par 69, SSS 70.

Visitors	preferred Mon & Thu.
Societies	must contact in advance.
Green Fees	not confirmed.
Facilities	⊗ ⊪ ⚲ ⚘ (Geoff Bleakley.
Location	518 Lisburn Rd (3m SW)
Hotel	★★★69% Stormont Hotel, 587 Upper Newtonards Rd, BELFAST ☎ (0232) 658621 106⇥ ℞

Cliftonville ☎ (0232) 744158
Parkland course with rivers bisecting two fairways.
9 holes, 5706mtrs, Par 70, SSS 70, Course record 66.
Club membership 430.

Visitors	may not play on Sat or on Sun mornings.
Societies	must contact in writing.
Green Fees	£12 (£15 Sun & bank holidays).
Facilities	⊪ by prior arrangement ⚲ ⚘ 🏠
Leisure	snooker.
Location	44 Westland Rd (Between Cavehill Rd & Cliftonville Circus)
Hotel	★★★69% Stormont Hotel, 587 Upper Newtonards Rd, BELFAST ☎ (0232) 658621 106⇥ ℞

Dunmurry ☎ (0232) 610834
Maturing very nicely, this tricky parkland course has several memorable holes which call for skilful shots.
18 holes, 5348mtrs, Par 69, SSS 68, Course record 68.
Club membership 840.

Visitors	may not play Tue, Thu & Sat after 5pm. Play restricted Fri & to after 12.30pm Sun.
Societies	must contact in writing.
Green Fees	£13 (£17 weekends).
Facilities	⊗ ⊪ ⅄ ⬛ (no catering Mon) ⚲ ⚘ 🏠 ⚘ (Paul Leonard.
Leisure	snooker.
Location	91 Dunmurry Ln
Hotel	★★★69% Stormont Hotel, 587 Upper Newtonards Rd, BELFAST ☎ (0232) 658621 106⇥ ℞

Royal Portrush

Portrush ☎(0265) 822311   **Map 01 D4**

John Ingham writes: It was more than thirty years ago that I first saw Royal Portrush, but the memory lingers on. That week in 1960, the great Joe Carr won the British Amateur Championship for his third, and last, time. But everyone there was a winner; the sun shone, and the course glistened as the foaming ocean was almost blown inland on to the briar roses that dotted the rough.

What a splendid seaside paradise this is, I wrote in a London evening newspaper, whose readers were keen to follow players such as Joe Carr and Michael Bonallack. There among the gallery was the late Fred Daly, winner of the 1947 Open and the only Irisman ever to win.

The man who designed this course was Harry S Colt, a name that appears as a creator of many fine courses. This one is considered among the six best in the United Kingdom. It is spectacular, breathtaking, but one of the tightest driving tests known to man because, if you get in the long stuff, you may stay there. On a clear day, you have a fine view of Islay and the Paps of Jura - seen from the 3rd tee. Then there's the Giant's Causeway, from the 5th, as good a downhill dogleg hole as you'll find anywhere.

While the greens have to be 'read' from the start, there are fairways up and down valleys, and holes called Calamity Corner and Purgatory for good reason. The second hole, called Giant's Grave, is 509 yards but there's an even longer one waiting for you at the 17th, while the last hole, a 479-yarder, nearly cost Max Faulkner his 1951 Open title. He hit a crooked drive, and had to bend his second shot with a wooden club. Dressed in primrose-coloured slacks, his colourful plumage and out-going attitude attracted most of the small crowd.

The Open did not return to Portrush and championship golf is the loser because the place is a gem. Founded in 1888, it was also the venue of the first professional golf event held in Ireland, when in 1895, Sandy Herd beat Harry Vardon in the final.

You'll love it.

Membership 1300

Visitors must contact in advance, and have a letter of introduction from their own club. Restricted Saturday and Sunday morning

Societies must apply in writing.

Green fees Dunluce Links £35 per day (£40 weekends); Valley Links £15 per day (£20 weekends); Skerries Course: £2

Facilities ⊗ 〽 🍴 🍺 ♀ (all day) ⛳ 🏪 ⛳ ((Dai Stevenson)

Leisure snooker

Location Bushmills Rd (0.5m from Portrush on main road to Bushmills)

45 holes. **Dunluce Links: 18 holes, 6794 yds, Par 72, SSS 73, course record 66**
Valley Links: 18 holes, 6273 yds, Par 70, SSS 70, course record 65
Skerries Course: 9 holes, 1187 yds

WHERE TO STAY AND EAT NEARBY

HOTELS:

PORTBALLINTRAE

★★ 60% Beach House, The Sea Front. ☎ (02657) 31214. 32 ⇆ 🐾 French cuisine

RESTAURANT:

PORTRUSH

✗ ✗ ✿✿ Ramore, The Harbour. ☎(0265) 824313. French cuisine

Fortwilliam ☎ (0232) 370770
Parkland course in most attractive surroundings. The course is bisected by a lane.
18 holes, 5771yds, Par 69, SSS 68.

Visitors	preferred weekday mornings.
Societies	preferred Thu. Must contact in advance.
Green Fees	not confirmed.
Facilities	⊗ ⅏ ♀ ℓ Peter Hanna.
Leisure	snooker, practice fairway.
Location	Downview Ave (Off Antrim road)
Hotel	★★★69% Stormont Hotel, 587 Upper Newtonards Rd, BELFAST ☎ (0232) 658621 106⇥ ▐

Knockbracken Golf, Ski & Leisure ☎ (0232) 401811
Inland parkland course which has recently been refurbished.
18 holes, 5391yds, Par 67, SSS 68.
Club membership 400.

Visitors	must contact in advance at weekends & bank holidays.
Societies	must contact in writing.
Green Fees	£9 (£11 weekends).
Facilities	⊗ ⅏ ⅃ ▼ ♀ ⚏ 🏠 ℱ ℓ D Jones/E Logue/ G Loughrey.
Leisure	snooker, driving ranges, bowls, ski slope.
Location	24 Ballymaconaghy Rd
Hotel	★★★69% Stormont Hotel, 587 Upper Newtonards Rd, BELFAST ☎ (0232) 658621 106⇥ ▐

Malone ☎ (0232) 612758
Two parkland courses, extremely attractive with a large lake, mature trees and flowering shrubs and bordered by the River Lagan. Very well maintained and offering a challenging round.
Course 1: 18 holes, 6433yds, Par 71, SSS 71.
Course 2: 9 holes, 5784yds, SSS 68.
Club membership 1300.

Visitors	may not play on 18 hole course on Tue, Wed & Sat.
Societies	apply in writing to council.
Green Fees	not confirmed.
Facilities	⊗ ⅏ ⅃ ▼ ♀ 🏠 ℓ
Location	240 Upper Malone Rd, Dunmurry (4.5m S)
Hotel	★★★69% Stormont Hotel, 587 Upper Newtonards Rd, BELFAST ☎ (0232) 658621 106⇥ ▐

Shandon Park ☎ (0232) 701799
Fairly level parkland offering a pleasant challenge.
18 holes, 6261yds, Par 70, SSS 70.
Club membership 1100.

Visitors	may not play on competition days. Must contact in advance and have a handicap certificate.
Societies	may play weekdays only.
Green Fees	not confirmed.
Facilities	⊗ ⅏ ⅃ ▼ ♀ ⚏ 🏠 ℱ ℓ Barry Wilson.
Leisure	snooker.
Location	73 Shandon Park (Off Knock road)
Hotel	★★★69% Stormont Hotel, 587 Upper Newtonards Rd, BELFAST ☎ (0232) 658621 106⇥ ▐

DUNDONALD   Map 01 D5

Knock ☎ Belfast (0232) 483251
Parkland course with huge trees, deep bunkers and a river cutting across several fairways. This is a hard but fair course and will test the best of golfers.
18 holes, 6407yds, Par 70, SSS 71.
Club membership 850.

Visitors	may not play on Sat.
Societies	must contact in advance.
Green Fees	£15 per day (£22 weekends & bank holidays).
Facilities	⊗ ⅏ ⅃ ▼ ♀ ⚏ 🏠 ℱ ℓ Gordon Fairweather.
Leisure	snooker.
Location	Summerfield
Hotel	★★★★70% Culloden Hotel, HOLYWOOD ☎ (0232) 425223 91⇥ ▐

NEWTOWNBREDA   Map 01 D5

The Belvoir Park ☎ Belfast (0232) 491693
This undulating parkland course is not strenuous to walk, but is certainly a test of your golf, with tree-lined fairways and a particularly challenging finish at the final four holes.
18 holes, 6501yds, Par 71, SSS 71, Course record 66.
Club membership 1076.

Visitors	may not play between 1 & 2pm or on Sat.
Societies	must contact in writing.
Green Fees	£25 per day (£30 Wed & Sun).
Facilities	⊗ ⅏ ⅃ ▼ ♀ ⚏ 🏠 ℱ ℓ Maurice Kelly.
Leisure	snooker.
Location	73 Church Rd (3m from centre off Saintfield/Newcastle rd)
Hotel	★★★69% Stormont Hotel, 587 Upper Newtonards Rd, BELFAST ☎ (0232) 658621 106⇥ ▐

CO DOWN

ARDGLASS   Map 01 D5

Ardglass ☎ (0396) 841219
A scenic cliff-top seaside course with spectacular views and some memorable holes.
18 holes, 5515mtrs, Par 70, SSS 69.
Club membership 762.

Visitors	must contact in advance at weekends.
Societies	must contact in advance.
Green Fees	£13 per round (£18 weekends & bank holidays).
Facilities	⊗ & ⅏ by prior arrangement ⅃ ▼ ♀ ⚏ 🏠 ℓ Kevin Dorrian.
Leisure	snooker.
Location	Castle Pl
Hotel	★★★60% Slieve Donard Hotel, NEWCASTLE ☎ (03967) 23681 120⇥

> Entries with a shaded background identify courses that are considered to be particularly interesting

ARDMILLAN
Map 01 D5

Mahee Island ☎ Killinchy (0238) 541234
An undulating parkland course, almost surrounded by water, with magnificent views of Strangford Lough and its islands, with Scrabo Tower in the background.
9 holes, 5588yds, Par 68, SSS 67, Course record 65.
Club membership 490.
Visitors may not play on Wed after 4pm or Sat before 5pm.
Societies restricted Wed evenings, Sat & some Sun ; must contact in advance.
Green Fees £10 per round (£14 weekends & public holidays).
Facilities ⊗ Ⅲ☕⅃ (catering by arrangement) ⌂ 🖻
Leisure pool table.
Location Comber (On Comber/Killyleagh road 0.5m from Comber)
Hotel ★★★69% Stormont Hotel, 587 Upper Newtonards Rd, BELFAST ☎ (0232) 658621 106⇥

BALLYNAHINCH
Map 01 D5

Spa ☎ (0238) 562365
Parkland course with tree-lined fairways and scenic views of the Mourne Mountains.
18 holes, 5938mtrs, Par 72, SSS 72.
Club membership 890.
Visitors must contact in advance but may not play on Sat; must play with member on Sun.
Societies must contact in advance.
Green Fees not confirmed.
Facilities ⅃⅄♀⌂
Leisure snooker.
Location 20 Grove Rd
Hotel ★★★⚑67% Ballynahinch Castle, BALLYNAHINCH ☎ (095) 31006 & 31086 28⇥

BANBRIDGE
Map 01 D5

Banbridge ☎ (08206) 62211
A picturesque course with excellent views of the Movene mountains. The holes are not long, but are tricky, and six new holes opened in 1992 completed the 18.
18 holes, 5003mtrs, Par 69, SSS 67, Course record 66.
Club membership 700.
Visitors may not play Tue, Sat or before 11am on Sun.
Societies must contact in writing.
Green Fees £7 (£12 weekends).
Facilities ⊗ Ⅲ⅃⅄ by prior arrangement ♀⌂
Location 116 Huntly Rd (0.5m along Huntly road)
Hotel ★★★60% Slieve Donard Hotel, NEWCASTLE ☎ (03967) 23681 120⇥

BANGOR
Map 01 D5

Bangor ☎ (0247) 270922
Undulating parkland course in the town. It is well maintained and pleasant and offers a challenging round, particularly at the 5th.
18 holes, 6490yds, Par 71, SSS 70.
Club membership 1150.
Visitors preferred on Mon & Wed.

Societies Mon & Wed. Must contact in advance.
Green Fees £17 (£21 Sun & bank holidays).
Facilities ⊗ Ⅲ⅃⅄♀⌂🖻ℓ N V Drew.
Location Broadway (1m from town on Donaghadee road)
Hotel ★★★63% Old Inn, 15 Main St, CRAWFORDSBURN ☎ (0247) 853255 32⇥ ℟

Carnalea ☎ (0247) 465004
A scenic course on the shores of Belfast Lough.
18 holes, 5574yds, Par 68, SSS 67, Course record 63.
Club membership 1100.
Visitors no restrictions.
Societies must contact in writing.
Green Fees £10 per round (£13 weekends & bank holidays).
Facilities ⊗ Ⅲ⅃⅄♀⌂🖣ℓ Michael McGee.
Leisure snooker.
Location Station Rd
Hotel ★★★63% Old Inn, 15 Main St, CRAWFORDSBURN ☎ (0247) 853255 32⇥ ℟

Clandeboyle ☎ (0247) 271767
Parkland/heathland courses. The Dufferin is the championship course and offers a tough challenge. Nevertheless, the Ava has much to recommend it, with a notable 2nd hole.
Dufferin Course: 18 holes, 6469yds, Par 71, SSS 71.
Ava Course: 18 holes, 5656yds, Par 70, SSS 68.
Club membership 1200.
Visitors must play with member at weekends.
Societies Mon-Wed & Fri, Apr-Sep; Mon & Wed, Oct-Mar. Must contact in advance.
Green Fees Dufferin: £17.50 per round (£23 weekends); Ava: £14 per round (£17.50 weekends).
Facilities ⊗ Ⅲ⅃⅄♀⌂🖻🖣ℓ Peter Gregory.
Location Tower Rd, Conlig, Newtownards (2m S on A21)
Hotel ★★★63% Old Inn, 15 Main St, CRAWFORDSBURN ☎ (0247) 853255 32⇥ ℟

CLOUGHEY
Map 01 D5

Kirkistown Castle ☎ Portavogie (02477) 71233
Popular with visiting golfers because of its quiet location, the course is exceptionally dry and remains open when others in the area have to close.
18 holes, 6167yds, Par 69, SSS 70.
Club membership 886.
Visitors must contact in advance, restricted Fri & weekends.
Societies must contact in advance.
Green Fees £12 per day (£20 weekends).
Facilities ⊗ Ⅲ⅃⅄♀⌂🖻ℓ Jonathon Peden.
Leisure snooker.
Location 142 Main Rd, Cloughey
Hotel ★★★63% Old Inn, 15 Main St, CRAWFORDSBURN ☎ (0247) 853255 32⇥ ℟

DONAGHADEE
Map 01 D5

Donaghadee ☎ (0247) 883624
Undulating seaside course requiring a certain amount of concentration. Splendid views.
18 holes, 6098yds, Par 71, SSS 69, Course record 65.
Club membership 900.
Visitors may not play Sat.
Societies apply in advance.
Green Fees £20 per day; £13.50 per round (£26/£17 Sun). ▶

Facilities ⊗ ⍔ ᥩ 🝙 ♀ ♨ 🏠 ⛳ ☏ Gordon Drew.
Leisure snooker.
Location Warren Rd
Hotel ★★★63% Old Inn, 15 Main St,
CRAWFORDSBURN ☎ (0247) 853255 32⇄ 🐾

DOWNPATRICK   Map 01 D5

Bright Castle ☎ (0396) 841319
Parkland course in elevated position with views of the
Mountains of Mourne. A good challenge for the energetic
golfer.
18 holes, 7300yds, Par 74, SSS 74.
Visitors no restrictions.
Societies must contact in advance.
Green Fees not confirmed.
Facilities ᥩ
Location 14 Coniamstown Rd, Bright (5m S)
Hotel ★★★60% Slieve Donard Hotel, NEWCASTLE
☎ (03967) 23681 120⇄

Downpatrick ☎ (0396) 612152 & 615947
This undulating parkland course has recently been extended,
with Hawtree & Son as architects. It provides a good
challenge.
18 holes, 6400yds, Par 70, SSS 69.
Club membership 800.
Visitors must contact in advance for groups of 20 or
more. May not play 7.30-10.30am at weekends
& bank holidays.
Societies must telephone in advance.
Green Fees £13 per day (£18 weekends & bank holidays).
Facilities ⊗ ⍔ ᥩ 🝙 ♀ ♨ 🏠 ⛳
Leisure snooker, putting green.
Location 43 Saul Rd (1.5m from town centre)
Hotel ★★★♨67% Ballynahinch Castle,
BALLYNAHINCH ☎ (095) 31006 & 31086
28⇄ 🐾

HOLYWOOD   Map 01 D5

Holywood ☎ (02317) 2138
Hilly parkland course with some fine views and providing an
interesting game.
18 holes, 5425mtrs, Par 69, SSS 68, Course record 64.
Club membership 800.
Visitors may not play between 1.30-2.15pm or on Sat.
Societies must contact in writing.
Green Fees not confirmed.
Facilities ⊗ ⍔ ᥩ 🝙 ♀ ♨ 🏠 ⛳ ☏ Michael Bannon.
Leisure snooker.
Location Nuns Wall, Demesne Rd
Hotel ★★★★70% Culloden Hotel, HOLYWOOD
☎ (0232) 425223 91⇄ 🐾

The Royal Belfast ☎ Belfast (0232) 428165
On the shores of Belfast Lough, this attractive course
consists of wooded parkland on undulating terrain which
provides a pleasant, challenging game.
18 holes, 5963yds, Par 70, SSS 69.
Club membership 1200.
Visitors may not play on Thu or Sat before 4.30pm;
must be accompanied by a member or
present a letter of introduction from their
own golf club.

Societies must contact in writing.
Green Fees not confirmed.
Facilities ⊗ (ex Sat) ⍔ ♀ ♨ 🏠 ⛳ ☏ David Carson.
Leisure hard tennis courts, squash, snooker.
Location Station Rd, Craigavad (2m E on A2)
Hotel ★★★★70% Culloden Hotel, HOLYWOOD
☎ (0232) 425223 91⇄ 🐾

KILKEEL   Map 01 D4

Kilkeel ☎ (06937) 62296
A very good parkland course, picturesquely situated at the
foot of the Mourne Mountains. A further nine holes are under
construction.
18 holes, 6576yds, Par 72, SSS 70.
Club membership 700.
Visitors restricted Sun mornings & Tue & Sat. Must
contact in advance.
Societies must contact in writing.
Green Fees £15 (£16 weekends & bank holidays).
Facilities ⊗ (Mar-Sep) ⍔ ᥩ 🝙 ♀ ♨
Location Mourne Park (On Newry road)
Hotel ★★★60% Slieve Donard Hotel, NEWCASTLE
☎ (03967) 23681 120⇄

NEWCASTLE   Map 01 D5

Royal County Down ☎ (03967) 23314
The remoteness of the links of the Royal County Down
and the backdrop of the Mountains of Mourne make this
a particularly exhilarating course to play, and there is a
wide variety in the challenges it presents. The greens,
always in good condition, can be tricky to read and some
of the tee shots are blind. The natural terrain of sand
dunes and gorse bushes may add to the hazards, but they
also contribute to the scenic beauty of the course.
*Championship Course: 18 holes, 6969yds, Par 71, SSS
73.*
No 2 Course: 18 holes, 4087yds, Par 65, SSS 60.
Visitors may not play on Sat; may not play on
Championship Course Sat, Sun & Wed.
Societies must contact in advance.
Green Fees Championship: £40 per round (summer);
£30 (winter)(£50 per round weekends).
Facilities ⊗ ᥩ 🝙 ♀ ♨ 🏠 ⛳ ☏ Kevan Whitson.
Hotel ★★★60% Slieve Donard Hotel,
NEWCASTLE ☎ (03967) 23681 120⇄

NEWTOWNARDS   Map 01 D5

Scrabo ☎ (0247) 812355
Hilly and picturesque, this course offers a good test of golf.
18 holes, 5699mtrs, Par 71, SSS 71, Course record 65.
Club membership 840.
Visitors may not play on Sat.
Societies must telephone in advance.
Green Fees not confirmed.
Facilities ⊗ ⍔ ᥩ 🝙 ♀ ♨ 🏠 ⛳ ☏ Billy Todd.
Leisure snooker.
Location 233 Scrabo Rd
Hotel ★★★69% Stormont Hotel, 587 Upper
Newtonards Rd, BELFAST
☎ (0232) 658621 106⇄ 🐾

WARRENPOINT   Map 01 D4

Warrenpoint ☎ (06937) 53695
Parkland course with marvellous views and a need for
accurate shots.
18 holes, 6288yds, Par 71, SSS 70.
Club membership 1120.
Visitors   preferred Mon, Thu & Fri.
Societies   must contact in advance.
Green Fees £15 (£21 weekends).
Facilities ⊗ ⅷ ⅼ 💺 ♀ 🛆 🖻 🏌 ⦗ Nigel Shaw.
Leisure   squash, snooker.
Location   Lower Dromore Rd (1m W)
Hotel   ★★★60% Slieve Donard Hotel, NEWCASTLE
     ☎ (03967) 23681   120🛏

CO FERMANAGH

ENNISKILLEN   Map 01 C5

Enniskillen ☎ (0365) 325250
Meadowland course in Castle Coole estate.
18 holes, 5476yds, Par 71, SSS 69.
Visitors   preferred on weekdays.
Societies   must contact in advance.
Green Fees not confirmed.
Facilities ⊗ & ⅷ by prior arrangement ♀ 🏌
Leisure   snooker.
Location   Castle Coole (1m E)
Hotel   ★★★58% Killyhevlin Hotel, ENNISKILLEN
     ☎ (0365) 323481   22🛏 ⦗ Annexe26rm

CO LONDONDERRY

AGHADOWEY   Map 01 C6

Brown Trout Golf & Country Inn
☎ Coleraine (0265) 868209
A challenging course with two par 5s. During the course of
the 9 holes, players have to negotiate water 7 times and all the
fairways are lined with densely packed fir trees.
9 holes, 2519mtrs, Par 70, SSS 68.
Club membership 150.
Visitors   no restrictions.
Societies   must contact by telephone.
Green Fees £7 per round (£10 weekends).
Facilities ⊗ ⅷ ⅼ 💺 ♀ 🛆 🖾 ⦗ Ken Revie.
Leisure   riding.
Location   209 Agivey Rd (junc of A54 & B66)
Hotel   ★★★66% Everglades Hotel, Prehen Rd,
     LONDONDERRY ☎ (0504) 46722   52🛏 ⦗

Remember – replace all divots, and repair
ball-marks or damage by spikes on
completion of the hole

CASTLEDAWSON   Map 01 C5

Moyola Park ☎ (0648) 68468
Parkland course with some difficult shots, calling for length and
accuracy. The Moyola River provides a water hazard at the 8th.
18 holes, 6517yds, Par 71, SSS 71, Course record 69.
Club membership 900.
Visitors   may not play Fri after 2pm. Must play with
     member Sat and may only play 1.30-2.30pm (by
     prior arrangement) Sun.
Societies   must contact in advance.
Green Fees £12 (£20 weekends).
Facilities ⊗ ⅷ ⅼ 💺 ♀ 🛆 🖻 🏌 ⦗ Vivian Teague.
Leisure   snooker.
Location   Shanemullagh (3m NE of Magherafelt)
Hotel   ★★★62% Adair Arms Hotel, Ballymoney Rd,
     BALLYMENA ☎ (0266) 653674   39🛏 ⦗

CASTLEROCK   Map 01 C6

Castlerock ☎ Coleraine (0265) 848314
A most exhilarating course with three superb par 4s, four
testing short holes and two par 5s. After an uphill start,
the hazards are many, including the river and a railway,
and both judgement and accuracy are called for. A
challenge in calm weather, any trouble from the elements
will test your golf to the limits.
Mussenden: 18 holes, 6687yds, Par 73, SSS 72.
Bann: 9 holes, 2457mtrs, Par 35, SSS 33.
Club membership 960.
Visitors   may not play at weekends or Fri during
     May-Aug.
Societies   must contact in advance.
Green Fees £13 per 18 holes (£25 weekends & bank
     holidays); £5 per 9 holes (£7 weekends &
     bank holidays).
Facilities ⅷ ⅼ 💺 ♀ 🛆 🖻 🏌 ⦗ Robert Kelly.
Leisure   snooker.
Location   65 Circular Rd (6m from Coleraine on A2)
Hotel   ★★60% Beach House Hotel, The Sea Front,
     PORTBALLINTRAE
     ☎ (02657) 31214   32🛏 ⦗

LONDONDERRY   Map 01 C5

City of Derry ☎ (0504) 46369
Two parkland courses on undulating parkland with good
views and lots of trees. The 9-hole course will particularly
suit novices.
*Prehen: 18 holes, 6406yds, Par 71, SSS 71, Course record
68.*
Dunhugh Course: 9 holes, 4708yds, Par 63.
Club membership 732.
Visitors   must make a booking to play on Prehen Course
     at weekends or before 4.30pm on weekdays.
Societies   must contact in advance.
Green Fees £12 (£14 weekends & bank holidays).
Facilities ⊗ & ⅷ by prior arrangement ⅼ (summer only)
     💺 by prior arrangement ♀ 🛆 🖻 ⦗ Michael
     Doherty.
Leisure   snooker.
Location   49 Victoria Rd (2m S)
Hotel   ★★★66% Everglades Hotel, Prehen Rd,
     LONDONDERRY ☎ (0504) 46722   52🛏 ⦗

PORTSTEWART   Map 01 C6

Portstewart ☎ (026583) 2015
Three links courses with spectacular views, offering a testing round on the Strand course in particular.
Strand: 18 holes, 6784yds, Par 72, SSS 72.
Town: 18 holes, 4733yds, Par 64, SSS 62.
3: 9 holes, 2622yds, Par 32.
Visitors   preferred on weekdays.
Societies   must contact in advance.
Green Fees not confirmed.
Facilities   ⊗ ⅲ ♀ ⬦ ⪦ ⓒ Alan Hunter.
Leisure   snooker, indoor bowling.
Location   117 Strand Rd
Hotel   ★★60% Beach House Hotel, The Sea Front, PORTBALLINTRAE
                 ☎ (02657) 31214 32⇄ ⟆

CO TYRONE

COOKSTOWN   Map 01 C5

Killymoon ☎ (06487) 63762
Parkland course on elevated, well drained land.
18 holes, 5498mtrs, Par 70, SSS 68.
Club membership 650.
Visitors   may not play on Sat afternoons. Must contact in advance and have a handicap certificate.
Societies   must contact in advance.
Green Fees £13 (£17 weekends & bank holidays).
Facilities   ⊗ ⅲ & ⬦ by prior arrangement
                 ⬦ ♀ ⪦ ⓒ Barry Hamill.
Leisure   snooker.
Location   200 Killymoon Rd
Hotel   ★★65% Royal Arms Hotel, 51 High St, OMAGH ☎ (0662) 243262 21⇄ ⟆

DUNGANNON   Map 01 C5

Dungannon ☎ (08687) 22098 or 27338
Parkland course with five par 3s and tree-lined fairways.
18 holes, 5433mtrs, Par 71, SSS 68, Course record 62.
Club membership 480.
Visitors   may not play on Sat.
Societies   must contact secretary in advance.
Green Fees £8-£10 per day (£10-£13 weekends & bank holidays).
Facilities   ♀ ⪦ ⬦
Leisure   snooker.
Location   34 Springfield Ln (0.5m outside town on Donaghmore road)
Hotel   ★★★69% Stormont Hotel, 587 Upper Newtonards Rd, BELFAST
                 ☎ (0232) 658621 106⇄ ⟆

NEWTOWNSTEWART   Map 01 C5

Newtownstewart ☎ (06626) 61466 & 61829
Parkland course bisected by a stream.
18 holes, 5468mtrs, Par 70, SSS 69, Course record 66.
Club membership 700.

Visitors   times may be booked in advance, restricted at weekends.
Societies   must contact in advance.
Green Fees £8 (£12 weekends & bank holidays).
Facilities   ⊗ by prior arrangement ⬦ ⬦ ♀ ⪦ ⓒ ⬦
Leisure   snooker.
Location   38 Golf Course Rd (2m SW on B84)
Hotel   ★★★62% Fir Trees Hotel, Melmount Rd, STRABANE ☎ (0504) 382382 26⇄ ⟆

OMAGH   Map 01 C5

Omagh ☎ (0662) 243160
Undulating parkland course beside the River Drumnagh.
18 holes, 5774yds, Par 70, SSS 68.
Visitors   may not play on Tue & Sat.
Societies   must contact in advance.
Green Fees not confirmed.
Facilities   ⬦ ♀
Leisure   snooker.
Location   83a Dublin Rd (On S outskirts of town)
Hotel   ★★65% Royal Arms Hotel, 51 High St, OMAGH ☎ (0662) 243262 21⇄ ⟆

STRABANE   Map 01 C5

Strabane ☎ (0504) 382271 & 382007
Testing parkland course with the River Mourne running alongside and creating a water hazard.
18 holes, 5552mtrs, Par 69, SSS 69.
Club membership 550.
Visitors   may not play on Sat.
Societies   must contact in writing.
Green Fees £10 per round (£12 weekends & bank holidays).
Facilities   ⬦ & ⬦ by prior arrangement ♀ ⪦
Leisure   snooker.
Location   Ballycolman Rd
Hotel   ★★★62% Fir Trees Hotel, Melmount Rd, STRABANE ☎ (0504) 382382 26⇄ ⟆

REPUBLIC OF IRELAND

CO CARLOW

CARLOW   Map 01 C3

Carlow ☎ (0503) 31695
Created in 1922 to a design by Tom Simpson, this testing and enjoyable course is set in a wild deer park, with beautiful dry terrain and a varied character. With sandy sub-soil, the course is playable all year round. There are water hazards at the 2nd, 10th and 11th and only two par 5s, both offering genuine birdie opportunities.
18 holes, 5599mtrs, Par 70, SSS 69.
Club membership 1000.
Visitors   are welcome, although play is limited on Tue and difficult on Sat & Sun. Must contact in advance.
Societies   must book in advance.

Green Fees IR£20 per day.
Facilities ⊗ ℳ ᛒ 🍺 ♀ 🛆 🏠 ⛳ ⛿ Andrew Gilbert.
Location Deerpark (2m N of Carlow)
Hotel ★★52% Royal Hotel, CARLOW
☎ (0503) 31621 34➯ ☞

CO CAVAN

BELTURBET   Map 01 C4

Belturbet ☎ Cavan (049) 22287
Beautifully maintained parkland course with predominantly
family membership and popular with summer visitors.
9 holes, 5480yds, Par 68, SSS 65, Course record 64.
Club membership 150.
Visitors restrictions the same as for members.
Societies must contact secretary or captain in advance.
Green Fees not confirmed.
Facilities ⊗ & ℳ by prior arrangement ᛒ 🍺 ♀ 🛆
Leisure snooker.
Location Erne Hill
Hotel ★★★♨75% Cromleach Lodge Country House
Hotel, Ballindoon, CASTLEBALDWIN
☎ (071) 65155 10➯ ☞

BLACKLION   Map 01 C5

Blacklion ☎ (0772) 53024
Parkland course established in 1962, with coppices of
woodland and mature trees. The lake comes into play on two
holes and there are some magnificent views of the lake,
islands and surrounding hills. It has been described as one of
the best maintained nine-hole courses in Ireland.
9 holes, 5614mtrs, Par 72, SSS 69.
Club membership 200.
Visitors may not play on Sun mornings & occasional
competition days.
Societies must contact in advance.
Green Fees IR£5 per day (IR£7 weekends & bank holidays).
Facilities ᛒ & 🍺 (afternoons only) ♀ 🛆
Leisure fishing.
Location Toam
Hotel ★★★67% Sligo Park Hotel, Pearse Rd, SLIGO
☎ (071) 60291 89➯ ☞

CO CLARE

ENNIS   Map 01 B3

Ennis ☎ (065) 24074
On rolling hills, this immaculately manicured course presents an
excellent challenge to both casual visitors and aspiring scratch
golfers, with tree-lined fairways and well protected greens.
18 holes, 5318mtrs, Par 69, SSS 68.
Club membership 965.
Visitors must contact in advance & be a member
of a golf club.
Societies apply in writing.
Green Fees IR£15 per day.

Facilities ⊗ ℳ by prior arrangement
ᛒ 🍺 ♀ 🛆 🏠 ⛳ ⛿ Martin Ward.
Leisure snooker.
Location Drumbiggle
Hotel ★★★65% Auburn Lodge Hotel, Galway Rd,
ENNIS ☎ (065) 21247 100➯ ☞

KILKEE   Map 01 A3

Kilkee ☎ (065) 56048
Well established course on the cliffs of Kilkee Bay, with
beautiful views.
9 holes, 6185yds, Par 69, SSS 68.
Club membership 600.
Visitors may not play on certain competition days.
Societies must contact in writing.
Green Fees not confirmed.
Facilities ⊗ ᛒ 🍺 ♀ 🛆 ⛳
Leisure squash, fishing, sauna.
Location East End
Hotel ★66% Halpin's Hotel, Erin St, KILKEE
☎ (065) 56032 11rm(7➯ ☞)

LAHINCH   Map 01 B3

Lahinch ☎ (065) 81003
Originally designed by Tom Morris and later modified by
Dr Alister MacKenzie, Lahinch has hosted every
important Irish amateur fixture and the Home
Internationals. The par five 5th - The Klondike - is
played along a deep valley and over a huge dune; the par
three 6th may be short, but calls for a blind shot over the
ridge of a hill to a green hemmed in by hills on three
sides.
Old Course: 18 holes, 6702yds, Par 72, SSS 73.
Castle Course: 18 holes, 4786mtrs, Par 67, SSS 66.
Club membership 1583.
Visitors handicap limit, men 28, ladies 36
Societies apply in writing
Green Fees Old Course IR£25 per round; Castle Course
IR£15 per round.
Facilities ⊗ ℳ ᛒ 🍺 ♀ 🛆 🏠 ⛳ ⛿ R McCavery.
Location 2m W of Ennistymon on N67
Hotel ★★70% Spa View Hotel, LISDOONVARNA
☎ (065) 74026 11➯ ☞

SHANNON AIRPORT   Map 01 B3

Shannon ☎ (061) 471849
Superb parkland course with tree-lined fairways, strategically
placed bunkers, water hazards and excellent greens, offering
a challenge to all levels of players - including the many
famous golfers who have played here.
18 holes, 6874yds, Par 72, SSS 74.
Club membership 700.
Visitors must contact in advance & have handicap
certificate. Restricted play at certain times.
Societies must contact in writing.
Green Fees IR£20 per day (IR£25 weekends & bank
holidays).
Facilities ⊗ ℳ ᛒ 🍺 ♀ 🛆 🏠 ⛳ ⛿ Artie Pyke.
Leisure pool table, putting green.
Location 2m from Shannon Airport
Hotel ★★★63% Fitzpatrick Shannon Shamrock Hotel,
BUNRATTY ☎ (061) 361177 115➯ ☞

CO CORK

BANDON Map 01 B2

Bandon ☎ (023) 41111
Lovely parkland course in pleasant rural surroundings.
18 holes, 5663mtrs, Par 70, SSS 69.
Club membership 800.
Visitors welcome but may not play during club competitions. Must contact in advance.
Societies must apply in writing.
Green Fees IR£12 (IR£15 weekends).
Facilities ⊗ ⅷ ⅼ ⾕ ♀ ☴ 🖢 ⚏ ⚏ Paddy O'Boyle.
Leisure hard tennis courts.
Location Castlebernard
Hotel ★★63% Innishannon House Hotel, INNISHANNON
☎ (021) 775121 13⇄ ⚏

BANTRY Map 01 A2

Bantry Park ☎ (027) 50579
An undulating 9-hole course with some magnificent sea views.
9 holes, 5882mtrs, Par 72, SSS 70.
Club membership 230.
Visitors course is restricted only during competition times.
Societies must apply in writing to Mr J Sheenan, Ardnagaoithe, Bantry.
Green Fees IR£10 per day.
Facilities ☴ ⚏
Location Donemark
Hotel ★★(red)♨♨ Sea View Hotel, BALLYLICKEY
☎ (027) 50073 & 50462
17⇄ ⚏ Annexe5rm

BLARNEY Map 01 B2

Muskerry ☎ (021) 385297 & 385104
An adventurous game is guaranteed at this course, with its wooded hillsides and the meandering Shournagh River coming into play at a number of holes. The 15th is a notable hole - not long, but very deep - and after that all you need to do to get back to the clubhouse is to stay out of the water.
18 holes, 6327yds, Par 71, SSS 70, Course record 66.
Club membership 706.
Visitors may not play Wed afternoon & Thu morning. Must play with member at weekends.
Societies must telephone in advance and then confirm in writing.
Green Fees IR£15 per day (£17 weekends).
Facilities ⊗ & ⅷ by prior arrangement ⅼ ⾕ ♀ ☴ 🖢 ⚏ ⚏ Martin Lehane.
Leisure snooker.
Location Carrigrohane (7.5m NW of Cork)
Hotel ★★★68% Blarney Park Hotel, BLARNEY
☎ (021) 385281 76⇄ ⚏

CASTLETOWNBERE Map 01 A2

Berehaven ☎ (027) 70039
Seaside links founded in 1902.
9 holes, 2380mtrs, Par 69, SSS 66.
Club membership 200.
Visitors no restrictions.
Societies must telephone (027) 70469 in advance.
Green Fees IR£8 per day (IR£10 weekends & bank holidays).
Facilities ⚏ (Jun-Aug) ☴ ⚏
Leisure hard tennis courts, outdoor swimming pool, fishing.
Location Millcove (2m E on Glen Garriff Rd)
Hotel ★★(red)♨♨ Sea View Hotel, BALLYLICKEY
☎ (027) 50073 & 50462
17⇄ ⚏ Annexe5rm

CHARLEVILLE Map 01 B2

Charleville ☎ (063) 81257
Wooded parkland course offering not too strenuous walking.
18 holes, 6434yds, Par 71, SSS 70, Course record 68.
Club membership 700.
Visitors may not play at weekends. Must contact in advance.
Societies must telephone in advance.
Green Fees not confirmed.
Facilities ⊗ ⅷ ⅼ ⚏ ♀ ☴
Location Ardmore
Hotel ★★★♨♨70% Longueville House Hotel, MALLOW
☎ (022) 47156 & 47306 17⇄ ⚏

CORK Map 01 B2

Cork ☎ (021) 353451
This championship-standard course is always kept in superb condition and is playable all year round. It has many memorable and distinctive features including holes at the water's edge and holes in a disused quarry.
18 holes, 6115mtrs, Par 72, SSS 72.
Club membership 705.
Visitors may not play 12.30-2pm or on Thu (Ladies Day), and only after 2.30pm Sat & Sun.
Societies must contact in advance.
Green Fees IR£23 per day (IR£26 weekends).
Facilities ⊗ ⅷ ⅼ ⚏ ♀ ☴ 🖢 ⚏
Location Little Island (5m E, on N25)
Hotel ★★★★66% Jurys Hotel, Western Rd, CORK
☎ (021) 276622 185⇄ ⚏

Mahon Municipal ☎ (021) 362480
Municipal course which stretches alongside the river estuary, with some holes across water.
18 holes, 4818mtrs, Par 67, SSS 66.
Visitors may not play mornings at weekends.
Green Fees not confirmed.
Facilities ⊗ ⅷ ⅼ ♀ ⚏ ⚏
Location Blackrock (2m from city centre)
Hotel ★★★65% Fitzpatrick Silver Springs Hotel, Tivoli, CORK
☎ (021) 507533 109⇄ ⚏

DOUGLAS
Map 01 B2

Douglas ☎ Cork (021) 362055 & 895297
Level inland course overlooking the city of Cork. Suitable for golfers of all ages and abilities.
18 holes, 5664mtrs, Par 70, SSS 69.
Club membership 750.
Visitors may not play Tue or Sat & Sun before 2.30pm.
Societies must contact in advance.
Green Fees IR£19 per day (IR£20 weekends).
Facilities ⊗ ᛗ ᛒ ♥ ♀ ♨ ⚑ ⚐ Ⴠ Garry Nicholson.
Leisure snooker.
Hotel ★★★★66% Jurys Hotel, Western Rd, CORK
☎ (021) 276622 185⇄ ⚑

FERMOY
Map 01 B2

Fermoy ☎ (025) 31472
Rather exposed heathland course, bisected by a road.
18 holes, 6370yds, Par 70, SSS 69.
Visitors preferred on weekdays.
Green Fees not confirmed.
Facilities ⊗ ᛗ ᛒ ♀ Ⴠ
Location Corrin Cross (2m SW)
Hotel ★★★♨♨70% Longueville House Hotel,
MALLOW ☎ (022) 47156 & 47306 17⇄ ⚑

LITTLE ISLAND
Map 01 B2

Harbour Point ☎ (021) 353094
A new championship-standard course in rolling countryside on the banks of the River Lee at Cork's scenic harbour. A distinctive and testing course for every standard of golfer.
18 holes, 6063yds, Par 72, SSS 72, Course record 72.
Club membership 250.
Visitors must contact in advance, may not play before 11am Sun.
Societies telephone for bookings.
Green Fees IR£10 per round before 11am Mon, Wed, Thu & Fri; IR£20 other times.
Facilities ⊗ ᛗ ᛒ ♥ ♀ ♨ ⚑ Ⴠ
Location Clash Rd (5m E of Cork)
Hotel ★★67% Ashbourne House Hotel,
GLOUNTHAUNE
☎ (021) 353319 & 353310 26⇄ ⚑

MALLOW
Map 01 B2

Mallow ☎ (022) 21145
A well wooded parkland course overlooking the Blackwater Valley, Mallow is straightforward, but no less a challenge for it. The front nine is by far the longer, but the back nine is demanding in its call for accuracy and the par 3 18th provides a tough finish.
18 holes, 5687yds, Par 72, SSS 70.
Visitors preferred on Mon, Wed, Thu & Fri.
Societies apply in writing.
Green Fees IR£13 (IR£16 weekends).
Facilities ⊗ ᛗ ᛒ ♥ ♀ ♨ ⚑ Ⴠ
Leisure hard tennis courts, squash, snooker, sauna.
Location Ballyellis
Hotel ★★★♨♨70% Longueville House Hotel,
MALLOW
☎ (022) 47156 & 47306 17⇄ ⚑

MIDLETON
Map 01 B2

East Cork ☎ (021) 631687
A well wooded course calling for accuracy of shots.
18 holes, 5207mtrs, Par 69, SSS 67.
Club membership 511.
Visitors may not play Sun mornings.
Societies must apply in writing.
Green Fees not confirmed.
Facilities ⊗ ᛒ ♥ ♀ ♨ Ⴠ
Leisure squash, fishing, riding, snooker.
Location Gortacrue (on the A626)
Hotel ★★67% Ashbourne House Hotel,
GLOUNTHAUNE
☎ (021) 353319 & 353310 26⇄ ⚑

MONKSTOWN
Map 01 B2

Monkstown ☎ (021) 841376
Undulating parkland course with five tough finishing holes.
18 holes, 5669mtrs, Par 70, SSS 69, Course record 66.
Club membership 914.
Visitors restricted Tue & busy weekends. Must contact in advance.
Societies must apply in writing.
Green Fees IR£20 Mon-Thu; IR£23 Fri-Sun.
Facilities ⊗ ᛗ ᛒ ♥ ♀ ♨ ⚑ Ⴠ Batt Murphy.
Location Parkgariffe
Hotel ★★★66% Rochestown Park Hotel, CORK
☎ (021) 892233 63⇄ ⚑

SKIBBEREEN
Map 01 B2

Skibbereen & West Carbery ☎ (028) 21227 & 22340
Expanded to an 18-hole course in May 1993. Slightly hilly course in scenic locatio.
18 holes, 4656mtrs, Par 72, SSS 70, Course record 63.
Club membership 376.
Visitors advisable to contact in advance.
Societies apply in writing.
Green Fees IR£12 per 18 holes (IR£15 July & August).
Facilities ⊗ (high season) ᛒ ♥ ♀ ♨ Ⴠ
Location Licknavar (20m S of Bantry, off N71)
Hotel ★★★55% Westlodge Hotel, BANTRY
☎ (027) 50360 90⇄ ⚑

YOUGHAL
Map 01 C2

Youghal ☎ (024) 92787
For many years the host of various Golfing Union championships, Youghal offers a good test of golf and is well maintained for year-round play. There are panoramic views of Youghal Bay and the Blackwater estuary.
18 holes, 5700mtrs, Par 70, SSS 69, Course record 67.
Club membership 600.
Visitors may not play Wed (Ladies Day) and should contact in advance for weekends.
Societies must apply in writing a few months in advance.
Green Fees not confirmed. ▶

Facilities ⊗ ⏛ by prior arrangement ⯑ ⯑ ⯑ ⯑ ⯑
⯑ ⯑ Ciaran Carroll.
Location Knockaverry
Hotel ★★63% Devonshire Arms Hotel, Pearse
Square, YOUGHAL
☎ (024) 92827 & 92018 10⇄ ⯑

CO DONEGAL

BALLINTRA   Map 01 B5

Donegal ☎ (073) 34054
This massive links course was opened in 1973 and
provides a world-class facility in peaceful surroundings.
It is a very long course with some memorable holes,
including five par 5s, calling for some big hitting.
Donegal is the home club of former Curtis Cup captain,
Maire O'Donnell.
18 holes, 6243mtrs, Par 73, SSS 73.
Club membership 550.
Visitors no restrictions.
Societies must apply in writing well in advance.
Green Fees IR£13 (IR£16 weekends).
Facilities ⊗ ⯑ ⯑ ⯑
Location Murvagh, Laghy (6m S of Donegal on
Ballyshannon road)
Hotel ★★★72% Sand House Hotel,
ROSSNOWLAGH ☎ (072) 51777 42⇄ ⯑

BALLYBOFEY   Map 01 C5

Ballybofey & Stranorlar ☎ (074) 31093
A most scenic course incorporating pleasant valleys backed
by mountains with three of its holes bordered by a lake. There
are three Par 3s on the first nine and two on the second. The
most difficult hole is the long uphill Par 4 16th. The only Par
5 is the 7th.
18 holes, 5328mtrs, Par 68, SSS 69.
Visitors may play on weekdays.
Green Fees not confirmed.
Facilities ⯑ ⯑
Location Stranorlar (0.25m from Stranorlar)
Hotel ★★★59% Kee's Hotel, Stranolar,
BALLYBOFEY ☎ (074) 31018 36⇄ ⯑

BUNCRANA   Map 01 C6

North West ☎ (077) 61027
A traditional-style links course on gently rolling sandy
terrain with some long par 4s. Good judgement is
required on the approaches and the course offers a
satisfying test coupled with undemanding walking.
18 holes, 6203yds, Par 69, SSS 69.
Club membership 500.
Visitors no restrictions.
Societies must contact in advance.
Green Fees IR£10 (IR£15 weekends).
Facilities ⊗ ⏛ ⯑ ⯑ (all catering by arrangement) ⯑
by arrangement ⯑ ⯑ ⯑ Seamus McBriarty.

Leisure snooker.
Location Lisfannon, Fahan
Hotel ★★63% Strand Hotel, BALLYLIFFEN
☎ (077) 76107 12⇄ ⯑

BUNDORAN   Map 01 B5

Bundoran ☎ (072) 41302
This popular course, acknowledged as one of the best in
the country, runs along the high cliffs above Bundoran
beach and has a difficult par of 69. Designed by Harry
Vardon, it offers a challenging game of golf in beautiful
surroundings and has been the venue for a number of
Irish golf championships.
18 holes, 5785mtrs, Par 70, SSS 71.
Club membership 400.
Visitors must contact in advance.
Societies must contact in advance.
Green Fees IR£12 (IR£20 weekends).
Facilities ⯑ & ⯑ by prior arrangement ⯑ ⯑ ⯑ ⯑ ⯑
Hotel ★★65% Dorrians Imperial Hotel,
BALLYSHANNON ☎ (072) 51147 26⇄ ⯑

DUNFANAGHY   Map 01 C6

Dunfanaghy ☎ Letterkenny (074) 36335
Overlooking Sheephaven Bay, the course has a flat central
area with three difficult streams to negotiate. At the Port-na-
Blagh end there are five marvellous holes, including one
across the beach, while at the Horn Head end, the last five
holes are a test for any golfer.
18 holes, 5066mtrs, Par 68, SSS 66, Course record 65.
Club membership 300.
Visitors restricted on Sat & Sun mornings.
Societies must telephone in advance.
Green Fees IR£10 per round (IR£12 weekends).
Facilities ⯑ ⯑ ⯑ ⯑ ⯑ ⯑
Location Kill (On N56)
Hotel ★★67% Arnold's Hotel, DUNFANAGHY
☎ (074) 36208 & 36142 34⇄ ⯑

GREENCASTLE   Map 01 C6

Greencastle ☎ (077) 81013
A typical links course along the shores of Lough Foyle,
surrounded by rocky headlands and sandy beaches. In 1992 to
celebrate its centenary, the club increased its size from 9 to
18 holes.
18 holes, 5118mtrs, Par 69, SSS 67.
Club membership 600.
Visitors no restrictions.
Societies must apply in writing in advance.
Green Fees IR£9 (IR£13 weekends).
Facilities ⏛ by prior arrangement ⯑ ⯑ ⯑ ⯑
Location Moville
Hotel ★★54% McNamara's Hotel, Foyle St,
MOVILLE ☎ (077) 82010 18rm(8⇄ ⯑)

Use the AA *Hotels* or *Bed and Breakfast*
Guides to extend your choice of
accommodation

LETTERKENNY   Map 01 C5

Letterkenny ☎ (074) 21150
The fairways are wide and generous, but the rough, when you
find it, is short, tough and mean. The flat and untiring terrain
on the shores of Lough Swilly provides good holiday golf.
Many interesting holes include the intimidating 1st with its
high tee through trees and the tricky dog-leg of the 2nd hole.
18 holes, 6239yds, Par 70, SSS 71, Course record 67.
Club membership 500.
Visitors   preferred Mon-Fri. Advisable to contact in
      advance for weekends and bank holidays.
Societies   apply by writing or telephone.
Green Fees IR£10.
Facilities   ⊗ ⅷ by prior arrangement ⅊ ♥ ♀ ⚘ ⚑
Leisure   snooker, table tennis.
Location   Barnhill (2m from town on Rathmelton road)
Hotel   ★★★59% Kee's Hotel, Stranolar,
      BALLYBOFEY ☎ (074) 31018 36⇆ ⋒

NARIN   Map 01 B5

Narin & Portnoo ☎ (075) 45107
Seaside links with every hole presenting its own special
feature. The Par 4 5th, for instance, demands a perfectly
placed drive to get a narrow sight of the narrow entrance to
the elevated green. Cross winds from the sea can make some
of the Par 4s difficult to reach with two woods.
18 holes, 5225mtrs, Par 69, SSS 68.
Visitors   preferred on weekdays.
Green Fees not confirmed.
Facilities   ⅊ ♀
Location   6m from Ardara
Hotel   ★★★61% The Hyland Central Hotel, The Diamond,
      DONEGAL ☎ (073) 21027 & 21090 72⇆ ⋒

PORTSALON   Map 01 C6

Portsalon ☎ (074) 59459
Another course blessed by nature. The three golden beaches
of Ballymastocker Bay lie at one end, while the beauty of
Lough Swilly and the Inishowen Peninsula beyond is a
distracting but pleasant feature to the west. Situated on the
Fanad Peninsula, this lovely links course provides untiring
holiday golf at its best.
18 holes, 5379mtrs, Par 69, SSS 68, Course record 66.
Club membership 300.
Visitors   may not play on competition days.
Societies   must apply in writing to club secretary.
Green Fees IR£10 per day.
Facilities   ⊗ ⅷ ⅊ & ♥ (Summer only) ♀ ⚘
Hotel   ★56% Pier Hotel, RATHMULLAN
      ☎ (074) 58178 16rm(11⇆ ⋒)

ROSAPENNA   Map 01 C6

Rosapenna ☎ (074) 55301
Dramatic links course offering a challenging round.
Originally designed by Tom Morris and later modified by
James Braid and Harry Vardon, it includes such features as
bunkers in mid fairway. The best part of the links runs in the
low valley along the ocean.
18 holes, 6271yds, Par 70, SSS 71.
Club membership 200.

Visitors   no restrictions.
Societies   must contact in advance.
Green Fees IR£12 (IR£15 Fri-Sun & bank holidays).
Facilities   ⅷ ⅊ ♥ ♀ ⚘ 🗇 ⚑ ⋒ ⚑ Simon Byrne.
Leisure   hard tennis courts, snooker.
Location   Downings
Hotel   ★★67% Arnold's Hotel, DUNFANAGHY
      ☎ (074) 36208 & 36142 34⇆ ⋒

CO DUBLIN

BALBRIGGAN   Map 01 D4

Balbriggan ☎ Dublin (01) 8412229
A parkland course with great variations and good views of
the Mourne and Cooley mountains.
18 holes, 5881mtrs, Par 71, SSS 71.
Club membership 600.
Visitors   no restrictions.
Societies   must apply in writing.
Green Fees IR£14 per round..
Facilities   ⊗ ⅷ ⅊ ♥ ♀ ⚘
Leisure   snooker.
Location   Blackhall
Hotel   ★★★60% Grand Hotel, MALAHIDE
      ☎ (01) 8450633 100⇆ ⋒

BRITTAS   Map 01 D3

Slade Valley ☎ (01) 582183
This is a course for a relaxing game, being fairly easy and in
pleasant surroundings.
18 holes, 5345mtrs, Par 69, SSS 69, Course record 65.
Club membership 700.
Visitors   preferred on Mon, Thu & Fri. Restricted
      weekends.
Societies   telephone in advance
Green Fees not confirmed.
Facilities   ⊗ ⅷ ⅊ ♥ ♀ 🗇 ⚑ ⚑ John Dignam.
Leisure   snooker.
Location   Lynch Park (9m SW of Dublin on N81)
Hotel   ★★★56% Downshire House Hotel,
      BLESSINGTON ☎ (045) 65199
      14⇆ ⋒ Annexe11⇆ ⋒

CLOGHRAN   Map 01 D4

Forrest Little ☎ (01) 401183
Testing parkland course.
18 holes, 5865mtrs, Par 70, SSS 70.
Visitors   preferred weekday mornings.
Green Fees not confirmed.
Facilities   ⅊ ♀ 🗇 ⚑ ⚑ Tony Judd.
Location   6m N of Dublin on N1
Hotel   ★★★61% Marine Hotel, Sutton, DUBLIN
      ☎ (01) 322613 27⇆ ⋒

If visiting a brand new course, be sure to
telephone before your visit to confirm the
course information is correct

DONABATE Map 01 D4

Beaverstown ☎ Dublin (01) 8436439 & 8436721
Well wooded course with water hazards at more than half of
the holes.
18 holes, 5855mtrs, Par 71, SSS 71.
Club membership 800.
Visitors may not play 12.30-2pm daily & must contact in
advance to play on Wed, Sat or Sun.
Societies must contact in writing.
Green Fees IR£12 (IR£20 weekends & bank holidays).
Facilities ⊗ ⊪ ⅃ ⊩ ♀ ⚲
Leisure snooker.
Location Beaverstown (5m from Dublin Airport)
Hotel ★★★60% Grand Hotel, MALAHIDE
☎ (01) 8450633 100⇄ ♠

Corballis Public ☎ (01) 8436583
Well maintained coastal course with excellent greens.
18 holes, 4971yds, Par 65, SSS 64.
Visitors no restrictions.
Societies book by telephone and confirm by letter.
Green Fees IR£7 per round (IR£8 weekends).
Facilities ⅃ ⊩ ⚲ ⊟
Location Corballis
Hotel ★★★60% Grand Hotel, MALAHIDE
☎ (01) 8450633 100⇄ ♠

Donabate ☎ (01) 8436346
Level parkland course.
18 holes, 5704yds, Par 70, SSS 69.
Visitors may not play on Wed or at weekends.
Green Fees not confirmed.
Facilities ⊗ ⊪ ⅃ ♀ ⊟ ⊶ ⸍ ℓ Hugh Jackson.
Hotel ★★★60% Grand Hotel, MALAHIDE
☎ (01) 8450633 100⇄ ♠

The Island ☎ (01) 8436104
Links course on a promontory, with sea inlets separating
some of the fairways. Accuracy as well as length of shots are
required on some holes and sand hills provide an additional
challenge.
18 holes, 6053mtrs, Par 71, SSS 72.
Club membership 800.
Visitors preferred on Mon, Tue & Fri.
Societies must apply in advance.
Green Fees IR£27 per round.
Facilities ⊗ ⊪ ⅃ ⊩ ♀ ⚲
Location Corballis
Hotel ★★★60% Grand Hotel, MALAHIDE
☎ (01) 8450633 100⇄ ♠

DUBLIN Map 01 D4

Castle ☎ (01) 904207
A tight, tree-lined parkland course which is very highly
regarded by all who play there.
18 holes, 5653mtrs, Par 70, SSS 69.
Club membership 1150.
Visitors restricted at weekends.
Societies must apply in writing.
Green Fees IR£25 per round.
Facilities ⊗ ⊪ (Tue-Sat) ⊩ ♀ ⚲ ⊟ ℓ
Leisure snooker.

Location Woodside Dr, Rathfarnham
Hotel ★★★★64% Jurys Hotel and Towers,
Ballsbridge, DUBLIN
☎ (01) 605000 284⇄ ♠ Annexe100⇄ ♠

Clontarf ☎ (01) 331892
The nearest golf course to Dublin city, with a historic
building as a clubhouse, Clontarf is a parkland type course
bordered on one side by a railway line. There are several
testing and challenging holes including the 12th, which
involves playihng over a pond and a quarry.
18 holes, 5459mtrs, Par 69, SSS 68, Course record 66.
Club membership 1000.
Visitors must contact in advance. May not play on Tue
between 1.30 & 2.30pm & Fri after 3pm; must
play with member at weekends. Mon is Ladies
Day. Dress code must be observed.
Societies Tue & Fri. Must contact in writing.
Green Fees IR£21 per day.
Facilities ⊗ ⊪ ⅃ ⊩ ♀ ⚲ ⊟ ⸍ ℓ Joe Craddock.
Leisure snooker, bowling green.
Location Donnycarney House, Malahide Rd
Hotel ★★★63% Central Hotel, 1-5 Exchequer St,
DUBLIN 2
☎ (01) 6797302 70⇄ ♠

Deer Park Hotel & Golf Course ☎ (01) 322624
Claiming to be Irelands largest golf/hotel complex, be warned
that its popularity makes it extremely busy at times and only
hotel residents can book tee-off times.
*St Fintans: 18 holes, 6647yds, Par 72, SSS 73, Course record
72.*
Old 9: 9 holes, 3130yds, Par 35.
Par 3: 12 holes, 1810yds, Par 36.
Club membership 200.
Visitors no restrictions.
Societies must contact by telephone.
Green Fees IR£7.50 (IR£9.50 weekends) 18 holes; IR£4/5 9
holes.
Facilities ⊗ ⊪ ⅃ ⊩ ♀ ⚲ ⊟ ⸍ ⊠
Leisure snooker.
Location Howth On right 0.5m before Howth Harbour.
Hotel ★★★53% Howth Lodge Hotel, HOWTH
☎ (01) 321010 46rm(41⇄ ♠)

Edmonstown ☎ (01) 931082 & 932462
A popular and testing parkland course situated at the foot of
the Dublin Mountains in the suburbs of the city. An attractive
stream flows in front of the 4th and 6th greens calling for an
accurate approach shot.
18 holes, 5663mtrs, Par 70, SSS 69.
Club membership 600.
Visitors must contact in advance as there are daily
restrictions.
Societies must contact in writing.
Green Fees IR£18 per round (IR£22 weekends & bank
holidays).
Facilities ⊗ ⊪ ⅃ ⊩ ♀ ⚲ ⊟ ℓ Andrew Crofton.
Leisure snooker.
Location Edmondstown Rd, Edmondstown
Hotel ★★★59% Hotel Montrose, Stillorgan Rd,
DUBLIN
☎ (01) 2693311 190⇄ ♠

Elm Park Golf & Sports Club ☎ (01) 2693438
Interesting parkland course requiring a degree of accuracy,
particularly as half of the holes involve crossing the stream.
18 holes, 5422mtrs, Par 69, SSS 68.
Club membership 1750.
Visitors telephone before arrival.
Societies apply in writing.
Green Fees IR£30 per round (IR£35 weekends).
Facilities ⊗ ⊪ 🏌 ⬛ ♀ ⚘ 📷 ⚑ 🥤 Seamus Green.
Leisure grass tennis courts.
Location Nutley House (3m from city centre)
Hotel ★★★★64% Jurys Hotel and Towers,
Ballsbridge, DUBLIN
☎ (01) 605000 284⇆ 🐾 Annexe100⇆ 🐾

Grange ☎ (01) 932889
Wooded parkland course which provides both interest and
challenge.
18 holes, 5517mtrs, Par 68, SSS 69.
Visitors preferred on weekdays.
Green Fees not confirmed.
Facilities ⊗ ⊪ 🏌 ♀ 📷 🥤 W Sullivan.
Location Rathfarnham (6m from city centre)
Hotel ★★★59% Hotel Montrose, Stillorgan Rd,
DUBLIN
☎ (01) 2693311 190⇆ 🐾

Howth ☎ (01) 323055
A moorland course with scenic views of Dublin Bay. It is
very hilly and presents a good challenge for the athletic
golfer.
18 holes, 5618mtrs, Par 71, SSS 69.
Club membership 1257.
Visitors may not play on Wed, Sat or Sun. Contact in
advance if more than 4 in party.
Societies must apply in writing.
Green Fees IR£16 Mon-Thu; IR£18 Fri.
Facilities 🏌 ⬛ ♀ ⚘ 📷 🥤 John McGuirk.
Leisure snooker.
Location St Fintan's, Carrickbrack Rd, Sutton
Hotel ★★★61% Marine Hotel, Sutton, DUBLIN
☎ (01) 322613 27⇆ 🐾

Milltown ☎ (01) 976090
Level parkland course on the outskirts of the city.
18 holes, 5638mtrs, Par 71, SSS 69, Course record 67.
Club membership 1200.
Visitors with member only on Sun and after 5pm daily.
Must contact in advance.
Societies welcome.
Green Fees not confirmed.
Facilities ⊗ ⊪ 🏌 ⬛ ♀ ⚘ 📷 🥤 John Harnett.
Leisure snooker.
Location Lower Churchtown Rd
Hotel ★★★★64% Jurys Hotel and Towers,
Ballsbridge, DUBLIN
☎ (01) 605000 284⇆ 🐾 Annexe100⇆ 🐾

Newlands ☎ (01) 593157
Mature parkland course offering a testing game.
18 holes, 5714mtrs, Par 71, SSS 70.
Club membership 1000.
Visitors must contact in advance and may play Mon,
Thu, Fri and Wed mornings only.
Societies must contact in writing.
Green Fees IR£25 per round.

Facilities ⊗ (Mon-Fri) ⊪ (by prior arrangement winter)
🏌 ⬛ ♀ ⚘ 📷 ⚑ 🥤 Karl O'Donnell.
Location Clondalkin
Hotel ★★★56% Green Isle Hotel, Clondalkin,
DUBLIN
☎ (01) 593406 48⇆ 🐾 Annexe35⇆ 🐾

Rathfarnham ☎ (01) 931201
Parkland course designed by John Jacobs in 1962.
9 holes, 5833mtrs, Par 71, SSS 70.
Club membership 554.
Visitors may not play Tue, Sat, or Thu pm.
Societies must apply in writing.
Green Fees not confirmed.
Facilities 🏌 ⬛ ♀ ⚘ 📷 🥤 Brian O'Hara.
Location Newtown
Hotel ★★★★64% Jurys Hotel and Towers,
Ballsbridge, DUBLIN
☎ (01) 605000 284⇆ 🐾 Annexe100⇆ 🐾

Royal Dublin ☎ (01) 336346 & 331262
A popular course with visitors, for its design subtleties,
for the condition of the holes and the friendly atmosphere.
Founded in 1885, the club moved to its present site in
1889 and received its Royal designation in 1891. A
notable former club professional was Christie O'Connor,
who was appointed in 1959 and immediately made his
name. Along with its many notable holes, Royal Dublin
has a fine and testing finish. The 18th is a sharply dog-
legged par 4, with out of bounds along the right-hand
side. The decision to try the long carry over the 'garden'
is one many visitors have regretted.
18 holes, 6262mtrs, Par 71, SSS 71, Course record 63.
Club membership 875.
Visitors must contact in advance & have handicap
certificate. Green fees not accepted on Wed
or Sat.
Societies must apply in writing.
Green Fees IR£35 per round (IR£45 weekends).
Facilities ⊗ ⊪ 🏌 ⬛ ♀ ⚘ 📷 ⚑ 🥤 Leonard Owens.
Leisure snooker, sauna, practice ground & nets,
putting green.
Location North Bull Island, Dollymount
Hotel ★★★63% Central Hotel, 1-5 Exchequer St,
DUBLIN 2 ☎ (01) 6797302 70⇆ 🐾

St Anne's ☎ (01) 336471
Links course, recently extended from 9 holes to 18.
18 holes, 5660mtrs, Par 70, SSS 69.
Club membership 500.
Visitors telephone for restrictions. Must have an
introduction from own club.
Societies must apply in writing.
Green Fees not confirmed.
Facilities ⊗ ⊪ 🏌 ⬛ ♀ ⚘ 🥤 Paddy Skerritt.
Location North Bull Island, Dollymount
Hotel ★★★63% Central Hotel, 1-5 Exchequer St,
DUBLIN 2 ☎ (01) 6797302 70⇆ 🐾

Stackstown ☎ (01) 942338 & 941993
Pleasant course in scenic surroundings.
18 holes, 5925mtrs, Par 72, SSS 72, Course record 70.
Club membership 1042.
Visitors preferred Mon-Fri.
Societies telephone in advance and confirm in writing.
Green Fees IR£14 (IR£18 weekeknd and bank holidays). ▶

Facilities ⊗ ⑂ ⑃ ♟ ♀ ⚘ 🏠 ⑁ Michael Kavanach.
Leisure snooker, sauna.
Location Kellystown Rd, Rathfarnham (9m S of city centre)
Hotel ★★★59% Hotel Montrose, Stillorgan Rd, DUBLIN ☎ (01) 2693311 190⇥ ⑁

DUN LAOGHAIRE Map 01 D4

Dun Laoghaire ☎ Dublin (01) 2803916
This is a well wooded parkland course, not long, but requiring accurate placing of shots.
18 holes, 5478mtrs, Par 70, SSS 69, Course record 66.
Club membership 1050.
Visitors with member only on Sun. Must contact in advance.
Societies must apply in writing.
Green Fees not confirmed.
Facilities ⊗ ⑂ (Apr-Oct) ⑃ ♟ ♀ ⚘ 🏠 ⑁ Owen Mulhall.
Location Eglinton Park, Tivoli Rd
Hotel ★★★59% Victor Hotel, Rochestown Av, DUN LAOGHAIRE ☎ (01) 2853555 & 2853102 64⇥ ⑁

KILLINEY Map 01 D3

Killiney ☎ Dublin (01) 2851983
The course is on the side of Killiney Hill with picturesque views over south Dublin and the Wicklow Mountains.
9 holes, Par 69.
Club membership 480.
Visitors welcome Thu, Sat & Sun am.
Green Fees not confirmed.
Facilities ⑃ ♟ ♀ ⚘ 🏠 ⑁ P O'Boyle.
Leisure snooker.
Location Ballinclea Rd
Hotel ★★★70% Fitzpatrick Castle Hotel, KILLINEY ☎ (01) 2840700 85⇥ ⑁

KILTERNAN Map 01 D4

Kilternan ☎ (01) 2955559
Interesting and testing course overlooking Dublin Bay.
18 holes, 4914mtrs, Par 68, SSS 67.
Club membership 789.
Visitors may not play before 1.30pm at weekends.
Societies must apply in writing.
Green Fees IR£12 (IR£15 weekends).
Facilities ⊗ ⑂ ⑃ ♟ ♀ ⚘ 🏠 ⑁ ⑁
Leisure hard tennis courts, heated indoor swimming pool, fishing, riding, snooker, sauna, solarium, gymnasium, dry ski slope, indoor tennis, night club.
Location Kilternan Hotel, Enniskerry Rd
Hotel ★★★70% Fitzpatrick Castle Hotel, KILLINEY ☎ (01) 2840700 85⇥ ⑁

A golf course name printed in **bold italics** means we have been unable to verify information with the club's management for the current year

---

LUCAN Map 01 D4

Finnstown Fairways ☎ (01) 6280644
A flat parkland 9-hole course based in grounds originally laid out in the 18th century. Very challenging 6th and 7th holes among many mature trees.
9 holes, 2695yds, Par 68, SSS 66.
Club membership 100.
Visitors time sheet in use.
Societies must reserve in advance.
Green Fees IR£10 per 18 holes (IR£12 weekends).
Facilities ⊗ ⑂ ⑃ ♟ ♀ ⚘ ⑁ 🏠
Leisure hard tennis courts, outdoor swimming pool, sauna, solarium, gymnasium, turkish bath.
Location Newcastle Rd (off N4)
Hotel ★★★57% Finnstown Country House Hotel & Golf Course, Newcastle Rd, LUCAN ☎ (01) 6280644 25⇥ ⑁

Hermitage ☎ (01) 6265049
Part level, part undulating course bordered by the River Liffey and offering some surprises.
18 holes, 6034mtrs, Par 71, SSS 70, Course record 65.
Club membership 1100.
Visitors must contact in advance and have an introduction from own club.
Societies must telephone well in advance.
Green Fees not confirmed.
Facilities ⊗ ⑂ (times vary with season) ⑃ ♟ ♀ ⚘ 🏠 ⑁ ⑁ David Daly.
Leisure snooker.
Location Ballydowd
Hotel ★★★57% Finnstown Country House Hotel & Golf Course, Newcastle Rd, LUCAN ☎ (01) 6280644 25⇥ ⑁

Lucan ☎ Dublin (01) 6282106
Founded in 1902 as a 9-hole course and only recently extended to 18 holes, Lucan involves playing across both the main road and a lane which bisects the course.
18 holes, 5958mtrs, Par 71, SSS 71, Course record 68.
Club membership 780.
Visitors with member only Sat & Sun, after 1pm Wed. Must contact in advance.
Societies must apply in writing.
Green Fees not confirmed.
Facilities ⊗ ⑂ ⑃ ♟ ♀ ⚘
Location Celbridge Rd
Hotel ★★★57% Finnstown Country House Hotel & Golf Course, Newcastle Rd, LUCAN ☎ (01) 6280644 25⇥ ⑁

MALAHIDE Map 01 D4

Malahide ☎ (01) 8461611
Parkland courses with water hazards at a number of holes.
Blue Course: 9 holes, 2888mtrs, Par 71, SSS 70.
Red Course: 9 holes, 2820mtrs, Par 71, SSS 70.
Yellow Course: 9 holes, 2632mtrs, Par 70, SSS 69.
Club membership 900.
Visitors must contact in advance, may not play on Sat & Sun mornings.
Societies must contact in advance.
Green Fees IR£21 per 18 holes (IR£31 weekends).

Facilities ⊗)⫟ 🯰 💺 ♀ 🧍 🏠 ⛳ 🍴
Leisure snooker.
Location Beechwood, The Grange (1m from coast road at Portmarnock)
Hotel ★★★60% Grand Hotel, MALAHIDE
☎ (01) 8450633 100⇌ 🐾

PORTMARNOCK   Map 01 D4

PORTMARNOCK See page 309

RATHCOOLE   Map 01 C3

Beech Park ☎ Dublin (01) 580100
Relatively flat parkland with heavily wooded fairways.
18 holes, 5730mtrs, Par 72, SSS 70, Course record 67.
Club membership 750.
Visitors restricted on some days, telephone in advance.
Societies apply in writing.
Green Fees not confirmed.
Facilities ⊗)⫟ 🯰 💺 ♀ 🧍
Leisure snooker.
Location Johnstown
Hotel ★★★57% Finnstown Country House Hotel & Golf Course, Newcastle Rd, LUCAN
☎ (01) 6280644 25⇌ 🐾

SKERRIES   Map 01 D4

Skerries ☎ (01) 8491567
Tree-lined parkland course on gently rolling countryside, with sea views from some holes. The 1st and 18th are particularly challenging. The club can be busy on some days, but is always friendly.
18 holes, 5994mtrs, Par 73, SSS 72.
Club membership 900.
Visitors must contact in advance.
Societies must contact well in advance in writing.
Green Fees IR£17 (IR£22 weekends).
Facilities ⊗)⫟ by prior arrangement
🯰 💺 ♀ 🧍 🏠 ⛳ 🍴 Jimmy Kinsella.
Leisure snooker.
Hotel ★★★60% Grand Hotel, MALAHIDE
☎ (01) 8450633 100⇌ 🐾

CO GALWAY

BALLINASLOE   Map 01 B4

Ballinasloe ☎ (0905) 42126
Well maintained parkland course, recently extended from a par 68 to a par 72.
18 holes, 6445yds, Par 72, SSS 70.
Club membership 800.
Visitors may not play on Sun.
Societies welcome on weekdays, apply in writing.
Green Fees not confirmed.
Facilities ⊗)⫟ 🯰 💺 (lunch/dinner summer only by arrangement) ♀ 🧍
Location Rossgloss
Hotel ★★★57% Hayden's Hotel, BALLINASLOE
☎ (0905) 42347 50⇌ 🐾

BALLYCONNEELY   Map 01 A4

Connemara ☎ Clifden (095) 23502
This championship links course is situated on the verge of the Atlantic Ocean in a most spectacular setting, with the Twelve Bens Mountains in the background. Established as recently as 1973, it is a tough challenge, due in no small part to its exposed location, with the back 9 the equal of any in the world. The last six holes are exceptionally long.
18 holes, 6173mtrs, Par 72, SSS 73.
Club membership 800.
Visitors must contact in advance and have a handicap certificate.
Societies must contact in writing.
Green Fees not confirmed.
Facilities ⊗)⫟ by prior arrangement
🯰 💺 ♀ 🧍 🏠 ⛳
Location 9m SW of Clifton
Hotel ★★★54% Abbeyglen Castle Hotel, Sky Rd, CLIFDEN ☎ (095) 21201 40⇌ 🐾

GALWAY   Map 01 B4

Galway ☎ (091) 22169
Designed by Dr Alister MacKenzie, this course is inland by nature, although some of the fairways run close to the ocean. The terrain is of gently sloping hillocks with plenty of trees and furze bushes to catch out the unwary. Although not a long course, it provided a worthy challenge as the venue of the Celtic International Tournament in 1984 and continues to delight the visiting golfer.
18 holes, 6376yds, Par 70, SSS 70.
Club membership 800.
Visitors preferred on weekdays, except Tue.
Societies must apply in writing.
Green Fees IR£20 per round.
Facilities ⊗)⫟ 🯰 💺 ♀ 🧍 🏠 ⛳ 🍴 Don Wallace.
Location Blackrock, Salthill (2m W in Salthill)
Hotel ★★★58% Great Southern Hotel, Eyre Square, GALWAY
☎ (091) 64041 117⇌ 🐾

GORT   Map 01 B3

Gort ☎ (091) 31336
A 9-hole course, bisected by a railway line and with out of bounds on most holes, six of which are bunkered.
9 holes, 2587mtrs, Par 34, SSS 67, Course record 67.
Club membership 220.
Visitors may not play on Sun mornings or Wed evenings.
Societies must contact club secretary or bar manager in advance.
Green Fees not confirmed.
Facilities 🯰 💺 ♀ 🧍 ⛳
Location Laughtyshaughnessy
Hotel ★★★66% Corrib Great Southern Hotel, Dublin Rd, GALWAY ☎ (091) 55281 178⇌ 🐾

This guide is up-dated annually – make sure you use the up-to-date edition

LOUGHREA

Map 01 B3

Loughrea ☎ Galway (091) 41049
An excellent parkland course with good greens and extended in 1992 to 18-holes. The course has an unusual feature in that it incorporates a historic souterrain (underground shelter/food store).
9 holes, 5860yds, Par 68, SSS 67.
Club membership 290.
Visitors may not play Sun mornings.
Societies must contact in advance.
Green Fees IR£10 per day (IR£12 weekends and bank holidays).
Facilities ⓑ ♥ ♀ ⌂
Location Bullaun Rd
Hotel ★★56% Westpark Hotel, PORTUMNA
☎ (0509) 41121 & 41112 29➪ ♟

ORANMORE

Map 01 B3

Athenry ☎ (091) 94466
Wooded parkland course, recently extended to 18 holes.
18 holes, 6100yds, Par 70, SSS 69.
Club membership 600.
Visitors may not play on Sun.
Societies must telephone in advance.
Green Fees IR£15 per round.
Facilities ⊗ Ⅲⓑ ♥ ♀ ⌂ ⌂ ♟
Location Palmerstown
Hotel ★★★66% Corrib Great Southern Hotel, Dublin Rd, GALWAY ☎ (091) 55281 178➪ ♟

OUGHTERARD

Map 01 B4

Oughterard ☎ (091) 82131
Well maintained parkland course with mature trees and shrubs. Some very challenging holes.
18 holes, 6060yds, Par 70, SSS 69.
Visitors preferred Mon-Fri.
Green Fees not confirmed.
Facilities ⊗ Ⅲ ⓑ ♀ ⌂ ♟ ♟ Michael Ryan.
Location 1m from town on Galway road
Hotel ★★★63% Connemara Gateway Hotel, OUGHTERARD ☎ (091) 82328 62➪ ♟

PORTUMNA

Map 01 B3

Portumna ☎ (0509) 41059
Parkland course with mature trees.
18 holes, 5205mtrs, Par 68, SSS 69, Course record 64.
Club membership 500.
Visitors must contact in advance to play on Sun.
Societies must contact in writing.
Green Fees not confirmed.
Facilities ⊗ by prior arrangement ⓑ ♥ ♀ ⌂ ♟
Location 1m from town on Scarriffe road
Hotel ★★56% Westpark Hotel, PORTUMNA
☎ (0509) 41121 & 41112 29➪ ♟

TUAM

Map 01 B4

Tuam ☎ (093) 24354
Interesting course with plenty of trees and bunkers.
18 holes, 6377yds, Par 73, SSS 70.

Visitors preferred Mon-Fri.
Green Fees not confirmed.
Facilities ⓑ ♀ ⌂ ♟
Location Barnacurragh (0.5m from town on Athenry road)
Hotel ★★★69% Ardilaun House Hotel, Taylor's Hill, GALWAY ☎ (091) 21433 92➪ ♟

CO KERRY

BALLYBUNION

Map 01 A3

BALLYBUNION See page 311

BALLYFERRITER

Map 01 A2

Ceann Sibeal ☎ (066) 56255
This most westerly golf course in Europe has a magnificent scenic location. It is a traditional links course with beautiful turf, many bunkers, a stream that comes into play on 14 holes and, usually, a prevailing wind.
18 holes, 6440yds, Par 72, SSS 71.
Club membership 300.
Visitors no restrictions.
Societies must telephone in advance.
Green Fees IR£21 per day; IR£16 per round.
Facilities ⊗ Ⅲ ⓑ ♥ ♀ ⌂ ⌂ ♟ ♟ Dermot O'Connor.
Hotel ★★★53% Benner's, Main St, DINGLE
☎ (066) 51638 25➪ ♟

GLENBEIGH

Map 01 A2

Dooks ☎ Tralee (066) 68205
Old-established course on the sea shore between the Kerry mountains and Dingle Bay. Sand dunes are a feature (the name Dooks is a derivation of the Gaelic word for sand bank) and the course offers a fine challenge in a superb Ring of Kerry location.
18 holes, 6010yds, Par 70, SSS 68.
Club membership 580.
Visitors no restrictions.
Societies must apply in writing.
Green Fees IR£15 per day.
Facilities ⊗ ⓑ ♥ ♀ ⌂
Hotel ★★★60% Gleneagle Hotel, KILLARNEY
☎ (064) 31870 177➪ ♟

KENMARE

Map 01 A2

Kenmare ☎ (064) 41291
Parkland course situated at the head of Kenmare Bay in very picturesque surroundings.
9 holes, 4410mtrs, Par 66, SSS 63, Course record 64.
Club membership 250.
Visitors may not play Wed or Sun.
Societies must contact secretary in writing.
Green Fees not confirmed. ▶

For a full list of all the golf courses included in this guide, see the index at the end of the Directory

⅁ortmarnock

Portmarnock ☎Dublin (01)8462 968   Map 01 D4

John Ingham writes: The night before our fourball tackled Portmarnock was spent, as I recall, in Dublin. Guinness in that city seems smoother, while the conversation with locals, ranged from why no southern Irish player ever won the Open to how such a small nation can boast so many great writers, wits and actors.

I can thoroughly recommend this preparation, prior to facing one of the world's great golfing challenges - providing you only intend playing eighteen holes in one day! Frankly, you will have to reach into the base of your golf bag to pull out every shot if you want to play to your handicap on this superb links.

An opening birdie, downwind, made me wonder what the fuss was about. Two hours later, with a backswing too fast and the breeze now something near a gale, I decided that a test of 7182 yards off the back tees was too man-size for me. Maybe it would be more enjoyable on a calm, summer evening!

I remember the course not for the way it humiliated me, but for the 1960 Canada Cup where I watched Sam Snead and Arnold Palmer winning with such skilful play. Even so, both took 75 in one round while scores by the mighty Gary Player ranged from 65 to 78.

There are no blind shots, unless you drive into sandhills. This is natural golf with no unfair carries off the tee and the only damage to your card is self-inflicted. True, there are a couple of holes of 560 yards and the 522-yard 16th is frightening as you tee up in a fierce wind.

It's incredible to think that Portmarnock was 'discovered' almost by accident in 1893 by a Mr Pickeman and the course architect, Ross. They had rowed a boat from Sutton to the peninsula where they came across a wilderness of bracken, duneland and natural-looking bunkers made by God. They were inspired to create the course, built a shack for a clubhouse and talked about the only real hazard left - a cow that devoured golf balls.

Today it's so very different - with a modern clubhouse filled with members delighted to belong to such an internationally well-known establishment.

Membership 1100

Visitors must apply in writing. Restricted Saturday, Sunday and Public Holidays

Societies must apply in writing

Green fees Monday-Friday (excluding Public Holidays) £IR40: Saturday, Sunday & Public Holidays £IR50 per day

Facilities ⊗ 胃 ⅃ ♀ (all day) ⟂ 🖻 ⊣⌐ ⟨ (Joey Purcell)

Location 12m from Dublin. 1m from village down Golf Rd

27 holes. Old Course: 18 holes, 7182 yds, Par 72, SSS 75, course record 74 (Sandy Lyle)
New Course: 9 holes, 3478yds, Par 37

WHERE TO STAY AND EAT NEARBY

HOTELS:

HOWTH

★★★ 53% Howth Lodge. ☎(01) 321010. 46 (41 ⇌) Irish & French cuisine

MALAHIDE

★★★ 60%Grand. ☎(01) 450633. 100 ⇌ 🖛. European cuisine

Facilities 🍺♟️⛱️📷🏌️
Location Kilgarvan Rd
Hotel ★★★★(red)🏨 Park Hotel, KENMARE
☎ (064) 41200 50🛏️ 🏌️

KILLARNEY
Map 01 A2

Killarney Golf & Fishing Club ☎ (064) 31034
Both of the courses are parkland with tree-lined fairways, many bunkers and small lakes which provide no mean challenge. Mahoney's Point Course has a particularly testing 5, 4, 3 finish and both courses call for great skill from the tee. Killarney has been the venue for many important events, including the Irish Open in 1991, and is a favourite of many famous golfers
Mahony's Point: 18 holes, 6152mtrs, Par 72.
Killeen: 18 holes, 6475mtrs, Par 72.
Club membership 1400.
Visitors must contact in advance & have a handicap certificate.
Societies must telephone in advance.
Green Fees not confirmed.
Facilities ⊗🍴🛒🍺♟️⛱️📷🏌️ Tony Coveney.
Leisure sauna, gymnasium.
Location O'Mahony's Point (On Ring of Kerry road)
Hotel ★★★★78% Aghadoe Heights Hotel, KILLARNEY ☎ (064) 31766 60 🛏️ 🏌️
Additional ★★★60% Gleneagle Hotel, KILLARNEY
Hotel ☎ (064) 31870 177🛏️ 🏌️

★★★
Gleneagle Hotel
KILLARNEY, CO. KERRY
TEL. 064-31870. FAX. 064-32646

Located in 25 acres of landscaped parkland, on the banks of the river Flesk, adjacent to the 25,000 acre National Park – the Gleneagle is ideally situated for a wide range of leisure holidays and general and special activities.

With 3 bars, 3 restaurants, 3 conference rooms, it is the ideal choice for meetings, seminars with a full business and social programme. Swimming pool, sauna, gym, jacuzzi, steam room, pitch and putt, tennis, squash, children's playground, creche – all on site. Lake cruises, coach tours, fishing, golf, pony trekking, cycle hire etc. are all arranged by the hotel.

Free colour brochure available.

IRELAND'S LEADING LEISURE HOTEL

PARKNASILLA
Map 01 A2

Parknasilla ☎ (064) 45122
Short, tricky 9-hole course, with 18 different tees which make the second 9 more interesting.
9 holes, 2447yds, Par 35, SSS 65, Course record 64.
Club membership 40.
Visitors may not play on competition days.
Societies must contact in advance.
Green Fees not confirmed.
Facilities ⊗🍴🛒🍺♟️⛱️📷🏌️🍽️ Charles McCarthy.
Leisure hard tennis courts, heated indoor swimming pool, riding, snooker, sauna.
Hotel ★★★★68% Great Southern Hotel, PARKNASILLA ☎ (064) 45122 25 🛏️ 🏌️ Annexe59 🛏️ 🏌️

TRALEE
Map 01 A2

Tralee ☎ (066) 36379
The first Arnold Palmer designed course in Europe, the magnificent 18-hole links are set in spectacular scenery on the Barrow peninsula. Perhaps the most memorable hole is the par four 17th which plays from a high tee, across a deep gorge to a green perched high against a backdrop of mountains.
18 holes, 6252mtrs, Par 73, Course record 66.
Club membership 1000.
Visitors may play before 4.30pm on weekdays but only 10.30am-12.15pm on Wed & 11am-12.30pm at weekends & bank holidays. Must have a handicap certificate. Must contact in advance.
Societies weekdays only; must contact in writing.
Green Fees not confirmed.
Facilities ⊗🍴🛒🍺♟️⛱️📷
Location West Barrow (8m W of Tralee on Spa-Fenit road)
Hotel ★★★63% The Brandon Hotel, TRALEE ☎ (066) 23333 160🛏️ 🏌️

WATERVILLE
Map 01 A2

Waterville ☎ (0667) 4102
On the western tip of the Ring of Kerry, this course is highly regarded by many top golfers. The feature holes are the par five 11th, which runs along a rugged valley between towering dunes, and the par three 17th, which features an exceptionally elevated tee. Needless to say, the surroundings are beautiful.
18 holes, 6549yds, Par 72, SSS 74, Course record 65.
Club membership 300.
Visitors must have a handicap certificate. May not play on Sun 8.30-9.30am & 2-3.30pm. Must contact in advance and have an introduction from own club.
Societies must contact in advance.
Green Fees not confirmed.
Facilities ⊗🍴🛒🍺♟️⛱️📷🏌️🍽️ Liam Higgins.
Leisure fishing, riding.
Hotel ★★64% Derrynane Hotel, CAHERDANIEL ☎ (0667) 5136 75🛏️

$\mathcal{B}$allybunion

Ballybunion ☎ **(068) 27146**　　　　　　　**Map 01 A3**

John Ingham writes: Since golf is a state of mind over muscle and a great day on the links is exhilarating, it is my view that memorable fairways tend not to be decorated with artificial lakes that are fun only for ducks and golf ball manufacturers.

Some of the best courses look natural, even though they may have been helped along by skilful architects such as Colt, Hawtree or Mackenzie. And in the Emerald Isle, it is entirely appropriate that, back in 1906, a Mr Murphy built Ballybunion on the West Coast of Ireland. Believe me, there are few greater adventures waiting to be tackled and not to play this old course is a crime.

In an American list of the world's top 100 courses, Ballybunion is in there at number eight and the reason is simple: it probably represents the ultimate links on as wild a stretch as you will find. The Atlantic waves crash into the shore and no golfer will ever feel closer to nature as he hunts his ball and flights it through crosswinds and breathtaking views. This course is a star even in a part of Ireland that is wall-to-wall golf courses of the highest calibre. The experience of taking on this classic will be remembered as long as you live.

There are now two courses at Ballybunion, separated only by a 19th hole that has heard all the wondrous stories before, as well as hosting such great names as Tom Watson, five times winner of the Open. Likeable Tom can't speak highly enough of the place and claims that before anyone builds a golf course, they should play Ballybunion.

Membership 1500

Visitors must contact in advance, and have a handicap certificate (maximum handicap 24; women 36)

Societies must book in advance

Green fees Old Course: £30 per round; New Course: £20 per round. Day ticket £40 (but Old Course cannot be played twice)

Facilities ⊗ ⊞ ⮯ ☕ ♀ ⛳ 🏠 ⚑ ✆ (Ted Higgins)

Location Sandhill Rd

36 holes. Old Course: 18 holes, 6593 yds, Par 71, SSS 72
New Course: 18 holes, 6130 yds, Par 71, SSS 72

WHERE TO STAY AND EAT NEARBY

HOTELS:
BALLYBUNION
★★ 70% Marine. ☎ (068) 27522 & 27139. 13 ⇆ 🐾
Irish & French cuisine

CO KILDARE

DONADEA   Map 01 C4

Knockanally Golf & Country Club ☎ (045) 69322
Home of the Irish International Professional Matchplay
championship, this parkland course is set in a former estate,
with a Palladian-style clubhouse.
18 holes, 6485yds, Par 72, SSS 72, Course record 66.
Club membership 320.
Visitors   may not play on Sun 8.30am-noon.
Societies   must contact in writing.
Green Fees IR£15 (IR£18 weekends).
Facilities   ⊗ & ⅷ by prior arrangement
                      ᴸ 🍷 ♀ ⚘ 🏌 🏌 (Peter Hickey.
Leisure   fishing.
Location   3m off main Dublin-Galway road
Hotel   ★★56% Curryhills House Hotel, PROSPEROUS
                      ☎ (045) 68150 10⇄ ⋒

KILDARE   Map 01 C3

Curragh ☎ (045) 41238
A particularly challenging course, well wooded and with
lovely scenery all around.
18 holes, 6003mtrs, Par 72, SSS 71.
Club membership 900.
Visitors   preferred on Mon, Thu & Fri.
Societies   apply in writing.
Green Fees not confirmed.
Facilities   ⊗ ⅷ (summer) ᴸ 🍷 ♀ ⚘ ⚘ 🏌 (Phil Lawlor.
Location   Curragh (Off N7 between Newbridge & Kildare)
Hotel   ★★56% Curryhills House Hotel, PROSPEROUS
                      ☎ (045) 68150 10⇄ ⋒

KILL   Map 01 D3

Killeen ☎ (045) 66003 & 66045
Set in pleasant countryside, the attractive course is
characterised by its many lakes. It provides a challenge to test
the skills of the moderate enthusiast and the more
experienced golfer.
18 holes, 4979mtrs, Par 69, SSS 66, Course record 71.
Club membership 300.
Visitors   may not play at weekends before 10am.
Societies   must contact in advance.
Green Fees IR£10 per round (IR£12 per round weekends &
                      bank holidays).
Facilities   ⊗ & ⅷ by prior arrangement ᴸ 🍷 ♀ ⚘ ⚘ 🏌
Leisure   snooker, putting green.
Location   Off N7 at Kill signposted
Hotel   ★★★70% Fitzpatrick Castle Hotel, KILLINEY
                      ☎ (01) 2840700 85⇄ ⋒

A golf course name printed in ***bold italics***
means we have been unable to verify
information with the club's management for
the current year

NAAS   Map 01 C3

Bodenstown ☎ (045) 97096
The old course in Bodenstown has ample fairways and large
greens, some of which are raised, providing more than a fair
test of golf. The Ladyhill course is a little shorter and tighter,
but still affords a fair challenge.
Bodenstown: 18 holes, 5788mtrs, Par 72, SSS 70.
Ladyhill: 18 holes, 5278mtrs, Par 71, SSS 68.
Club membership 650.
Visitors   may not play on Bodenstown course at
                      weekends.
Societies   must contact by telephone.
Green Fees not confirmed.
Facilities   ⊗ ⅷ ᴸ 🍷 ♀ ⚘
Leisure   snooker.
Location   Sallins (4m from town near Bodenstown
                      graveyard)
Hotel   ★★★56% Downshire House Hotel,
                      BLESSINGTON ☎ (045) 65199
                      14⇄ ⋒ Annexe11⇄ ⋒

Naas ☎ (045) 97509
Scenic parkland course with different tees for the return 9.
9 holes, 3000mtrs, Par 36, SSS 70, Course record 68.
Club membership 800.
Visitors   may not play on Sun, Tue or Thu.
Societies   must contact in advance.
Green Fees not confirmed.
Facilities   ᴸ 🍷 ♀ ⚘
Leisure   snooker.
Location   Kerdiffstown (1m from town on Sallins-
                      Johnstown road)
Hotel   ★★★56% Downshire House Hotel,
                      BLESSINGTON ☎ (045) 65199
                      14⇄ ⋒ Annexe11⇄ ⋒

CO KILKENNY

KILKENNY   Map 01 C3

Kilkenny ☎ (056) 22125 & 65400
One of Ireland's most pleasant inland courses, noted for
its tricky finishing holes and its par threes. Features of
the course are its long 11th and 13th holes and the
challenge increases year by year as thousands of trees
planted over the last 30 years or so are maturing. As host
of the Kilkenny Scratch Cup annually, the course is
permanently maintained in championship condition. The
Irish Dunlop Tournament and the Irish Professional
Matchplay Championship have also been held here.
18 holes, 5824mtrs, Par 71, SSS 70, Course record 65.
Club membership 1000.
Visitors   restricted weekends & Tue. Must contact in
                      advance.
Societies   must contact in advance.
Green Fees IR£15 (IR£17 weekends).
Facilities   ⊗ ⅷ ᴸ 🍷 ♀ ⚘ ⚘ 🏌 (Noel Leahy.
Leisure   snooker.
Location   Glendine (1m from centre on Castlecomer road)
Hotel   ★★★65% Hotel Kilkenny, College Rd,
                      KILKENNY ☎ (056) 62000 60⇄ ⋒

CO LAOIS

MOUNTRATH
Map 01 C3

Mountrath ☎ (0502) 32558
Small picturesque course at the foot of the Slieve Bloom Mountains in central Ireland. The course is in the process of being extended to 18 holes, due to be completed by summer 1994.
9 holes, 4634mtrs, Par 68, SSS 66.
Club membership 300.
Visitors no restrictions.
Societies must contact in advance.
Green Fees IR£7 (£8 weekends).
Facilities ⓛ ♥ ⚲ ⚴
Location Knockanina (1.5m from town on Dublin-Limerick road)
Hotel ★★★50% Killeshin Hotel, Dublin Rd, PORTLAOISE ☎ (0502) 21663 44⇋ ⭍

PORTARLINGTON
Map 01 C3

Portarlington ☎ Portlaoise (0502) 23115
Lovely parkland course beside the River Barrow and surrounded by 10,000 trees.
9 holes, 5264mtrs, Par 68, SSS 68.
Club membership 400.
Visitors must be accompanied by member, contact in advance and have an introduction from own club.
Societies must contact in writing.
Green Fees not confirmed.
Facilities ⊗ ⽶ ⓛ & ♥ by prior arrangement ⚲ ⚴
Location Garryhinch (4m from town on Mountmellick road)
Hotel ★★★56% Hotel Montague, Portlaoise, EMO ☎ (0502) 26154 75⇋ ⭍

PORTLAOISE
Map 01 C3

The Heath ☎ (0502) 46533
One of the oldest clubs in Ireland. The course is set in pretty countryside and offers a good challenge.
18 holes, 5721mtrs, Par 71, SSS 70.
Club membership 700.
Visitors preferred on weekdays.
Societies apply in writing
Green Fees IR£10 per day (IR£16 weekends and bank holidays).
Facilities ⊗ ⽶ by prior arrangement
ⓛ ♥ ⚲ ⚴ ⮱ ⭍ ⭤ Eddie Doyle.
Leisure snooker.
Location 5m NE
Hotel ★★★50% Killeshin Hotel, Dublin Rd, PORTLAOISE ☎ (0502) 21663 44⇋ ⭍

We make every effort to ensure that our information is accurate but details may change after we go to print

---

CO LEITRIM

BALLINAMORE
Map 01 C4

Ballinamore ☎ (078) 44346
A very dry and very testing 9-hole parkland course along the Ballinamore/Ballyconnell Canal.
9 holes, 5680yds, Par 68, SSS 66, Course record 68.
Club membership 100.
Visitors restricted occasionally. Must contact in advance.
Societies must contact in writing.
Green Fees not confirmed.
Facilities ⓛ ♥ ⚲ ⚴
Leisure fishing.
Hotel ★★61% Royal Hotel, BOYLE ☎ (079) 62016 16⇋ ⭍

CO LIMERICK

LIMERICK
Map 01 B3

Castletroy ☎ (061) 335753
Parkland course with out of bounds on the left of the first two holes. The long par five 10th features a narrow entrance to a green guarded by a stream. The par three 13th has a panoramic view of the course and surrounding countryside from the tee and the 18th is a daunting finish, with the drive played towards a valley with the ground rising towards the green which is protected on both sides by bunkers. In recent years the club has hosted the finals of the Irish Mixed Foursomes and the Senior Championships.
18 holes, 5793mtrs, Par 71, SSS 71.
Club membership 1066.
Visitors must contact in advance & have handicap certificate but may not play Sun or 1-2.30pm weekdays.
Societies must contact in advance.
Green Fees IR£20 per day/round.
Facilities ⊗ ⽶ ⓛ ♥ ⚲ ⚴ ⮱ ⭍ ⭤ Noel Cassidy.
Leisure snooker.
Location Castletroy (3m from city on Dublin road)
Hotel ★★★69% Jurys Hotel, Ennis Rd, LIMERICK ☎ (061) 327777 95⇋ ⭍

Limerick ☎ (061) 414083
Tree-lined parkland course which hosted the 1991 Ladies Senior Interprovincial matches. The club are the only Irish winners of the European Cup Winners Team Championship.
18 holes, 5890mtrs, Par 72, SSS 71, Course record 69.
Club membership 1350.
Visitors may not play after 4pm or on Tue & weekends.
Societies must contact in writing.
Green Fees IR£20 per day.
Facilities ⊗ ⽶ ⓛ ♥ ⚲ ⚴ ⮱ ⭍ ⭤ John Cassidy.
Leisure snooker.
Location Ballyclough (3m S on Fedamore road)
Hotel ★★★69% Jurys Hotel, Ennis Rd, LIMERICK ☎ (061) 327777 95⇋ ⭍

CO LOUTH

ARDEE   Map 01 C4

Ardee ☎ (041) 53227
Pleasant parkland course with mature trees and a stream.
18 holes, 6100yds, Par 69, SSS 69.
Visitors may normally play on weekdays (except Wed).
Green Fees not confirmed.
Facilities ⌘ ⅊ ♀
Location Townparks
Hotel ★★★65% Ballymascanlon House Hotel,
DUNDALK ☎ (042) 71124 36⇄

BALTRAY   Map 01 D4

County Louth ☎ Drogheda (041) 22329
Generally held to have the best greens in Ireland, this
links course was designed by Tom Simpson to have well
guarded and attractive greens without being overly
dependant on bunkers. It provides a good test for the
modern champion, notably as the annual venue for the
East of Ireland Amateur Open.
18 holes, 6577yds, Par 73, SSS 72.
Club membership 1000.
Visitors must contact in advance and have a
handicap certificate.
Societies must contact in writing.
Green Fees IR£27 (IR£33 weekends).
Facilities ⊗ ⌘ ⅊ ♀ 🍴 Paddy McGuirk.
Leisure snooker.
Location 5m NE of Drogheda
Hotel ★★★62% Boyne Valley Hotel,
DROGHEDA ☎ (041) 37737 35⇄ ♠

DUNDALK   Map 01 D4

Dundalk ☎ (042) 21731
A tricky course with extensive views.
18 holes, 6115mtrs, Par 72, SSS 72.
Club membership 1000.
Visitors must contact in advance and may not play Tue or
Sun.
Societies must apply in writing 3 to 6 months in advance.
Green Fees not confirmed.
Facilities ⊗ ⌘ ⅊ ♀ 🍴 James Cassidy.
Leisure sauna.
Location 2.5m S on coast road
Hotel ★★★65% Ballymascanlon House Hotel,
DUNDALK ☎ (042) 71124 36⇄

GREENORE   Map 01 D4

Greenore ☎ Dundalk (042) 73212
Situated amidst beautiful scenery on the shores of Carlingford
Lough, the trees here are an unusual feature on a links course.
There are quite a number of water facilities, tight fairways
and very good greens.
18 holes, Par 71, SSS 71, Course record 68.
Club membership 500.

Visitors must contact in advance at weekends. A letter of
introduction is desirable, but not essential.
Societies must contact in writing well in advance.
Green Fees not confirmed.
Facilities ⊗ ⌘ ⅊ ♀ ♀
Hotel ★★★65% Ballymascanlon House Hotel,
DUNDALK
☎ (042) 71124 36⇄

CO MAYO

BALLINROBE   Map 01 B4

Ballinrobe ☎ (092) 41448
Mainly flat terrain with some very interesting features.
Although no other club plays on the course, its landlords, The
Ballinrobe Race Company, hold races there five or six times a
year.
9 holes, 5790yds, Par 72, SSS 68, Course record 67.
Club membership 250.
Visitors may not play on Tue after 5pm or on Sun.
Societies must contact Secretary in advance on 092 41659.
Green Fees IR£8 per day; IR£10 per day Jun-Aug.
Facilities ⅊ (summer only) ♀ ♀
Leisure snooker.
Location Castlebar Rd
Hotel ★★★60% Breaffy House Hotel, CASTLEBAR
☎ (094) 22033 40⇄

BALLYHAUNIS   Map 01 B4

Ballyhaunis ☎ (0907) 30014
Undulating parkland course with 9 holes, 10 greens and 18
tees.
18 holes, 5393mtrs, Par 69, SSS 68.
Club membership 185.
Visitors may not play Thu & Sun. Must contact in
advance.
Societies must contact in advance.
Green Fees IR£6 per day.
Facilities ⊗ ⌘ & ⅊ by prior arrangement ♀ ♀
Leisure putting green.
Location Coolnaha
Hotel ★★★60% Breaffy House Hotel, CASTLEBAR
☎ (094) 22033 40⇄

CASTLEBAR   Map 01 B4

Castlebar ☎ (094) 21649
Pleasant parkland course with a particularly interesting 9th
hole.
18 holes, 5591yds, Par 71, SSS 69, Course record 67.
Club membership 600.
Visitors no restrictions.
Societies must contact in advance.
Green Fees IR£10 per day.
Facilities ⊗ by prior arrangement ⅊ ♀ ♀
Location Rocklands (1m from town on Belcarra road)
Hotel ★★★60% Breaffy House Hotel, CASTLEBAR
☎ (094) 22033 40⇄

KEEL

Map 01 A4

Achill ☎ (098) 43202
Seaside links in a scenic location on the edge of the Atlantic Ocean.
9 holes, 2723yds, Par 70, SSS 66.
Club membership 50.
Visitors no restrictions.
Societies must telephone in advance.
Green Fees IR£4 per day.
Facilities ⛳ ⚑
Location Achill, Westport
Hotel ★★★♨74% Newport House Hotel, NEWPORT
☎ (098) 41222 & 41154 13⇄ ⚐ Annexe7⇄ ⚐

SWINFORD

Map 01 B4

Swinford ☎ (094) 51378 & 51729
A pleasant parkland course with good views of the beautiful surrounding countryside.
9 holes, 5901yds, Par 70, SSS 68, Course record 70.
Club membership 237.
Visitors no restrictions.
Societies must contact in writing.
Green Fees IR£5 per day.
Facilities ⛳ & ☕ (afternoon) ⚐ ⛳
Leisure squash, fishing, riding, snooker.
Location Brabazon Park
Hotel ★★★60% Breaffy House Hotel, CASTLEBAR
☎ (094) 22033 40⇄

WESTPORT

Map 01 A4

Westport ☎ (098) 25113
This is a beautiful course with wonderful views of Clew Bay, with its 365 islands, and the holy mountain called Croagh Patrick, famous for the annual pilgrimage to its summit. Golfers indulge in a different kind of penance on this challenging course with many memorable holes. Perhaps the most exciting is the par five 15th, 580 yards long and featuring a long carry from the tee over an inlet of Clew Bay.
18 holes, 6959yds, Par 73, SSS 73, Course record 68.
Club membership 650.
Visitors may not play Wed 8-9.30pm & 1.45-3pm, or Sat & Sun 8-10am & 1-3pm.
Societies must write for application form.
Green Fees not confirmed.
Facilities ⊗ �🍴 ⛳ ☕ ⚐ ⛳ ⚑ ⚑ Alex Mealia.
Location Carrowholly
Hotel ★★★61% Hotel Westport, WESTPORT
☎ (098) 25122 49⇄ ⚐

CO MEATH

BETTYSTOWN

Map 01 D4

Laytown & Bettystown ☎ (041) 27170
A very competitive and trying links course, home of famous golfer, Des Smyth.
18 holes, 5652mtrs.
Club membership 950.

Visitors may not play 1-2pm. Must contact in advance.
Societies must contact in writing.
Green Fees not confirmed.
Facilities ⛳ ⚑ ⚑ ⚑
Leisure tennis courts, snooker.
Hotel ★★★62% Boyne Valley Hotel, DROGHEDA
☎ (041) 37737 35⇄ ⚐

DUNSHAUGHLIN

Map 01 C4

Black Bush ☎ (01) 8250021
Recently constructed 18-hole course in lovely parkland, with a lake providing a hazard at the 1st. The 9-hole course is less of a challenge.
Course 1: 18 holes, 6930yds, Par 72, SSS 73.
Course 2: 9 holes, 3020yds, Par 35, SSS 35.
Club membership 850.
Visitors may not play Tue afternoons.
Societies must apply in writing.
Green Fees IR£12 per round (IR£14 weekends).
Facilities ⊗ & 🍴 by prior arrangement (Mon-Fri)
⛳ ☕ ⚐ ⛳
Leisure snooker, driving range.
Location Thomastown (1.5m from village on Dublin-Navan road)
Hotel ★★★57% Finnstown Country House Hotel & Golf Course, Newcastle Rd, LUCAN
☎ (01) 6280644 25⇄ ⚐

KELLS

Map 01 C4

Headfort ☎ (046) 40146
A delightful parkland course which is regarded as one of the best of its kind in Ireland. There are ample opportunities for birdies, but even if these are not achieved, Headfort provides for a most pleasant game.
18 holes, 6480yds, Par 72, SSS 70, Course record 65.
Club membership 650.
Visitors must contact in advance.
Societies must contact in writing.
Green Fees not confirmed.
Facilities ⛳ ☕ ⚐ ⛳ ⚑ ⚑ Brendan McGovern.
Hotel ★★57% Conyngham Arms Hotel, SLANE
☎ (041) 24155 16rm(15⇄ ⚐)

NAVAN

Map 01 C4

Royal Tara ☎ (046) 25244 & 25508
Pleasant parkland course offering plenty of variety. Situated close to the Hill of Tara, the ancient seat of the Kings of Ireland.
18 holes, 5757mtrs, Par 71, SSS 70, Course record 66 or 9 holes, 3184yds, Par 35, SSS 35.
Club membership 1000.
Visitors preferred Mon, Thu & Fri.
Societies welcome Mon & Thu-Sat, apply in writing or telephone.
Green Fees IR£14 per round (IR£18 weekends & bank holidays).
Facilities ⊗ 🍴 ⛳ ☕ ⚐ ⛳ ⚑ ⚑ Adam Whiston.
Leisure snooker.
Location Bellinter (6m from town on N3)
Hotel ★★57% Conyngham Arms Hotel, SLANE
☎ (041) 24155 16rm(15⇄ ⚐)

CO MONAGHAN

CO OFFALY

CARRICKMACROSS — Map 01 C4

Nuremore ☎ Dundalk (042) 61438
Picturesque parkland course of championship length which offers an excellent test of golf.
18 holes, 6206mtrs, Par 72, SSS 73.
Club membership 275.
Visitors restricted for short periods at weekends.
Societies must contact in advance.
Green Fees IR£15 per day (IR£18 weekends & bank holidays).
Facilities ⊗ ⅲ ᴸᴸ 🍴 ♀ 🏊 🏠 ⛳ 🎿 🥢
Maurice Cassidy.
Leisure grass tennis courts, heated indoor swimming pool, squash, fishing, snooker, sauna, solarium, gymnasium.
Location S on Dublin road
Hotel ★★★65% Ballymascanlon House Hotel, DUNDALK ☎ (042) 71124 36⇄

CASTLEBLAYNEY — Map 01 C4

Castleblayney ☎ (042) 40197
Scenic course on Muckno Park estate, adjacent to Muckno Lake and Blayney Castle.
9 holes, 5345yds, Par 68, SSS 66, Course record 68.
Club membership 175.
Visitors may not play during competitions.
Societies must contact in advance.
Green Fees not confirmed.
Facilities 🏊
Leisure hard tennis courts.
Location Onomy
Hotel ★★★65% Ballymascanlon House Hotel, DUNDALK ☎ (042) 71124 36⇄

MONAGHAN — Map 01 C5

Rossmore ☎ (047) 81316
An undulating parkland course amidst beautiful countryside. At the time of going to press the course was being extended from 9 to 18 holes, the design commissioned from Des Smyth Golf Design.
18 holes, 6000yds, Par 70, SSS 68, Course record 66.
Club membership 350.
Visitors may not play on competition days.
Societies must contact in writing.
Green Fees not confirmed.
Facilities ⊗ ⅲ ᴸᴸ 🍴 ♀ 🏊
Leisure snooker.
Location Rossmore Park (2m S on Cootehill road)
Hotel ★★★65% Ballymascanlon House Hotel, DUNDALK ☎ (042) 71124 36⇄

Entries with a shaded background identify courses that are considered to be particularly interesting

BIRR — Map 01 C3

Birr ☎ (0509) 20082
The course has been laid out over undulating parkland utilising the natural contours of the land, which were created during the ice age. The sandy subsoil means that the course is playable all year round.
18 holes, 6262yds, Par 70, SSS 70.
Club membership 450.
Visitors may not play on Sun except 11am-noon; some restrictions on Sat.
Societies must contact in writing.
Green Fees not confirmed.
Facilities ⊗ by prior arrangement ᴸᴸ 🍴 ♀ 🏊
Location Glenns
Hotel ★★62% County Arms Hotel, BIRR ☎ (0509) 20791 & 20193 18⇄ 🏨

EDENDERRY — Map 01 C4

Edenderry ☎ (0405) 31072
A most friendly club which offers a relaxing game in pleasant surroundings. The course was extended to 18 holes in 1992.
18 holes, 6047yds, Par 71, SSS 69.
Club membership 350.
Visitors restricted Thu & weekends.
Societies may not play on Thu & Sun; must contact the secretary in writing.
Green Fees IR£7 per day.
Facilities ⊗ ᴸᴸ 🍴 ♀ 🏊
Leisure pool table.
Hotel ★★56% Curryhills House Hotel, PROSPEROUS ☎ (045) 68150 10⇄ 🏨

TULLAMORE — Map 01 C4

Tullamore ☎ (0506) 21439
Well wooded parkland course.
18 holes, 6314yds, Par 71, SSS 70.
Club membership 950.
Visitors must contact in advance, restricted on Tue & at weekends.
Societies must contact in writing.
Green Fees IR£12 (IR£15 weekends).
Facilities ⊗ ⅲ ᴸᴸ 🍴 ♀ 🏊 🏠 ⛳ 🥢 John E Kelly.
Location Brookfield (2.5m SW on Kinnity road)
Hotel ★★★58% Prince Of Wales Hotel, ATHLONE ☎ (0902) 72626 72⇄ 🏨

Remember – prior to playing a stroke or making a practise swing, the players should ensure that no one is standing close by and that no one should move, talk or stand close to or directly behind the ball or the hole when a player is addressing the ball or making a stroke

CO ROSCOMMON

ATHLONE
Map 01 C4

Athlone ☎ (0902) 92073

A picturesque course with a panoramic view of Lough Ree. Overall, it is a tight, difficult course with some outstanding holes and is noted for its magnificent greens.

18 holes, 5880mtrs, Par 71, SSS 70, Course record 64.
Club membership 1100.

Visitors	may not play on Sun & competition days. Afternoon only on Sat.
Societies	must contact in advance.
Green Fees	IR£12 (IR£15 weekends).
Facilities	⊗ & �𝕄 by prior arrangement ⯑ ⯑ 𝍢 ⯑ ⯑ ⯑ Martin Quinn.
Leisure	snooker.
Location	Hodson Bay (4m from town beside Lough Ree)
Hotel	★★★58% Prince Of Wales Hotel, ATHLONE ☎ (0902) 72626 72⇌ ⯑

BOYLE
Map 01 B4

Boyle

Situated on a low hill and surrounded by beautiful scenery, this is an undemanding course where, due to the generous fairways and semi-rough, the leisure golfer is likely to finish the round with the same golf ball.

9 holes, 5324yds, Par 67, SSS 66, Course record 65.
Club membership 260.

Visitors	no restrictions.
Societies	must contact in writing.
Green Fees	not confirmed.
Facilities	⯑ ⯑ 𝍢 ⯑ ⯑
Location	Roscommon Rd
Hotel	★★61% Royal Hotel, BOYLE ☎ (079) 62016 16⇌ ⯑

CARRICK-ON-SHANNON
Map 01 B4

Carrick-on-Shannon ☎ (079) 67015

A pleasant 9-hole course overlooking the River Shannon.

9 holes, 5545mtrs, Par 70, SSS 68.
Club membership 200.

Visitors	restricted on competition days & some Sun.
Societies	must contact in advance.
Green Fees	IR£10 per day.
Facilities	⯑ ⯑ 𝍢 ⯑ ⯑
Leisure	snooker.
Location	Woodbrook (4m W beside N4)
Hotel	★★61% Royal Hotel, BOYLE ☎ (079) 62016 16⇌ ⯑

Each golf-course entry has a recommended AA-appointed hotel. For a wider choice of places to stay, consult *AA Hotels in Britain and Ireland* and *AA Inspected Bed and Breakfast in Britain and Ireland* available from your local book shop or AA shops

CO SLIGO

ENNISCRONE
Map 01 B5

Enniscrone ☎ (096) 36297

In a magnificent situation with breathtaking views of mountain, sea and rolling countryside, this course offers some unforgettable golf. It has been designated by the Golfing Union of Ireland as suitable for major national and provincial championships and offers an exciting challenge among its splendid sandhills. A particularly favourite hole is the tenth, with a marvellous view from the elevated tee and the chance of a birdie with an accurate drive.

18 holes, 6620yds, Par 72, SSS 72.
Club membership 700.

Visitors	may not play before 10.30am or between 1.30 & 3pm on Sun.
Societies	must telephone in advance.
Green Fees	IR£15 per day May-Oct; IR£10 per day Nov-Feb ; IR12 per day Mar & Apr.
Facilities	⊗ 𝕄 ⯑ ⯑ 𝍢 ⯑ ⯑
Location	0.5m S on Ballina road
Hotel	★★★61% Downhill Hotel, BALLINA ☎ (096) 21033 51⇌ ⯑

SLIGO
Map 01 B5

County Sligo ☎ (071) 77134

Now considered to be one of the top links courses in Ireland, County Sligo is host to a number of competitions, including the West of Ireland Championships. Set in an elevated position on cliffs above three large beaches, the prevailing winds provide an additional challenge.

18 holes, 6003mtrs, Par 71, SSS 72, Course record 66.
Club membership 930.

Visitors	must contact in advance. Must play on medal course (white tee markers).
Societies	must contact in writing & pay a deposit.
Green Fees	IR£15 per round (IR£20 weekends & bank holidays).
Facilities	⊗ 𝕄 ⯑ ⯑ 𝍢 ⯑ ⯑ ⯑ Leslie Robinson.
Location	Rosses Point
Hotel	★★★58% Ballincar House Hotel, Rosses Point Rd, SLIGO ☎ (071) 45361 26⇌ ⯑

Strandhill ☎ (071) 68188

This scenic course is situated between Knocknarea Mountain and the Atlantic, offering golf in its most natural form amid the sand dunes of the West of Ireland. The 1st, 16th and 18th are Par 4 holes over 364 metres in length; the 2nd and 17th are testing Par 3s which vary according to the prevailing wind; the Par 4 13th is a testing dogleg right. This is a course where accuracy will be rewarded.

18 holes, 5045mtrs, Par 69, SSS 68.

Visitors	preferred on weekdays, except Thu.
Green Fees	not confirmed.
Facilities	⊗ 𝕄 by prior arrangement ⯑ ⯑
Location	Strandhill (5m from town)
Hotel	★★★58% Ballincar House Hotel, Rosses Point Rd, SLIGO ☎ (071) 45361 26⇌ ⯑

CO TIPPERARY

CLONMEL   Map 01 C2

Clonmel ☎ (052) 24050
Set in the scenic, wooded slopes of the Comeragh Mountains, this is a testing course with lots of open space and plenty of interesting features. It provides an enjoyable round in exceptionally tranquil surroundings.
18 holes, 5785mtrs, Par 71, SSS 70.
Club membership 850.

Visitors	may not play at weekends & bank holidays. Must contact in advance.
Societies	must contact in advance.
Green Fees	IR£12 per round (IR£15 weekends).
Facilities	⊗ & ⅷ by prior arrangement ᒼᕈ ᄝ ♀ ᗑ ☎ ⌥ { Robert Hayes.
Leisure	snooker, pool table, table tennis.
Location	Lyreanearla, Mountain Rd
Hotel	★★★65% Minella Hotel, CLONMEL ☎ (052) 22388 & 22717 45⇄ ℟

NENAGH   Map 01 B3

Nenagh ☎ (067) 31476
Interesting gradients call for some careful approach shots. Some magnificent views.
18 holes, 5996yds, Par 69, SSS 68, Course record 64.
Club membership 600.

Visitors	preferred weekdays.
Societies	must apply in writing.
Green Fees	IR£12 per round (IR£15 weekends).
Facilities	⊗ ⅷ ᒼᕈ ᄝ ♀ ᗑ ⌥ { John Coyle.
Location	Graigue (At Beechwood, 5m from town)
Hotel	★★★59% Castle Oaks House Hotel, CASTLECONNELL ☎ (061) 377666 11⇄ ℟

TEMPLEMORE   Map 01 C3

Templemore ☎ (0504) 31400
Parkland course with newly planted trees which offers a pleasant test to visitors without being too difficult. Walking is level too.
9 holes, Par 68, SSS 67, Course record 68.
Club membership 220.

Visitors	may not play on Sun during Special Events & Open weeks.
Societies	must contact in advance.
Green Fees	not confirmed.
Facilities	ᄝ by prior arrangement ♀ ᗄ
Location	Manna South (0.5m S)
Hotel	★★68% Leix County Hotel, BORRIS-IN-OSSORY ☎ (0505) 41213 19⇄

THURLES   Map 01 C3

Thurles ☎ (0504) 21983
Superb parkland course with a difficult finish at the 18th.
18 holes, 5904mtrs, Par 72, SSS 71.
Club membership 700.

Visitors	preferred on Mon, Wed, Thu & Fri.
Societies	must book one year in advance.
Green Fees	apply for details.

Facilities	⊗ & ⅷ by prior arrangement ᒼᕈ ᄝ ♀ ᗑ ⌥ { Sean Hunt.
Leisure	squash, snooker.
Location	1m from town on Cork road
Hotel	★★★★⚚70% Cashel Palace Hotel, CASHEL ☎ (062) 61411 20⇄

CO WATERFORD

DUNGARVAN   Map 01 C2

Dungarvan ☎ (058) 41605
Due to open in June 1993. A championship-standard course beside Dungarvan Bay, with seven lakes and hazards placed to challenge all levels of golfer.
18 holes, 6134yds, Par 72, SSS 72.
Club membership 400.

Visitors	no restrictions.
Societies	apply in writing.
Green Fees	IR£12 per round (IR£15 weekends).
Facilities	⊗ ᒼᕈ ᄝ ♀ ᗄ ᗑ ⌥
Location	Knocknagrannagh (off N25 between Waterford & Youghal)
Hotel	★★★59% Lawlors Hotel, DUNGARVAN ☎ (058) 41122 & 41056 89⇄ ℟

LISMORE   Map 01 C2

Lismore ☎ (058) 54026
Scenic inland parkland course with mature deciduous trees.
9 holes, 5196mtrs, Par 69, SSS 67.
Club membership 450.

Visitors	may not play Wed & Sun.
Societies	must telephone in advance to play on weekdays (contact in writing for weekends).
Green Fees	IR£8 per day (IR£10 weekends & bank holidays).
Facilities	ᄝ (summer & weekends only) ♀ (summer/weekends) ᗄ
Location	Ballyin
Hotel	★★⚚53% Ballyrafter House Hotel, LISMORE ☎ (058) 54002 12rm(4⇄)

TRAMORE   Map 01 C2

Tramore ☎ (051) 86170
This course has matured nicely over the years to become a true championship test and has been chosen as the venue for the Irish Professional Matchplay Championship and the Irish Amateur Championship. Most of the fairways are lined by evergreen trees, calling for accurate placing of shots, and the course is continuing to develop.
18 holes, 5999mtrs, Par 72, SSS 71, Course record 66.
Club membership 1203.

Visitors	preferred on weekdays.
Societies	apply in writing.
Green Fees	IR£17 (IR£21 weekends & bank holidays).
Facilities	⊗ ⅷ ᒼᕈ ᄝ ♀ ᗄ ᗑ ⌥ ⋈ { Paul McDaid.
Leisure	squash, snooker.
Location	Newtown Hill
Hotel	★★★★⚚75% Waterford Castle Hotel, The Island, WATERFORD ☎ (051) 78203 19⇄ ℟

WATERFORD
Map 01 C2

Waterford ☎ (051) 78489
Undulating parkland course in pleasant surroundings.
18 holes, 6237yds, Par 71, SSS 70.
Visitors preferred on weekdays.
Green Fees not confirmed.
Facilities ⊗ ⅏ ⅃ ⅄ 🍴 ⅊ ⚐ E Condon.
Location Newrath (1m N)
Hotel ★★★65% Jurys Hotel, Ferrybank,
WATERFORD ☎ (051) 32111 98⇥ ⋒

CO WESTMEATH

MULLINGAR
Map 01 C4

Mullingar ☎ (044) 48366
The wide rolling fairways between mature trees provide
parkland golf at its very best. The course, designed by the
great James Braid, offers a tough challenge and annually
hosts one of the most important amateur events in the
British Isles - the Mullingar Scratch Cup. It has also been
the venue of the Irish Professional Championship. One ad-
vantage of the layout is that the clubhouse is never far away.
18 holes, 6451yds, Par 72, SSS 71.
Club membership 900.
Visitors preferred on weekdays, except Wed.
Societies must contact in advance.
Green Fees IR£15 per round (IR£20 weekends & bank
holidays).
Facilities ⊗ ⅏ ⅃ ⅄ 🍴 ⅊ ⚐ John Burns.
Leisure snooker.
Location 3m W
Hotel ★★★58% Prince Of Wales Hotel,
ATHLONE ☎ (0902) 72626 72⇥ ⋒

CO WEXFORD

ENNISCORTHY
Map 01 C3

Enniscorthy ☎ (054) 33191
A pleasant course suitable for all levels of ability.
18 holes, 5382mtrs, Par 70, SSS 70.
Club membership 650.
Visitors preferred on weekdays. Must contact in advance.
Societies must book in advance.
Green Fees IR£10 per day (IR£12 weekends & bank holidays).
Facilities ⊗ ⅏ ⅃ ⅄ ⅊ ⚐
Leisure snooker.
Location Knockmarshall (2m from town on New Ross road)
Hotel ★★53% Murphy-Flood's Hotel, Market Square,
ENNISCORTHY ☎ (054) 33413 21rm(5⇥13 ⋒)

GOREY
Map 01 D3

Courtown ☎ (055) 25166
A pleasant parkland course which is well wooded and
enjoys views across the Irish Sea near Courtown
Harbour.

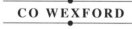

18 holes, 5852mtrs, Par 71, SSS 70, Course record 67.
Club membership 700.
Visitors may not play on major competition days or
5-7pm in Jul & Aug.
Societies must contact in advance.
Green Fees not confirmed.
Facilities ⊗ & ⅏ (Jun-Aug) ⅃ ⅄ ⅊ 🍴 ⚐ John
Coone.
Location Kiltennel (Off Courtown Road)
Hotel ★★★(red)≙ Marlfield House Hotel,
GOREY ☎ (055) 21124 19⇥ ⋒

ROSSLARE
Map 01 D2

Rosslare ☎ (053) 32203 & 32238
This traditional links course is within minutes of the ferry
terminal at Rosslare, but its popularity is not confined to
visitors from Fishguard or Le Havre. It is a great
favourite with the Irish too. Many of the greens are
sunken and are always in beautiful condition, but the
semi-blind approaches are among features of this course
which provide a healthy challenge.
Old Course: 18 holes, 6542yds, Par 72, SSS 71.
New Course: 9 holes, 3153yds, Par 70, SSS 70.
Club membership 900.
Visitors book in advance.
Societies apply in writing.
Green Fees Old: IR£17 per round (IR£23 weekends).
New: £IR12 per 18 holes.
Facilities ⊗ ⅏ ⅃ ⅄ ⅊ 🍴 ⚐ Austin Skerritt.
Leisure snooker.
Location Rosslare Strand (Near the ferry terminal)
Hotel ★★★(red) Kelly's Strand Hotel,
ROSSLARE ☎ (053) 32114
Annexe96⇥ ⋒

St Helen's Bay Golf & Country Club
☎ (053) 33234 & 33669
A championship-standard golf course designed by Philip
Walton. Parkland with water hazards, bunkers and trees
incorporated generously.
18 holes, 6213yds, Par 72, SSS 65.
Club membership 300.
Visitors advisable to contact in advance.
Societies advisable to book.
Green Fees IR£14-IR£15 (IR£18-IR£20 weekends &
bank holidays).
Facilities ⊗ ⅏ ⅃ ⅄ ⅊ 🍴 ⚐ ⋒
Leisure grass tennis courts.
Location St Helens, Kilrane
Hotel ★★★57% Hotel Rosslare, ROSSLARE
HARBOUR
☎ (053) 33110 & 33312 25rm(22⇥ ⋒)

WEXFORD
Map 01 D2

Wexford ☎ (053) 42238
Parkland course with panoramic view of the Wexford
coastline and mountains.
18 holes, 6100yds, Par 71, SSS 69.
Club membership 800.
Visitors must contact in advance but may not play
Thu & weekends.

Societies must contact in writing.
Green Fees IR£14 per day (IR£15 weekends & bank holidays).
Facilities ⊗ & 🍽 by prior arrangement 🛒 ⬤ ♀ ♨ 📷 ℓ G Ronayne.
Leisure pool table.
Location Mulgannon
Hotel ★★★69% Talbot Hotel, Trinity St, WEXFORD
☎ (053) 22566 100⇆ ⌨

CO WICKLOW

ARKLOW
Map 01 D3

Arklow ☎ (0402) 32492
Scenic links course.
18 holes, 5404mtrs, Par 68, SSS 67, Course record 66.
Club membership 450.
Visitors may play Mon-Fri.
Societies must apply in writing.
Green Fees IR£12 (IR£15 weekends).
Facilities ⊗ & 🍽 by prior arrangement
🛒 ⬤ ♀ ♨ 📷
Location Abbeylands (0.5m from town centre)
Hotel ★★★(red)🏵 Marlfield House Hotel, GOREY
☎ (055) 21124 19⇆ ⌨

BLAINROE
Map 01 D3

Blainroe ☎ (0404) 68168
Parkland course overlooking the sea on the east coast, offering a challenging round to golfers of all abilities.
18 holes, 6159mtrs, Par 72, SSS 72.
Club membership 700.
Visitors restricted Mon and weekends. Must contact in advance.
Societies must apply in writing.
Green Fees IR£18 (IR£25 weekends and bank holidays).
Facilities ⊗ 🍽 🛒 ⬤ ♀ ♨ 📷 ⛳ ℓ John McDonald.
Location S of Wicklow, on coast road
Hotel ★★★🏵74% Tinakilly Country House & Restaurant, RATHNEW
☎ (0404) 69274 29⇆ ⌨

BLESSINGTON
Map 01 C3

Tulfarris Hotel & Country Club ☎ Naas (045) 64574
Designed by Eddie Hackett, this course is on the Blessington lakeshore with the Wicklow Mountains as a backdrop.
9 holes, 2806mtrs, Par 36, SSS 69, Course record 78.
Club membership 150.
Visitors tee booking advisable; may not play Sun. Must contact in advance.
Societies must contact in writing.
Green Fees not confirmed.
Facilities ⊗ 🍽 🛒 ⬤ ♀ ♨ 📷 ⛳ ⚑
Leisure hard tennis courts, heated indoor swimming pool, fishing, sauna, gymnasium.
Hotel ★★★56% Downshire House Hotel, BLESSINGTON
☎ (045) 65199 14⇆ ⌨ Annexe11⇆ ⌨

BRAY
Map 01 D3

Old Conna ☎ (01) 2826055
Fairly young but interesting course with a number of shots across water.
18 holes, 6551yds, Par 72, SSS 71, Course record 71.
Club membership 900.
Visitors may not play 12.30-2pm or at weekends unless with member. Must contact in advance.
Societies must telephone well in advance.
Green Fees IR£20 (£IR25 weekends & bank holidays).
Facilities ⊗ 🍽 🛒 ⬤ ♀ ♨ 📷 ⛳ ℓ Niall Murray.
Leisure snooker.
Location Ferndale Rd
Hotel ★★64% Royal Hotel, Main St, BRAY
☎ (01) 2862935 67⇆ ⌨

Woodbrook ☎ Dublin (01) 2824799
Pleasant parkland with magnificent views and bracing sea breezes which has hosted a number of events, including the Irish Close and the Irish Open Championships. A testing finish is provided by an 18th hole with out of bounds on both sides.
18 holes, 5996mtrs, Par 72, SSS 71, Course record 65.
Club membership 960.
Visitors must contact in advance and have a handicap certificate.
Societies must contact in advance.
Green Fees not confirmed.
Facilities ⊗ 🍽 🛒 ⬤ ♀ ♨ 📷 ⛳ ℓ Billy Kinsella.
Leisure snooker.
Location Dublin Rd (11m S of Dublin on N11)
Hotel ★★64% Royal Hotel, Main St, BRAY
☎ (01) 2862935 67⇆ ⌨

DELGANY
Map 01 D3

Delgany ☎ (01) 2874536
An undulating parkland course amidst beautiful scenery.
18 holes, 5414mtrs, Par 69, SSS 67.
Club membership 800.
Visitors preferred on Mon, Thu & Fri.
Societies normally Mon & Thu.
Green Fees IR£17 per round (IR£20 weekends & bank holidays).
Facilities ⊗ 🍽 🛒 ⬤ ♀ ♨ 📷 ⛳ ℓ E Darcy.
Leisure snooker.
Location Greystones (0.75m from village)
Hotel ★★64% Royal Hotel, Main St, BRAY
☎ (01) 2862935 67⇆ ⌨

GREYSTONES
Map 01 D3

Greystones ☎ (01) 2876624 & 2874136
A part level and part hilly parkland course.
18 holes, 5401mtrs, Par 69, SSS 68.
Club membership 941.
Visitors may only play Mon, Tue & Fri morning. Must contact in advance.
Societies must contact in writing.
Green Fees IR£20 per round (IR£24 weekends).
Facilities ⊗ & 🍽 (Wed-Sun only) 🛒 ⬤ ♀ ♨ 📷 ⛳ ℓ Kevin Daly.
Hotel ★★★56% Downshire House Hotel, BLESSINGTON ☎ (045) 65199 14⇆ ⌨ Annexe11⇆ ⌨

Index to Counties

Index to Golf Courses

The first name is the name of the course or club; the second (in italic) is the name of the town under which the course or club appears in the gazetteer

INDEX TO GOLF COURSES ....

KEY TO ATLAS

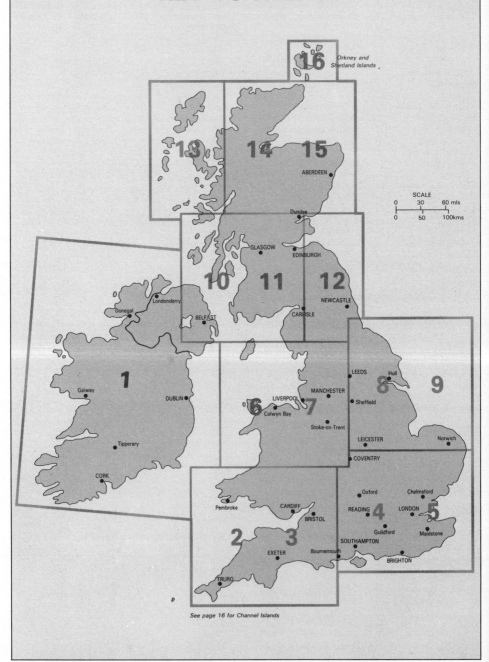

See page 16 for Channel Islands

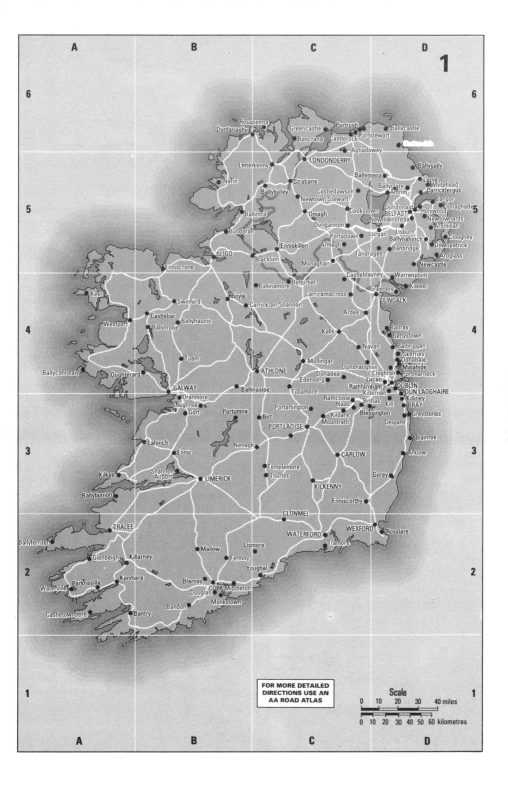

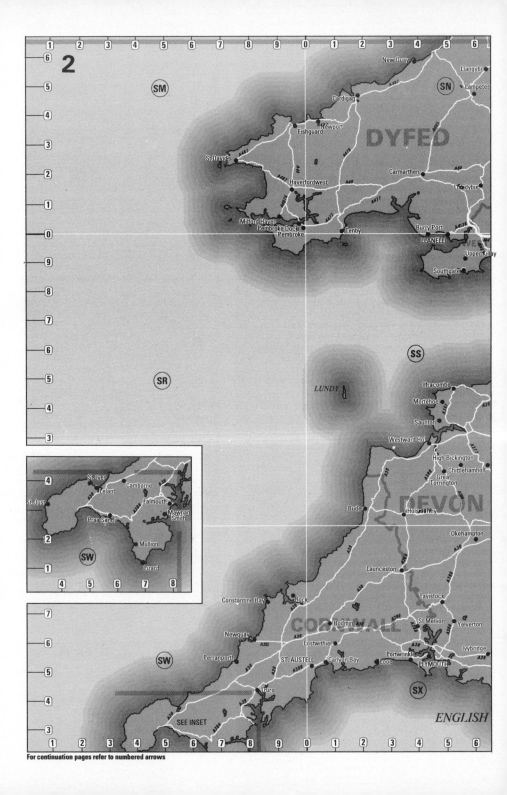

2

For continuation pages refer to numbered arrows

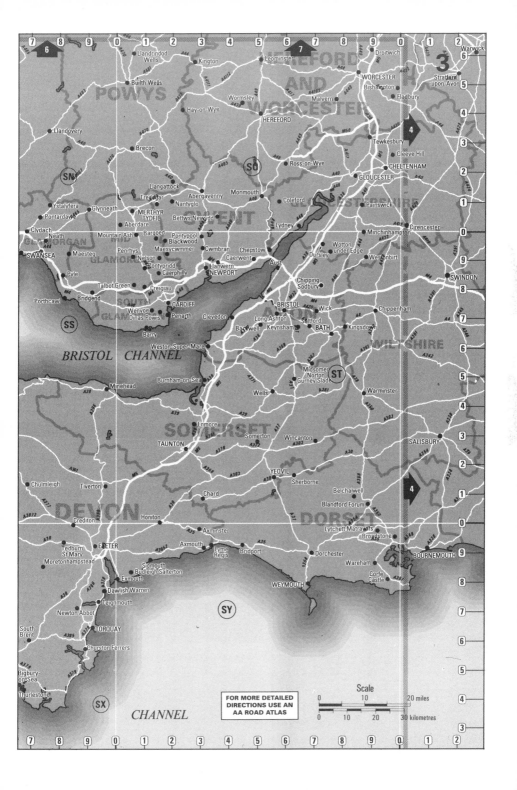

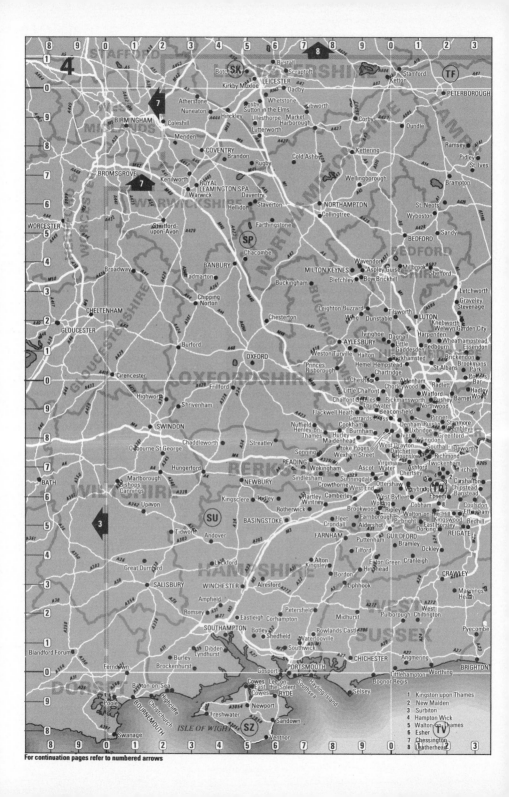

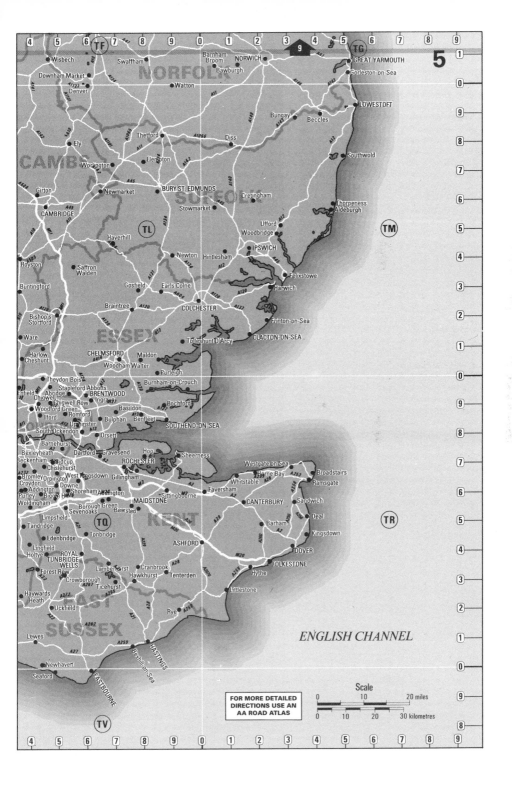

ENGLISH CHANNEL

FOR MORE DETAILED
DIRECTIONS USE AN
AA ROAD ATLAS

Scale
0   10   20 miles
0   10   20   30 kilometres

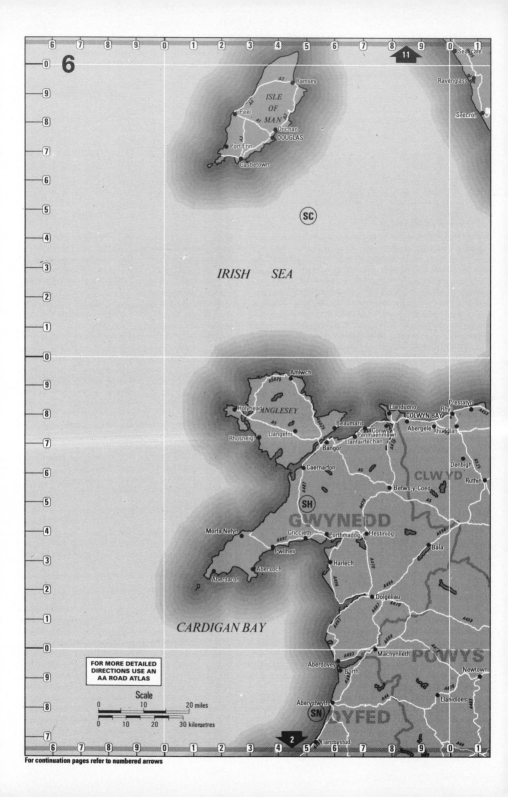

ISLE
OF
MAN

Ramsey

Peel
Onchan
DOUGLAS
Port Erin
Castletown

Seascale
Ravenglass
Silecroft

(SC)

IRISH   SEA

Amlwch

Holyhead   INGLESEY   Beaumaris
Rhosneigr   Llangefni   Bangor   Penmaenmawr
Caernarfon   Llanfairfechan

Llandudno   Prestatyn
COLWYN BAY   Rhyl
Conwy   Abergele   Rhuddlan

Denbigh
CLWYD   Ruthin

(SH)

Betws-y-Coed

GWYNEDD

Morfa Nefyn   Criccieth   Porthmadog   Ffestiniog
Pwllheli   Harlech   Bala
Abersoch
Aberdaron

Dolgellau

CARDIGAN BAY

POWYS

Machynlleth
Aberdovey   Newtown
Borth

Aberystwyth   Llanidloes
(SN)   DYFED
Llanrhystud

FOR MORE DETAILED
DIRECTIONS USE AN
AA ROAD ATLAS

Scale
0   10
20 miles
0   10   20   30 kilometres

CUMBRIA
NORTH YORKSHIRE
LANCASHIRE
SOUTH YORKSHIRE
DERBYSHIRE
CHESHIRE
STAFFORDSHIRE
WARWICKSHIRE

Ravenstonedale
Richmond
Bowness-on-Windermere
Kendal
Sedbergh
Askham-in-Furness
Ulverston
Grange-over-Sands
Silverdale
Bentham
Settle
BARROW-IN-FURNESS
MORECAMBE
Heysham
LANCASTER
Knott End-on-Sea
Fleetwood
Skipton
HARROGATE
York
Malton
Poulton-le-Fylde
BLACKPOOL
Longridge
PRESTON
Clitheroe
Barnoldswick
Silsden
Ilkley
Keighley
Bingley
Riddlesden
Shipley
Baildon
BRADFORD
LEEDS
Lytham St Anne's
Blackburn
Haslingden
Wilpshire
Rishton
Accrington
Whalley
Great Harwood
Burnley
Colne
Nelson
Hebden Bridge
Halifax
Leyland
Pleasington
Darwen
Bacup
Todmorden
Sowerby Bridge
Elland
Holywell Green
HUDDERSFIELD
SOUTHPORT
Chorley
Whitworth
Outlane
Marsden
Meltham
Shevington
Rochdale
Milnrow
Ormskirk
Upholland
Wigan
Horwich
Bolton
Bury
Whitefield
Middleton
Oldham
Uppermill
Ashton-under-Lyne
DONCASTER
Formby
Hindley
Leigh
Worsley
Swinton
Prestwich
Brinnington
West-houghton
Cross
Walkden
Failsworth
Denton
Stalybridge
Glossop
Ashton-in-Makerfield
MANCHESTER
Blundellsands
Bootle
St Helens
Newton-le-Willows
Flixton
Sale
Stockport
Hyde
Romiley
Mellor
SHEFFIELD
Wallasey
BIRKENHEAD
Hoylake
LIVERPOOL
Huyton
Widnes
Warrington
Altrincham
Cheadle
Bramhall
New Mills
Caldy
Heswall
Bebington
Runcorn
Lymm
Hale
Disley
Eastham
Bromborough
Woodford
Poynton
Pott Shrigley
Chapel-en-le-Frith
Brynford
Flint
Ellesmere Port
Sandway
Alderley Edge
Wilmslow
Mottram
St Andrew
Prestbury
Buxton
Pantymwyn
Hawarden
Helsby
Knutsford
MACCLESFIELD
Mold
Delamere
Winsford
Congleton
MANSFIELD
SJ
CHESTER
Eccleston
Tarporley
Sandbach
CREWE
Leek
Goldsithall
Ashbourne
NOTTINGHAM
WREXHAM
Alsager
DERBY
Llangollen
Newcastle-under-Lyme
STOKE-ON-TRENT
Onneley
Whitchurch
Barlaston
Uttoxeter
Oswestry
Pant
Market Drayton
Stone
Weston
Weston-under-Redcastle
STAFFORD
Lilleshall
Brocton
Hazleslade
Welshpool
SHREWSBURY
Meole Brace
Wellington
TELFORD
Shifnal
Lichfield
Tamworth
LEICESTER
Church Stretton
Perton
Wolverhampton
Walsall
Aldridge
Sutton Coldfield
Lea Marston
Bridgnorth
Pattingham
Himley
Dudley
West Bromwich
BIRMINGHAM
Stourbridge
Halesowen
Solihull
COVENTRY
Knighton
Ludlow
Bewdley
Blakedown
Hollywood
Wythall
Tanworth-in-Arden
Bowness
Kidderminster
Alvechurch
Redditch
HEREFORD AND WORCESTER
SHROPSHIRE

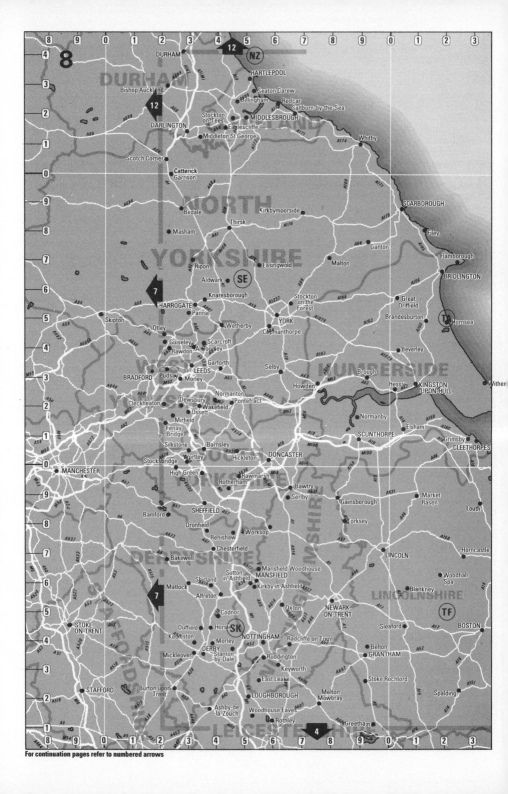

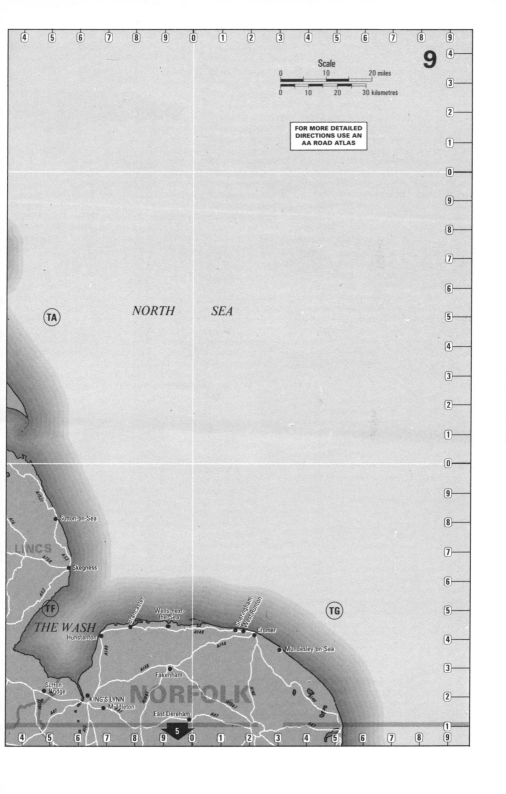

Scale

0   10   20 miles
0   10   20   30 kilometres

**FOR MORE DETAILED
DIRECTIONS USE AN
AA ROAD ATLAS**

NORTH   SEA

TA

Sutton-on-Sea

LINCS

Skegness

TF

TG

THE WASH

Brancaster

Wells-next-
the-Sea

Sheringham
West Runton

Cromer

Hunstanton

Mundesley-on-Sea

Fakenham

Sutton
Bridge

NORFOLK

KING'S LYNN

Middleton

East Dereham

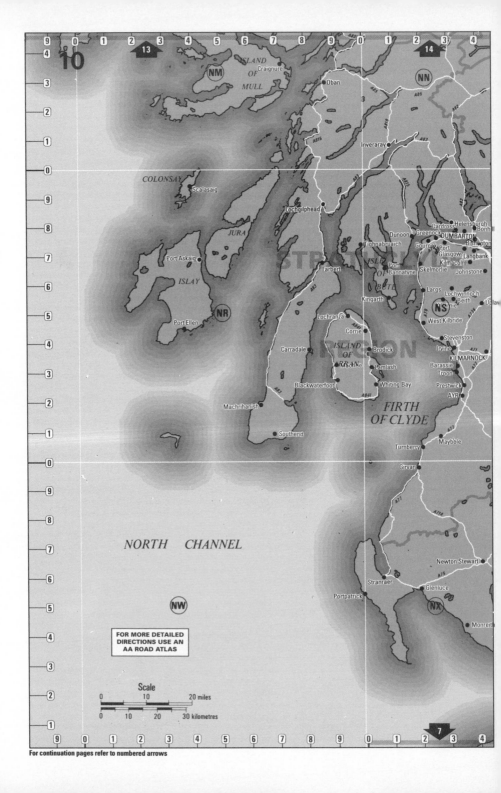

For continuation pages refer to numbered arrows

TAYSIDE REGION

CENTRAL REGION

FIFE REGION

LOTHIAN REGION

BORDERS REGION

DUMFRIES AND GALLOWAY REGION

NORTHUMBERLAND

CUMBRIA

DURHAM

NN NO NT NX NY

15 12 7

Killin, St Fillans, Comrie, Crieff, Muthill, Dunkeld, DUNDEE, PERTH, Callander, Aberfoyle, Dunning, Auchterarder, Ladybank, Cupar, Falkland, Leslie, Glenrothes, Markinch, Leven, Milnathort, Kinross, Thornton, Muckhart, Dollar, Dunblane, Bridge of Allan, Tillicoultry, Lochgelly, STIRLING, Alloa, Saline, Kincardine, Dunfermline, KIRKCALDY, Kinghorn, Burntisland, Aberdour, Larbert, Bonnybridge, Polmont, South Queensferry, Dunbar, Drymen, Lennoxtown, Kirkintilloch, Kilsyth, Falkirk, Linlithgow, EDINBURGH, Prestonpans, Musselburgh, Bearsden, Lenzie, Balmore, Muirhead, Gartcosh, Cumbernauld, Bathgate, Uphall, Bathgate, Livingstone, Ratho, Clydebank, Renfrew, Bishopbriggs, Airdrie, Whitburn, West Calder, Dalkeith, Paisley, Cambuslang, Coatbridge, Shotts, Bonnyrigg, GLASGOW, Bellshill, Uddingston, Penicuik, Barrhead, Burnside, Motherwell, Clarkston, Carmyle, Wishaw, Carluke, Newton Mearns, East Kilbride, Larkhall, Hamilton, West Linton, Berwick-upon-Tweed, Eaglesham, Strathaven, Lesmahagow, Lanark, Carnwath, Kelso, Galston, Biggar, Peebles, Innerleithen, Galashiels, Mauchline, Leadhills, Hawick, Jedburgh, New Cumnock, Sanquhar, Moffat, New Galloway, Thornhill, Lochmaben, Langholm, Lockerbie, DUMFRIES, Wigtown, Castle Douglas, Cummertrees, Hexham, Gatehouse of Fleet, Kirkcudbright, Colvend, Southerness, CARLISLE, Silloth, Maryport, Cockermouth, Penrith, WORKINGTON, Keswick, Borrowdale, St Bees, Grasmere, Ambleside

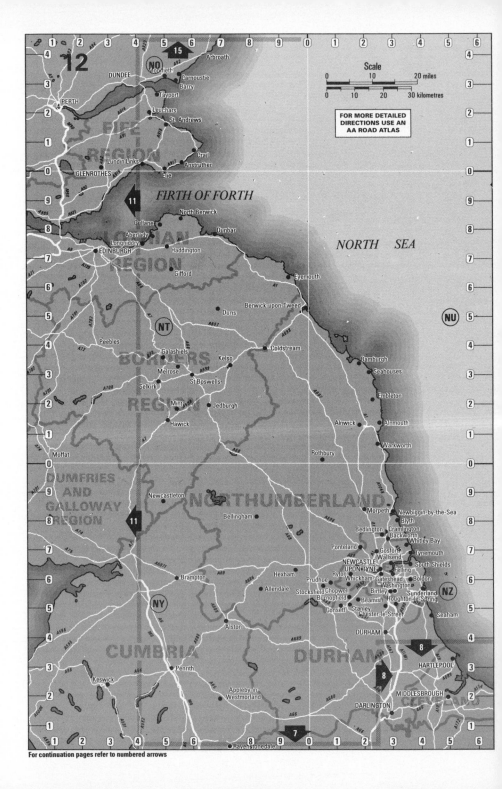

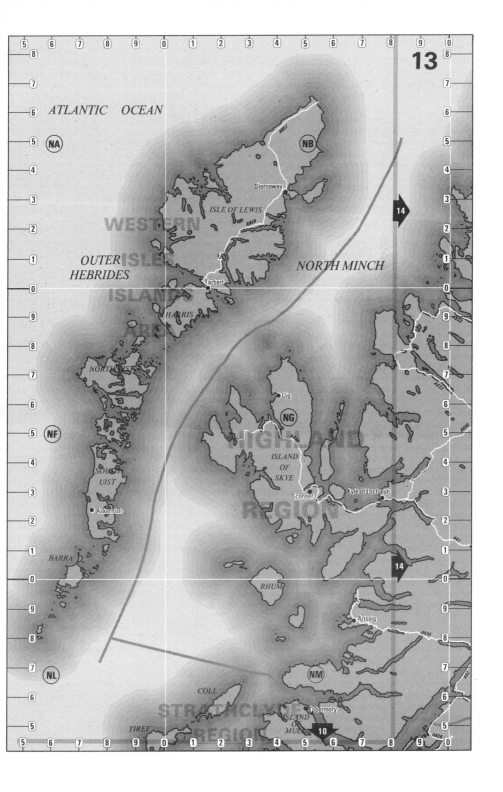

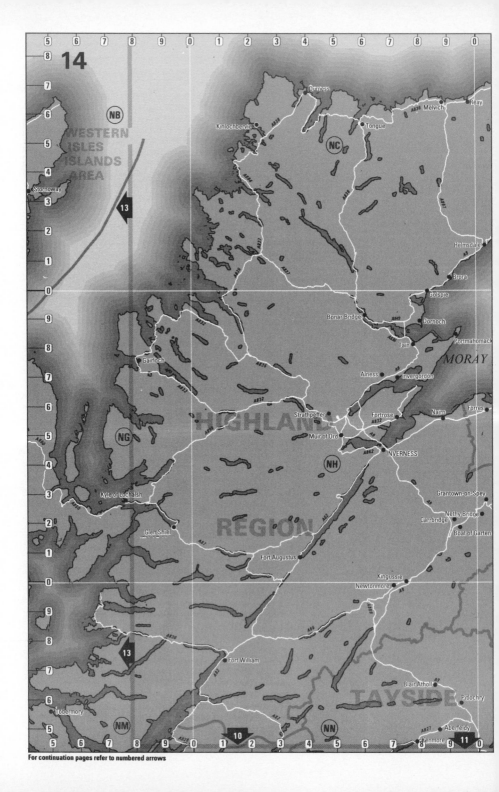

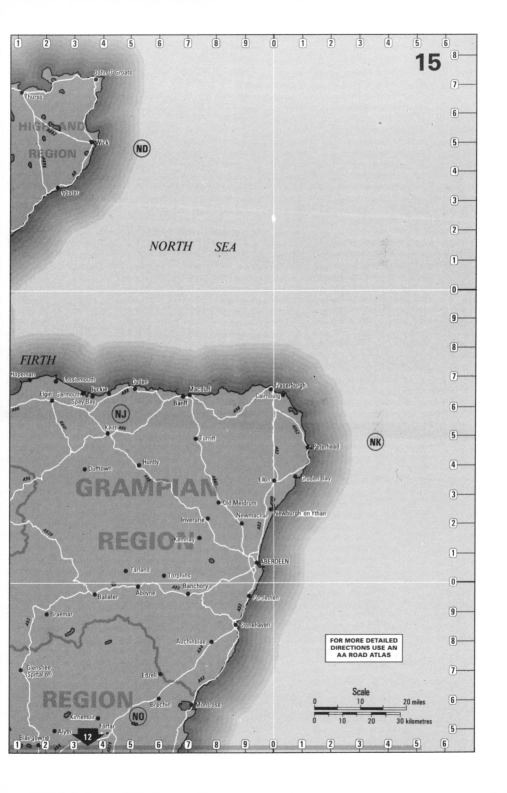

NORTH SEA

FIRTH

HIGHLAND REGION

GRAMPIAN

REGION

REGION

John O' Groats

Thurso

Wick

Lybster

Hopeman

Lossiemouth

Cullen

Macduff

Fraserburgh

Elgin Garmouth

Buckie

Banff

Cairnbulg

Spey Bay

Keith

Turriff

Peterhead

Dufftown

Huntly

Ellon

Cruden Bay

Old Maldrum

Newburgh on Ythan

Inverurie

Newmachar

Kemnay

Tarland

Torphins

ABERDEEN

Aboyne

Banchory

Ballater

Portlethen

Braemar

Stonehaven

Auchinblae

Glenshee
(Spittal of)

Edzell

Brechin

Montrose

Kirriemuir

Forfar

Alyth

Blairgowrie

12

ND

NJ

NK

NO

FOR MORE DETAILED
DIRECTIONS USE AN
AA ROAD ATLAS

Scale

0   10   20 miles

0   10   20   30 kilometres

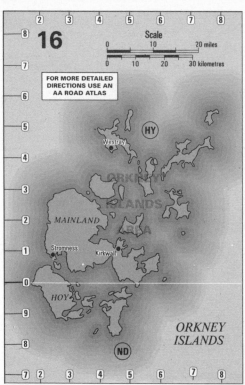
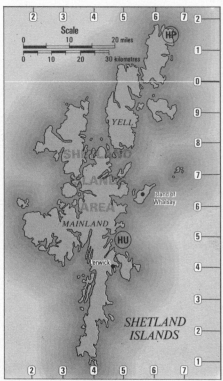
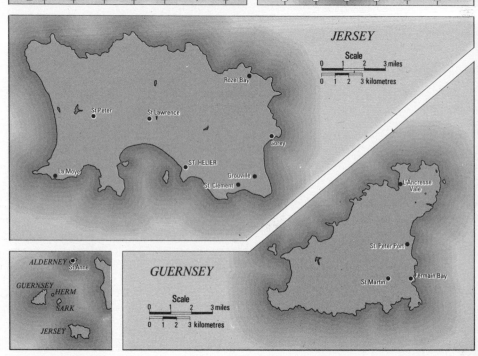

FOR MORE DETAILED
DIRECTIONS USE AN
AA ROAD ATLAS

Scale
0   10   20 miles
0   10   20   30 kilometres

(HY)

Westray

ORKNEY
ISLANDS
AREA

MAINLAND

Stromness
Kirkwall

HOY

ND

*ORKNEY
ISLANDS*

Scale
0   10   20 miles
0   10   20   30 kilometres

HP

YELL

SHETLAND
ISLANDS
AREA

MAINLAND

Island of
Whalsay

HU

Lerwick

*SHETLAND
ISLANDS*

JERSEY

Scale
0   1   2   3 miles
0   1   2   3 kilometres

Rozel Bay

St Peter   St Lawrence

Gorey

ST HELIER

La Moye

Grouville

St Clement

L'Ancresse
Vale

St Peter Port

GUERNSEY

Scale
0   1   2   3 miles
0   1   2   3 kilometres

St Martin   Fermain Bay

ALDERNEY
St Anne

GUERNSEY   HERM

SARK

JERSEY